D0871224

Conference on Ocean Wave Spectra, Easton, Md., 1961.
III

OCEAN WAVE

SPECTRA; *proceedings*

of a conference

PROCEEDINGS OF A CONFERENCE

sponsored by

THE U.S. NAVAL OCEANOGRAPHIC OFFICE*

and the

DIVISION OF EARTH SCIENCES,
NATIONAL ACADEMY OF SCIENCES
NATIONAL RESEARCH COUNCIL

EASTON, MARYLAND
MAY 1–4, 1961

*Formerly U. S. Navy Hydrographic Office

PRENTICE-HALL INTERNATIONAL, INC., *London*
PRENTICE-HALL OF AUSTRALIA, PTY., LTD., *Sydney*
PRENTICE-HALL OF CANADA, LTD., *Toronto*
PRENTICE-HALL OF FRANCE, S.A.R.L., *Paris*
PRENTICE-HALL OF JAPAN, INC., *Tokyo*
PRENTICE-HALL DE MEXICO, S.A., *Mexico City*

Library of Congress Catalog Card Number: 63-8927

Printed in the United States of America
62999-C

REAR ADMIRAL E. C. STEPHAN, USN

INTRODUCTION

May I express our pleasure at the fine spirit of cooperation that has existed between the National Academy of Sciences and the Hydrographic Office in the planning and organizing of this conference. We appreciate the very large amount of detailed organizational planning called for, and we feel fortunate to have available an organization with the Academy's experience and interest to which we may turn for assistance.

Gentlemen, on behalf of the Chief of Naval Operations, Admiral Burke, and the U. S. Navy's Hydrographic Office, I take pleasure in welcoming you to the Conference on Ocean Wave Spectra. I wish you every success in your discussions, and I hope that your deliberations will result in an increased wave research effort and more complete understanding of ocean waves. This knowledge is of great importance to all countries that must perform operations at sea, whether these operations be concerned with transportation, mining, fisheries, or naval activity. There is no operation carried out at sea that is not limited, sometimes seriously, by some characteristic of ocean waves. Therefore, an organized effort to understand the spectrum completely should produce valuable scientific knowledge that will also have many practical applications.

In a very real sense this conference has been called by you gentlemen rather than by any organization. Over the past ten years, there has been no field of marine science more active than wave research. Your untiring pioneering efforts have resulted not only in a vast amount of new scientific knowledge but also in several differences of opinion, each view being enthusiastically and ably defended by its proponents. I believe that this is all to the good. In this way we learn.

It is appropriate that we begin the conference with a summary of the present status of knowledge of the ocean wave spectrum. It is equally appropriate that this summary be presented by Dr. George Deacon, Director of the National Institute of Oceanography in England since 1949. A large portion of the pioneering work in the ocean wave field accomplished in recent years has been done by scientific workers at the National Institute of Oceanography under his direction.

CONTENTS

3 TWO-DIMENSIONAL SPECTRA

DR. G. E. R. DEACON
CHAIRMAN

4 NONLINEAR ASPECTS OF THE SPECTRUM

DR. CARL ECKART
CHAIRMAN

5 RECENT MEASUREMENT AND ANALYSIS TECHNIQUES

JAMES M. SNODGRASS
CHAIRMAN

FOREWORD

During the past few years statistical methods have been applied with increasing success to the complex problem of describing and understanding wind-generated ocean waves. However, different methods, different data, and, perhaps, different geographical environments have led to different conclusions concerning the characteristics of the ocean-wave spectrum.

The Conference on Ocean-Wave Spectra was called to consider and possibly resolve some of these differences. Participated in by 70 scientists, engineers, and artisans concerned with ocean-wave research, the conference was held at Easton, Maryland, May 1–4, 1961. Formal morning and afternoon sessions were supplemented by informal sessions in the evenings and by many small spontaneous group discussions.

A great deal of information was exchanged and new ideas generated in the course of the conference. Many of the participants returned to their laboratories with intensified interest in ocean-wave spectra, anxious to put new ideas to the test of experimental and theoretical criteria.

Both the conference and this book were made possible by financial support from the Hydrographic Office of the U. S. Department of the Navy, which also provided the original impetus for the conference which was organized and carried out under the auspices of the Earth Sciences Division of the NAS/NRC.

Many persons contributed their time and talents behind the scenes in planning and staging the conference and in publishing this report. Among those whose contributions should be acknowledged here are the members of the Organizing Committee: Charles L. Bretschneider, B. King Couper, Richard W. James, Feenan Jennings, Wilbur Marks, John J. Schule, Jr., and Alver E. Sik. The Chairmen of the sessions — Admiral E. C. Stephan, John J. Schule, Jr., Wilbur Marks, R. Dorrestein, Carl Eckart, G. E. R. Deacon, James M. Snodgrass, and Walter Munk — all influenced and shaped the course of the conference. Special thanks are due Dr. G. E. R. Deacon, who brought a substantial part of the staff from the National Institute of Oceanography to the conference.

RICHARD C. VETTER,
Executive Secretary
Committee on Oceanography
National Academy of Sciences
National Research Council

G. E. R. DEACON

PRESENT STATUS OF WAVE RESEARCH

To assess the present status of a vigorously expanding subject is never easy, and it is particularly difficult in the case of research on waves, where the advances seem to be made by relatively few specialists, and there is not much effort to spare for building up background literature and writing summaries and surveys. The reference books tend either to be elementary or to be dominated by the special interests of the authors.

All-round study of waves is a recent activity. The sailing ship part of the nineteenth century was a great era for marine research because it was important to find the best tracks for ships to follow. Since that time, however, the supremacy of powerful steamships has meant that nothing less than a catastrophe could create much demand for research. The decline of important fisheries and disasters such as the sinking of the *Titanic* have launched expeditions and founded laboratories, but the day-to-day cost of loss, damage, and delay from waves has been accepted with little question. Not until the Second World War did it become urgent to make both a practical and theoretical effort to learn something about one of the biggest and most troublesome things in Nature. Now, in the midst of the subsequently rapid and impressive growth, we must make certain that adequate attention is paid to systematic long-term studies, and perhaps less direct approaches, as well as to those that have been immediately successful.

Before the War there were theoretical conclusions based on the laws of classical mechanics, and generalizations based on makeshift observations. The practical men had some excuse, no doubt, for considering the theoretical ideas insufficiently developed to be of much practical value; and the theoretical workers could well despair at the difficulty of making observations sufficiently precise to test detailed theories. There was also the difficulty of understanding each other's language and point of view.

A survey of the advances of the past fifteen years and of the papers presented here affords abundant evidence of the success of joint action, but there is still some tendency for theoretical and practical workers to feel more at home in opposite camps, with blackboard and chalk predominating in one and heavy engineering in the other. It is doubtful whether either approach can be fully effective until it uses the best weapons of the other. Hydraulic laboratories must find room for models designed to test theoretical principles, and theoretical workers must design and make their own experiments.

GENERATION OF WAVES BY WIND

The question of how waves are generated must be regarded as one of overriding importance. Until the flow of air over waves and the interaction

PRESENT STATUS OF

WAVE RESEARCH

E. C. STEPHAN

CHAIRMAN

between waves is understood, all theoretical conclusions and empirical generalizations used to relate the waves to the wind must have inherent weaknesses. Progress in the study of ship motion in relation to waves was slow because too much attention was concentrated on the way in which ships moved rather than on what made them move. The realization of this interaction alone ought to have prompted wave researchers to study the air as well as the water.

Several of the papers contributed to the conference deal with this outstanding, intrinsic problem. They deal especially with the two kinds of mechanism now believed to be most important: the effect of travelling pressure disturbances associated with atmospheric turbulence, and the growth of the interfacial disturbance as an instability in the shearing flow of the air over the water. They confirm the growing conviction that a combination of the two ideas is the most promising, the waves being initiated by the turbulent pressure fluctuations in the air stream and augmented by the instability in the shearing flow.

The experience of the past few years has demonstrated the difficulty of making measurements sufficiently precise to test such advanced ideas, but substantial progress is nevertheless reported. Preliminary conclusions are drawn from continuous recordings of pressure fluctuations above ocean waves, and useful evidence has been obtained from measurements of the angular distribution of energy with respect to the direction of the wind. If the transfer of energy from the air to the waves is due to the effect of pressure fluctuations acting on the surface of the water, the angular distribution should be such that waves of particular lengths and speeds would be preferentially energized in the directions where the component of wind velocity.is the same as the wave speed. This is likely to be modified by the effect of the existing waves on the pressure fluctuations. One of the papers presented to the conference indicates that the shear instability tends to narrow the spread at all frequencies, though it has a greater effect on the longer waves and the short waves are probably spread out again by non-linear mechanisms, such as breaking. The use of wave-recording buoys, supplemented as much as possible with recordings of the microbarometric fluctuations above the waves, seems to be a very promising method of testing and building on the new ideas.

Another notable advance during the past few years is progress in the study of second-order effects, such as the interaction among waves and

between waves and currents. This is an essential preliminary to full understanding of the wave spectrum.

PROPAGATION AND DECAY

Recent work on wave statistics represents an outstanding scientific achievement. It is remarkable how precise a description can be given of the geometry of a surface that can be described in no other way; and it is remarkable how easily such information as the probability of given wave heights, slopes, and accelerations can now be obtained from relatively few and simple measurements of a wave record. Statistical expressions of the oscillatory motions and stresses in ships can be calculated from the wave information and ship characteristics. It is no exaggeration to say that the precise description of the sea surface provided by oceanographers and the methods of spectrum analysis they have used have brought research on the design and sea-keeping qualities of ships to the threshold of new and exciting developments. This data provides a similar basis for studies of the reflection of light and radio waves from the sea surface. Combined with the idea of the wave spectrum it is essential to studies of wave generation and decay.

But while it is necessary to treat a wave record of short duration (say twenty minutes) as noise with constant statistical parameters, the underlying physical conception of a large number of component wave trains forming a continuous spectrum and travelling from the generating area with the group velocities appropriate to their periods is still a good guide in dealing with the products of a storm as a whole and trying to predict the energy level in a given area at known times and distances from the generating areas that are contributing to it. The accumulating experience of wave forecasters must provide valuable information about the effects of dispersion and of the angular spread and attenuation of different wave components in a range of weather conditions, but it seems very desirable that more specific studies should be made with measuring programmes designed for each purpose.

WAVE PREDICTION

With the physics of generation and decay so little known, and with no comprehensive network of wave measurements, it is not surprising that methods used to forecast waves differ from one exponent to another and one area to another. Perhaps all the methods give useful results when used by the men who invented them to forecast the sort of observations on which they were based in more or less the same place and conditions. Some of the difference is due no doubt to the type of wave recorder, standard of visual estimate, amount of data, and nature of physical hypotheses. But even when one man makes entirely empirical generalizations from what seems to be an adequate number of measurements, with the same well-tried instrument, he finds that different formulae are needed for deep and shallow water. There is no doubt much to be learnt about the effect of the bottom, especially when it is irregular, and of the modifications due to varying tides and currents, as well as the influence of opposing winds and encounter with other waves.

There are growing demands for wave predictions, and we must work hard at improving the methods, but it seems very doubtful whether we can learn much about the waves themselves by trying to compare them too closely at this early stage. Till we have more observations that we can rely on, more knowledge of the physics of generation, propagation, and decay, and even more precise methods of inferring surface winds over the sea from weather charts, our theoretical workers, at least, should insist on a more systematic approach.

WAVES IN SHALLOW WATER

The geometry of refraction as waves enter shallow water is well understood, and we know how the statistical properties of the wave pattern change. The decrease and increase in height due to changes in phase and group velocity are known, at least for small waves, till the waves are near the breaking point. There are good prospects for further theoretical research on the transport of momentum towards a beach; experiments have shown that under certain conditions there is a rise in mean level on the shore to which the waves are travelling, and a fall in other conditions. Such studies will have an important bearing on the relationship between surf beats and the alternation of high and low groups of waves, and on the formation of rip currents.

Theoretical methods taking account of turbulence, viscosity, and the boundary effects in shallow water have led to a more complicated structure than was expected from Stokes' theory. They have explained the apparently anomalous forward movement of bottom material in earlier tank experiments, and have also been confirmed by new measurements just below the surface. The generation of longshore currents and the effect of oblique approach of the waves and roughness of the bottom have been carefully studied, but we need more theoretical guidance in the studies of breaking waves.

MEASUREMENT OF WAVES

I have left this till the last because it seems that the immediate problem to be solved must generally determine the type of measuring instrument to be used. Some of the more obvious needs, such as measurement of the larger and more important-looking waves to a first order of accuracy, seem to be well provided for, but it must be emphasized that the necessary equipment is often sufficiently complex to need some attention by a specialist who understands it thoroughly and who is available when required to inspect and service it after installation. It is probably fair to say that more failures are due to lack of such care and understanding than to weakness in design. It is, of course, up to the designer to give a good idea of the limitations as well as the advantages of the instrument; they are not all meant to work in very exposed situations. Damage to electric cables is perhaps one of the most frequent causes of failure so that there seems to be some advantage in using frequency-modulated systems or digital systems, which are not so dependent on the state of the cable as voltage and current systems. Unexpected radio interference seems to make the maintenance of continuous radio links with offshore installations very difficult.

Perhaps one of the greatest weaknesses is in measurement of very short waves and ripples, which seem to be important in studies of wave generation and of the varying roughness of the sea. There is not much difficulty in tanks and lakes where a thin vertical wire can be supported from a mast or other rigid structure, but it is difficult to make an apparatus that can be used to measure little waves on big waves. Perhaps wave-recording buoys can be designed to carry a vertical wire and made to distinguish between the waves and their own movements. The glitter method gives useful information about the statistics of the fine structure on waves, but it would be useful to have a method that would record the detail on a wave profile under any condition.

Stereophotography is a very positive method, but the problems involved in its planning and execution and the difficulty and labour of analysing the photographs seem to reduce its applicability. The growing numbers of wave-recording buoys that measure wave slope in two directions as well as vertical accelerations afford a ready method of studying the two-dimensional spectrum of waves. But the most outstanding need is suitable radar equipment for making rapid measurements of wave profiles from aircraft. Initial success has been obtained with prototypes, and further development and use ought to be fairly straightforward, though perhaps expensive; it will be very simple and cheap in comparison with what goes into space ships, and at least as important.

FUTURE RESEARCH

It seems superfluous to insist that the greatest need is still for closer integration of theory and experiment. Observations of one sort and another are urgently required for a variety of purposes, but a lot of effort will be saved when we have better understanding of the physical processes involved. A systematic approach is not only more satisfying, it is forced on us by the scope and difficulty of the problems that have still to be solved. We must not be afraid of venturing outside the circle of past experience nor should we persist in trying plausible but ill-imagined things till we are only turning over stones.

In particular we must make as serious a study of the flow of turbulent air over a water surface as is made of the flow of air over the wings of an aircraft. It is perhaps just as difficult and rewarding and requires the same collaboration between advanced science and engineering.

Tank experiments must be an essential part of future work, but to be fully effective they must be designed more frequently to test individual theoretical conclusions. It seems, for example, rather doubtful whether model experiments blowing air over water will give much information about wave generation unless great care is taken to control and measure the turbulence and shear in the air stream.

* * *

The usefulness of an elementary appreciation of this subject is likely to be limited, but I hope my comments will help some persons who, like myself, are keenly interested but unable to go deeply enough into the essential theoretical and practical problems of the subject. It shows what I feel, but I work with an active group and probably reflect a sort of smoothed outline of their views.

We all have cause to be grateful to the organisers of the Conference, which will do much to stimulate the exchange of ideas. On behalf of those taking part, particularly the overseas visitors, I should like to thank the National Academy of Sciences – National Research Council and the U. S. Navy for providing such a unique opportunity for us to discuss how further progress can best be made.

ONE-DIMENSIONAL GRAVITY

WAVE SPECTRA

JOHN J. SCHULE, JR.

R. DORRESTEIN

CHAIRMEN

GERHARD NEUMANN
WILLARD J. PIERSON, JR.

ONE

KNOWN AND UNKNOWN PROPERTIES OF
THE FREQUENCY SPECTRUM OF A WIND-GENERATED SEA

THE PROCESS

The motion of the surface that forms the boundary between air and water is a function of space and time. This surface presents the appearance of a series of irregular moving ridges and hollows that gradually grow and shrink with time. Spray rising into the air and air bubbles in the water should perhaps be considered as well as the masses of water overhanging a pocket of air. If they are not considered, this surface is then a single-valued function of x, y, and t, $\eta(x, y, t)$. The air motions above this surface and the water motions below it must satisfy the nonlinear equations for fluid motions and a nonlinear boundary condition at this surface. These equations have never been solved exactly.

Even under the above simplifications of the nature of the problem, the surface, $\eta(x, y, t)$, has an amazingly complex structure involving distances ranging from centimeters to thousands of meters and hundreds of kilometers to describe its spatial appearance, and times ranging from 0.01 seconds to many days to describe its temporal variation. The function $\eta(x, y, t)$ has not yet been measured exactly over a volume of the x, y, t space. Nor has the function $\eta(x, y, t)$ for fixed t ever been measured exactly over a large area as to the complete structure described above. Also $\eta(x, y, t)$

has never been measured exactly for x and y fixed as a function of t. At the present stage of instrumental techniques it will be necessary to look at parts of the structure of $\eta(x, y, t)$ with different instrumentation systems of varying precision under a wide variety of uncontrolled conditions, and only for a limited number of controlled conditions in wind tunnels and wave tanks.

The water at and below $\eta(x, y, t)$ is set into motion by the motion of the air above. The water motion, being dominantly oscillatory in character, extracts energy from the air motion and stores it in the form of potential and kinetic energy. This energy is dissipated in turn by eddy viscosity and by a process that destroys patches of organized motion and converts it into regions of disorganized motions with strong dissipative shear zones. However, these dissipative effects are not as rapid or as strong as the generative effects in the beginning stages. A considerable motion in the water accompanied by appreciable variation in $\eta(x, y, t)$ often continues for a number of hours after the air motion weakens. Moreover, the disturbance in the water can propagate out of an area of strong air motion to areas of relative calm, traveling for many hundreds of kilometers.

Although considerable success has been achieved by making numerous assumptions about the nature of the motion of the water (potential inviscid flow with linearizing assumptions), the motion of the air immediately over the water is much less well understood. The air is a compressible, viscous, highly turbulent fluid whose motions depend on the temperature difference between the air and water and the space-time properties of the surface $\eta(x, y, t)$. The case of interest is the one in which the air motion produces a mean wind that has eddies of various sizes embedded in it (as opposed to convective type zero mean circulations). This mean wind generally increases with elevation, and at times it appears to follow approximately some form of a logarithmic law, in the lowest ten meters or so, with elevation for those cases in which $\eta(x, y, t)$ has a range of less than about two meters.

Measurements of the air motion over the water are in an even less satisfactory state than measurements of $\eta(x, y, t)$. Some measurements have been made, and others are being attempted when $\eta(x, y, t)$ has a small range, but when large oscillations occur, little can be done to measure the air motion through a range of elevations above the moving water surface. Also many previous observations of air motion have neglected the measurement of $\eta(x, y, t)$, and many measurements of $\eta(x, y, t)$ have been obtained with only crude measurements of the air motion.

SOME THEORY

Although the equations that govern the motions under consideration have never been completely solved, various simplifications and approximations are possible that lead to results not totally divorced from reality. Classical linear and nonlinear periodic wave theory contains some of these results in which the air over the water is neglected to a greater or lesser extent. The linear theory when properly randomized and when interpreted in a probabilistic sense describes many of the properties of $\eta(x, y, t)$. In very recent results some effects of the wind over the water have been included.

The highly irregular moving surface $\eta(x, y, t)$ has properties that do not appear to be properly described by a linear theory. For example, one can tell immediately if it is upside down. The very small motions under the control of both surface tension and gravity are recognizably different in form from the larger motions under the dominant effect of gravity. In the absence of air motion with surface tension neglected the equations governing the behavior of $\eta(x, y, t)$ have been extended so as to obtain a probabilistic model correct to the second order that shows these properties.

THE OBSERVATIONS

The moving surface described above is, of course, one of the features of the wind-generated sea caused by the wind over the water. These seas affect many of mankind's activities by limiting the speeds of ships, causing the loss of ships in extreme conditions, obscuring radar targets by a background of sea clutter, and stirring the layer of water nearest the surface, thus affecting the depth of the thermocline. For example, its form must in some way determine the stress of the wind at the water surface and hence the storm tides caused by hurricanes. It is thus rather important to understand these waves in nature — both how the waves are generated and affected by the wind as well as how the wind field immediately over the waves is affected by the waves. There is a close coupling between wave and air motion in immediate contact at the air-sea boundary.

At the present time, waves as observed by ships at sea are described by four numbers: the dominant direction to 36 parts of a circle, the average of the heights of a "well defined sequence of waves," and the average of the "periods" of these same waves. The definition for both wave height and wave period is inadequate. Even discounting the difficulty of estimating a wave height at sea, ten different people could get ten different answers differing easily by a factor of two from the greatest to the least, depending on the particular sequence of "well defined waves" that was chosen and on the number of waves in this "well defined sequence." Visual wave observations really ought to include a complete sequence of 51 to 102 waves with all heights estimated, and the average height of the 17 or 34 highest waves in the sequence should be reported. This will provide at least a crude estimate of sampling variability. This technique of visual wave observations was used by G. Neumann (1952) in 1950–51. He also included sequences of apparent wave-period observations for 50 to 100 waves at given sea state conditions.

MEASUREMENT

If attention is concentrated for the moment on measurements at a fixed point (more or less) as a function of time, techniques of varying degrees of precision have been developed to measure $\eta(t)$. In wind tunnels, for variations of the order of one-half a centimeter, $\eta(t)$ has been measured at time scales that involve time intervals of the order of 0.02 seconds, and $\partial\eta(t)/\partial x$ has been measured at time scales that involve 0.01 second to define the record properly by a series of points. For variations of the order of $\frac{1}{8}$ to 2 meters, wires or poles have been developed. For variations of the order of 2 to 6 meters, $\eta_{tt}(t)$ has been measured by a small free floating raft that senses the vertical acceleration. For a variation of the order of 10 to 20 meters, a shipborne recorder has been developed.

However, all such measurement devices have serious design problems. Although there is some understanding of how they function within the framework of a drastically linearized theory, some of the more important questions that are currently of interest will be difficult to answer because of the shortcomings of these devices and because of inadequate theoretical development. As examples, the poles and wires are too coarse to measure the rapid low oscillations defined at the 0.01-second time scale. The shipborne recorder cannot sense the $\frac{1}{8}$- to 2-meter, 2- to 3-second oscillations superimposed on the 10- to 18-meter, 10- to 20-second oscillations much less the 0.5-cm, 0.02-second oscillations.

SYNOPTIC WAVE-RECORDING SYSTEM

The only organization to record waves on a systematic synoptic basis is the National Institute of Oceanography in Great Britain. They have been recording waves since before 1953 on British weather ships with an instrument developed by M. J. Tucker (1956). It would be highly desirable to have all of the weather ships in the North Atlantic Ocean record waves by similar techniques on a synoptic basis. But this alone is not enough because it often takes many months before such records are reduced to a form where they can be used in a practical way, and thus an immediate determination of the spectral form would be highly desirable. Recommendations given in a recent report edited by E. V. Lewis and G. Gerard (1959) are of interest here. It is most heartening that the Hydrographic Office of the U. S. Navy is planning to set up a wave recording and data reduction program on a synoptic basis.

The data that are presently available, in view of the location of the vessels that obtain them, are, in the opinion of the writers, not enough to help solve the problems connected with an adequate description of the spectrum of a wind-generated sea.

THE PROBLEM

Given such wave recordings obtained as a function of time on the open ocean, the problem of how to analyze these records arises. If the assumption is made that they are samples from a quasi-stationary random process that is approximately Gaussian, the techniques for the analysis of such records are available. If the records are varying too rapidly (for example, if the average wave height is sensibly increasing throughout a twenty-minute interval) or if the records are decidedly non-Gaussian in character, techniques have yet to be developed. Nevertheless, the techniques for the analysis of stationary Gaussian processes are the most logical and the most adaptable to this particular problem. Moreover, it would seem that most wave situations are such that the lack of stationarity for twenty- or thirty-minute observation and the departure from normality will not seriously distort the interpretation of an analysis based on the stationary Gaussian assumption. This is true especially for the interpretations that the writers have in mind at this time.

Assuming, therefore, that we wish to proceed to analyze the records as if they were samples from a stationary Gaussian process, what is the best technique? It must be recognized that a finite sample is being analyzed, that the sample has been subject to sampling variability, and that spectra estimated from different finite samples from a truly stationary Gaussian process differ. It is, therefore, essential to separate this sampling variability from the variability caused by the weather, the winds, and the propagation of disturbances from one area to another on the open ocean. This is one of the reasons why the spectral analysis of time records should prove so fruitful because it gives the analyst an additional dimension in which to work to determine the causative mechanisms that determine the properties of the sea surface that has been observed.

In addition to sampling variability, the spectra that can be obtained or recovered from a given finite sample are distorted by the effect of a convolution with some filter function in the frequency domain. It is quite likely that some of the differences of opinion as to the form of the spectrum are due to the fact that different scientists have applied different data-reduction techniques, and hence different convolution functions, to their data. Only a few investigators have used the results of R. B. Blackman and J. W. Tukey (1958) for the reduction of such time series. The procedure of analyzing a record by considering the equally weighted sums of the squares of the values of the Fourier spectral components within a certain band, and weighting adjacent bands by factors of $\frac{1}{4}$, $\frac{1}{2}$, and $\frac{1}{4}$, definitely applies a quite different filter to the form of the spectrum. One of the results of a conference like this perhaps might be agreement on a standardized system of data reduction. The writers believe that the standardized system should follow the procedures outlined by Blackman and Tukey for digital computations and that analogue devices should be constructed that will parallel these procedures as closely as possible. W. Marks and P. Strausser (1959) have constructed an analogue analyzer that reproduces in almost exact detail the spectrum that would be obtained by a Tukey analysis. Given a number of such spectra, it may well be worthwhile to attempt to devise a technique that will unconvolve the computed spectra and try to recover something more like the original spectrum.

It would be most educational if a particular record, obtained both as an analogue voltage signal and as a chart paper record, could be analyzed by every technique that has been used in the reduction of wave records to date. The spectra that would be so obtained would perhaps differ, and this would be one reason why different investigators have come up with different theoretical forms for such spectra.

Another possible source of such discrepancies is the instrumentation that has been used to record the waves. The instrument developed by Tucker attenuates the high frequencies in the signal. The device used by Kinsman fills in the troughs of the waves and may perhaps cause one to question the reliability of the skewness and kurtosis values that he obtained as an indication of the departure from normality in the marginal distribution of the points read from a wave record. In the study of waves no instrument that could be considered a primary standard of calibration exists. Whenever waves have been recorded simultaneously in the same area by two different recording techniques, the results have not been made to agree (to the authors' present knowledge). From the theoretical point of view it would be highly desirable to be able to take wave observations by two different recording systems and to explain whatever discrepancies existed between the spectra resulting from the two observations, apart from sampling variability, on the basis of the response of the different instruments.

THE KNOWN PROPERTIES OF THE SPECTRUM

A great many different scientific papers have been published on the form of the spectrum of a wind-generated sea. They differ in many ways. As many as possible of these papers are listed in the bibliography at the end of this paper.

If we simplify the situation by eliminating those cases in which swells or dead seas have contaminated the spectrum and made it double- or multi-peaked, the spectrum that is computed from a wave record obtained when the wind was actually acting on the sea surface and generating the waves has a wide variety of forms, depending upon some of the more obvious variables that might be expected to influence the situation. For fetches of the order of 12 or 15 feet, when the waves are recorded in a wind tunnel, the area under the spectrum which is proportional to the square of the significant height yields a significant height near $\frac{1}{2}$ cm. Fetches of the order of kilometers for a constant wind yield heights of a few feet. On the open ocean observed significant heights have ranged from several feet to 40 or 50 feet or more. Thus the area under the spectrum increases as a function of fetch for a constant wind velocity.

The spectra computed from what are effectively infinite durations for this range of fetches all have a number of properties in common. First, from zero up to a certain frequency that shall be designated f_0 the activity in the spectrum is quite low. There is some question as to just what this activity actually is. It may be due to nonlinear interactions between the various frequencies in the more dominant part of the spectrum where it must be recognized a second order theory may not account for all of what could occur. On the other hand, it may be due to basically linear motions that are independent of most of the spectrum of the sea and that are propagating at their own linear phase speed (with the appropriate group velocities) for each frequency that is involved. There is still a third possibility that the instrumentation has introduced these frequencies by spurious drifts. This portion of the frequency range is of considerable interest, however, and ways to separate these three possibilities, such as those proposed by W. Munk, F. E. Snodgrass, and M. J. Tucker (1959), need to be developed. In quite a bit of the past work oceanographers (including the present authors) have tended to attribute this portion of the frequency range to instrumental discrepancies. Recent theoretical work suggests that this may not be the case.

Near the frequency f_0 the spectral intensity increases very rapidly over a narrow spectral range to a very sharp and well pronounced peak. On the other side of the peak the spectral intensities fall off much more gradually and approach zero at very high frequencies. It would appear that the rise to the forward peak of this spectrum is almost vertical. Of course, this is due partly to the scale of frequencies plotted on the abscissa. All of the present systems of data reduction and analysis have tended to ignore the fact that the spectrum has been convolved with a convolving function. If the rise to the peak is essentially vertical and if the spectral analysis (being digital at times) involves a frequency band that straddles the vertical rise in the spectrum, the first point of the forward face will be considerably lowered. The data reduction techniques described above for the reduction of the spectrum of stationary Gaussian processes and those actually used in wave record analysis are all relatively insensitive to a sharp forward face on such a spectrum, and no published results contradict the hypothesis that this face could be treated as if it were essentially vertical.

With reference to the high frequency side, literature dealing with the tail of the spectrum has advocated all possible high frequency asymptotic behaviors, including exponential, k/ω^7, k/ω^6, $k/\omega^{5.5}$, $k/\omega^{5.xxx}$, (carried out to a number of significant figures on the basis of least square fits to a large mass of data), and k/ω^5. The form, k/ω^6, appears to be near the center of this range of values. B. Kinsman (1960) has also stoutly contended that the question of the particular number that would go into the exponential of ω on the basis of the average of a large number of records is rather a nonsense question because the nonlinear interactions in the second and higher order effects of the spectrum are obscured when the spectra are averaged. This may well be the case, and some of the discrepancies and debate may be due to the fact that some authors are considering a linear system and others are working with data that involve nonlinear effects and certainly involve corrections at the high frequency end of the spectrum.

O. M. Phillips (1958) has pointed out that sharp-crested waves in the space domain imply a spectrum that behaves like $\alpha g^2/\omega^5$. His analysis, however, is based on dimensional arguments. Moreover, the analysis involved depends on highly nonlinear features. One might also suggest, for example, that the high-frequency behavior of the spectrum depends on $\alpha g^2 \omega_0^p/\omega^{5+p}$, where ω_0 is the peak of the spectrum and controls the total power under the spectrum. It is also interesting to note that R. W. Burling (1959) now leans more toward $k/\omega^{5.5}$ upon further analysis of his observations.

It should also be pointed out that waves not only are sharp-crested on the open sea, but they also break, and it is the belief of the writers that the eventual explanation for the high-frequency behavior of the spectrum of a wind-generated sea will be found in a study of the probability structure of breaking waves. The high-frequency behavior of the spectrum of a wind-generated sea is undoubtedly determined by nonlinear considerations.

It is, however, very likely that with increasing wave motion and the appearance of high, breaking seas, partial obliteration of wave energy at the high-frequency end of the spectra occurs in patchlike patterns at the sea surface. This may result in a decrease of energy at the high-frequency end with increasing sea state conditions, on the average, for the whole sea surface. In general, we note that the higher the exponent of ω, the higher the waves.

THE OPEN SEA

Given a wave record as a function of time obtained at a particular point $x_0 y_0$ on the open ocean for, say, twenty minutes, the waves recorded will depend upon the state of the sea over the whole ocean for the times previous to the time of the observation and upon the velocity field in the air, from the surface of the water up to a considerable elevation, over the entire ocean prior to the time of the observation. A particular observation may have a swell in it that has traveled a great distance to the point of observation. The swell in turn may have been generated many hours ago and often many hundreds of kilometers away, and it has taken this time to travel to the area of observation. Similarly, with the wind velocity field varying in speed and direction over the ocean, a certain sea state probably existed over the same area a day or so before the time of the observation, and one must check to see whether it has had time to travel away from the place of observation before a new local sea generated by the more recent winds develops. The wind field itself is a complicated structure, and it is questionable whether or not different turbulent properties in the wind field for the first ten meters or so above the surface of the water can produce different spectra for the same mean wind at ten meters. One of the more controversial questions here concerns air-sea temperature differences. Whether or not the air-sea temperature difference produces differences in the observed wave height and in observed spectra, with all other conditions kept the same, is not the question. The question is what the differences are.

There are a great number of different wave forecasting procedures available today developed by a number of different authors. The differences between them are very striking. One would almost question whether the various authors were working on the same planet with the same weather conditions. The argument has been advanced that the ocean waves on one side of the Atlantic are remarkably different from ocean waves on the other side of the Atlantic on the basis of different results from different forecasting techniques. It is the belief of the writers that ocean waves on one side of the Atlantic are not different from ocean waves on the other side of the Atlantic and that a properly devised wave forecasting technique (including the depth of the water) will work in any ocean at any time under any circumstances and will predict the conditions in a wind-generated sea to within plus or minus ten percent. Some of the forecasting techniques must obviously be wrong, and given the synoptic observations described above on a routine basis for all weather ships on the Atlantic, it should not take too long to decide which ones are wrong. (They may all be wrong to a greater or lesser extent.) In what follows some of the major discrepancies between the different forecasting techniques will be pointed out, and observational procedures will be described that will make it possible to decide which procedures are most nearly correct. An important goal should be that of properly forecasting the state of the sea on the open ocean as a function of the geographical boundaries of the ocean and of the weather and winds over the ocean. This goal should not be delayed much longer.

THE OPEN SEA FORECASTING PROBLEM

At the present time there are a number of wave forecasting techniques that are based on the concept of wave spectra and a number of techniques that are based on some of the features of wave spectra but that do not use the spectra explicitly in the forecasting procedure. The methods of J. Darbyshire (1959), W. J. Pierson, Jr., G. Neumann, and R. W. James (1955), and C. L. Bretschneider (1959) are based on wave spectra concepts. The method of H. Walden (1958) is based on wave spectra, but it is not necessary to appeal to the form of the spectrum to prepare a given forecast. Some of the recent work by S. C. Wen (1960) is of interest in this regard.

Darbyshire's method has one rather decided advantage over all of the other procedures in that it is based on wave records actually obtained at sea for a great many years. However, in many respects, this method is in contradiction to the concepts employed in the other forecasting methods. In fact, there appears to be a dichotomy between the results of Darbyshire and the results of other investigators. It is rather important to delineate the areas in which these discrepancies arise and to attempt to formulate procedures that will resolve some of these differences.

The results of Darbyshire essentially call for fully developed seas nearly all of the time. That is, his techniques imply that there is very little lag between the state of the sea and the presently observed wind speed. It has also been stated that there is little effect of fetch for any fetch greater than 100 nautical miles in length regardless of the speed of the wind. The results of Darbyshire are not clear on how rapidly a given sea state will die down once the wind has died down, and there is no evidence in his work that the so-called Filter IV method in PNJ actually works on the open ocean. If there is no effect of viscosity and friction in causing the decrease of the height of waves in a fetch where the waves have been aroused to some given significant height, then the Filter IV method would yield the result that waves in a large fetch would die down less rapidly than waves in a small fetch, especially at the down-wind edge of the fetch.

In contrast, all of the other methods for forecasting waves imply time lags of greater or lesser magnitude. The state of the sea is not simply a function of the wind velocity observed in a particular instant of time. With a wind of constant velocity and a sufficiently long fetch, the sea can continue to grow in height until a steady state is reached at a much later time. These other methods all predict that with a high wind speed, a long time is needed for a full build-up of the sea and that this full build-up cannot occur unless there are fetches of greater length than 100 nautical miles over the oceans. These other methods all disagree as to how high the highest possible waves are for a given wind speed, and as to what fetches and durations are needed to achieve waves of a certain height and period. However, they all disagree more sharply with the results of Darbyshire than they do with each other.

In most cases of storm waves, with wind speeds exceeding 50 knots in the North Atlantic, both duration and fetch around the storm center appear too short with the passage of the storm to generate a fully developed sea. Exceptions may be observed in the higher southern latitudes, where a sequence of storms may continue to increase the wave energy at certain time intervals during which the decay of the waves does not exceed the energy input by the following storm. The question of the highest possible waves for a given wind speed is, therefore, a question of the minimum fetches and minimum wind durations required for the given wind speed.

It would seem that the best way to check these different procedures one against the other would be to prepare wave forecasts for the open sea and see which technique actually performs the best. However, in this respect the weather over the oceans is not too cooperative. We seldom find a wind of 60 knots that switches on suddenly at a time $t = 0$, and blows for three days over a fetch of 1000 nautical miles. Should such an event actually occur, we would probably not have the right wave measuring devices in the vicinity to make proper wave observations.

Extratropical cyclones at sea have a time scale and a scale of dimensions that are unique unto themselves. Exceptionally long durations and fetches occur only when the cyclone is blocked and builds to a scale of great intensity without moving across the ocean. Exceptional storms with winds over 50 knots and durations of a day or more and fetches of 500 or 600 nautical miles are rare in the literature and deserve a special write-up and description of the conditions that are observed during such storms. Also, the old observations by Graf von Larisch (1925) in the Southern Hemisphere, especially around the Cape Horn region, and his motion pictures taken of the seas in these latitudes deserve attention.

One such storm has been studied by Darbyshire (1955), Pierson (1959), and Walden (1960). Bretschneider's results were given by Pierson (1959). The results of the analysis served only to show that each of the forecasting procedures gave results that were more or less in agreement with that which was observed. As far as spectral detail is concerned, neither the results of Darbyshire nor those of Pierson, Neumann and James agree perfectly with the spectra that were computed from the observations. The spectral forms of Walden and Bretschneider have not as yet been compared with the observed spectra. Thus, despite the wide discrepancies in the bases of the various forecasting techniques, these techniques did equally well in forecasting the average sea state (significant height, periods, etc.) when applied to a fairly severe storm that produced waves with significant heights of about 40 feet. The determination of the spectra, or spectral details, is obviously a much more delicate procedure.

Also, it must be pointed out that Darbyshire (1957) has documented at least one case where fetches of great length and winds of long duration did not result in steadily growing waves — at a wind speed where some of these methods would have forecasted a steady wave growth.

Moreover, H. Walden (1959) has compared some formulas given by N. N. Djounkovski and P. K. Bojitch with those of other authors. These results agree more with Darbyshire than with the other forecasts. For durations of 12 hours and fetches of 100 nautical miles, the waves, even for a 40-knot wind, are nearly fully developed. However, Walden points out that some of the observations, on which the curves are based, were taken in shallow water, and the results may have been influenced by this.

It may well be that the truth lies somewhere between these two extremes. To believe that waves almost instantaneously follow the wind is very difficult. Possibly, the gradual increase of wind speed in a region of high winds, an increase from, say, 30 knots to 55 or 60 knots, over a period of a day and a half is so slow compared with the actual growth of the waves for a long enough fetch, that instantaneous agreement between the wind and the waves could be expected. This possibility needs much more intensive checking than it has been given up to the present time. An understanding of wave spectra and their growth as a function of duration and fetch should, however, exclude directly "built in" locations or special meteorological situations. These should be accounted for by more general factors, involving time and space, so that the method or the spectral form can be applied to any given meteorological situation.

These questions can be settled only by a large collection of simultaneous instrumental wave recordings and instrumental wind speed observations. The currently available wind speed estimates and data from visual observations of waves are not adequate in our opinion since the problem of resolving the errors in these observations is just as difficult as that of resolving the discrepancies in the various forecasting methods. However, given adequate instrumental wave observations and a proper definition of wind speeds at the time that the waves were observed, it is possible to propose various experiments that would concentrate on these differences one by one and resolve the conflicts in the different methods. Observations with clearly defined and quasi-stationary meteorological conditions are necessary. This would eliminate, at least to some degree, the little known effects of varying wind speeds and directions (moving fetches).

EXPERIMENTS ON THE EFFECT OF FETCH IN LIMITING WAVE HEIGHTS

Perhaps one of the greatest discrepancies between the methods of Darbyshire and the others is in the concept of fetch. If a fetch of 100 nautical miles only is needed to achieve a fully developed sea state for any wind speed, the problem of wave forecasting would be greatly simplified. However, the open ocean between Iceland and England and the Atlantic to the west of England is hardly the place to define fetches of the scale of 100 nautical miles accurately from the synoptic weather observations made in this region. The effect of fetch can best be studied when offshore winds blow over a given region of the ocean for a sufficient distance offshore to establish fetches of various lengths. At the same time the condition that the duration be sufficiently long over the fetch can be established. Preferably also the water should be quite deep immediately offshore from the continental land

mass. This last requirement is the most difficult to meet, and there is some question whether or not the east coast of the United States will fulfill this requirement because of a continental shelf that extends quite a distance out to sea.

However, with the help of the U. S. Navy Hydrographic Office an experiment is to be carried out to test these concepts for conditions offshore from the east coast of the United States. The wave recording instrument that is being used is the Splashnik (R. G. Tuckerman [1960]) developed at the David Taylor Model Basin. A brief description of the technical part of this experiment as set forth in some memoranda to the Hydrographic Office follows:

Required Synoptic Conditions

One of the difficulties in the verification of the results of Darbyshire is that his observations were taken from a weather ship halfway between Iceland and England. It is difficult to decide upon the dimensions of the fetches that are involved on the open ocean. Here on the east coast there is an advantage in that, if a well-defined synoptic situation develops such that the winds are definitely offshore from the continental land mass, the fetch can more accurately be delineated. There is a difficulty that cannot be treated at the moment theoretically in that the shoal waters of the continental shelf may limit the height of the waves. Nevertheless, it is felt that the experiment should be carried out without taking this feature into consideration and that perhaps later it can be accounted for subjectively by testing to see if the water was deep enough so that it would not affect the dominant part of the spectrum. The first requirement is, therefore, nearly uniform offshore winds over an extensive area of the east coast that have lasted long enough to establish a steady state as a function of fetch as measured from the coast. For the sake of the design of the experiment the required durations for the offshore wind will be those of H. O. Pub. 603, and this of course requires an increase in duration with increasing wind speed so that a steady state is established. It would be on the safe side to add about 10 percent to each of the required durations in H. O. Pub. 603 so as to be sure of a fully developed sea. For the short fetches this involves a large safety factor, and for the long fetches perhaps even longer durations would be better.

Another rather important feature of the synoptic situation should be that the chance of swell from a distance opposing and running through the local sea should be a minimum. This is, of course, quite difficult to realize and there may well be some swell from a distance. The experimental program should not be abandoned if this is the case but some attempt to make sure that the swell is contained in a frequency band quite different from that of the local sea should be made. If the frequency band of the swell is markedly different from that of the local sea it can be eliminated from the spectrum after the acceleration records have been analyzed.

Experimental Procedure

The accompanying table shows the experimental procedure that is to be used. The first row of the table gives the mean wind speed at anemometer level in knots. The next row gives the theoretical fetch for a fully developed sea for the tabulated wind speed. The third row gives the required duration. The next three rows give the significant height for that fully developed sea, and one-third and two-thirds of that same height. The last three rows give the fetches at which one-third of the significant height is realized, two-thirds of the significant height is realized, and that value of the fetch that is one and a half times the fetch

required for a fully developed sea. It would thus seem that four observations made with the Splashniks for each particular wind speed at the four values of the fetch that are tabulated would be the proper procedure to check out on this concept of fetch limitation of wave heights. For example, if the offshore wind speed averaged to about 26 knots for more than 17 hours, one would then proceed to attempt to take Splashnik observations at offshore distances of 31 nautical miles, 85 nautical miles, 180 nautical miles, and 270 nautical miles. These observations could be taken at any time and in any sequence as long as the average wind stayed at 26 knots and the duration was over 17 hours.

If the wind was increasing from 26 to, say, 28 knots, then one would proceed to allow for the increasing duration that was needed. Suppose that on proceeding toward shore the wind had picked up from 26 to 28 knots and had lasted, after having been 26 knots for more than 19 hours, for five or six hours at 28 knots. Then it would only be necessary to change the distances from 31 nautical miles to 48 nautical miles and from 85 nautical miles to 130 nautical miles in order to still obtain useful information concerning the effect of fetch. All fetches tabulated can be safely changed by plus or minus 10 percent.

The observational program can be simplified even further. For a range of 14 to 32 knots in steps of 2 knots, 40 different Splashnik observations need to be taken at the indicated values of $F_{1/3}$, $F_{2/3}$, F, and $1.5F$ for each wind

TABLE TO DISCRIMINATE THE EFFECT OF FETCH IN LIMITING THE HEIGHT
OF WIND-GENERATED SEAS

V	14	16	18	20	22	24	26	28	30	32
(3) F^*	28	40	55	75	100	130	180	230	280	340
$\left(\begin{array}{l}+10\% \text{ at}\\ \text{least}\end{array}\right)t$	5.2	6.6	8.3	10	12	14	17	20	23	27
$\overline{H}_{1/3}$	3.23	4.51	6.1	7.9	10.0	12.4	15.2	18.3	21.7	25.5
$\sim H/3$	1.1	1.5	2	2.7	3.3	4	5	6.1	7	8.5
$\sim 2H/3$	2.2	3.0	4	5.2	6.7	8	10	12.2	14	17
(1) $F_{1/3}^*$	5	8	11	16	20	28	31	48	60	70
(2) $F_{2/3}^*$	11	21	31	43	60	70	85	130	150	180
(4) $1.5F^*$	42	60	75	112	150	195	270	345	420	510

NOTATION: * ±10% for all tabulated fetches.
F = fetch, t = duration, $\overline{H}_{1/3}$ significant height fully developed sea,
$H/3$ one third of this height, $2H/3$ two thirds of this height.
$F_{1/3}$ fetch at which waves are $\frac{1}{3}$ of full height according to H. O. Pub. 603,
$F_{2/3}$ fetch at which waves are $\frac{2}{3}$ of full height according to H. O. Pub. 603.

speed. Any observation that meets these requirements can be taken at any time and in any sequence, and eventually the data will be useful in resolving this question.

However, although seven or eight observations could be taken following this perfectly general procedure, they might not be close enough and form a tight enough sequence within the elements of the table to permit the question to be decided. It would therefore be preferable, although not absolutely necessary, to concentrate on two different wind speeds. For example, if the observations could be completed for a wind speed of 18 knots by making observations at fetches of 11, 31, 55, and 90 nautical miles, this would form a very useful sequence. Similarly, the observations for a wind of 26 knots at 31, 85, 180, and 270 nautical miles would also form a very useful sequence as conditions are sufficiently different at these two wind speeds from the 100 nautical mile fetch for all wind speeds proposed by Darbyshire to make discrimination possible.

Requirements of Splashnik Records

A twenty minute long Splashnik record is the minimum time acceptable. Even longer records would be better. The high frequencies in the acceleration record should be recorded if possible in all cases.

Measurements were taken in this program, but they turned out to be not good enough to provide answers to this problem. Further attempts will be made to carry out the plans described above.

EXPERIMENTS ON LIMITATION OF WAVE HEIGHT BY DURATION OF WINDS

Resolution of the problems concerning the effect of duration is rather difficult. Observations made every six hours are not sufficiently close in time resolution to permit good discrimination for the lower wind speeds. Perhaps here a sequence of observations every hour or so for the lower wind speeds would provide insight into what actually occurs. Moreover, there is a difficulty of the advection of a given sea state by the winds as it moves across the ocean. The discussions in H. O. Pub. 603 on the effects of a passing cold front and of the sudden increase of wave height behind the

cold front is of interest in this connection. The observed durations at a fixed point are not truly representative of the conditions that would occur if a wind field of a certain speed were to spring up suddenly over an entire fetch that had previously been covered by very low waves.

One technique for studying the effects of duration is to begin immediately to assemble pertinent data on exceptional storms at sea. If a number of storms can be found that have the same long fetch and initial build-up of winds, and then if the duration of the peak of the storm is different (with say, one storm providing 50-knot winds for only 6 hours and another providing 50-knot winds for 24 hours), then a comparison of the state of the sea at the end of the 6-hour period and at the end of the 24-hour period can be made that will perhaps shed some light on the problem of the effect of duration. One such storm that occurred in December 1959 is being studied by these techniques at the present time, but as of the date of this writing nothing definitive has been learned. Many such storms will have to be documented thoroughly before some of these questions can be settled.

HIGHEST WAVES FOR A FULLY ARISEN SEA

Last but not least is the question of the highest waves for a fully arisen sea. Here the range of possible answers is extremely broad, and a wide variety of spectra is therefore implied. In general, the results of Darbyshire provide the lowest upper bound on the highest waves for a fully arisen sea. If his basic conclusions as outlined above — namely that the seas follow the winds practically instantaneously — are correct, then his results would be correct in this final conclusion. However, if longer durations and greater fetches do actually produce higher waves, as the other forecasting methods predict, then the sample of points that Darbyshire has used to fit his H proportional V^2 curve does not represent a sample of wave heights for the highest possible sea for a given wind.

This also brings up the question of the wave spectra that should exist for fully developed seas for given speeds. This question has two sides to it. For low winds there is the decided possibility that the spectra have been contaminated by the waves left over from previously higher winds or by waves that have traveled into the area from a distance. For the high winds again, the fully developed state may not have been attained. This is perhaps part of the reason for the great discrepancies in the theoretical forms for the spectra of fully developed seas that have been published. The PNJ method especially considers much higher wave heights at storm wind speeds for fully arisen seas than do other methods.

The fetch and duration experiments that have been described above will help to settle this question. If certain low frequencies are not present in waves generated offshore from a continental land mass, and if a fully developed state is achieved for a given fetch so that the spectrum can be believed to be fully representative of a fully developed state for that particular wind, then some of the discrepancies between the various theoretical spectra will be eliminated. Similarly, if the duration experiments should prove that the waves continue to grow for a given high wind speed as the durations become larger for a long enough fetch, then it will become evident that the data presently used to fit the curve for the significant heights of fully developed seas do not represent the worst conditions for each wind speed. It would therefore seem that pursuing the procedures described above with reference to fetch and duration will also shed some light on the problem of the highest waves for a given wind speed.

Should it turn out that the observations that are needed to describe the fully arisen sea for a given wind speed have not yet been taken, then there arises the data collection problem. We simply must wait for a ship to be in the right place at the right time and for the fetch and duration to be more than adequate to provide a fully developed sea, and then the sea must be observed. At this time and only at this time will it be possible to settle on the appropriate law that governs wave height in relation to wind speed.

AIR-SEA TEMPERATURE DIFFERENCE

Another area of considerable difference of opinion lies in the effects of air-sea temperature differences in the generation of waves of a given height. One must be careful to differentiate between the use of air-sea temperature differences to predict the surface wind from the gradient wind and their use to modify a given wave-height forecast based on the surface wind. The first of these two procedures is a standard technique for filling in missing areas of synoptic wind data. The second technique actually assumes that different sea states result

from different air-sea temperature differences and the same wind as observed at the anemometer level. It is agreed that there may be some effect of air-sea temperature differences on the height of the waves in a given weather situation. However, it is the opinion of the writers that this effect has not been properly separated out from the other more dominant effects — those of wind speed, fetch, and duration. The air-sea temperature differences strongly correlate with wind speed, the fetch and the duration. If the air is much colder than the water, this implies a high wind speed because the air must have traveled rapidly from the land along a relatively straight fetch to the point of observation. It therefore would not have had much time to have been modified by its trajectory over water. In this sense, therefore, a condition in the which the air is much colder than the water is automatically associated with a longer fetch and a higher wind speed than is usual for a given place of observation.

Given the inaccuracies of present wind speed estimates, and the difficulties in determining the actual trajectories over the water, it would seem that the problem of air-sea temperature differences cannot be resolved by comparing all the heights observed for the same wind speed for different air-sea temperature differences simply because the effects of duration and fetch are still present and have not been properly separated out. It therefore seems that the effects of air-sea temperature differences should be investigated as, in a sense, a residual effect that would reduce the discrepancies in forecasts that were very strongly dependent upon the more dominant parameters of wind speed, fetch, and duration. With discrepancies in the various forecasting methods of the order of many feet for a given meteorological condition, it does not seem justifiable at the present time to add 5 or 10 percent corrections one way or the other in order to try to take into account the effects of air-sea temperature differences.

SUMMARY AND CONCLUSIONS

In many ways the problem under investigation is complex. The mechanisms that cause the waves on the open ocean are decidedly nonlinear, and they are not well understood. The fully developed sea for a given wind speed and for a long enough fetch and duration is limited by nonlinear effects, as is evidenced by the presence of whitecaps and spindrift on the open ocean.

Little agreement exists in the literature at the present time about the form of the spectrum of a fully arisen sea or about the successive stages of growth of the spectrum of a wind-generated sea. The only areas of agreement may be that the spectrum has essentially a vertical forward face and that it behaves like k/ω^n, with n somewhere between 4 and 8 at the high frequencies.

The effects of fetch, duration, wind speed, and air-sea temperature difference are not settled. Experiments have been described that may help settle these questions. The differences of opinion among various scientists in this area are great enough so that these differences can be subjected to scientific tests in order to contrast the results that have been presented and to settle on the ones that prove to be more nearly correct.

* * *

ACKNOWLEDGMENTS

The research reported in this paper has been supported by the Office of Naval Research under Contract Nonr-285(03). Reproduction in whole or in part for any purpose of the United States Government is permitted.

REFERENCES AND BIBLIOGRAPHY

Blackman, R. B. and J. W. Tukey, "The Measurement of Power Spectra from the Point of View of Communications Engineering." Parts I and II. *Bell System Tech. J.*, Jan. 1958, Mar. 1958. (Also available in book form from Dover Publications, Inc., New York.)

Bracelin, P., *Observing, Forecasting and Reporting Ocean Waves and Surf.* Naval Weather Service, Memo. No. 147/52, 1952.

Bretschneider, C. L., *Wave Variability and Wave Spectra for Wind Generated Gravity Waves*, Beach Erosion Board, Tech. Memo. No. 118, 1959.

Burling, R. W., "Surface Waves on Enclosed Bodies of Water." *Proc. 5th Conf. on Coastal Engineering*, Grenoble, Sept. 1954. Printed 1955.

Burling, R. W., "The Spectrum of Waves at Short Fetches," *D.H.Z.*, Band 12, Heft 2, (1959) 45–119.

Cote, L. J., J. O. Davis, W. Marks, R. J. McGough, E. Mehr, W. J. Pierson, Jr., J. F. Ropek, G. Stephenson and R. C. Vetter, "The Directional Spectrum of a Wind Generated Sea as determined from Data obtained by the Stereo Wave Observation Project." *Meteor. Papers*, II, No. 6 (June 1960). New York University, College of Engineering.

Cox, C. S., "Measurements of Slopes of High-frequency Wind Waves" *J. Mar. Res.*, XVI (1958a) 199–225.

Cox, C. S., "Comments on Dr. Phillip's Paper," *J. Mar. Res.*, XVI (1958b) 241–245.

Darbyshire, J., "An Investigation of Storm Waves in the North Atlantic Ocean" *Proc. Roy. Soc.* A, No. 230 (1955) 560.

Darbyshire, J., "An Investigation into the Generation of Waves when the Fetch of the Wind is less than 100 Miles," *Quart. J. Roy. Meteor. Soc.*, LXXXII, No. 354 (1956) 461.

Darbyshire, J., "A Note on the Comparison of Proposed Wave Spectrum Formulae," *D.H.Z.*, X (1957) 184.

Darbyshire, J., "A Further Investigation of Wind-generated Waves," *D.H.Z.*, XII (1959) 1.

Djounkovski, N. N. and P. K. Bojitch, *La Houle et son Action sur les Côtes et les Ouvrages Côtiers.* Paris, 1959.

*Hicks, B. L., "Contributions for the Easton Conference on Ocean Wave Spectra." C.S.L. Univ. of Illinois, Urbana, Ill., March, 1961.

Kinsman, B., *Surface Waves at Short Fetches and Low Wind Speeds — a Field Study.* Tech. Report XIX, vols. 1, 2, and 3 (1960) ref. 60–1, Chesapeake Bay Institute, The Johns Hopkins University.

Lewis, E. V. and G. Gerard, *A Long-Range Research Program in Ship-Structural Design.* Ship Structure Committee, for Bu-Ships Contract Nobs-72285, National Academy of Sciences — National Research Council, 1959.

Marks, W. and P. Strausser, *Reduction of Sea-Keeping Data at the David Taylor Model Basin.* D. T. M. B. Rep. 1363, 1959.

Miles, J. W., "On the Generation of Surface Waves by Shear Flow," *J. Fluid Mech.*, III (1957) 185.

Munk, W., F. E. Snodgrass and M. J. Tucker, "Spectra of Low-Frequency Ocean Waves," *Bull. Scripps Inst. Ocean.*, VII No. 4 (1959) 283–362.

Neumann, G., "Über die komplexe Natur des Seeganges. 1. Teil: Neue Seegangsbeobachtungen im Nordatlantischen Ozean, in der Karibischen See und im Golf von Mexico (M. S. "Heidberg," Oktober 1950–Februar 1951). 2. Teil: Das Anwachsen der Wellen unter dem Einfluss des Windes." *D. H. Z.*, V (1952) see 95, 252.

Neumann, G., "Zur Charakteristik des Seeganges," *Archiv für Meteorol., Geophys. und Bioklim.*, ser. A, VII (1954) 352.

---

* More references to Hicks are to the paper cited above.

Neumann, G. and W. J. Pierson, Jr., "A Detailed Comparison of Theoretical Wave Spectra and Wave Forecasting Methods," *D. H. Z.*, X (1957) see 73, 134.

Phillips, O. M., "On the Generation of Waves by Turbulent Wind," *J. Fluid Mech.*, II (1957) 417–445.

Phillips, O. M., "The Equilibrium Range in the Spectrum of Wind-Generated Waves," *J. Fluid Mech.*, IV (1958a) 426–434.

Phillips, O. M., "Wave Generation by Turbulent Wind over a Finite Fetch," *Proc. Third Natl. Cong. Appl. Mech.* (1958b) 785–790.

Phillips, O. M., "On Some Properties of the Spectrum of Wind-Generated Ocean Waves," *J. Mar. Res.*, XVI (1958c) 231–240.

Phillips, O. M., "Comments on Dr. Cox's Paper." *J. Mar. Res.*, XVI (1958d) 226–230.

Pierson, W. J., Jr., "Wind-Generated Gravity Waves," *Advances in Geophysics*, II (1955) 93. New York: Academic Press.

Pierson, W. J., Jr., "A Note on the Growth of the Spectrum of Wind-Generated Gravity Waves as determined by Non-Linear Considerations," *J. Geophys. Res.*, LXIV (1959a) 1007–1011.

Pierson, W. J., Jr., "A Study of Wave Forecasting Methods and of the Height of a Fully Developed Sea on the Basis of some Wave Records obtained by the O. W. S. Weather Explorer during a Storm at Sea," *D. H. Z.*, Bd. 12, Heft 6, 1959b.

Pierson, W. J., Jr., "Surface Waves," *Trans. Amer. Geophys. Un.*, XLI, No. 2 (1960).

Pierson, W. J., Jr., G. Neumann and R. W. James, *Practical Methods for Observing and Forecasting Ocean Waves by Means of Wave Spectra and Statistics.* H. O. Pub. 603, U. S. Navy Hydrographic Office.

Rattray, M., Jr., and W. V. Burt, "A Comparison of Methods for Forecasting Wave Generation," *Deep Sea Research*, III No. 2 (1956) 140.

Roll, H. U., "Über Grössenunterschiede der Meereswellen bei Warm- und Kaltluft," *D. H. Z.*, V (1952) 111.

Roll, H. U., "Oberfluchenwellen des Meeres," *Handbuch der Physik*, No. 48. Berlin, Göttingen, Heidelberg.

Roll, H. U. and G. Fischer, "Eine kritische Bemerkung zum Neumann-Spektrum des Seeganges," *D. H. Z.*, 9, Heft 9 (1956).

Symposium, *Proceedings of the Symposium on the Behavior of Ships in a Seaway* (Sep. 7 to 10, 1957). Pt. I, papers; Pt. II, discussions. Netherlands Ship Model Basin, Wageningen, 1957.

Tick, L. J., "A Non-Linear Random Model of Gravity Waves," *J. Math. and Mech.*, VIII (1959) 643–652.

Tucker, M. J., "A Ship-Borne Wave Recorder," *Trans. Inst. Naval Arch.*, XCVIII (1956a) 236. London.

Tucker, M. J., *Comparison of Wave Spectra as measured by the NIO Ship-Borne Wave Recorder installed in the R. V. Atlantis and the Woods Hole Oceanographic Institution Wave Pole.* NIO International Report No. A. 6.

Tucker, M. J. and H. Charnock, "A Capacitance-Wire Recorder for Small Waves," *Proc. 5th Conf. Coastal Engineering*, Grenoble, Sept. 1954, p. 177. Printed 1955.

Tuckerman, R. G., "Wave Height Buoy System." Instrument Division David Taylor Model Basin Project No. 6, 230–179, 1960.

Tukey, J. W., "The Sampling Theory of Power Spectrum Estimates," *Symposium on Application of Autocorrelation Analysis to Physical Problems.* Woods Hole, Mass. (13–14 June 1949) 47. Washington, D. C., Office of Naval Research.

von Larisch-Moennich, "Sturmsee und Brandung," *Monographien zur Erdkunde*, 33 (1925). Bielefeld und Leipzig.

Walden, H., "Die Wellenhöhe neu angefachter Windsee nach Beobachtungen atlantischer Wetterschiffe und des Fischereischutzbootes 'Meerkatze'," *Ann. Meteorol.* VI (1953/54) 296.

Walden, H., "Ein neues Diagramm zur Berechnung des Seegangs aus den Windverhältnissen," *Ann. Meteorol.*, VII (1955/56) 213.

Walden, H., "Stau der Wellenenergie im wandernden Windfeld," *D. H. Z.*, IX (1956) see 225, 280.

Walden, H., "Die winderzeugten Meereswellen, Teil I," *Deutsch. Wetterd., Seewetteramt, Einzelveröff*, No. 18, Heft 2, 1958. Hamburg.

Walden, H., "Bemerkungen zu einer von Djounkovski und Bojitch angegebenen Beziehung zur Berechnung des Seegangs aus den Winterverhältnissen," *D. H. Z.*, Band 12, Heft 6, 1959.

Walden, H., "Der hohe Seegang auf 61°N, 150°W am 16 November 1953 als Ergebnis der Energie-Akkumulation in einem wandernden Sturmfeld," *D. H. Z*, Band 13, Heft 2, 1960.

Wen, S. C., "Generalized Wind Wave Spectra and their Applications," *Scientia Sinica*, IX, No. 3 (1960) 377–402.

Williams, A. J. and D. E. Cartwright, "A Note on the Spectra of Wind Waves," *Trans. Amer. Geophys. Un.*, XXXVIII (1957).

DISCUSSION

Mr. Schule: Although there is considerable interest and a lot of experimentation on the nonlinear aspects of the wave spectrum and the two-dimensional spectrum, the one-dimensional spectrum requires a considerable amount of our attention. There is a much larger body of research data available on this subject, and for some time to come most of the measurements that will be available to us on a more or less continual basis will be time-series measurements of the sea surface, without any directional resolution. Most of the hypotheses for testing prediction methods and theoretical spectra of this sort will be based on the one-dimensional spectrum.

One other matter: Dr. Dorrestein felt that there might be some confusion as to terminology and notations used by the authors. Since you can't tell the ballplayers without a score card, he has prepared a score card, in which he has attempted to clarify their terminology. This should be a big help, and we appreciate Dr. Dorrestein's taking the time to do it.

Dr. Burling: I believe that my data underestimates the slope in the low-frequency part of the spectrum. Averages of five successive peaks in a Fourier analysis were taken. If proper consideration were taken of the effect of energy in nearby, higher parts of the spectrum, the slope would be much steeper. In other words, the slope of 6.6 found by Dr. Hicks is a considerable underestimate.

Dr. Pierson: We make the statement that the rise of the forward face is very steep because nearly every one that I have seen in the Tukey analysis of storm-sea spectra, has the feature that as you plot the points, irrespective of what resolution you decided to use to start with, the spectrum rises to the peak of the forward face in about three points.

The convolution function that is used in the analysis is just about the right shape (roughly triangular, with the width of the spectral band being $2\frac{1}{2}$ frequency intervals to each side of the centers) for a rise of this nature. I think it all checks out that the spectrum is very steep on the forward face.

ONE-DIMENSIONAL WAVE SPECTRA NOMENCLATURES USED BY VARIOUS AUTHORS

R. Dorrestein

Kon. Nederl. Meteorologisch Inst., De Bild, The Netherlands

Say σ^2 = mean-square deviation of sea elevation from its mean (recommended unit: m² or cm²). If spectrum narrow (Rayleigh distribution for extrema), mean-square wave height $\overline{H^2}$ = approx. $8\sigma^2$.

Then: wave energy density is $g\rho\sigma^2$ = approx. $\frac{1}{8} g\rho\overline{H^2} \left(\text{unit } \frac{\text{Joule}}{\text{m}^2}\right)$

Recommendation: use as abscissa of spectral curve f = cycles per sec exclusively (Bretschneider also uses the symbol ν).

Author(s)	Ordinates of spectral curve:	Integral of spectrum:
Burling a.o. use:	$W(f)$ = contribution to ms deviation per unit f	σ^2
Neumann,	$E_f = 2W(f)$	$E = 2\sigma^2$
Walden a.o. use:	$\left(\text{Walden denotes this by } \frac{H_f^2}{4}\right)$	
Darbyshire a.o. use:	H_f^2 = (by definition) $4E_f$ = $8W(f)$	$H^2 = 4E = 8\sigma^2$
Bretschneider* uses:	$S_{H^2}(f)$ = (by definition) $4E_f$ = $8W(f)$	$\int_0^\infty S_{H^2}(f)\, df = 8\sigma^2$
	Wave energy density per unit f:	Total wave energy density:
Neumann:	$g\rho W(f)$	$g\rho\sigma^2$
Darbyshire ⎫ :	$\frac{1}{2} g\rho E_f$	$\frac{1}{2} g\rho E$
Walden ⎭	$\frac{1}{8} g\rho H_f^2$	$\frac{1}{8} g\rho H^2$
Bretschneider:	$\frac{1}{8} g\rho S_{H^2}(f)$	$\frac{1}{8} g\rho \int_0^\infty S_{H^2}(f)\, df$

Expression for "significant" height for relatively narrow spectrum:
$H_{\text{sign}}^2 = 16.0\sigma^2 = 8.0E = 2.0\overline{H^2}$

* (See his "Discussion")

I would like to see someone do the type of analysis, in this area of the forward face, that would best locate the position of that frequency where the very steep rise occurs. It would be rather interesting to handle a problem like that.

Dr. Hicks (Prepared comment): The authors of the first paper have touched on numerous important aspects of the energy spectra of wind waves. My discussion relates to other papers as well as that of these authors. My theme is that there are so many difficult questions about the generation of wind waves that we will find time and energy to solve them only if we exploit fully the advantages of studying small wind waves.

The authors ask, in effect, for a more or less complete characterization of the wind fields if we are to understand wave generation. I agree that this characterization is needed, but it should be spelled out carefully in a hierarchical series of specifications, each one more complete than its predecessor and each in turn becoming possible as instrumentation, data-processing, and our own understanding advances. At a low level of specification we should recognize the "region of influence" of the wind stress at one point (x, y, t) in producing wave energy that appears at other points (x', y', t'). The dimensions of a region of influence depend of course upon the wave frequency. We must also recognize that the wind stress at a point on the water surface is in part determined by the past history of the winds and by the nature of the surface it has blown past on its way to the point in question.

It was not the authors' purpose to examine instrumentation in any considerable detail. Unfortunately their brevity is dangerous, for it leaves two false impressions: first, that the lack of good instrumentation is all that blocks the making of excellent wave studies; and second, that the range and reliability of existing instruments are very poor. What has blocked good wave studies in the past is inadequate experimental design (sometimes unavoidably inadequate). Let me cite one example. In how many water-wind tunnel measurements has the air boundary layer been characterized (with respect to turbulence and velocity profile) upstream and along the fetch and compared with the boundary layers that produce natural wind waves?

Although the authors' suggestion of comparing wave data taken by two different instruments in the same area is a good one, I would also maintain that several types of instruments are already reliable enough to be useful when they are used by experimenters who understand fully the capabilities of each instrument. In our own studies we found our instrumentation to be very reliable and of measured accuracy that exceeded the demands of the experiments we made. This instrumentation was used in the range of frequencies up to 30 cps and rms wave amplitudes from 0.04 to 1.2 mm.

One cannot quarrel with the authors' hope for a "properly devised wave forecasting technique" that will predict to ± 10 per cent the wave conditions in any ocean, except to note that the specification of ± 10 per cent means little without collateral specification of the errors in the input data and knowledge of the effect of these errors on the accuracy of the forecast. In testing a forecasting method both hypotheses and the procedures for testing the hypotheses should be set up before the data are collected or analyzed if the results are to have scientific significance. The techniques of such proper design of experiments have been well developed for simpler situations and can presumably be elaborated sufficiently so as to apply to studies of wave spectra and of forecasting. One particular item in connection with the program outlined in the paper (pages 16–18 might be mentioned: the fetch (and possibly the shear properties) of an off-shore wind vary appreciably with wind direction.

Each application of an energy spectrum may place characteristically different requirements on the accuracy and fidelity of the spectrum. In our work we sought in part to answer the question, "With what accuracy can the energy spectra of small wind waves be considered to depend *only* upon the average wind speed and average fetch?" A clear answer to this question for ocean waves would obviously be relevant to the design of wave-forecasting methods. In either case we are not concerned primarily with the mode of departure of individual spectra from the "average spectrum" for the same values of V and F. In seeking to understand the physical nature of the processes of wave generation by the wind or of energy transfer across the spectrum, then we certainly are concerned with individual spectra, or, more accurately, with variation of the energy in specific frequency bands as a function of variation of the wind field $\vec{V}(x, y, t)$.

On the basis of some of the preceding remarks I may mention that the determination of various properties of an "average spectrum" requires different experimental and analytical tools, but the need for some of these tools has not been appreciated. For example, Dr. Walden, in his paper, points to the wide variation among different "theoretical" spectra that have been proposed in predicted values of total wave energy and of frequency of the peak of the spectrum. That these obvious features of a spectrum cannot at present be predicted or measured well indicates that less obvious features, such as the logarithmic slopes on either side of the peak, are even more uncertain. The tool or capability required for determination of these slopes is linearity of wave-sensing over a wide dynamic range, which was achieved for small waves by CSL instrumentation. The results of the studies* of small waves by CSL and by Burling yield slopes of the low-frequency face of the energy spectrum of 1.3 ± 0.2 and 6.6 ± 0.3. These values are not compatible with the statement of Pierson and Neumann that this face should be treated as if it were vertical. (The results also suggest that the boundary layers in the two sets of experiments were, on the average, rather different.)

Another correction to the authors' paper is in order at this point. The CSL analysis of the data of CSL and of Burling solved three problems simultaneously: the deconvolution of spectra that had been measured with a broad band filter; least-squares fitting of these deconvolved (experimental) spectra to eight-parameter spectral functions; and estimation of the probable errors of the values of the parameters obtained by the least-squares analysis. Our techniques were first described in detail in CSL reports issued last year. It is not, therefore, correct to imply that a suitable method for deconvolution is yet to be developed.

In conclusion I wish to give specific examples of vague wording that serves no useful purpose but appears all too commonly in our oceanographic literature. The statement that "there is a close coupling between wave and air motion in immediate contact at the air sea boundary" is meaningful only in the trivial sense that there is no slip at the interface. I can just as well say, thinking of a slab of air whose thickness is ten times $H_{1/3}$, that there is only very loose coupling between the air and the water. To be meaningful, the "closeness" of the coupling must be specified in terms of the changes produced by one medium acting upon the other and in comparison with the

---

* Hicks, B. L., "Estimation of the Spectrum Function for Small Wind Waves," Paper for the Easton Conference on Ocean Wave Spectra, May 1–4, 1961.

changes that occur in the absence of coupling. In a similar vein of criticism I would say that the authors' parameter f_0 (below which "the activity in the spectrum is quite low") would be more useful if it were defined as that frequency, less than the peak frequency $f°$, at which the spectral energy density is a given fraction, say one-tenth, of the value of the energy density at the peak.

Dr. Darbyshire (prepared comment): I am in the main in agreement with this paper in that it indicates that a good deal more work will have to be done and many more observations taken before we finally settle the question of the one-dimensional wave spectrum. I think, however, that they underestimate the value of the locations of "India" and "Juliett." Although it may be difficult to assess the fetch accurately at these places, they are at the receiving end of waves generated by Atlantic depressions which generally move east or northeast, and they must be more typical of ocean conditions than is a point near the U. S. eastern seaboard, from which the depressions would be moving away.

Mr. Harris: There are at least two reasons for studying the wave spectra. One may study the spectra to learn more of the physics that ocean-waves generate and to devise a system for synoptic forecasts. One may try to make engineering predictions about both, but the observations that yield the best results for one do not necessarily give good results for the other. In different parts of their papers the authors sound as though they are writing about one problem or the other. These differences, coupled with the uncertainty of the wind speeds over the oceans, adequately explain many of the discrepancies in the different systems.

Dr. Walden (prepared comment): I agree with the paper of Professors Neumann and Pierson on nearly all points.

I have a supplement to my remark on the effect of Filter IV after PNJ (see page 67). The filter concerns the case where the wind ceases within the fetch. If the state of the fully arisen sea had been reached at P before the beginning of the decrease of the wind, the sea will decrease at an observation point P less rapidly in a long fetch than in a short fetch in any case or after any method. Under Darbyshire's assumption, these cases would occur generally more frequently because the "minimum fetch" is assumed to be very short. Moreover, in the case of a really fully arisen sea generated at P, the sea would decrease much less rapidly under Darbyshire's method than under the others. The same is generally true when the sea is not fully developed.

* * *

Concerning the effect of the air-sea temperature differences on the properties of the sea (see page 19), it may be noted as a matter of course that the principal factor influencing the state of the sea is turbulence or gustiness in the air. It is, in general, closely related to the temperature difference; however, an originally stable continental air mass needs a rather long time (or way) over comparatively warm water until it becomes unstable and therefore turbulent. Thus, it may happen that the sea will not become higher and longer than with equal temperatures, although a high negative difference between air and water is observed.

On the other hand, it may be regarded as certain that, in the open ocean, far away from land, the cold air will have become warmer and damper in the low layers and consequently will have become turbulent and gusty.

A "statistical" investigation has been made of the effect of air-sea temperature differences on the period of the sea from observations of various Ocean Weather ships. The periods were a little longer for cold air over warm water than for (approximately) equal temperatures.

In my opinion, corresponding corrections could be used in the regions far from the continents.

Dr. Wiegel: I have one comment on the air-sea temperature difference. Most people are familiar with the ocean observations. We tried to reproduce them in the laboratory using a wind of nearly constant temperature, cutting out any large turbulence in the wind by forcing it through a filter such as one uses in a wind tunnel, and then changing the water temperature.

First we heated the water (with the air temperatures at 50°F.) until we had the water temperature and air temperature almost identical. We then cooled the water to about 35°F. We got results that were in conflict with open ocean observations in that the hot water and cool air gave the lowest waves. The highest waves were given by cold water and warm air. The problem is complicated because it involves the growth of the boundary layer in the air after it has left the wind tunnel filter. We are now looking into the level and the size of turbulence.

Dr. Kinsman: I would like to add a plea for a little closer look at the structure of the wind field. When I first went out to measure waves, I decided that I would look at the wind structure as well as I could and was able to round up three anemometers. The results of a preliminary trial in the summer were so bizarre that I added a fourth anemometer to the stack before I went out again in November. Dr. Montgomery told me that this was the wrong move, that I should have taken one out and things would have become more simple. Ever since then I have been treasuring in the back of my files a group of deformed wind profiles that you hide like a two-headed baby in the family. I was recently encouraged by Dr. Stewart who told me that in his travels about the country he had discovered that almost every file he saw contained interesting specimens of this sort. Specifically, what I got was a low sheet, about 75 centimeters off the water, of high-speed air moving much more rapidly than either the lower layer or the upper layer.

Dr. Burling: May I also offer myself for confession. I observed some mean wind profiles, but because time was limited, I handed them over to someone else. It does seem that the logarithmic form is not always a suitable profile for wind over water. We ought to attempt to measure profiles and at the same time turbulent fluctuations to compute Reynold's stresses. We will try to do this shortly, but it will require many measurements under different circumstances to make much progress.

THE ONE-DIMENSIONAL WAVE SPECTRUM

IN THE ATLANTIC OCEAN AND IN COASTAL WATERS

One hundred and ten wave records were selected from those taken by the O.W.S. "Weather Explorer" and frequency analysed by the N.I.O. analyser; 46 of these were discussed in the earlier paper in 1955 and 64 in the 1959a paper. The wave records were so chosen that the waves recorded were entirely wind waves and the effect of extraneous swell was insignificant. The fetch varied from 200 to 2000 miles, the duration from 4 to 48 hours, and the wind force from 3 to 11. The stability conditions varied from an "air minus sea temperature difference" of less than $-10°$ to $7°$F.

A plot of all the energy densities (1959a) showed that they could be represented by:

$$\frac{H_f^2}{H^2} df =$$

$$23.9 \exp - \left\{ \frac{(f - f_0)^2}{0.0085[(f - f_0) + 0.042]} \right\}^{1/2} df \quad (1)$$

$$= 0 \text{ when } (f - f_0) < -0.042$$

where $\frac{1}{8}g\rho H_f^2$ is the wave energy per unit frequency and $H^2 = \int_0^\infty H_f^2 \, df$. If W is the surface wind speed in knots, then:

$$H = 0.0081 W^2 \text{ (ft)} \quad \text{and} \quad \frac{1}{f_0} =$$

$$1.94 W^{1/2} + 2.5 \times 10^{-7} W^4 \text{ (secs)} \quad (2)$$

(See Figs. 8, 9, 10, 11, and 12, 1959a.)

These results were obtained from the 64 analyses used in 1959, but some of those described in the 1955 paper have since been analysed digitally by W. J. Pierson and they also fit this curve.

The ship-borne wave recorder was calibrated by using the formula:

$$\left(\frac{\text{wave amplitude}}{\text{recorded amplitude}} \right) =$$

$$0.83[1 + (8.8 \times 2\pi f)^{-2}]^{3/2} \exp \frac{4\pi^2 f^2 d}{g} \quad (3)$$

but recent work by Cartwright on the Weather Reporter records has shown that this is not correct but that an approximation to the true result can be obtained if $2d$ is substituted for d in the formula, d being the depth of the recorder below the water line in feet. Such a correction was probably also necessary for the "Weather Explorer," and so the energy densities for wind speeds of force 3, 4 and 5 were recalculated on the basis of this new calibration. But, as shown in figure 2-2-1, there is no significant difference in the distribution of the points, and as the periods for this range of wind speeds are the most affected, there is no likelihood of a change in the distribution for higher wind speeds.

Several points follow from the spectrum formula, one being that H_f^2 increases for any value of f with wind speed. A plot of values over the whole range of frequency considered is shown in

VARIATION OF SPECTRAL DENSITY USING NEW
CALIBRATION FOR WINDS OF FORCE 3, 4, & 5

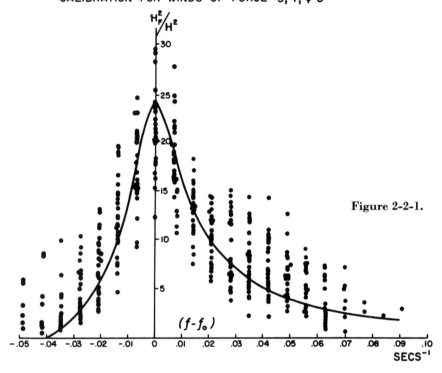

Figure 2-2-1.

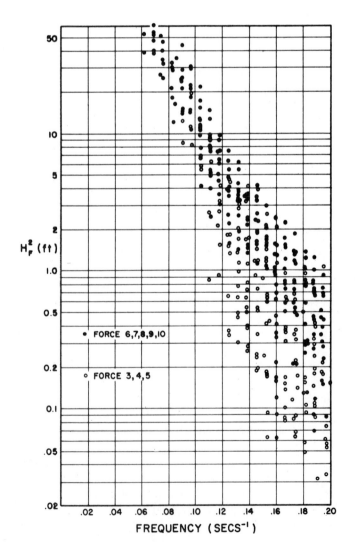

Figure 2-2-2, using a logarithmic scale. The solid circles represent wind speeds of force 6, 7, 8, 9, and 10, and the open circles wind forces 3, 4, and 5. The plot shows clearly that there is a very marked tendency for an increase with wind speed, and it is difficult to reconcile this with a constant equilibrium value proportional to f^{-5}, as is suggested by many workers, but the periods considered here only go down to 5 secs.

Although the points obtained represent a large range of wind speed, fetch, and duration, there appear to be no significant differences between them. Figure 2-2-3 shows the variation of maximum wave height for the reasonably narrow wind range force 8–9 to force 9. The fetch was taken to be the observed fetch or the product of the duration and the group velocity corresponding to the significant period, whichever was the lower. There is clearly no trend towards an increase after 200 miles although according to Pierson, Neumann, and James (1955), the values should reach saturation only after 500–900 miles for these wind speeds.

The effect of a short fetch on the spectrum formula was discussed in 1959a, where it was found that the formula could be extended to short

Figure 2-2-2.

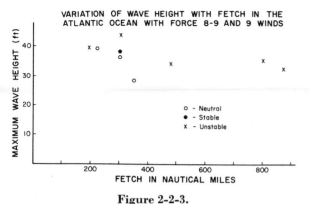

Figure 2-2-3.

fetches if $y(f - f_c)$ was substituted for $(f - f_0)$ so that the formula became:

$$\frac{H_f^2}{H^2} =$$

$$23.9y \exp - \left\{ \frac{y^2(f - f_0)^2}{0.0085[y(f - f_0) + 0.042]} \right\}^{1/2} \quad (4)$$

where

$$y = \frac{x^3 + 3x^2 + 65x}{x^3 + 12x^2 + 260x + 80} \quad \begin{array}{l} x \text{ being the fetch in} \\ \text{nautical miles} \end{array}$$

and

$$y = \frac{H_x}{H_{\text{sat}}} = \frac{f_0(\text{sat})}{f_0(\text{at } x)}$$

This formula appeared satisfactory in that it agreed with wave spectra taken at Lough Neagh

with fetches up to 15 miles and those taken by Burling with fetches up to 1 mile at Staines Reservoir. It does, however, lead to a result that H_f for a given value of f decreases with increasing fetch. This seems to be an unreasonable result as it is difficult to see why the energy should not continually increase with increasing fetch (up to the saturation point) as it does with increasing wind speed. Two examples will be given that illustrate this decrease.

(1) Wind speed 50 knots, $f_0 = 0.065$, and, as the formula holds only for $-0.042 < f - f_0 < 0.12$, the highest frequency we are concerned with is $0.12 + 0.065 = 0.185$; and this becomes the modal frequency when

$$y = \frac{0.065}{0.185} = 0.35$$

and then

the energy density $= 23.9 \times 0.35^3 \times H_{\text{sat}}^2$
$$= 23.9 H_{\text{sat}}^2 \times 0.043,$$

but at infinite fetch, the energy density at $f = 0.185$ is $23.9 \times H_{\text{sat}}^2 \times 0.038$ so there is a slight drop in value.

(2) Wind speed 15 knots, $f_0 = 0.133$, and thus highest frequency considered $\lambda = 0.253$, and then, for this frequency when it is modal,

$$H_f^2 = 23.9 \times 0.525^3 H_{\text{sat}}^2$$
$$= 23.9 \times 0.145 H_{\text{sat}}^2$$

whilst at infinite fetch the value is again $23.9 H_{\text{sat}}^2 \times 0.038$.

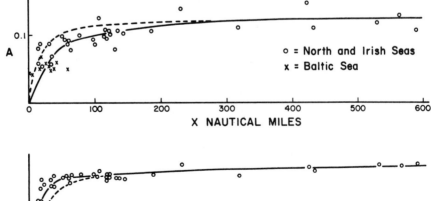

VARIATION OF WAVE HEIGHT AND PERIOD
WITH FETCH IN COASTAL WATERS

o = North and Irish Seas
x = Baltic Sea

X NAUTICAL MILES

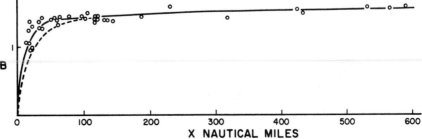

Figure 2-2-4. *Plot of A and B against fetch where* $H_{\text{max}} = AW^{3/2}$ $T_{1/3} = BW^{1/2}$

X NAUTICAL MILES

The effect is thus more pronounced at low wind speeds. The fault lies not in the spectrum formula but in the assumption that

$$\frac{H_x}{H_{\text{sat}}} = \frac{f_0(\text{sat})}{f_0 \ (\text{at } x)} \qquad (5)$$

Recent work on coastal waves (M. Darbyshire, 1960) has shown that

$$\frac{H_x}{H_{\text{sat}}} = \frac{f_0^n(\text{sat})}{f_0^n \ (\text{at } x)} \qquad (6)$$

where n lies between 2 and 3. The work showed (see Figs. 6 and 7 1959a.) that height ratio was less than y and the period ratio greater. We shall assume that $n = 2$ and that $H_{\text{sat}}/H_x = y^{3/2}$ and $T_{\text{sat}}/T_x = y^{3/4}$.
We shall work the last example again on this new basis. Now

$$y^{3/4} = \frac{0.133}{0.253}$$
$$= 0.525$$

and thus $y = 0.42$, and thus

$$H_f^2 \text{ at } f = 0.253 = 23.9 H_{\text{sat}}^2 \times 0.425^4$$
$$= 23.9 H_{\text{sat}}^2 \times 0.034$$

which is less than the value at infinite fetch, which was:

$$23.9 H_{\text{sat}}^2 \times 0.038$$

so that there is an increase of energy with increasing fetch.

From these formulae, it follows that the steepness of the highest waves given by H/T^2 remains constant independent of fetch for a constant wind speed. It can be shown, however, that the mean square slope increases with increasing fetch. The spectrum formula cannot be integrated directly, and approximate expansions for the integral of the slope spectrum were given in 1959a and b. These have since been shown to give values far too low, and integration carried out by computer has shown that the mean square slope for 20 knots and $y = 0.17$ (corresponding to a fetch of less than a mile),

$$\sigma^2 = 0.0033$$

whilst for the same wind speed at infinite fetch

$$\sigma^2 = 0.0051$$

This value of σ^2 increases very steeply with increasing wind speed becoming equal to 0.23 at 60 knots. It is doubtful, however, if the spectrum

formula, which has been only experimentally verified over the range

$$-0.042 < y(f - f_0) < 0.12 \qquad (7)$$

can be applied at very high frequencies.

The investigation of waves in coastal waters has already been mentioned in connection with the effect of fetch. The results found were:

$$H_{\text{max}} = 0.125 y^{3/2} W^{3/2} \qquad (8)$$

and

$$T_f = 1.55 y^{3/4} W^{1/2} \qquad (9)$$

These are different from those derived for the deep ocean, in the case of the period, the constant being different whilst the power of the wind speed is different in the height formula.

Originally (1959b) a spectrum formula

$$\frac{H_f^2 \, df}{0.1 \, T_f H^2} = 23.9 \exp -$$
$$\left\{ \frac{0.01 T_f^2 (f - f_0)^2}{0.0085 \left[0.1 T_f (f - f_0) + 0.042 \right]} \right\}^{1/2} \cdot df \quad (10)$$

was found where $T_f = 1/f_0$.
But if the formulae for height and period given above for coastal waters are used for H and f_0 (taking $H_{\text{max}} = 2.30 H$), then the deep water spectrum formula applies just as well.

CONCLUSIONS

In all cases the spectral energy density can be expressed by:

$$\frac{H_f^2 \, df}{H^2} = 23.9 y \exp -$$
$$\left\{ \frac{y^2 (f - f_0)^2}{0.0085 \left[y(f - f_0) + 0.042 \right]} \right\}^{1/2} \cdot df \quad (11)$$
$$= 0 \text{ when } y(f - f_0) < -0.042$$

where

$$y = \frac{x^3 + 3x^2 + 65x}{x^3 + 12x^2 + 260x + 80}$$

x being fetch in nautical miles.
And for ocean conditions:

$$H = 0.0081 y^{3/2} W^2,$$
$$f_0 = \frac{1}{y^{3/4}} (1.94 W^{1/2} + 2.5 \times 10^{-7} W^4)$$
$$(\text{ft., secs.})$$

and for coastal waters:

$$H = 0.054 y^{3/2} W^{3/2}, \quad f_0 = \frac{1}{1.55 y^{3/4} W^{1/2}}$$

REFERENCES

J. Darbyshire, "An Investigation of Storm Waves in the North Atlantic Ocean," *1955 Proc. Roy. Soc.* A, 230, 560.
"A further Investigation of Wind-Generated Waves," *Deutsche Hydrogr. Zeit.* 12, 1. 1959a.
"The Spectra of Coastal Waves," *D. H. Z.* 12, 4. 1959b.

M. Darbyshire, *Waves in the North Sea.* Dock & Harbour Authority, Nov. 1960, p. 225.

Pierson, W. J., Jr., G. Neumann, R. W. James, 1955: *Practical Methods for Observing and Forecasting Waves By Means of Wave Spectra and Statistics.* U. S. Navy Dept., Hydrogr. Office, Pub. No. 603, Wash. D.C.

DISCUSSION

Dr. Burling (prepared comment): I believe that Dr. Darbyshire's results are of very great importance.

Formulae to represent the spectra of ocean waves have been sought both as necessary information for forecasting procedures, and to represent wave systems in the study of physical processes acting to cause generation and decay of waves. For the former purpose, forecasts may, if necessary, be performed using only winds observed near the particular location, with little or no knowledge of the general distribution of winds nor of the movements of meteorological systems. Since it will be a long time before adequate synoptic observations are available over all regions of the oceans, many forecasts must depend on a knowledge of the average wave conditions associated with (but not necessarily generated by) particular winds at the location. Since much scatter in data is introduced by neglecting the movements of storms, only a reasonable fit to the data is to be expected. Dr. Darbyshire's results will be extremely useful for application to those parts of the oceans where storms are similar to, and approach the forecasting region in a manner similar to, those approaching the region of the northeastern Atlantic Ocean.

However, for the study of the generation of waves by wind a more precise spectral representation is required, and the distribution of properties associated with the wind in time and space must be known. These studies will also determine the optimum representations of wave spectra for application to forecasting waves in any area when adequate synoptic meteorological data are available.

Dr. Darbyshire's second figure shows that the spectral density at high frequencies increases with wind velocity for waves in the North Atlantic Ocean. In an earlier paper (Darbyshire, 1959) it was shown that the Darbyshire spectrum appropriate to short fetches of 500 to 1300 m is nearly proportional to f^{-5} at frequencies of 1 to 2 cycles per second, and is comparable with the shape found by Burling (1959, referred by Darbyshire to an earlier unpublished work). Phillips (1958) showed, from a dimensional analysis and also from the condition that a water surface can contain no more than an enumerable number of discontinuities, that the equilibrium spectrum at high frequencies should be proportional to Af^{-5}.

The data in Dr. Darbyshire's Figure 2-2-2 appear to fit curves Af^{-5} quite well for each grouping of winds. It is interesting to compare rough values for A estimated from the figure for each of the three wind groups with the asymptotic spectra observed by others. In the following table Af^{-p} is expressed in units cm² sec and is the high-frequency asymptotic form of the spectrum which, integrated over all frequencies, equals the mean square surface elevation. Sources of data are: Hicks, Huber and Berg (1958); Burling (1959); Kinsman (1960).

It is apparent that besides increasing with wind velocity, the (dimensional) constant A decreases with fetch. On each set of data the scatter is quite large, and A varies with different estimates of P in each set; also, corrections required to compensate for instrumental response and/or for factors imposed by the various techniques of analysis may affect these results. A more detailed

Observer	Spectrum Af^{-p} cm² sec		Range of Wind Veloc. m/sec	Range of Fetch
	A	P		
Hicks, *et al.*	12	4.9	0.3 to 3	16 to 300 m
Burling	12	5.5	5 to 9	500 to 1300 m
Kinsman	2.5	4.5	5 to 10	1700 to 3000 m
Darbyshire	∼1	∼5	3.5 to 10	Greater than 350 km
Darbyshire	∼2	∼5	11 to 16	Greater than 350 km
Darbyshire	∼3	∼5	17 to 27	Greater than 350 km

analysis must await further observations; moreover, the shape of the spectrum at high frequencies may also be influenced by the nonlinear properties of waves.

A decrease of spectral densities at high frequencies with fetch implies that the revision of his spectrum proposed by Dr. Darbyshire is unnecessary.

REFERENCES

Burling, R. W., "The Spectrum of Waves at Short Fetches," *Dt. Hydrogr. Z.*, XII (1959) 45–64, 96–117.

Darbyshire, J., "A further Investigation of Wind Generated Waves," *Dt. Hydrogr. Z.*, XII (1959) 1–13.

Hicks, B. L., E. A. Huber and G. Berg, *The Growth of Small Water Waves with Wind Speed and Fetch*. Report I-77, Control Systems Laboratory, University of Illinois, Urbana, Ill., 1958.

Kinsman, B., *Surface Waves at Short Fetches and Low Wind Speeds — A Field Study*. Tech. Report XIX, vol. 1 (1960) reference 60–1, Chesapeake Bay Institute, The Johns Hopkins University.

Phillips, O. M., "The Equilibrium Range in the Spectrum of Wind Generated Ocean Waves." *J. Fluid Mech.*, IV (1958) 426–434.

Dr. Walden (Prepared comment on Dr. Darbyshire's paper): In a large ocean, it is a rare event when a pure wind sea, being generated by steady winds in a well defined fetch and not superimposed by an extraneous swell, is observed or even recorded. If one has a large series of observations, it is difficult to find those cases which fulfill the conditions of a pure wind sea. In most cases, when the wind waves are not too low, the existence of a minor swell will not be perceivable. The situation concerning swell must be worked out by using a series of weather maps. From our experiences in Hamburg, it appears remarkable that Dr. Darbyshire succeeded in finding such a large number of pure (or approximately pure) wind sea records.

Concerning the fetch it may be pointed out that its length at a certain moment cannot be considered valid if the wind field is moving along at any angle to the wind direction. It has been shown that a rather high sea is generated also in short fetches if the displacement of the fetch agrees approximately with the movement of the wave energy. Thus, in order to investigate the relations between the length of the fetch and the state of the sea, it is necessary to consider only those cases in which the fetch does not move. Whether or not this has been done is important for the validity of the slide "Variation of Wave Height with Fetch in the Atlantic Ocean . . . ."

If the slide "Variation of Wave Height and Period with Fetch in Coastal Waters" also is to support the assumption that short fetches are sufficient for the generation of a fully arisen sea, it may be noted that, unfortunately, the Baltic Sea data are not totally uninfluenced by swell effects.

As for the spectrum formula for coastal waters, the question arises whether it is expedient to establish a formula valid for *all* different water depths. There exists a close relation between the water depth and the frequency of maximum energy (f_0) if our conception is correct that a wave or "wave component" begins to collapse as soon as it begins to "feel" the bottom; and it is generally assumed that this is the case when the water depth becomes less than half the wave length. At a bank or a bar in the bottom the long components of a sea are destroyed, whilst the short ones are left and are able to pass the obstacle. Thus, in my opinion, such a formula should contain the physical quantities that affect the form and the area under the curve of the spectrum in an obviously decisive way.

Dr. Neumann: I would like to comment on the statements made by Dr. Walden. I think the effect of shoal water on the wave spectrum involves more than just the long waves. If the sea runs over the shoaling water, the long waves are first affected. The long waves break, the turbulence in the water increases, and the high-frequency end of the spectrum is considerably reduced. So the shoal water affects the spectrum on both ends.

Dr. Barber: Why should the high frequencies be reduced?

Dr. Neumann: When the long wave components in the spectrum start feeling the bottom and these longer components in the spectrum break (or lead to an increase of white caps), the turbulence increases as it would, let us say, in the wake of a ship. One can follow the wake of a ship as the result of obliteration of high-frequency waves. That is, the small wave components at the high-frequency end are obliterated by increased turbulence.

Dr. Bretschneider: I think that what Dr. Neumann has said is true in part, but his comments may not necessarily apply in all situations. I believe that this might be the case for a relatively steep continental shelf; however, I think that there could exist a continental shelf sufficiently flat so that the long-period or low-frequency waves would never trigger the high-frequency components of the spectrum. The long waves can be damped out by bottom friction, and it would not necessarily be due to any breaking waves. If one considers a steep continental shelf, it would enhance breaking waves. Perhaps it is correct to say that breaking of the long waves would destroy some of the high-frequency components.

Dr. Darbyshire: I think bottom friction is the answer. This is a very gradual process. The waves may not be breaking. The turbulence will be near the sea bottom, which the shorter waves will not touch or feel.

Dr. Pierson: I think all wind-generated seas are breaking, are they not?

Dr. Darbyshire: But it is suggested that they are breaking more than usual in this case.

Dr. Munk: Is it perhaps not more likely that some of the effects of the waves are associated with the increased tidal flow rather than with some of the processes mentioned earlier?

Dr. Neumann: Yes, that is certainly true. There are, however, oceanic regions that are well known for extremely rough sea conditions as a result of shoaling waters. One of them is the region west of the English Channel, south of Lizard Point, with southwest gales. I know this region well from my own experience when I sailed there.

In the open ocean, the ship behaves quite well. But when you come over the grounds and are passing the 100- or 200-fathom line, then it gets rough. The wind speed is the same. There is terrific breaking. I would like to mention that this is the region where many ships have been lost, according to records of the last forty or fifty years.

There was the last unfortunate accident of the "Flying Enterprise," which broke in half some years ago. This is the effect of shoaling water on waves when the long rolling sea from the Atlantic Ocean passes over the grounds of the Continental Shelf.

Dr. Deacon: I have had some experience on the Burdwood Bank, between Cape Horn and the Falkland Islands. The seas are very uncomfortable in the approaches to the bank, but I think they are not so bad on top of the bank. The old sailing directions for the Indian Ocean comment on the remarkable effect of the Agulhas Bank in quieting the heavy seas that roll up to it. "A vessel may be exposed to a most turbulent and irregular sea while in deep water outside the bank, endangering her spars and threatening to break over the ship and swamp her; but the moment soundings are gained in 60 or 70 fathoms, the sea comes comparatively tranquil in a remarkable manner" (*Directory for the Navigation of the Indian Ocean,* Findlay, 1870, p. 101). The previous paragraphs emphasize the effect of the Agulhas current on waves but do not suggest that it is the currents that protect the bank.

Dr. Pierson: At the edge of the bank were there a lot of breakers?

Dr. Deacon: Steeper waves, and I believe more of them were breaking. Now that we have ship-borne recorders and prospect of an airborne recorder, we ought to make some measurements.

Dr. Bretschneider: Another interesting question is what happens after the waves break? Perhaps the breaking waves will destroy high-frequency components, but does this type of breaking generate new waves? Does the wind act again to generate continuously short-period, high-frequency waves, which eventually form larger and lower-frequency waves, which again might break?

Dr. Longuet-Higgins: I would like to suggest that the dynamics of the generation of waves by either of the two processes that are now under general discussion will depend upon whether the waves are in deep water or in water of finite depth. Consider, for example, the mechanism of wave generation by turbulence in the atmosphere. A pressure fluctuation of a given wave length applied to the surface of the sea can produce a quite different response if the depth of the water is finite.

I should imagine that there would be some difference also in the instability caused by shear flow (which has been proposed as a mechanism for wave generation). The degree of instability would depend on the depth of the water.

Dr. Phillips (prepared comment): The first two papers seem to me most valuable in their clear presentation of the lack of agreement between different sets of observations made in the field.

I would like to make a number of comments that are germane to both papers.

The first concerns the equilibrium range. The paper by Pierson and Neumann suggests a little misunderstanding of the basic argument underlying this idea. Although the dynamics of the high-frequency wave components certainly has non-linear features, the basic point concerns the surface stability. For the free surface to be stable, the particle acceleration downward cannot exceed g, the gravitational acceleration. If a portion of the surface momentarily becomes unstable, the wave breaks, energy is lost from the wave motion, ending up as turbulent energy, and the surface stability is restored. If this process is the dominant one at the high frequencies, then the frequency spectrum is determined by the two physical parameters ω and g, and we immediately ascertain by dimensional analysis that the limiting or saturated value of the spectrum $\Phi(\omega)$ is given by

$$\Phi(\omega) = \alpha g^2 \omega^{-5} \qquad (1)$$

for large values of ω. The beauty of dimensional analysis is that the physical mechanism serves only to guide our choice of appropriate parameters, and its details are irrelevant. Clearly, the presence of breaking waves does not upset the argument. On the contrary, it is a good indication that the high-frequency components are virtually saturated, or in a state of statistical equilibrium between the physical processes of energy input (largely from the wind in most cases) and energy loss by wave breaking.

The presence of sharp crests is inferred by a similar analysis for the two-dimensional wave-number spectrum $\Psi(\mathbf{k})$, from which it appears that for large k,

$$\Psi(\mathbf{k}) = f(\theta)k^{-4} \qquad (2)$$

where θ is the direction of wave propagation relative to the wind. This asymptotic form for large k implies, according to the theory of Fourier Analysis, that there exist at any instant somewhere in the wave field, discontinuities in slope, or sharp crests. It does not imply anything about what is going to happen to these crests. They may break or they may just subside.

It is clear that, if g is the only relevant parameter, then the spectra must asymptotically be of the forms (1) and (2) under saturated conditions. It is not a matter of curve-fitting; there is just no alternative. The fact that the best instrumented and most reliable observed spectra have asymptotic forms between about $\omega^{-4.5}$ and $\omega^{-5.5}$ suggests that the dominant parameter is indeed g and that the various other alternatives are of lesser significance.

If, however, an observed spectrum is very different from (1), this necessarily implies that some other process besides the surface stability is important. Let us suppose that the high-frequency components are saturated. It is difficult to say very much about the unsaturated case. From two points of view, we know that (1) gives a reasonably good first approximation — theoretically because the surface stability condition is certainly operative and observationally because the exponents are of the same order as -5. What is significant is the ratio between the expression (1) and our observed spectrum and not the value of the exponent that happens to fit our data best. If we wish to seek a second approximation to account for this difference, we must invoke some other physical mechanism, and there are a number of possibilities.

One possibility is mentioned by Pierson and Neumann. It is that the frequency of the spectral peak ω_0 is in some way coupled to the higher-frequency components. Dr. Kinsman in his comments also presents arguments along these lines. Such a coupling is undoubtedly present for frequencies near $2\omega_0$ at any rate because of the distortion of the wave profiles as described by second order theory. However, the influence of ω_0 can hardly be felt for higher frequencies than this since the coupling is both weak and indirect; the energy input to the high-frequency components is much more dependent on the wind than on nonlinear interactions. In any event, there is no reason to suppose that this effect will simply modify the exponent of the power law (1); the most we can say is that the spectrum will be of the form

$$\Phi(\omega) = \alpha g^2 \omega^{-5} F\frac{\omega}{\omega_0} \qquad (3)$$

where F is an undetermined dimensionless function. In view of the very small coupling between ω_0 and high frequencies, it is likely that

$$F\frac{\omega}{\omega_0} \to 1 \quad \text{as} \quad \frac{\omega}{\omega_0} \to \infty \qquad (4)$$

Another possibility can be inferred from the recent work of Longuet-Higgins and Stewart (1960). If a train of short waves is riding on a larger wave of much greater wavelength, then on the forward face of the large wave, the amplitude of the small waves is enhanced by the contraction effect and they may become saturated locally and break. On the rear face of the large wave, on the other hand, the amplitudes are diminished, and in an extreme case may be almost flattened out. The net result is that the small components may be saturated over something like half the water surface; the high frequency values of the spectrum may be smaller than (1) by a factor of order 2.

A third possibility is that, in very high winds, the wave profiles themselves may be distorted, but I do not know how significant this effect would be. One thing is certain, however: if we are to consider any of these secondary effects, then we have no justification for assuming that fitting a power law to the high-frequency components has any basic significance at all. A much more meaningful procedure would be to seek an explanation of the differences between the form (1) and our observed spectra in terms of these and perhaps other mechanisms that we might envisage.

Let me turn to another aspect of these observations that is, I think, of profound significance. Drs. Pierson and Neumann mention the steep forward face of the observed spectra and, indeed, it is one of their most striking properties. I think

that the recent theories of wave generation can do three things: (i) they can provide a natural explanation of this steep forward face, (ii) they can offer some new predictions that are capable of testing in the field and (iii) they can even interpose an olive branch in the dispute between the very different results obtained by Darbyshire and by other workers.

The relevant part of the theory has been worked out by Dr. Miles (1960; see also Phillips & Katz, 1961). He considers the growth under action of the wind, of a particular wave component as a function of time, taking into account the two dominant mechanisms for energy input to the waves, namely the resonance with the convected turbulent pressure fluctuations and the back-reaction of the waves on the wind, which has a sheltering effect. The results of this analysis are shown in Figure 1, which shows the time history of the energy content in a small frequency band of the spectrum $\Phi(\omega)$. Starting off from an initial condition at rest, the energy content grows slowly, and linearly with time under the dominant influence of the convected atmospheric turbulent pressure fluctuations. If the phase speed c of the

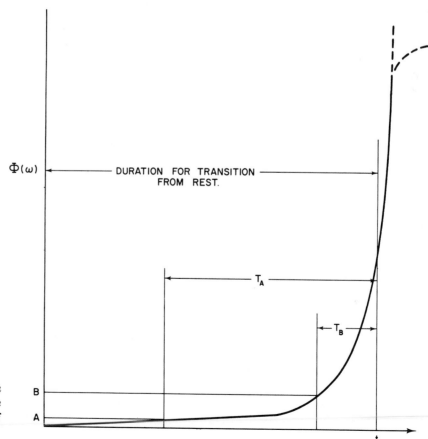

Figure 2-2D-1. *Growth of a particular component of the Spectrum $P(\Phi)$ as ω function of time $(C < u)$.*

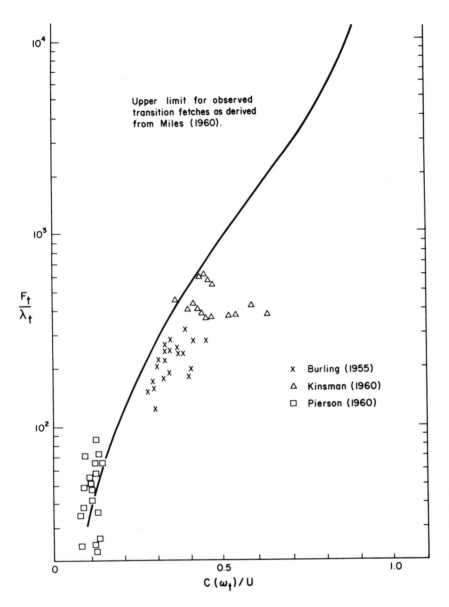

Figure 2-2D-2. *The transition fetch, expressed as number of wavelengths of the waves undergoing transition as a function of C/U.*

Upper limit for observed transition fetches as derived from Miles (1960).

X Burling (1955)
△ Kinsman (1960)
□ Pierson (1960)

waves is less than the wind-speed v, then after a certain time, the "sheltering" mechanism becomes operative, and the rate of growth increases enormously. The value of Φ then increases very rapidly until presumably the saturation limit is attained. The interesting point is that the time interval between the onset of the wind, when there are no waves, and this transition from the one made of energy input to the other is determined by Miles' stability analysis and can be calculated without arbitrary constants. The physical model that Miles uses is likely to be quite realistic except perhaps when c/v is very small.

Now, I want to relate these results to the observations. Let us consider a sequence of wave spectra measured at increasing duration of the wind (or equivalently, at increasing fetch). As Drs. Pierson and Neumann have pointed out, the spectra have steep forward faces, which occur at

lower and lower frequencies. To put the same thing another way, if we look at the same frequency for each of the records, then at a short duration, the energy content is very low, until suddenly it shoots up as the steep forward face moves past our observation frequency to lower values. This is exactly the behaviour predicted by the theory, and it makes almost inevitable an identification between the frequency at which the steep forward face is found at a particular fetch or duration and the frequency undergoing transition in the sense described above.

From this chain of reasoning, a number of conclusions follow that are, as I have said, of great importance. In the first place, it provides a perfectly natural explanation of the *steepness* of the forward face. Second, the frequency at which this forward face occurs is calculable without arbitrariness for a given wind speed and fetch or duration, *assuming that the sea was initially at rest.* This last condition is very important; if initially there is some energy in this frequency component, say at the level A in Figure 2-2D-1, the duration necessary before transition may be very much less even if A is small. At any rate, for a steady wind, the duration cannot be longer than the value found by taking initial conditions at rest. As a first test of this concept, Mr. E. J. Katz and I plotted the frequencies of the steep forward faces of as many spectra as we could find and compared the corresponding wind fetches with the values given by the theory. The results are shown in Figure 2-2D-2, and it is striking that most of the experimental points lie on or below the theoretical line, as we would expect. For very small values of c/v, the theoretical curve is very sensitive to small changes in the wind velocity profile, and is inclined to be rather unreliable when compared to experiments where the profile is not known accurately.

This comparison is enough to suggest that we are on the right track, but not enough to clinch it absolutely since we must attribute the degree to which the points fall below the line to an initial wave state of low energy, which, though undoubtedly present, is not measured. Fortunately, however, we can make a further prediction which, if borne out by experiment, should be quite convincing. This concerns the directional distribution of the components at frequencies near that of the spectral maximum. According to the theory, the transition occurs soonest for components travelling in the direction of the wind, so that the frequency of the steep forward face is strictly the transition frequency for components travelling in the wind direction. Components with the same frequency, but travelling at an angle to the wind will not have undergone transition, so that the directional distribution of frequency components near the spectral peak should be strongly oriented towards the direction of the wind. At a slightly higher frequency, transition will have occurred over a range of angles, and the directional distribution should be much broader. Methods are now becoming available for measuring the directional distribution of components of a given frequency, and this prediction of the theory should soon be tested. Perhaps some relevant measurements already exist.

One word of caution, though. This argument and the prediction above is relevant to frequencies where c/v is not nearly equal to unity. For very long durations or fetches, there may be substantial energy in the components for which $c \sim v$.

For these, the "sheltering" or instability mechanism is very inefficient, so that most of the energy input to the waves must be by means of the resonance between the turbulent atmospheric pressure fluctuations and the waves. The directional distributions would then be much broader, and may show the bi-modal behaviour, with maxima at angles to the wind, predicted by the resonance theory (Phillips, 1958).

We have therefore provided an explanation for the steepness of the steep forward face, and I have extended my neck by making a prediction on purely theoretical grounds. What about the olive branch for Darbyshire *vs* the rest?

The dichotomy appears to be real — there seems to be too much evidence and too much competence on either side to attribute the differences to errors in recording or analysis. The most striking difference, as Pierson and Neumann point out, is that Darbyshire's results show that the sea becomes "fully developed" much more rapidly under his conditions than it does under the conditions where most of the other data have been obtained. A very plausible explanation of this difference can be found in the theoretical results shown in Figure 1. It will be recalled that the duration required to produce transition (and the consequent rapid growth for the spectral value at a particular frequency ω) is given by the theory when we specify that the water is initially at rest when the wind starts to blow. If there is a background sea existing, so that the initial value of this spectral component is A, say, then the duration required is much less, and if the level is, say, B, the duration of wind required to saturate this component may be very short indeed. Now, the region of the North Atlantic where the O.W.S. "Weather Explorer" is stationed is not noted for initial conditions at rest; indeed, the background wave activity is likely to be considerably higher than it is in most other places. It follows then that the wind durations required to generate a "fully developed" sea (i.e., one for which most components in which $c < v$, are approximately saturated) will be very much less than those observed in waters where the background activity is less. If we accept the guidance of the theory, it is difficult to see how the differences between Darbyshire's results and the others could be any less profound than they are.

Two final remarks emerge as a consequence of these considerations. The first concerns the crucial importance of the initial sea state on which the wind acts, even though it may be small. It is quite clear that the initial sea does not just "add on" to the final wave field, since the growth curve of Figure 1 is so nonlinear. Instead, the initial sea state can serve as a *trigger* to set off a rapid rate of growth long before it would be expected in the absence of this initial wave field. This conclusion suggests some important experiments that can be done, but I will not go into them now; it also emphasizes the profound importance of the initial sea state, a factor that has been largely neglected in the past.

The second remark is merely to indicate the obvious point that, although the various empirical spectra provide excellent summaries of the data on which they are based, it would be rash to try to extrapolate them to very different conditions.

I hope that these comments may excite discussion, particularly from those present who are very experienced in observation of this complex phenomenon.

REFERENCES

Longuet-Higgins, M. S. and R. W. Stewart, *J. Fluid Mech.* VIII (1960) 565–583.

Miles, J. W., *J. Fluid Mech.* VII (1960) 469–478.

Phillips, O. M., *J. Mar. Res.* XVI (1958) 226–230.

Phillips, O. M. and E. J. Katz, *J. Mar. Res.* (in press).

Dr. Darbyshire (prepared reply): Dr. Phillips' ideas about a small amount of energy in a spectral component triggering off the growth of a large amount of wave energy is an interesting one. Some points have to be borne in mind, though. It is true the ocean is seldom still, but there are often occasions when the energy in a given spectral component, particularly if it is on the low frequency side, is very low, less than the background level of the analysis. A more plausible explanation for this triggering might be that the effect of weaker winds, which usually occur before the strong wind, may be more important than is generally supposed as weak winds can impart some energy to the lower frequency parts of the spectrum.

I cannot see, however, that the conditions under which my observations were taken are particularly different from those of the observations used by other workers. The Neumann spectrum was based largely on observations taken during a sea voyage across the N. Atlantic Ocean. The ideas about saturation at long fetches started with the

work of Sverdrup, Munk, and Suthons, and they included a large number of ocean observations in their work. Moreover, I found the fetch effect first from observations at Perranporth, Cornwall, and the same conditions seem to apply in the Irish and North Seas. I think Dr. Phillips' suggestion would be a good explanation of the difference between the results of sea observations and those taken in an experimental storm basin or a small lake and might be the answer why, from my observations, I just cannot find any evidence to support the equilibrium f^{-5} rule.

I agree that the spectrum formulae obtained in the N. Atlantic cannot be applied anywhere outside it without reservation. As I point out in my paper, different rules apply in shallow waters. It is possible that the depth should be taken into account in any general formula.

I have now extended my method and forecast simultaneously over all the North Atlantic for ship-routing purposes. I use a directional spectrum that uses the two modes suggested by Dr. Phillips. The results seem to be satisfactory so far.

Several speakers mention the lapse rate and its effect on wave generation. Our experience in the Irish Sea was that this effect was important only when the conditions were unsaturated and ceased to be important after one hundred miles.

Dr. Neumann: I would like to ask a question concerning the equilibrium range. In the case of a growing sea before it reaches the fully-developed stage, the turbulence in the water increases. Wouldn't that affect the equilibrium range in such a way that at least patch-wise over the ocean surface the smaller waves would be obliterated much more than in the previous stage where the sea started to grow? That would indicate that there is no equilibrium range with a growing sea.

Dr. Phillips: Unless the velocities of the turbulent motion are comparable with the velocities of a wave of the same scale, turbulence tends to scatter. It doesn't absorb very much.

I have tried to examine the interaction of turbulence and waves very carefully. If the turbulent froude number is less than one, the striking thing is that very little happens!

Dr. Neumann: I am thinking mostly in terms of observations. When the storm seas approach the fully-arisen state, we have these high breakers. One observes shorter waves riding on top of long waves, and on top of the long waves we find the heavy breakers. There is an increased stirring of the water. The leeward slope of the wave is not as smooth as the windward slope after breaking. So I think that patch-wise over the ocean surface the energy at the high-frequency end of the spectrum is smaller than in the early stages of a developing sea.

Dr. Phillips: Yes. Another fact is that as the wave breaks forward, there is an expansion effect of the type you talked about, and the wave slope is drastically reduced. I should have said that the equilibrium range has tended to be an upper limit. It is perfectly possible to find a spectrum that lies underneath this.

Dr. Neumann: The second question I have is, under these conditions, wouldn't the equilibrium range tend to approach a proportionality frequency to the minus sixth?

Dr. Phillips: No. You can't jiggle around the dimensions if you suppose that the important parameters don't change in the study.

Dr. Longuet-Higgins: In the paper that I hope will be presented on Wednesday morning, we have some evidence, derived from the directional spread of energy in the spectrum, that something is taking place that is similar to what Dr. Phillips has been claiming.

That is to say, at very low frequencies the directional spread is rather small (corresponding to the resonance angle). Then, as the frequency increases, the directional spread increases with the resonance angle, but not quite as rapidly, owing to the shear instability tending to reduce the spread. Finally, at high frequencies you get an increase again, which can be attributed to wave breaking and nonlinear effects.

Professor Pierson: Parenthetically, the way that the spectrum grows is the way that we assumed it would grow in H.O. Pub. 603 in 1953.

Dr. Barber: What led you to assume it?

Professor Pierson: Because all of the available data at that time suggested that this was a reasonable assumption — namely, that the period of the wave increased with increasing fetch.

Dr. Phillips: I never said that.

Professor Pierson: Fetch and duration then.

Dr. Phillips: The period of the wave doesn't change.

Professor Pierson: Our assumption was that the "period" increases with the fetch and duration. We assumed that the spectrum moves from the high frequencies to the low with the sudden appearance of each spectral component. So it may not have been too far off.

Dr. Neumann: Dr. Pierson said: "The observations that were available at that time." At that time we had no other observations available than a few visual observations at short fetches.

Professor Pierson: Except for shallow water observations.

Dr. Neumann: Yes.

CHARLES L. BRETSCHNEIDER

THREE

A ONE-DIMENSIONAL

GRAVITY WAVE SPECTRUM

ABSTRACT

A one-dimensional gravity wave spectrum might be interpreted as a frequency analysis of a continuous recording of the sea surface elevations at a particular point, where the recording mechanism is a blind staff, itself not knowing from which direction or directions the undulations approach. This is of no concern to the recorder since the recorder cannot think for itself. The analysis and the interpretation of the data is the responsibility of the professional scientist. If the spectrum is to be nonlinear, then there should be present no higher harmonic components. In nature it is a well known fact that the sea surface undulations are quite irregular in direction of approach, in the peaks or the maximums, and in successions of zero elevations. There is much use in having a knowledge of the one-dimensional linear spectrum, both in practical engineering works and as a basis for studying actual deviations therefrom as might be required in other scientific problems.

The present text is limited primarily to the nonlinear, one-dimensional wave spectrum, although it is not always possible to disassociate the nonlinear factors. It is not intended to make comparisons of the various proposed wave spectra, which is a separate task in itself. The development of the wave spectra given by Bretschneider (1959) is discussed, together with a brief summary of, and some additions to, the derivation. Although the spectrum of Neumann (1952) is mentioned for illustrative purposes, comparing some of the similarities and dissimilarities with the spectrum of Bretschneider (1959), it is not intended to impede the other proposed wave spectra found in the literature, i.e., Darbyshire (1952, 1955, 1959), Roll and Fisher (1956), among others.

A number of seemingly justified assumptions are used to derive the theoretical wave spectrum. These assumptions are discussed in detail, and a number of computed wave spectra are given to illustrate the principles used in this derivation. No attempt is made to compare the computed wave spectra with a special form of the theoretical wave spectrum, which is also presented. This phase of the investigation is incomplete to date.

Finally, it is quite important to understand that the problem of the linear wave spectrum is not yet solved, except perhaps as a weak first approximation. Certainly the nonlinear and directional wave spectrum is far more complicated and difficult to capture from both theoretical and practical points of view. A break-through in this aspect would certainly be of great value for understanding more fully the linear one-dimensional spectrum. For the above reasons it is believed that the present paper offers some encouragement that one should like to find in a progress report.

INTRODUCTION

For application to the design of coastal engineering structures there is greater practical need for knowledge of the joint probability distribution function for wave heights and periods than there is for the actual wave spectrum. However, the present trend in practices at the Beach Erosion Board is to record waves on magnetic tape to be analyzed by use of an analog type spectrum analyzer (Williams and Caldwell, 1961). One of the reasons for this practice is to eliminate the tremendous work involved in analysing the paper charts. Thus the problem is created of how to convert the wave spectrum to the joint probability distribution of wave heights and periods. It is hoped that this problem will soon be solved.

A previous report (Bretschneider, 1959) proposed a wave spectrum, after a detailed analysis of wave height variability and period variability, in an attempt to investigate the joint probability relationship between wave height and wave period. Conventional methods were used to define the individual wave heights and periods. Both the method of Putz (1952) and that of Pierson (1954) were used. Strictly speaking, neither method is correct, but the zero upcrossing method proposed by Pierson was more easily adapted. In the investigation of the marginal distribution of wave heights it was found that the Rayleigh distribution was applicable, which is in agreement with the theoretical work of Longuet-Higgins (1952), and which is also in close agreement with the Gamma type distribution presented by Putz (1952). The work of Darlington (1954), Walters (1953), and Czepa and Schellenberger (1959), among others, support the Rayleigh distribution. Deviations from the Rayleigh distribution were apparent in many of the records, and an attempt was made by Cartwright and Longuet-Higgins (1956) to explain certain deviations therefrom. It certainly appears that the Rayleigh distribution can be used as an adequate model for representing wave height variability.

In regard to wave period variability, the first work was presented as a Gamma type distribution by Putz (1952). Later a distribution function for wave period variability was presented by Bretschneider (1959), and this distribution function is in very close agreement over a certain range of mean wave periods with that given by Putz (1952). It was found by Bretschneider (1959) that the wave lengths (or periods squared) could also be represented by the Rayleigh distribution function to the same degree of accuracy as for the wave heights. The wave period distribution function was then obtained by transformation of the Rayleigh distribution of periods squared.

Utilizing the similarities between the wave height and period squared, an attempt was made to investigate the joint probability of the two variates. Figure 2-3-1 is a typical example of scatter diagrams of wave height versus wave period squared. The ordinate is given by $\eta = H/\overline{H}$, where $\overline{H}$ is the mean wave height, and $\lambda = T^2/\overline{T^2}$, where $\overline{T^2}$ is the mean squared wave period. From Figure 2-3-1 it is seen that η and λ could easily be interchanged without much effect on the actual positions of the data. Other such figures were similar to Figure 2-3-1, but some were of quite different nature. A schematic plot, similar to this figure together with certain assumptions, can be used as a typical model of wave height-period squared variability, from which one might derive a wave period spectrum.

ASSUMPTIONS

A number of assumptions are made which permit a derivation of a wave spectrum:

1. It is assumed that the wave record obtained with respect to time at a given point, such as recorded on a vertical staff, is of sufficient duration over a steady state or near steady state period so that the statistical distributions of wave heights will be sufficient and complete for all ranges of frequency. The analysis of the wave record then can be based on a particular interpretation that the wave record consists of groups or wave trains made up of individual waves of variable heights and variable frequencies (or periods). The record can be analyzed by the zero up-crossing method of Pierson (1954), and the individual wave heights can be grouped into M classes from $i = 1$ to $i = M$, according to the apparent wave periods $(T_i \pm \frac{1}{2}\Delta T)$, or in terms of frequency $(f_i \pm \frac{1}{2}\Delta f_i)$. The duration of the wave record must be long enough so that the number of wave heights in each class i are sufficient to be statistically significant. This assumption is more realistic in theory than in practice, since it is not always possible to obtain a long enough wave record to satisfy the statistical requirements for all classes i, particularly for the higher and the lower frequency ends of the spectrum.

2. It is assumed that there should be present

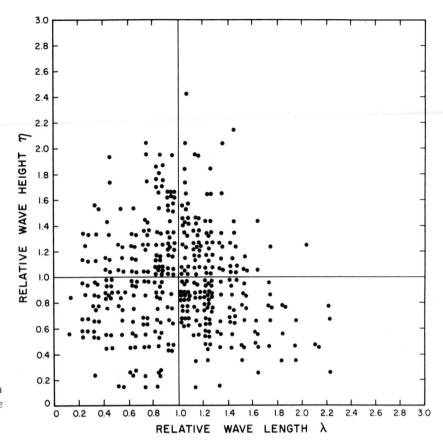

Figure 2-3-1. *Scatter diagram of η and λ for 400 consecutive waves in the Gulf of Mexico.*

only one wave spectrum system from only one storm. This assumption is required in order to avoid difficulties resulting from a composite wave spectrum made up of two or more linear wave spectra, each having a separate fundamental peak of its own. Such a composite wave spectrum of two or more peaks is not necessarily a nonlinear spectrum. This assumption is not required for computing a composite wave spectrum from the wave data of the record.

3. It is assumed that the waves are unidirectional and that the water surface displacements are small relative to horizontal distances between maximums. This assumption is general for every nonlinear one-dimensional wave spectrum.

4. It is assumed that all the individual surface elevations for each class i, when averaged at corresponding phase positions result in a simple sinusoidal wave having a mean amplitude A_i and a frequency f_i (or period T_i), whence the mean amplitude for class i is determined from

$$\overline{A}_i = \frac{1}{2N_i} \sum_1^{N_i} H_i \qquad (1)$$

where H_i are the individual wave heights of class i and the individual wave height H_i is defined as the total vertical displacement between two consecutive zero up-crossings. The equation for this mean surface profile will be

$$\xi_i = \overline{A}_i \cos \theta_i \qquad (2)$$

where $\theta_i = (k_i X - \omega_i t)$ is the phase position: $k_i = \dfrac{2\pi}{L_i}$ wave number; and $\omega_i = \dfrac{2\pi}{T_i}$, wave angular frequency. ξ_i is the surface elevation measured with respect to the undisturbed still water elevation. For each class i, $T_i - \frac{1}{2}\Delta T$ to $T_i + \frac{1}{2}\Delta T$, T_i will be a constant as ΔT approaches zero, and for deep water (constant T_i and constant L_i) the wave length (Lamb, 1945) will be given by

$$L_i = \frac{g}{2\pi} T_i^2 \qquad (3)$$

5. It is assumed that the root mean square surface elevations of assumption 4 above result in an equation of the root mean square surface profile for class i as follows:

$$\sqrt{\overline{\xi_i^2}} = \sqrt{\overline{A_i^2}} \cos \theta_i \qquad (4)$$

where

$$\overline{A_i^2} = \frac{1}{4N_i} \sum_1^{N_i} H_i^2 \qquad (5)$$

It then follows that the energy coefficient for class i is given by

$$\overline{\eta_i^2} = \frac{\overline{A_i^2}}{(\overline{A}_i)^2} = \frac{\overline{H_i^2}}{(\overline{H}_i)^2} \qquad (6)$$

6. It will be assumed that the energy coefficient $\overline{\eta_i^2}$ is the same for all classes taken independently. The over-all energy coefficient $\overline{\eta^2}$ is not necessarily the same as $\overline{\eta_i^2}$. The over-all energy coefficient will be given by

$$\overline{\eta^2} = \frac{\sum N_i \overline{H_i^2}}{\sum N_i (\overline{H}_i)^2} = \frac{\overline{H^2}}{(\overline{H})^2} \qquad (7)$$

which is the weighted average over all classes from $i = 1$ to $i = M$.

$\overline{\eta_i^2}$ is also related to the second moment of the data about the mean value of $\overline{\eta}_i = 1.0$ for class i, whereas $\overline{\eta^2}$ is related to the second moment about the mean value of $\overline{\eta} = 1.0$ for all classes $i = 1$ to $i = M$ taken as one large class. The second moment is related to the standard deviation, and it can be seen that the standard deviation within each class will be between zero and the standard deviation of all classes taken as one large class.

DERIVATION

Based on the above assumption, a period spectrum can be derived from an expression for the joint probability distribution function. Instead of selecting H and T as the variates, it was found more desirable to select H and T^2. The statistical analysis of the data indicated satisfactorily that linear or near-linear regression existed between H and T^2, whereas this was not true of the regression lines between H and T.

In the development it is convenient to use the following identities:

$$\eta = H/\overline{H}$$
$$\lambda = T^2/\overline{T^2}$$
$$\tau = T/\overline{T} \qquad (8)$$
$$\lambda = a\tau^2$$

$$\overline{H} = \frac{1}{N} \sum N_i H_i$$

where

$$a = \frac{\overline{T^2}}{(\overline{T})^2}$$

$$\overline{T^2} = \frac{1}{N} \sum N_i T_i^2$$

$$\overline{T} = \frac{1}{N} \sum N_i T_i \qquad (9)$$

$$N = \sum N_i$$

and the summation is over all classes i.

The general form of the joint distribution function (Uspensky, 1937) for two dependent variates can be written as the product of two functions

$$\mathcal{P}(\eta,\lambda) = \mathcal{P}(\lambda) \cdot \mathcal{P}_\lambda(\eta) \qquad (10)$$

which states that the probability of both a particular value of λ and η occurring simultaneously is equal to the probability that η will occur times the probability that λ will occur, assuming that λ occurred. $\mathcal{P}(\lambda)$ is the marginal distribution function for λ, and $\mathcal{P}_\lambda(\eta)$ is the conditional probability function of η, the condition being that λ occurred.

$\mathcal{P}(\eta)$ is the marginal distribution function for η, and is given by

$$\mathcal{P}(\eta) = \int_0^\infty \mathcal{P}(\eta, \lambda)\, d\lambda = \mathcal{P}(\eta) \int_0^\infty \mathcal{P}_\eta(\lambda)\, d\lambda \quad (11)$$

For the joint probability function there will be a linear correlation coefficient defined by

$$r = r(\eta, \lambda) = \frac{\overline{\eta\lambda} - 1}{[(\overline{\eta^2} - 1)(\overline{\lambda^2} - 1)]^{1/2}} \qquad (12)$$

where

$$\overline{\eta\lambda} = \int_0^\infty \int_0^\infty \eta\lambda \mathcal{P}(\eta, \lambda) d\eta\, d\lambda$$

$$\overline{\eta^2} = \int_0^\infty \eta^2 \mathcal{P}(\eta) d\eta$$

$$\overline{\lambda^2} = \int_0^\infty \lambda^2 \mathcal{P}(\lambda) d\lambda$$

The linear correlation coefficient measures the strength of the relationship between the two variables, assuming that the relationship is linear. That is, it is assumed that the two regression equations of η on λ and λ on η are straight lines of the form $y = mx + b$. The condition of linear regression is not necessarily correct, but the data seem to indicate that the regression equations are approximately straight lines, at least over the greatest concentration of the points.

Using the above-mentioned assumptions, a λ-

spectrum of η (also for η^2) is derived as follows: All values of η are summed for each class i of λ_i between $\lambda_i - \frac{1}{2}\Delta\lambda$ and $\lambda_i + \frac{1}{2}\Delta\lambda$, and in theory $\Delta\lambda$ approaches zero. Denoting this sum as $S_\eta(\lambda)$, meaning the sum of η with respect to λ, the mathematical definition of this summation function or the λ-spectrum of η is

$$S\eta(\lambda) = \int_0^\infty \eta \mathscr{P}(\eta, \lambda) d\eta \qquad (13)$$

or using equation 20

$$S_\eta(\lambda) = \mathscr{P}(\lambda) \int_0^\infty \eta \mathscr{P}_\lambda(\eta) d\eta \qquad (14)$$

The integral of equation 14 is nothing more than the equation of the regression line of η on λ. It can be shown that the equation for linear regression of η on λ is given by

$$\bar{\eta}_\lambda = 1 + r(\lambda - 1) \qquad (15)$$

where the correlation coefficient r remains defined by equation 12. Thus,

$$S_\eta(\lambda) = [1 + r(\lambda - 1)] \mathscr{P}(\lambda) \qquad (16)$$

Equation 16 can be defined as the summation function or the λ-spectrum of η.

In a similar manner the λ-spectrum of η^2 can be developed. Each value of η is squared, and then all values of η^2 are summed for each class i of λ_i between $\lambda_i - \frac{1}{2}\Delta\lambda$ and $\lambda_i + \frac{1}{2}\Delta\lambda$, as before. Denoting this sum as $S_{\eta^2}(\lambda)$, meaning the sum of all η^2 for each λ, the mathematical definition of this summation function or the λ-spectrum of η^2 is

$$S_{\eta^2}(\lambda) = \int_0^\infty \eta^2 \mathscr{P}(\eta, \lambda) d\eta \qquad (17)$$

or, using equation 10,

$$S_{\eta^2}(\lambda) = \mathscr{P}(\lambda) \int_0^\infty \eta^2 \mathscr{P}_\lambda(\eta) d\eta. \qquad (18)$$

One may suppose that the integral of equation 18 evaluates by definition

$$\overline{\eta_\lambda^2} = \int_0^\infty \eta^2 \mathscr{P}_\lambda(\eta) d\eta; \qquad (19)$$

thus,

$$S_{\eta^2}(\lambda) = \overline{\eta_\lambda^2} \mathscr{P}(\lambda). \qquad (20)$$

In order to evaluate $\overline{\eta_\lambda^2}$, it will be assumed that

$$\overline{\eta_\lambda^2} = K(\bar{\eta}_\lambda)^2 \qquad (21)$$

Where K is a constant and can be determined from the condition that the area under the

λ-spectrum of η^2 is equal to the energy coefficient $\overline{\eta^2}$, then

$$\overline{\eta^2} = \int_0^\infty S_{\eta^2}(\lambda) d\lambda, \qquad (22)$$

or

$$\overline{\eta^2} = K \int_0^\infty [1 + r(\lambda - 1)]^2 \mathscr{P}(\lambda) d\lambda \qquad (23)$$

or, expanding and by definition,

$$\int_0^\infty \mathscr{P}(\lambda) d\lambda = 1.0$$

$$\int_0^\infty \lambda \mathscr{P}(\lambda) d\lambda = \bar{\lambda} = 1.0$$

$$\int_0^\infty \lambda^2 \mathscr{P}(\lambda) d\lambda = \overline{\lambda^2} \qquad (24)$$

whence

$$\overline{\eta^2} = K[1 + r^2(\overline{\lambda^2} - 1)] \qquad (25)$$

thus

$$S_{\eta^2}(\lambda) = \frac{\overline{\eta^2}[1 - r + r\lambda]^2}{1 + r^2(\overline{\lambda^2} - 1)} \mathscr{P}(\lambda) \qquad (26)$$

Equation 26 can be defined as the summation function or the λ-spectrum of η^2.

It might be noted that $\overline{\eta_i^2}$, the energy coefficient for each class i, is given by

$$\overline{\eta_i^2} = \frac{\overline{\eta^2}}{1 + r^2(\overline{\lambda^2} - 1)} \qquad (27)$$

When $r = 0$, $\overline{\eta_i^2} = \overline{\eta^2}$, and η and λ are completely independent of each other. When $r = \pm 1$, $\overline{\eta_i^2} = \overline{\eta^2}/\overline{\lambda^2}$, and for linear regression all the data fall on a straight line of the form $y = mx + b$.

TRANSFORMATION OF λ-SPECTRUM TO τ-SPECTRUM

The λ-spectrum can be transformed into a corresponding period of τ-spectrum by use of the following:

$$S_\eta(\lambda) d\lambda = S_\eta(\tau) d\tau$$
$$S_{\eta^2}(\lambda) d\lambda = S_{\eta^2}(\tau) d\tau \qquad (28)$$
$$\mathscr{P}(\lambda) d\lambda = \mathscr{P}(\tau) d\tau$$
$$\lambda = a\tau^2$$
$$d\lambda = 2a\tau d\tau,$$

with λ, τ, and a given above in equation 8.

Thus

$$S_\eta(\tau) = [1 + r(a\tau^2 - 1)]\mathscr{P}(\tau), \qquad (29)$$

and

$$S_{\eta^2}(\tau) = \overline{\eta^2}\, \frac{(1 - r + ar\tau^2)^2}{1 + r^2(a^2\tau^4 - 1)}\, \mathscr{P}(\tau), \qquad (30)$$

with r as defined in equation 12.

TRANSFORMATION OF τ-SPECTRUM TO ν-SPECTRUM

The period or τ-spectrum can be transformed into a corresponding frequency or ν-spectrum by use of the following:

$$S_\eta(\tau)d\tau = -S_\eta(\nu)d\nu$$

$$S_{\eta^2}(\tau)d\tau = -S_{\eta^2}(\nu)d\nu$$

$$\mathscr{P}(\tau)d\tau = -\mathscr{P}(\nu)d\nu \qquad (31)$$

$$\tau = b\nu^{-1}$$

$$d\tau = -b\nu^{-2}\, d\nu$$

$$\nu = \frac{\omega}{\overline{\omega}} = \frac{f}{\overline{f}}$$

$$\omega = \frac{2\pi}{T}$$

$$f = \frac{1}{T}$$

Thus

$$S_\eta(\nu) = [1 + r(ab^2\nu^{-2} - 1)]\mathscr{P}(\nu) \qquad (32)$$

and

$$S_{\eta^2}(\nu) = \overline{\eta^2}\, \frac{[1 - r + ab^2r\nu^{-2}]^2}{1 + r^2(a^2b^4\overline{\nu}^{-4} - 1)}\, \mathscr{P}(\nu) \qquad (33)$$

where r remains as defined in equation 12, and

$$\frac{1}{\overline{\nu^2}} = \frac{(\overline{\omega})^2}{\overline{\omega^2}} \qquad (34)$$

$$\frac{1}{\overline{\nu^4}} = \frac{(\overline{\omega})^4}{\overline{\omega^4}} \qquad (35)$$

Equations 16 and 26 are the general forms of the theoretical λ-spectrum of η and the theoretical λ-spectrum of η^2, respectively, for the primary assumption of linear regression between η and λ. The corresponding τ-spectrum of η and of η^2, and ν-spectrum of η and of η^2 are given in equations 29, 30, 32, and 33, respectively, also for the primary assumption of linear regression between η and λ,

or between η and τ^2 or η and ν^{-2}, as the case might be. The general forms of these spectra become special forms when the marginal distribution function $p(\lambda)$ is specified. Therefore, the accuracy of a special form of the spectrum depends on the accuracy of the distribution of λ, τ, or ν, as the case may be.

λ AND τ-DISTRIBUTION FUNCTIONS

In order to complete the derivation of, and obtain a definite expression for, the λ-spectrum or the τ-spectrum, it is necessary to have the proper distribution function for wave λ or wave τ variability. Such a marginal distribution function must be obtained by use of theory or data, or both theory and data. The work of Putz (1952) was the first attempt to obtain such a function, which in this case was of the Gamma type based on statistical analysis of individual wave periods obtained from 25 separate ocean wave records. The work of Bretschneider (1959) resulted in a distribution function for wave-period variability which was in very close agreement with that given by Putz (1952). It was found that the data for λ fitted the Rayleigh distribution function equally as well as did the wave height data for η. This being a simple mathematical expression, it was found convenient to assume that the Rayleigh distribution was adequate, although some other Gamma type function might be an improvement. The Rayleigh distribution function has the following form

$$p(\lambda) = K\lambda e^{-B\lambda^2} \qquad (36)$$

where it can be shown that

$$K = \frac{2}{\overline{\lambda^2}} = \frac{\pi}{2}$$

and

$$B = \frac{1}{\overline{\lambda^2}} = \frac{\pi}{4}$$

since

$$\overline{\lambda^2} = \frac{4}{\pi}$$

The wave-period distribution function, corresponding to $p(\lambda)$ above, can be obtained by use of relations 28, whence

$$p(\tau) = K_1\tau^3 e^{-B_1\tau^4} \qquad (37)$$

where it can be shown that

$$K_1 = \pi (\overline{\tau^2})^{-2} = 2.70$$

$$B_1 = \frac{\pi}{4} (\overline{\tau^2})^{-2} = 0.675$$

since

$$\overline{\tau^2} = 1.07871$$

The wave frequency distribution function, corresponding to $p(\tau)$ above, can be obtained by use of relations 31, whence

$$p(\nu) = K_2 \nu^{-5} e^{-B_2 \nu^{-4}} \qquad (38)$$

where it can be shown that

$$K_2 = \frac{4}{\pi} (\overline{\nu^2})^2 = 1.772$$

and

$$B_2 = \frac{1}{\pi} (\overline{\nu^2})^2 = 0.443$$

since

$$\overline{\nu^2} = 1.1803.$$

Finally, the corresponding τ- and ν-spectra become

$$S_\eta(\tau) =$$
$$2.7[(1-r) + 0.927 r \tau^2] \tau^3 e^{-0.675 \tau^4} \quad (39)$$

$$S_{\eta^2}(\tau) =$$
$$2.7 \overline{\eta^2} \frac{[(1-r) + 0.927 r \tau^2]^2}{1 + 0.273 r^2} \tau^3 e^{-0.675 \tau^4} \quad (40)$$

$$S_\eta(\nu) =$$
$$1.772[(1-r) + 0.606 r \nu^{-2}] \nu^{-5} e^{-0.443 \nu^{-4}} \quad (41)$$

and

$$S_{\eta^2}(\nu) =$$
$$1.772 \overline{\eta^2} \frac{[(1-r) + 0.606 r \nu^{-2}]^2}{1 + 0.273 r^2} \nu^{-5} e^{-0.443 \nu^{-4}} \quad (42)$$

where r still remains defined by equation 12.

THE SPECIAL CASE FOR $r = 0$

It is of interest to investigate in more detail the special case of the wave spectrum for $r = 0$, although similar deductions can be made for the general case. Setting $r = 0$, the general form of the τ-spectrum reduces to

$$S_\eta(\tau) = K_1 \tau^3 e^{-B\tau^4} \qquad (43)$$

and

$$S_{\eta^2}(\tau) = \overline{\eta^2} S_\eta(\tau) \qquad (44)$$

where K_1 and B_1 are given before for the τ-distribution function. The corresponding frequency spectrum reduces to

$$S_\eta(\nu) = K_2 \nu^{-5} e^{-B_2 \nu^{-4}} \qquad (45)$$

and

$$S_{\eta^2}(\nu) = \overline{\eta^2} S_\eta(\nu) \qquad (46)$$

where K_2 and B_2 are given before the ν-distribution function.

It is shown by Bretschneider (1959) that the Neumann spectrum, corresponding to the form of equation 45, can be written as follows:

$$S_{\eta^2}(\nu) = 7.95 \nu^{-6} e^{-1.77 \nu^{-2}} \qquad (47)$$

Figure 2-3-2 shows a comparison between equation 46 and equation 47.

ALTERNATE FORM OF τ-SPECTRUM AND ν-SPECTRUM

For the above special case it will be convenient to write equations 43 and 45 in alternate forms. If equation 43, for example, is differentiated and set equal to zero, one obtains

$$B_1 = \tfrac{3}{4} \tau_0^{-4}$$

and

$$K_1 = e^{3/4} \tau_0^{-3} S_\eta(\tau_0)$$

where τ_0 is the peak of the period spectrum, or corresponds to that period for which $S_\eta(\tau) = S_\eta(\tau_0)$, the maximum value.

It then follows that the period spectrum can be written as follows:

$$S_\eta(\tau) = S_\eta(\tau_0) \left(\frac{\tau}{\tau_0}\right)^3 e^{-3/4[(\tau/\tau_0)^4 - 1]} \qquad (48)$$

A similar operation can be performed on the frequency spectrum, whence

$$B_2 = \tfrac{5}{4} \nu_0^4$$

and

$$K_2 = e^{5/4} \nu_0^5 S_\eta(\nu_0)$$

where ν_0 is the peak of the frequency spectrum and corresponds to that frequency for which $S_\eta(\nu) = S_\eta(\nu_0)$, the maximum value.

It then follows that the frequency spectrum can be written

$$S_\eta(\nu) = S_\eta(\nu_0) \left(\frac{\nu_0}{\nu}\right)^5 e^{-5/4[(\nu_0/\nu)^4 - 1]} \qquad (49)$$

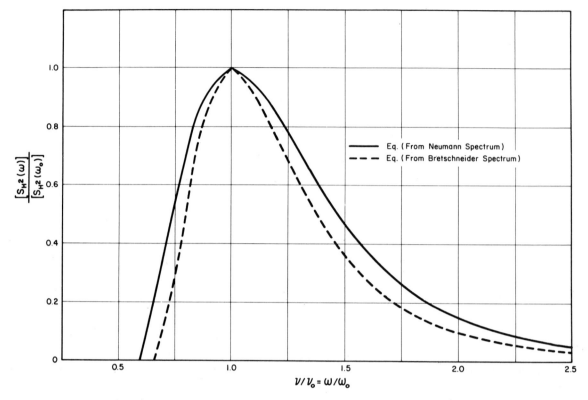

Figure 2-3-2. *Non-dimensional form of frequency spectra (in terms of ω_0).*

Comparing equations 43 and 48 and also 45 and 49, it will be found that

$$\tau_0^4 = \frac{3}{\pi}\,(\overline{\tau^2})^2$$

$$\tau_0 S_\eta(\tau_0) = 3e^{-3/4} \qquad (50)$$

$$\nu_0^4 = \frac{4}{5\pi}\,(\overline{\nu^2})^2$$

$$\nu_0 S_\eta(\nu_0) = 5e^{-5/4}$$

It might be mentioned that any type of exponential continuous linear-wave spectrum can be written as follows:

$$S_\eta(\tau) = K_1 \tau^M e^{-B_1 \tau^N} \qquad (51)$$

Applying the above operation it will be found that

$$B_1 = \frac{M}{N}\,\tau_0^{-N}$$

and

$$K_1 = e^{M/N}\tau_0^{-M} S_\eta(\tau_0)$$

thus

$$S_\eta(\tau) = S_\eta(\tau_0)\left(\frac{\tau}{\tau_0}\right)^M e^{-M/N[(\tau/\tau_0)^N-1]} \qquad (52)$$

According to the period spectrum by Neumann (1952), $M = 4$ and $N = 2$, whence the Neumann spectrum can be written as follows:

$$S_\eta(\tau) = S_\eta(\tau_0)\left(\frac{\tau}{\tau_0}\right)^4 e^{-2[(\tau/\tau_0)^2-1]} \qquad (53)$$

The general form of the linear-frequency spectrum can be written

$$S_\eta(\nu) = K_2 \nu^{-m} e^{-B_2 \nu^{-n}} \qquad (54)$$

where it can be shown that

$$B_2 = \frac{m}{n}\,\nu_0^n$$

and

$$K_2 = e^{m/n}\nu_0^m S_\eta(\nu_0)$$

thus

$$S_\eta(\nu) = S_\eta(\nu_0)\left(\frac{\nu}{\nu_0}\right)^{-m} e^{-m/n[(\nu/\nu_0)^{-n}-1]} \qquad (55)$$

According to the frequency spectrum of Neumann (1952), $M = 6$ and $N = 2$, whence the Neumann spectrum can be written

$$S_\eta(\nu) = S_\eta(\nu_0)\left(\frac{\nu}{\nu_0}\right)^{-6} e^{-3[(\nu/\nu_0)^{-2}-1]} \qquad (56)$$

Figure 2-3-3 shows a comparison between the frequency spectra given by equations 49 and 56. Comparison with other proposed wave spectra might also have been made. The important factor is that the shape of the spectrum is determined by the exponents M and N, which are also functions of the state of sea. $S_\eta(\nu_0)$ and ν_0, the peak values, are also functions of the state of sea.

COMPOSITE WAVE SPECTRUM

The discussions of the linear wave spectrum should not be concluded without first making an attempt to investigate a composite wave spectrum. A composite wave spectrum is one made up of two or more primary components, and is not necessarily a nonlinear wave spectrum but may take on some nonlinear appearances. This consideration becomes important in order that a proper interpretation can be attached to the significance of the linear wave spectrum and also for the proper interpretation of a computed wave spectrum.

For example, such a composite wave spectrum acts frequently on the California coast, where short period wind waves of 4 to 6 seconds are superimposed on 12- to 14-second swell.

It will be sufficient for illustrative purposes to assume that each component of the composite spectrum will be similar to that given by equa-

tion 49, although equation 55 or 56 might also have been used. Corresponding to equation 59, the composite frequency spectrum can be written as follows:

$$S_\eta(\nu) = \sum_1^N K_N \left(\frac{\nu_{0N}}{\nu}\right)^5 e^{-5/4(\nu_{0N}/\nu)^4} \quad (57)$$

where $K_N = K_1, K_2, K_3$, etc., as $N = 1, 2, 3$, etc. are the corresponding constants for each linear spectrum taken separately; and $\nu_{0N} = \nu_{01}, \nu_{02}, \nu_{03}$, etc. as $N = 1, 2, 3$, etc. are the corresponding peak frequencies for each linear spectrum taken separately. It then follows from equation 57:

$$K_N = e^{5/4}S_\eta(\nu_{0N}),$$

whence

$$K_1 = e^{5/4}S_\eta(\nu_{01})$$

$$K_2 = e^{5/4}S_\eta(\nu_{02})$$

$$K_3 = e^{5/4}S_\eta(\nu_{03}), \text{ etc.}$$

It would be relatively easy to construct a composite spectrum by direct addition of the corresponding linear spectra. Once a composite spectrum is constructed, as under natural conditions, it is more difficult to separate the composite spectrum into the corresponding linear spectra. Although peaks may be apparent in the composite spectrum, they do not necessarily correspond in magnitude or frequency of the corresponding spectra taken separately. No attempt is made to

Figure 2-3-3. *Non-dimensional form of frequency spectra.*

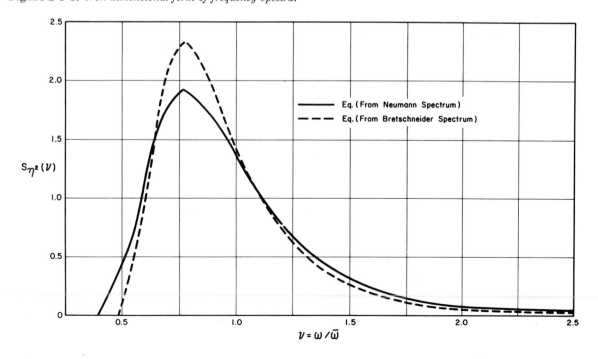

set up techniques for the general solution of the problem, which normally would require curve fitting and the use of a high speed computer. Instead, only a special case will be considered for illustrative purposes. For example, if one considers the case for which $\nu_{01} = \nu_0$, $\nu_{02} = 2\nu_0$, and $\nu_{03} = 3\nu_0$, and no additional terms, then one can write from equation 68

$$S_\eta(\nu_0) = K_1 e^{-5/4} + 2^5 K_2 e^{-20} + 3^5 K_3 e^{-405/4}$$

$$S_\eta(2\nu_0) = (\tfrac{1}{2})^5 K_1 e^{-5/64} + K_2 e^{-5/4} + (\tfrac{3}{2})^5 K_3 e^{-405/64}$$

$$S_\eta(3\nu_0) = (\tfrac{1}{3})^5 K_1 e^{-5/364} + (\tfrac{2}{3})^5 K_2 e^{-20/81} + K_3 e^{-5/4}$$

It will be noted that $S_\eta(\nu_0)$ is essentially equal to $S_\eta(\nu_{01})$, but $S_\eta(2\nu_0)$ does not equal $S_\eta(\nu_{02})$, and $S_\eta(3\nu_0)$ does not equal $S_\eta(\nu_{03})$. It then follows essentially that

$$K_1 = e^{5/4} S_\eta(\nu_0)$$

$$K_2 = e^{5/4}[S_\eta(2\nu_0) - (\tfrac{1}{2})^5 K_1 e^{-5/4(1/2)^4}]$$

and

$$K_3 = $$
$$e^{5/4}[S_\eta(3\nu_0) - (\tfrac{1}{3})^5 K_1 e^{-5/4(1/3)^4} - (\tfrac{2}{3})^5 K_2 e^{-5/4(2/3)^4}]$$

It can easily be seen that the fourth term would be

$$K_4 = $$
$$e^{5/4}[S_\eta(4\nu_0) - (\tfrac{1}{4})^5 K_1 e^{-5/4(1/4)^4} - (\tfrac{2}{4})^5 K_2 e^{-5/4(2/4)^4}$$
$$- (\tfrac{3}{4})^5 K_3 e^{-5/4(3/4)^4}]$$

Figure 2-3-4 shows a plot of the components of a composite frequency spectrum for the case where $\nu_{01} = \nu_0$, $\nu_{02} = 2\nu_0$ and $\nu_{03} = 3\nu_0$, using the shape of equation 49 and normalizing to unity the area under each of the three curves. The actual spectrum in each case would have to take into account the corresponding mean wave heights. It is interesting to note that the spectrum corresponding to $\nu_{02} = 2\nu_0$ has no effect on the peak value $S_\eta(\nu_0)$ nor on the peak frequency ν_0. A similar conclusion can be made for the Neumann spectrum, and perhaps it is a general conclusion.

It might also be considered that ν_{02} and ν_{03} are the second and third harmonics of the fundamental ν_0, and it can further be concluded that the second and higher harmonics of a nonlinear spectrum have no effect on the peak value of the fundamental. It therefore seems to be the case that the two most valuable parameters of the linear frequency spectrum are $S_\eta(\nu_0)$ and ν_0, and it is these two parameters that should be related to the wind-wave generation parameters and perhaps also to the decay parameters. The low frequency components, those lower than ν_0, are also not affected by higher harmonics. In fact, over half of the fundamental of the linear spectrum is not affected by the second or higher harmonics. The high frequency components of the spectrum will always be mixed with the higher harmonics, and therefore a difficult problem arises as to what are the high frequency components and what are the higher harmonics of the lower frequency components.

Figure 2-3-4. *Illustrative example of individual spectra of a particular composite spectrum in non-dimensional form.*

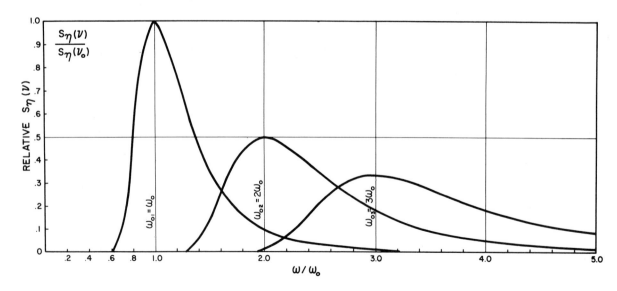

COMPUTED WAVE SPECTRA

A few wave records have been analyzed to obtain individual wave heights and periods, using the zero upcrossing method (Pierson, 1954).

The wave records were obtained at the Beach Erosion Board gaging station at Atlantic City, New Jersey. The wave staff is the step-resistance wave gage installed in about 17 feet mean low water. The surface elevations at the gage are recorded simultaneously on the Brush recorder type wave gage and also on a magnetic tape. The individual wave heights and periods were tabulated for grouping. The grouping of the heights was made according to equal increments of the frequency $f = 1/T$. It was found desirable to use a smoothing technique, since a 20-minute wave record is not usually long enough to obtain enough statistics for each range of frequency. Although other methods of smoothing the data might prove more satisfactory and be used at some later date, the method discussed below appears rather simple to use. The frequencies were grouped according to $f = 0.02 \pm 0.02$, $f = 0.04 \pm 0.02$, $f = 0.06 \pm 0.02$, etc., but applied respectively to $f = 0.02 \pm 0.01$, $f = 0.04 \pm 0.01$, $f = 0.06 \pm 0.01$, etc. In this way many of the same wave heights were entered in one, two, or three classes of f, and the total number of waves (N) for statistical purposes is increased accordingly. Since the period T and not f is read directly from the paper record, it was found convenient to prepare Table I for the range in periods to be used with each centroid frequency, 0.02, 0.04, 0.06, etc. It can be seen from Table I, except for the very long wave periods, that the

groupings are still over reasonably small ranges of wave period. The wave periods from the wave records are read accurately to the closest one-half second and estimated to the closest 0.1 second.

TABLE I
CENTROID FREQUENCIES FOR VARIOUS RANGES
IN WAVE PERIOD

f seconds^{-1}	Range in Periods seconds	f seconds^{-1}	Range in Periods seconds
0.04	16.5–50	0.30	3.2–3.6
0.06	12.6–25	0.32	3.0–3.4
0.08	10.0–16.6	0.34	2.8–3.2
0.10	8.4–12.6	0.36	2.6–3.0
0.12	7.2–10.0	0.38	2.6–2.8
0.14	6.2– 8.4	0.40	2.4–2.6
0.16	5.6– 7.2	0.42	2.2–2.6
0.18	5.0– 6.2	0.44	2.2–2.4
0.20	4.6– 5.6	0.46	2.0–2.2
0.22	4.2– 5.0	0.48	2.0–2.2
0.24	3.8– 4.6	0.50	2.0–2.0
0.26	3.6– 4.2	0.52	1.8–2.0
0.28	3.4– 3.8	0.54	1.8–1.8

Each individual wave height of a particular wave period was entered on a table according to the appropriate row or rows of f (see Table I), from which $S_H(f)$ and $S_{H^2}(f)$ were determined. $S_H(f)$ represents the sum of all the individual wave heights for each class of f, and $S_{H^2}(f)$ represents the sum of all the squares of the individual wave heights for each class of f. For presentation purposes, it was found convenient to determine

$$S_\eta(f) = [S_H(f)] \div N\overline{H} \quad \text{and} \quad S_{\eta^2}(f) = [S_{H^2}(f)] \div N\overline{H^2}$$

TABLE II
SUMMARY OF $\overline{H}$ AND $\overline{H^2}$ FROM INDIVIDUAL WAVE HEIGHTS
AND FROM GROUPED WAVE HEIGHTS

Record Date	Time	Fig. No.	From Individual Wave Heights			From Grouped Wave Heights		
			$\overline{H}$ feet	$\overline{H^2}$ feet^2	N	$\overline{H}$ feet	$\overline{H^2}$ feet^2	N
4-5-60	2000*	5	5.26	31.14	62	5.23	30.80	134
1-3-60	2000	6	6.87	51.41	134	6.94	52.27	293
9-29-59	0404	7	4.04	18.90	154	4.03	20.63	345
8-7-59	2000	8	2.06	4.99	173	2.04	4.91	399
4-23-59	1245	9	3.87	17.27	155	3.80	16.88	342
8-8-59	1600*	10	2.29	6.28	66	2.36	6.59	167
9-11-60	2000	11	1.86	4.09	193	1.79	3.81	491
9-11-60	2400	12	1.99	4.68	214	1.92	4.38	557
9-12-60	0400	13	3.24	11.97	190	3.21	11.93	547
9-12-60	0800	14	5.37	33.96	203	5.15	32.67	528
9-12-60	1200	15	6.32	47.71	127	6.04	45.78	281
Averages			3.92	21.13	152	3.86	20.97	371

* Indicates 7-minute wave records; the other records are of 20-minute duration.

where N represents the total number of entries of H for all f for each record, and $\overline{H}$ and $\overline{H^2}$ are the corresponding mean wave height and mean square wave height, respectively. N as used here is different from the total number of individual waves of the wave record because of the method of grouping of the data, and $\overline{H}$ and $\overline{H^2}$ might be somewhat different from the corresponding true values. The true value of $\overline{H}$ and $\overline{H^2}$ were also determined from the wave records and were found to be within a few percent of $\overline{H}$ and $\overline{H^2}$ determined from the grouped data.

Table II shows a comparison of $\overline{H}$ and $\overline{H^2}$ from individual wave heights respectively, with $\overline{H}$ and $\overline{H^2}$ obtained from the grouped data.

It can be seen from Table II below that the two sets of $\overline{H}$ and $\overline{H^2}$ are essentially the same, and that the wave statistics are increased by the ratio of $371/152 = 2.44.$

Figures 2-3-5 through 2-3-15 are typical wave spectra computed according to the methods presented in this paper. No attempt was made to compare these spectra with a theoretical spectrum of the exponential type because the present study and analysis is not completed to date. Furthermore, some of these records are not ideal for comparison with a linear wave spectrum because of their composite nature of a mixture of wind waves and swell. The effect of wave refraction would also have to be accounted for before such a comparison could be made. Wave records of Hurricane Donna were also recorded on magnetic tape, the analysis of which is discussed in the paper by Williams and Caldwell (1961). No attempt was made to compare the computed wave spectra with those obtained from the analog spectrum analyzer because of possible nonlinear effects combined with the composite nature of these spectra.

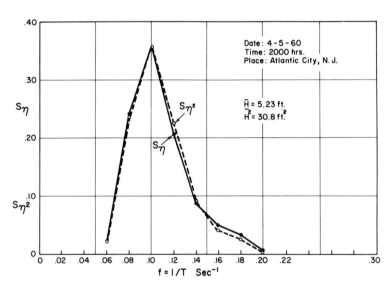

Figure 2-3-5. *Computed wave spectra.*

Figure 2-3-6. *Computed wave spectra.*

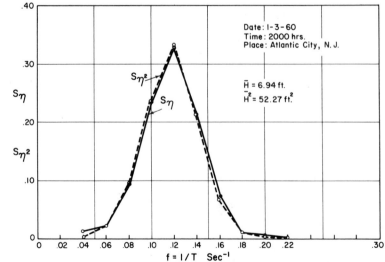

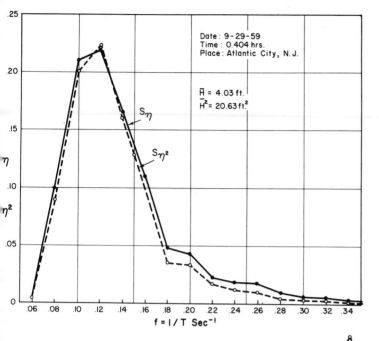

Date: 9-29-59
Time: 0.404 hrs.
Place: Atlantic City, N.J.

$\bar{H}$ = 4.03 ft.
$\overline{H^2}$ = 20.63 ft.²

$S\eta$

$S\eta^2$

η

η^2

f = 1/T Sec⁻¹

Figure 2-3-7. *Computed wave spectra.*

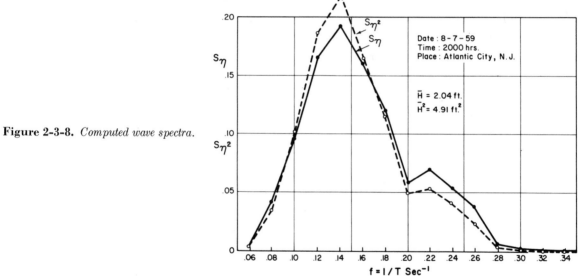

$S\eta$

$S\eta^2$

$S\eta^2$
$S\eta$

Date: 8-7-59
Time: 2000 hrs.
Place: Atlantic City, N.J.

$\bar{H}$ = 2.04 ft.
$\overline{H^2}$ = 4.91 ft.²

f = 1/T Sec⁻¹

Figure 2-3-8. *Computed wave spectra.*

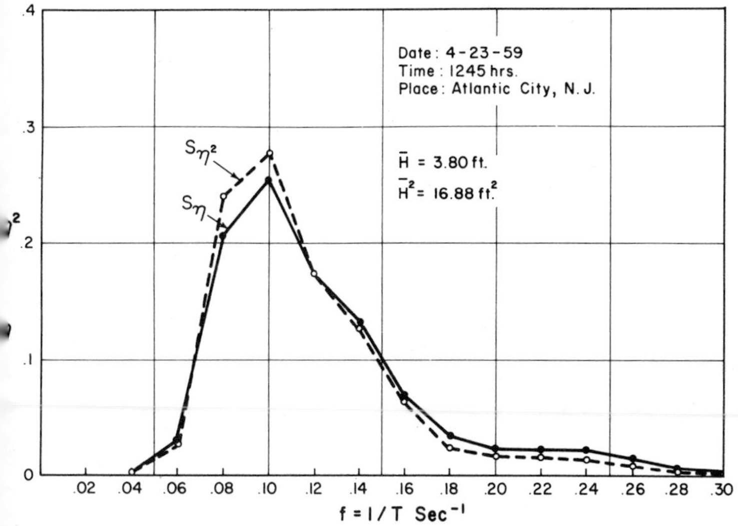

Date: 4-23-59
Time: 1245 hrs.
Place: Atlantic City, N.J.

$\bar{H}$ = 3.80 ft.
$\overline{H^2}$ = 16.88 ft.²

$S\eta^2$

$S\eta$

f = 1/T Sec⁻¹

Figure 2-3-9. *Computed wave spectra.*

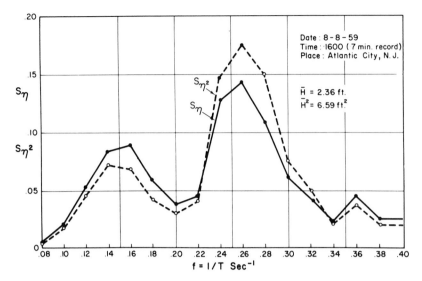

Figure 2-3-10. *Computed wave spectra.*

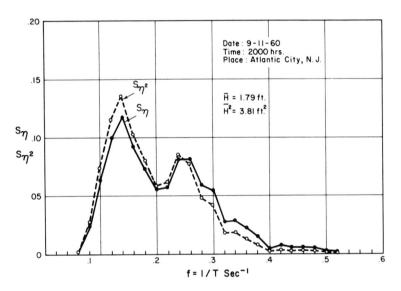

Figure 2-3-11. *Computed wave spectra.*

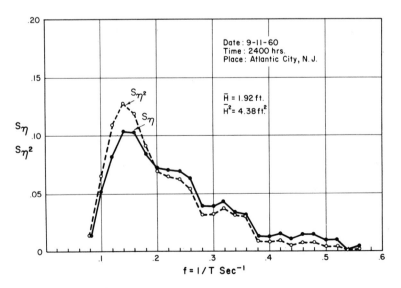

Figure 2-3-12. *Computed wave spectra.*

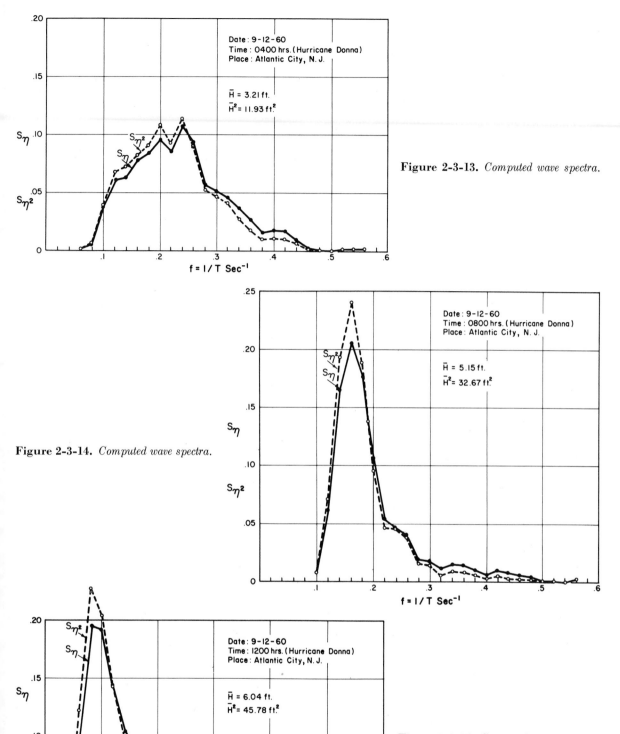

Figure 2-3-13. *Computed wave spectra.*

Figure 2-3-14. *Computed wave spectra.*

Figure 2-3-15. *Computed wave spectra.*

FUTURE PLANNING

At present the U. S. Army Engineer District, Walla Walla, Washington, in cooperation with the Beach Erosion Board, is conducting a wind-wave gaging program on one of the reservoirs of the Columbia River. The fetch is limited, and the wave spectra should not be of the same composite nature as those obtained at Atlantic City, New Jersey. It is believed that wave records obtained on the Columbia River Reservoir will permit a fair test of numerical procedures used to obtain the computed wave spectra and perhaps permit a reasonable interpretation of the recorded wave spectrum with the joint distribution of wave heights and periods. The ultimate goal is to install magnetic tape recorders at all future gaging stations and analyze the records by use of the analog-type spectrum analyzer. From these wave spectra an attempt will be made to relate $S_H(f_0)$ and f_0, as well as $\overline{H}$ and $\overline{T}$, to the wave generation parameters. Finally, an attempt will be made to verify and modify, if necessary, the present form of the proposed wave spectrum given in this paper, so that the joint distribution of H and T (or H and $f = 1/T$) can be deduced accurately from the wave spectrum.

There are some design problems for which it is enough to know only the significant wave height and period, using the distribution functions presently available to obtain the higher wave heights and the range in periods of the design spectrum. There are other design problems for which a knowledge of the wave variability within each range of periods would be more desirable.

* * *

ACKNOWLEDGMENTS

Appreciation is extended to the Beach Erosion Board for making available the time and personnel needed for this investigation. In particular, Messrs. Demetrius Dumm, Gary Hampton, Horacio Avelino, and Louis Meyerle participated in the wave record analysis and computations. Mrs. Kathryn Rees did the typing.

REFERENCES

Bretschneider, C. L., *Wave Variability and Wave Spectra for Wind-Generated Gravity Waves.* Beach Erosion Board, Tech. Memo. 118 (1959) 192 pp.

Cartwright, D. E. and M. S. Longuet-Higgins, "The Statistical Distribution of the Maxima of a Random Function." *Proc. R. Soc.*, A, No. 237 (1956) 212–232.

Czepa, O. and G. Schellenberger, "Zur Charakteristik Winderzeugter Oberflächen Wellen von Binnenseen," *Gerlands Beiträge zur Geophysik*, 68, Heft 3 (1959) 171–187.

Darbyshire, J., "The Generation of Waves by Wind," *Proc. R. Soc.*, A No. 215 (1952) 299–328.

"An Investigation of Storm Waves in the North Atlantic Ocean," *Proc. R. Soc.*, A No. 230 (1955) 299–328.

"Further Investigation of Wind Generated Waves." *Deut. Hydr. Zs.* XII (1959) 1–13.

Darlington, C. R., "The Distribution of Wave Heights and Periods in Ocean Waves" *Q. J. R. Met. Soc.*, LXXX (1954) 619–626.

Longuet-Higgins, M. S., "On the Statistical Distribution of the Heights of Sea Waves," *Jour. Marine Res.*, XI, No. 3 (1952) 345–366.

Neumann, G., *On Ocean Wave Spectra and a New Method of Forecasting Wind-Generated Sea*, Beach Erosion Board, Tech. Memo. 43 (1952) 42 pp.

Pierson, W. J., Jr., "An Interpretation of the Observable Properties of 'Sea' Waves in Terms of the Energy Spectrum of the Gaussian Record." *Trans. Am. Geophys. Union*, XXXV (1954) 747–757.

Putz, R. R., "Statistical Distribution for Ocean Waves," *Trans. Am. Geophys. Union* XXXIII, No. 5 (1952) 685–692.

Roll, H. U. and G. Fischer, "Eine Kritische Bemerkung Zum Neumann-Specktrum der Seeganger," *Deut. Hydr. Zs.*, IX (1956) 9–14.

Uspensky, J. V., *Introduction to Mathematical Probability.* New York: McGraw-Hill Book Company, Inc., 1937 411 pp.

Watters, Jessie K. A., "Distribution of Height in Ocean Waves," *New Zealand Journal of Science and Technology*, Sec. B, XXXIV (1953) 408–422.

Williams, L. C. and J. M. Caldwell, "The Beach Erosion Board's Wave Spectrum Analyzer and Its Purpose" Presented at 1961 Conference on Wave Spectra.

DISCUSSION

Dr. Dorrestein: I think we have come upon an argument over what the word "spectrum" means. It should be clear that we use it in different senses — "spectrum" in the strict sense and "spectrum" in the wider sense. Of course, everyone knows what you mean by it, and we can keep these different concepts separate. The problem is what is the relation between the two.

The other problem is what does Dr. Bretschneider mean by a "wave system." The definition of a wave system is not easy. We tried to develop a suitable definition for instructions to observers aboard ship. Everyone knows what is meant by "one-wave system," but a good definition is needed.

* * *

Mr. Cartwright: It has often occurred to me that Bretschneider's type of representation of quasi-period and wave height is what is needed for certain engineering problems. In fact, I have frequently talked with engineers about spectra, and we seem to be in agreement for a time, until suddenly I realize that I am talking about a normal sort of spectrum while they are talking about the sort of thing Dr. Bretschneider dealt with.

It is obviously very valuable to consider this and try to find the relation between this new type of spectrum and the more conventional type. Dr. Bretschneider certainly built up a remarkable structure to describe the statistics of his sort of spectrum, which is based on six assumptions that appear qualitatively reasonable at first sight. But I think it would be difficult to build up a rigorous mathematical model from them, or to relate them to the properties of the conventional spectrum. However, starting with a Gaussian model and an autocovariance function, one could rigorously derive the joint probability distribution of H and T (or more easily, the mean and variance of H as a function of T) with the following definitions:

$$Y(0) - Y(T) = H,$$

$$Y'(0) = 0 = Y'(T),$$

$$Y'(\tfrac{1}{2}T) < 0,$$

$$Y''(0) < 0,$$

$$Y''(T) > 0$$

The numerical work would not be prohibitive with an automatic computer, and would follow on similar lines to that of Ehrenfeld, Pierson, and others on the zero-crossing problem. The result would be a mathematical realisation of something very close to Dr. Bretschneider's spectrum.

* * *

Mr. Farmer (prepared comments): Dr. Bretschneider has pointed out the need in coastal engineering for knowledge about joint frequency distribution of wave heights and wave periods and about how this distribution might be related to the wave energy spectrum. The joint frequency distribution is obtained using wave heights and apparent wave periods (by zero up-crossings), which are measured from actual wave records. Longuet-Higgins has shown that for a narrow spectrum wave heights follow the Rayleigh distribution.

Bretschneider has found that the distribution of the square of the apparent wave period also appears to fit the Rayleigh distribution. The joint distribution of the wave height and the square of the apparent wave period is then characterized by a correlation coefficient and the requirement that the marginal distribution be that of Rayleigh.

In terms of this bivariate frequency function, a summation function, equation 13, is defined, and following equation 16 it is stated to be the wave spectrum. Other spectrum functions are similarly defined. These equations are still in terms of weighted wave heights and apparent wave periods as they would be measured from a wave record. No statement is made, however, about the interpretation of these apparent wave periods or frequencies in terms of spectral wave frequencies, as used, for example, by Blackman and Tukey and others.

Since it is proposed to compare this spectrum function with observed spectra determined by analogue or digital computers, some assumption relating these two quite different types of frequencies has been tacitly made.

The spectrum function which results is just the Rayleigh frequency distribution with an added proportionality factor that is dependent on the correlation coefficient of the bivariate distribution. In the case of zero correlation, the Rayleigh distribution then becomes the amplitude (in contrast to energy) spectrum, equations 16 and 43. For the energy spectrum the distribution is multiplied by the mean square conditional nondimensional wave height, equations 20 and 44.

A possible similarity in shape between this modified Rayleigh distribution and observed wave spectra may well exist, but to attempt a derivation by claiming this statistical frequency distribution to be the energy spectrum seems a very questionable procedure.

If it can be shown that this spectrum does adequately describe the observed spectra and that the joint distribution of wave heights and apparent periods can be theoretically or even empirically related to the spectral density and frequencies, then, indeed, a very useful result has been achieved.

Dr. Burling (prepared comments): The stimulating paper by Dr. Bretschneider presents an approach to a general study of the wave spectrum that may ultimately be of immense value. The value, of course, will depend upon adequate testing of the basic assumptions.

Because of the method's potential, but at the risk of being presumptuous, I would like to suggest a new set of assumptions. The first assumptions apply to a random variable (or stochastic process), which is defined in a general enough way to apply to ocean waves generated by one steady definable wind acting over a given fetch. Further assumptions are required on observed samples that might be used to test Dr. Bretschneider's theory or on which the theory may be applied. Subject to test, the assumptions could make the theory much more powerful and more generally applicable. To be worth while the formulations should be sufficiently precise, and should draw attention to some points that have often escaped notice.

The best method of exploring details of the spectrum is undoubtedly to measure it according to its definition, but the facilities are not always available.

THE VARIABLE

Let $x(t)$ be a real random process which varies with some ordinary variable t, such that

$$E\{x(t)\} = 0 \tag{1}$$

$$E\{x(t)x(t + s)\} = R(s), \tag{2}$$

where $R(s)$ is the autocovariance function with lag s and where $E\{f(x)\}$ is the average value of a function of x in probability (Cramer, 1946, p. 170). We may write, putting $x_i = x(t_i)$,

$$E\{f(x_1, x_2)\} = \int_0^\infty \int f(x_1, x_2)p(x_1, x_2)\, dx_1\, dx_2 \tag{3}$$

where $p(x_1, x_2)$ is the joint probability that x_1 lies between x_1 and $x_1 + dx_1$ and x_2 lies between x_2 and $x_2 + dx_2$. Conditional and marginal distributions are defined by relations shown in equations 10 and 11 in Dr. Bretschneider's paper. Suitable references for the following paragraphs are Bartlett (1955) and Doob (1953).

Let $x(t)$ be continuous except at an enumerable number of discrete values of t_j (that is, the t_j may be arranged in a sequence even if infinite in number [Cramer, 1946, p. 3]; also compare breaking waves); then $R(s)$ is continuous. If there are no discrete frequency components in $x(t)$ (for general ocean "waves" this seems to exclude only tidal constituents, and possibly certain components with much longer periods), then $x(t)$ has a spectral density $S(w)$ defined by

$$R(s) = \int_0^\infty S(w) \cos ws\, dw \tag{4}$$

which has the reciprocal relation

$$S(w) = \int_0^\infty R(s) \cos ws\, ds \tag{5}$$

where w is the angular frequency.

An important result from condition (1), corresponding to no trend, is that time averages of $f(x)$ over very long times, denoted by $\overline{f(x)}$, may be used instead of probability averages (that is, the ergodic property), and we write (compare also equation 3 above)

$$\overline{f(x)} = E\{f(x)\} \tag{6}$$

If any variable $x(t)$ is such that the left hand sides of (1) and (2) exist and are independent of time, then the variable is described as stationary to the second order. A normal or Gaussian process with the same properties has stationary moments of all orders, but this is not necessarily true of third and higher order moments of $x(t)$. Thus, although $R(s)$ is not a function of t, but only of s, the higher order moments may actually vary with time in the probability sense, and the ergodic property would not be true for averages of functions incorporating higher order moments than the second, even though the spectrum and autocovariance remain constant. Values of $\bar{x}$, $R(s)$, and $S(w)$ computed from observed data thus have a scatter inherent in the distribution of $x(t)$ and dependent on the duration of the observations, but values of $\overline{x^n}$ $(n \geqslant 3)$ may have additional scatter. We should test to see if this is so; if not, the process is stationary to a higher order.

ASSUMPTIONS

Let h, k, H, and T be normalized variables defined on $x(t)$ in a manner corresponding to that in which Dr. Bretschneider (equation 8) defined η, λ, H and T, respectively, on the elevations of the wave record. Let $p(h, k)$, $p(k)$ and $p_k(h)$ be probability densities defined in the manner corresponding to his equation 10.

We define a function

$$S_{h^2}(k) = \overline{h_k^2}\, p(k) \qquad (7)$$

analogous formally to the relations shown in his equations 17 to 20. $S_{h^2}(k)$ will be called the k spectrum of h^2. $\overline{h_k^2}$ is the mean square value of all h occurring simultaneously with values of k in the interval $k - (dk/2)$, $k + (dk/2)$, and it is some function of k, say $\overline{h_k^2} = G(k)$. Then

$$S_{h^2}(k) = G(k)p(k). \qquad (8)$$

Assumption 1.
It is assumed that $k = T^2/\overline{T^2} = (1/w^2)/(1/\overline{w^2})$ and that

$$a\overline{T^2}\overline{H^2}S_{h^2}(k)\, dk = S(w)\, dw, \qquad (9)$$

where $S(w)$ is defined by equation 5 above, a is constant, $-dk = (8\pi^2/\overline{T^2}w^3)\, dw$ and where the integral of each side (0 to ∞) is $\overline{x^2}$. Either spectrum (S or S_{h^2}) may be expressed in terms of w, $f = 1/T$, $T = 1/f$, T^2, etc., or corresponding non-dimensional quantities.

Assumption 2.
It is assumed that $G(k)$ and $p(k)$ are some particular functions. The particular functions may either be derived theoretically or may be functions suggested or determined empirically from observed data. Dr. Bretschneider assumed that $G(k)$ is $mk + b$, and that $p(k)$ is the probability density of the Rayleigh distribution, both having been suggested from the analysis of earlier observations.

Assumption 3.
It is assumed that data used to test both assumptions, and on which the second assumption was based (if the empirical method was used), is drawn from a process $x(t)$ defined above.

The choice of quantity of discrete data or the duration of a record or parts of records depends solely on the level of significance desired if the data is yet to be observed. If a given number of data is already at hand, then its use will allow the determination of significance to some level.

Several features mentioned by Dr. Bretschneider are such that perhaps special attempts should be made to avoid them in future test data, either from precise information on conditions in the generating area or by monitoring (for example through the spectra) the data and selecting uncontaminated and sufficiently stationary parts of the records.

It is remarked that assumptions equivalent to the above were used by Neumann (1953) in his development of a form for the spectrum.

FURTHER DISCUSSION

An extremely useful proposition used in the general theory is that to every random process $x(t)$ there corresponds a normal or Gaussian process with the same moments of first and second order (that is $f(x_1, x_2) = x_1^n x_2^m$ in equation 3, where $n + m = 1$ or 2, for $n \geqslant 0$ and $m \geqslant 0$). A consequence is that any property of $x(t)$ which is derived from first and second moments only can be derived from the normal distribution with the same first and second moments.

Hence the functions $R(s)$ and $S(w)$ and the variance of $x(t)$ are precisely those of the corresponding normal distribution. However, this is not true for the distribution of $x(t)$ itself and associated joint distributions which contain moments higher than the second. Notably, properties such as the mean number of zeros (see Bartlett, 1955, p. 188) and the distribution of maxima or of minima, and many others (some are given by Longuet-Higgins, 1957) are not accurately approximated by expressions found from the normal distribution for terms containing moments of $x(t)$ higher than the second, and odd moments do not appear at all in the approximations.

For actual water surface elevations the approximations have been tested in a few cases; for example, it was shown by Kinsman (1960) that the distribution of actual elevations is significantly non-Gaussian and that errors will be large for properties involving third order moments. Dr. Bretschneider (1959) plots many observations of wave height distributions, and they appear to conform to an expected Rayleigh distribution. However, no statistical test was applied, and quoted skewness coefficients are quite large. All other tests on wave-height distributions appear to have been applied to data obtained by recording the pressures beneath the surface. This has the effect of applying a low frequency filter and the spectrum of frequencies recorded is effectively narrower than the spectrum of surface elevations. Cartwright and Longuet-Higgins (1956) show that as the width of the spectrum decreases, the distribution of wave crests, approximated by that appropriate to that of the corresponding normal distribution, tends towards a Rayleigh distribution; thus, the statistically significant correspondence of observed data to that estimated from the normal distribution suggests that the pressures may be regarded as being normally distributed; but it is by no means certain that this is true for surface elevations.

It appears that attempts should be made to get records of actual surface elevations and test the distribution of the data itself. This would eliminate ambiguities introduced by substituting Gaussian moments for the higher order moments of the distribution, which also eliminates odd order moments completely. Since computers are fairly generally available, adequate testing should present no great difficulty if suitable data can be selected.

It may be that the assumption of a Rayleigh distribution for wave heights is sufficient for most purposes or at long fetches, or for swell. However, it is noted here that in records of waves at short fetches which I have observed, there is a significant difference between the distribution of wave crests and the distribution of wave troughs, the former being scattered more widely about their mean than are the troughs about the mean depression of troughs. This cannot be a function of a normal distribution with a wide spectrum, since this distribution is symmetrical for crests and troughs, but must result from the lack of normality of the data.

It is clear that the estimate of any statistic that depends on the third or higher order moments may not conform with what would be expected if the surface elevations were normally distributed. Such properties as the distribution of zero crossings or the distribution of crests are thus liable to give incorrect information on the spectrum or other properties which depend only on first and second order moments.

It is also noted that Bretschneider (1959) examined the distribution of wave periods squared; λ was plotted against the cumulative frequency and compared with the curve for the Rayleigh distribution. The comparison appears to be reasonable, but no test was applied. However, a test was applied to the regressions between η and λ, and it was found that the deviation of the data from the regression of λ on η was not significant, while the deviation from the regression of η on λ was significant. Since the latter regression is that important to the development of Dr. Bretschneider's method, it is apparent that some relation other than linear may be applicable.

It is interesting that Dr. Bretschneider's spectra may be written in terms of frequency and dimensional, non-constant parameters

$$Af^{-p} \exp(-Bf^{-r}), \quad (p = 5, r = 4)$$

Other investigators who have approximated the spectrum by a similar form have found p to lie in the range 5 to 6, and r to have the value 2 in all but one case (Burling, 1959), in which r was found to lie roughly between the values 5 and 9.

REFERENCES

Bartlett, M. S., *An Introduction to Stochastic Processes.* Cambridge University Press, 1955, 312 pp.

Bretschneider, C. L., *Wave Variability and Wave Spectra for Wind-Generated Gravity Waves.* Beach Erosion Board, Technical Memorandum No. 118, 1959.

Burling, R. W., "The Spectrum of Waves at Short Fetches." *Dt. Hydrogr. Z.*, XII (1959) 45–64, 96–117.

Cartwright, D. E. and M. S. Longuet-Higgins, "The Statistical Distribution of the Maxima of a Random Function," *Proc. R. Soc.*, A, CCXXXVII (1956) 212–232.

Cramer, H., *Mathematical Methods of Statistics.* Princeton University Press 1946, 575 pp.

Doob, J. L., *Stochastic Processes.* New York: John Wiley and Sons, and London: Chapman and Hall, 1953, 654 pp.

Kinsman, B., *Surface Waves at Short Fetches and Low Wind Speeds — a Field Study.* Tech. Report XIX, vol. 1 (1960) ref. 60–1, Chesapeake Bay Institute, The Johns Hopkins Univ.

Longuet-Higgins, M. S., "The Statistical Analysis of a Random Moving Surface," *Phil. Trans., R. Soc.,* A, CMLXVI (1957) 321–387.

Neumann, G., *On Ocean Wave Spectra and a New Method of Forecasting Wind-Generated Sea.* Beach Erosion Board, Tech. Memo. 43, 1953.

Rice, S. O., "Mathematical Analysis of Random Noise," *The Bell System Tech. Jour.,* XXIII (1944), 282–332 and XXIV (1945) 46–156.

Dr. Bretschneider (in reply to comments): If I build up a so-called spectrum by the method about which I have been talking, then it pretty much implies that a small sinusoidal wave represents a small sample of the record. Let us just consider this one wave having a particular wave height and wave length. Now if this is a wave of finite height, then there will exist higher harmonics. Consider now only the fundamental and second harmonic of this wave, and one will note that there is no change in the number of zero up-crossings and that the wave length is still the same as the fundamental. The wave height is still the vertical distance between the crest and the trough, and the second harmonic does not contribute to any vertical distance between the crest and the trough. By my method of analysis, the second harmonic does not exist, and one obtains only the linear wave spectrum.

What is difficult is that the wave spectrum analyzer separates the fundamental from the second harmonic, and after we consider the linear average from the spectrum analyzer, there will be a peak at the fundamental and a peak at the second harmonic. Now when any waves of various frequencies are considered by the spectrum analyzer, many of the fundamentals of the higher frequency components will combine with the second harmonics of the lower frequency components; and when these are all added to give the total area under the spectrum, then the situation becomes difficult since we can no longer say that this area is the mean wave height. That is, for example, if we have a 10-foot fundamental wave height and the second harmonic is 2 feet, my method of analysis would say the wave height is 10 feet. The wave spectrum analyzer would give the wave height as 10 + 2 or 12 feet.

The problem is not so difficult in regard to the square average since the spectrum analyzer would square 10 and obtain 100 and square 2 and obtain 4, the total being 104 feet square.

Dr. Dorrestein: Thank you. I now invite remarks pertaining to Dr. Burling's discussion.

Dr. Barber: The fact that steep waves do not have a sinusoidal shape certainly worried me and perhaps led me to pay more attention to long travelled swell, where you don't have this problem. It has occurred to me for some time that we may not be measuring waves in the best way. The motion of a floating buoy in a steep wave is very much more sinusoidal than the profile of the wave itself; although the wave may have a peak crest, a buoy is carried rapidly through the trough and dwells a longer time on the crest.

The motion of the buoy is much nearer to a sinusoidal motion. That is perhaps why I am very much interested in the remark, made earlier in the session, that Professor Pierson is considering developing a wave theory from the point of the motion of the particles and not the profile and fixed coordinates. I would be glad if we could hear something about that.

Dr. Pierson: I would like to ask if the Beach Erosion Board has or will have an analogue spectrum analyzer in operation; if they have one now, why not use it?

Dr. Bretschneider: We are using it. We need the records.

Dr. Pierson: Yes, but get down to a spectral technique that is being used in many other fields and many other areas and has a considerable background of theory. The joint density of the period squared and the amplitude, used by Dr. Bretschneider, may or may not be effective as an engineering approximation.

In some work that Dr. Burling referred to, we found certainly that the marginal distribution of the period is not Rayleigh, nor is the marginal distribution of the square of the period Rayleigh.

If you start squaring periods in the wave record, you lose count. The random process is a little more devilish than a series of pieces of sine waves. I suppose we are equally guilty. This is the way that Dr. Neumann got his spectrum. But there are structural faults in this type of analysis that are very difficult to eliminate.

If anything, the distribution of the period, or the apparent periods, in the wave record is extremely complicated and, among other things, depends on the presence of multiple peaks in the spectrum if you have sea and swell.

There is some work — Dr. Longuet-Higgins' work and ours — that comes up with fairly reasonable "period" distributions that fit into place. The theories blow up, or the solution dives below zero and becomes negative, which is impossible, for very high values.

Nevertheless, I think it is very dangerous to use a Rayleigh distribution for the distribution of the "period." A spectrum, when we think of it, is simply the resolution of the total variance of the record into frequencies. If the process is linear, that is all you need to know to describe the record completely. If the record is nonlinear, you need more information, but the spectrum is still useful.

This, of course, will be discussed in detail by Dr. Tick. You can add that second harmonic properly in a nonlinear model and correct a linear model for the second harmonic effects by the procedures that he has developed. Of course, the reverse problem is unsolved at the moment. If you have a spectrum computed from a free surface record that is highly nonlinear, very steep waves, sharp crested, with not only the second harmonic but the second, third, fourth, fifth, sixth, and nth in there, there is no way that we know of to go back to what one might think of as the underlying linear part. Then you get into trouble. You dare not use the available statistical techniques on the spectrum because of the danger of coming up with horribly wrong answers in terms of derivatives and curvatures.

Dr. Bretschneider: I have one question I would like to ask Dr. Pierson. You remarked that your data on wave periods did not agree with my distribution function for period squared. I would like to ask you where your measurements were made?

Dr. Pierson: From highly linear bottom pressure recorders in fifty or sixty feet of water.

Dr. Bretschneider: What location? The Atlantic Ocean?

Dr. Pierson: From Chesapeake Bay out into the Atlantic, giving a very wide spectrum. But that doesn't matter because the theory is general enough to go for any spectrum.

Dr. Bretschneider: The records I have shown are from Atlantic City, New Jersey, and I know that for these records these periods do not fit my distribution function; the reason being that more than one wave train is present, and swell, in particular, will combine with wind waves, resulting in a very complex type of distribution. My distribution function fits quite well for data collected from reservoirs and inland lakes, where only one wave system is present. The distribution system also fits quite well some of the data that Putz obtained from the Pacific Ocean. I will, however, concede that my distribution function does not fit all of the data obtained from Atlantic City, New Jersey, because of the contribution of swell. If one could eliminate this swell, then one would find better agreement with the distribution function for the remaining wind waves.

Dr. Pierson: I think the point is this: If you go about trying to solve this distribution with the techniques that statisticians use in the study of time series, you reach the conclusion that it is not Rayleigh.

Dr. Bretschneider: The distribution of wave periods is very nearly normal, but the periods squared on the wave lengths fit the Rayleigh distribution function quite well.

Mr. Wiegel: I would like to comment on the point that Dr. Pierson brought up — that the original Neumann spectrum was obtained by a method somewhat similar to the one Bretschneider is using. Ten years ago Ursell questioned whether this gave you anything that was connected with the spectrum as defined by a statistician. Does your more recent work show the same sort of distribution? In other words, using the Tukey approach, is the spectrum the same as originally obtained by Neumann?

Dr. Pierson: No.*

Dr. Wiegel: The problem has been posed. Can it be proven one way or another?

Dr. Pierson: Yes.

Mr. Wiegel: You have perhaps not proved it mathematically, but you apparently have compared these distributions?

Dr. Pierson: At the time it was a very valiant attempt, and I have supported the spectrum quite vehemently, but I think it went wrong in certain places. The question is: What is a spectrum? If you consider a function of frequency and say that it resolves the total variance into frequency components, you have a spectrum. Whether what you ended up with by this process is the correct spectral analysis procedure is wide open. I don't think it is.

Mr. Putz: These concepts of wave-by-wave analysis, looking at the time intervals between readily observable events on the time history, never seem to die (and I don't think they should necessarily); whenever you try to interpret wave records to people who make practical use of them, they always look at time intervals between successive peaks or troughs or between successive zero crossings, whether they are up-crossings or down-crossings.

We do have to communicate with people who make use of the results of our work. Even though we don't know the true spectrum, we have to try to interpret these things. These concepts are

---

* I would like to discuss this question further. The derivation due to Neumann really ought to be reviewed by all concerned to clarify this point. The distribution of $H/\tilde{T}^2$ versus $(\tilde{T}/v)^2$ was used solely to conclude that for apparent "periods" that were small compared to the wind speed the spectral energy was saturated. This led to the ω^{-6} part of the spectrum. It also led to the conclusion that the spectral energy was not saturated when $\tilde{T}$ was large compared to the wind speed. The analysis resulted in the shape only of the spectrum. For the available observations at the time, the shape is remarkably close to what is now obtained by computation. The joint density of height and period does not enter strongly in the derivation.

When I answered "No" to Dr. Wiegel's question, I was thinking in the context of using the spectrum to compute the joint density of height and period, and for the reasons given in the discussion, this cannot be done.

related to the spectrum. The distribution of the heights of the peaks measured from the mean ordinant level has been obtained. It was pointed out by Cartwright and Longuet-Higgins, and also by myself, that the work of Steven Rice was directly applicable to the distribution of these peak heights. As far as the periods are concerned — the "periods," as Dr. Pierson calls them — these are also directly related to the spectrum, although one has to look at more than the time intervals between successive crossings.

One also has to consider the time intervals between crossings that are separated by one or more crossings. There are two problems here. One is the problem that Pierson and Tick worked on, which was referred to a few moments ago, the so-called problem of first return. In other words, when a time history passes through zero, what is the probability distribution for the time interval elapsing between the next zero crossing and the first one?

This is a very difficult problem and has not been completely solved. The inverse (second) problem has been solved, and one can determine the spectrum explicitly from the joint distributions of all of the various orders of zero-crossing differences.

These concepts can be related to the spectrum. However, the joint distribution of both the periods and the height is something else again. I did want to point out that some of these problems have been solved, and there is a direct relation to some extent between these concepts and the true spectrum.

Dr. Neumann: Physical oceanographers should be very thankful to statisticians for opening their eyes to all the mistakes that have been made in the past. Concerning the wave spectrum that I proposed almost ten years ago, at that time I had only visual observations for arriving at the spectrum. I am surprised that it is not farther from reality. There is one particular thing I would like to ask the statisticians about and that concerns the time intervals between successive crests, which can be observed with a stop-watch. I did that for more than 20,000 observations under different conditions. The frequency distribution of these time intervals between successive crests is definitely non-Gaussian. It is very definitely skewed.

Is there any means by which mathematical statistics can determine from a given wave spectrum — a truly theoretical wave spectrum — this time interval between successive crests?

Dr. Dorrestein: I think Dr. Pierson and Dr. Longuet-Higgins have done some work on this.

Dr. Longuet-Higgins: I believe the answer to Dr. Neumann's question is that there is no exact solution known, but there are various approximate methods of trying to obtain the distribution of intervals between successive zeros from the frequency spectrum in the usual sense.

A number of these methods have been studied by Professor Pierson, and I am sure you are familiar with his report on his zero-crossing distribution. I have also done some work on this myself, and there are many references to work on this problem, which I will be very glad to give you if you are interested.

There is one feature of these solutions that I would like to point out: If the fourth moment of the distribution of energy in the spectrum is finite, then the distribution of intervals between zero crossings can be shown to tend to zero at small intervals. If we plot the probability density of the interval between successive zeros against intervals then at small intervals, as a rule, the curve comes to a maximum and falls off. If you have a very sharp cut-off in the spectrum, you sometimes get a secondary maximum, but this is not common. On the other hand, if the fourth moment is infinite, which can happen if the spectrum behaves like (frequency)$^{-4}$ at infinity, then you get a positive probability density at the origin.

Cases like this have been studied experimentally, and some theoretical work has been done by McFadden. The nature of this positive density has been investigated in a forthcoming paper [*Phil. Trans. Roy. Soc. A* **254**, 557–599]. McFadden got an approximate answer, and we think we have an answer which is a decimal place better. The fact that the fourth moment being finite is the more common would be some rough justification for assuming that the distribution is like the Rayleigh distribution. However, it is only an approximate assumption because you can get something quite different.

Dr. Burling: I believe that by deliberately selecting stationary, that is, steady state records and looking at the distribution of the data, we have a chance of estimating the error of various statistical estimates. If at the same time we measure the spectrum, we would then know much more about what its errors might be.

Today a lot of data are given in digits, and the use of computers is available to many. Therefore, estimates of the statistics we require are surely not a very difficult nor time-consuming process today.

Dr. Pierson: The reason why we have never tried any of the zero-crossing results on theoretical spectra to compare with his visual observations is twofold. First, if you look at the time interval between crests, it is the equivalent of the time interval between the zeros of the derivative of the process, relative maxima and minima. That puts a differentiation on the record so that fourth moments become sixth moments. All the theoretical spectra are incorrect in this respect. The moments don't exist and you can't do it.

Second, it has been a question of relating the visual observations, with some sort of human filter interposed between what was there and what was written down, and these theoretical spectra forms.

Dr. Neumann: If one has *only* a frequency spectrum, and *no* wave record, is it possible to derive the time intervals between successive crests from such a spectrum without any other information?

Dr. Pierson: No. You get an approximate answer, but that is all.

Dr. Tick: I don't think we are seriously interested in this problem because if we were, a simple analogue computer with counting circuits and noise generator would answer it in about an hour.

Dr. Barber: We are discussing what is called a one-dimensional spectrum. This talk of a wave of finite height makes me wonder whether it really is. After all, the wave surface, if the waves are traveling in the same direction, is a function of both distance and time. We can reduce it to a one-dimensional spectrum, providing we assume that all the waves are traveling with a velocity appropriate to their length.

But this is clearly not true when we consider the harmonics of a wave of finite length, travelling at the same velocity as the fundamental wave. Are we being forced, therefore, even if the waves travel all in the same direction, into considering a two-dimensional spectrum in which we display both frequency and wave length? This is not a very helpful suggestion. If we took it seriously, it would mean that one wave recorder was not enough. We should have to have a line of recorders. Then, because waves don't in fact travel all in the same direction, we should be forced into considering the directional spectrum.

Dr. Darbyshire: Mr. Cartwright remarked that we are also interested in this problem because civil engineers want to know how dangerous a given wave length is. For instance, lightship people are concerned. A lightship may be 100 feet long, and they want to know the height of waves 100 feet long. This is almost impossible to estimate from the wave spectrum as normally defined. So I did some work similar to Bretschneider's on this matter.

First, we chose an ordinary wave record, and took not the zero crossings but the intervals between crests. Then we split them into one-second intervals and plotted the mean height for each crest to crest period against the period. I got something that looked reasonable, but it didn't look at all like the frequency spectrum that I also had. Any resemblance was purely coincidental. Nevertheless, I thought this was very important in its own right.

On the same wave records that I showed to you yesterday, I did another sort of analysis. In this case I took the elevation between the two minima. Occasionally you get negative values. I did plot them against the mean period in seconds for various wind speeds from about force three to force nine. They were published in 1960.

I did not try to fit any formula to them because they are of use only to civil engineers and others who are interested only in this particular answer. I would not try to relate it to a spectrum as normally defined.

H. WALDEN

FOUR

COMPARISON OF ONE-DIMENSIONAL WAVE SPECTRA

RECORDED IN THE GERMAN BIGHT

WITH VARIOUS "THEORETICAL" SPECTRA

I. Within the past ten years several authors have worked out, and afterwards published, various so-called "theoretical" wave spectra, the properties of which vary greatly. Let us consider first the spectra for the fully developed wind sea. They are all based, to some extent, on visual observations or measurements, and I think it not surprising that the differences are so great (Figure 2-4-1). The spectra are supposed to be valid for ocean waves and, consequently, the open sea; however, on comparing the spectra for some different given wind velocities v, we find the relatively best agreement among the various curves for wind speeds of about 20 to 30 knots (Figures 2-4-2 and 2-4-3), while the accord is poorest for light winds and, on the other side, for storm forces. This is not very surprising for the following reasons, which are chiefly of a meteorological nature:

1. Wind speeds of about 15 to 30 knots are frequent in most parts of the world, and the corresponding fetch is quite often long enough for the occurrence of a fully arisen sea. The latter is not the case with strong winds or gales, while weak winds often are less steady in speed and direction.

2. The sea generated by medium wind forces can be estimated visually rather easily and can be

recorded satisfactorily by most instruments.

3. A sea produced by light winds often is superimposed on swell-like "foreign" waves of sometimes considerable energy, while the area of a fetch with medium winds more frequently is large enough to exclude minor swells from the near neighborhood.

The graphs for $v = 10$ knots (Figure 2-4-1) and for $v = 60$ knots (Figure 2-4-4) show the extremely great differences among some of the various ocean wave spectra. The legend to the curves may be found on the figures or at their edge. On the abscissa, the quantity f is the frequency or the reciprocal value to the period T. The spectrum DSA II has been established by the Frenchmen R. Gelci, H. Cazalé, and J. Vassal (1957). The spectrum of Roll/Fischer (1956) is given in the form modified by R. W. Burling (1959) in Figure 2-4-1 and in its original form. C. L. Bretschneider's curve has been plotted for his expression $F_2 = 1.95$ (a fully developed sea after a very long duration) in Figures 2-4-1 and 2-4-2 and for $F_2 = 1.45$ in Figure 2-4-2. The spectrum of J. Darbyshire is that published in 1955, while Neumann's spectrum originates from 1953. The ordinate gives the f-spectral energy density in cm^2

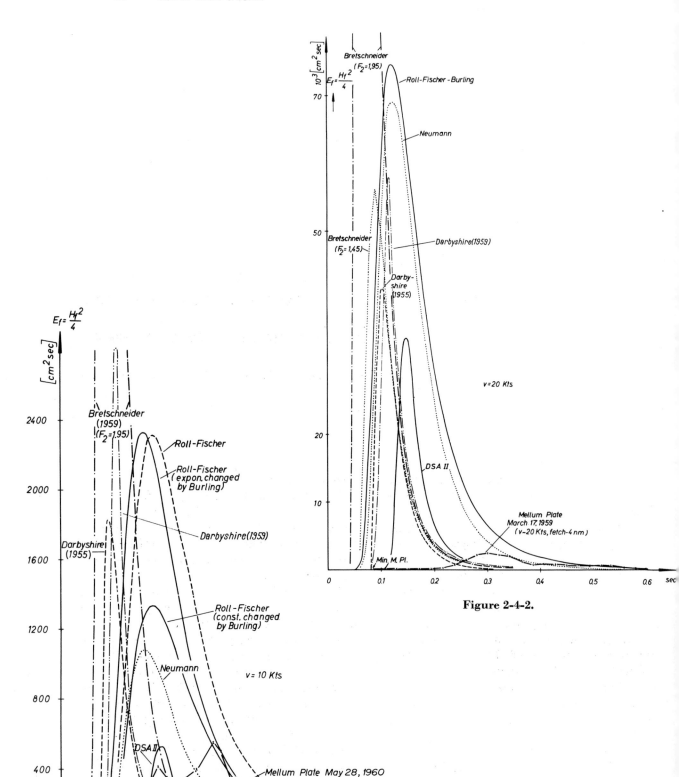

Figure 2-4-2.

Figure 2-4-1.

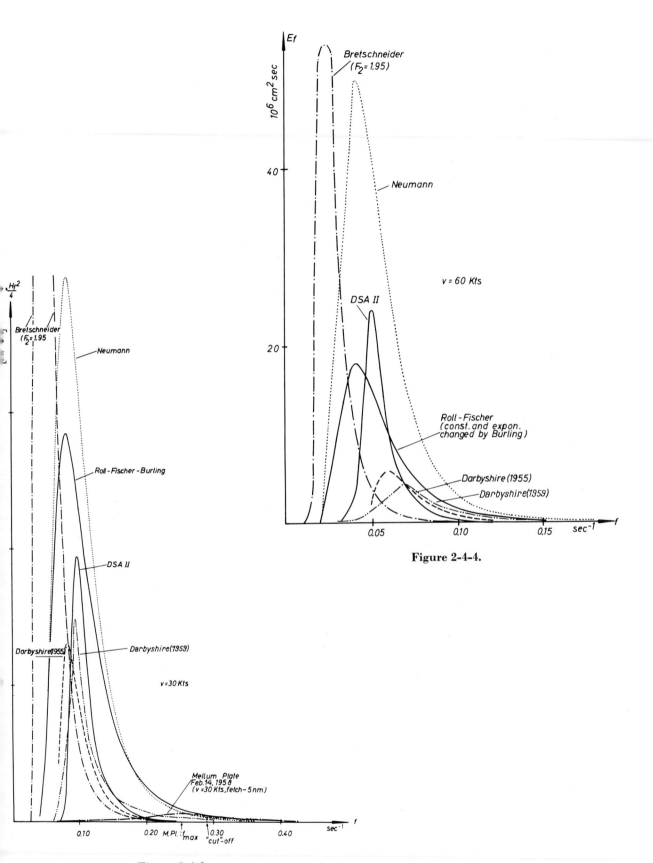

Figure 2-4-4.

Figure 2-4-3.

sec and corresponds to the quantity E of G. Neumann and the doubled value $H_f^2/8$ (after Burling) or $= H_f^2/4$. The figures giving the various spectra for the fully arisen sea of the different wind velocities also show the spectra of Darbyshire (1959). It is interesting that these spectra have a large total energy (compared with other spectra) for light winds, while the energy is strikingly small with high wind velocities.

The differences between the various spectra concern the area under the spectrum, or the "total energy," as well as the distribution of the energy density along the frequency scale. Particularly disappointing is the poor agreement of the frequencies of maximum energy (tops of the curves). This is the case even for medium wind velocities.

The reasons for this alarming disaccord may be found in the different methods of observing, measuring, and perhaps analyzing the sea. Some observations, utilized as bases for the spectra, possibly were invalidated by the effects of "foreign" swells or, in other cases, by the influence of shallow water, or even by the effect of turbulence in the air connected with the air-water temperature difference.

For practical hindcasting or forecasting the wind sea and the swell from the meteorological conditions, one of these spectra must be regarded as correct, or an intermediate or even an average curve must be used. This decision is facilitated when a comparison with observations or measurements is possible.

The *Seewetteramt* and the *Instrumentenamt* of the *Deutscher Wetterdienst* have been taking wave records near the German lighthouse *Mellum Plate*, a tower that is totally surrounded by water, located in a bight on the North Sea coast. The water depth amounts to 10 to 15 meters in its environs. A pole was erected (total length 28 m) 85 meters distant from the lighthouse (Figure 2-4-5). At the outer side of a 3-meter wide frame, a vertical scale was fastened. Using a movie-camera, we took 16 or, in other cases, 10 photographs per second of the water surface at the pole and evaluated these records, which were from 10 to 30 minutes duration. For the first time we also utilized a gauge for measuring the electrical conductivity between vertical staffs of 3-meter length, each being fastened at the frame of the pole. The electrical current varies due to the change in the water level at the staffs and yields a record of the waves. The gauge was calibrated and tested by means of cinematographic pictures.

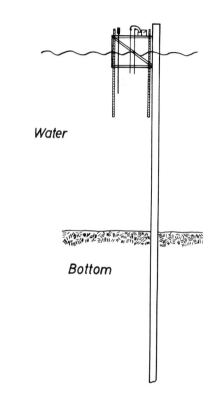

Water

Bottom

Figure 2-4-5.

The results were so satisfactory that the record could be considered perfect within a very broad frequency band. The spectra from all these records have been computed by the autocorrelation method after Pierson and Marks (1952).

These measurements were aimed at testing and, if possible, at calibrating an accelerometer constructed by A. Lang (1960). It was floating on the water surface at a distance of about 15 meters from the pole. It may be mentioned here, by the way, that these experiments have not yet been finished, and there were the well-known difficulties with the double integration of the acceleration records and with choosing an optimal filter. It was found that this way of calibrating the results from the acceleration measurements should be possible for a low sea, but that at the long-period end of the energy spectrum there are "disturbances" which are so enlarged by the double integration as to preclude the determination of the upper limit of the spectrum. In Figure 2-4-6 the unbiased cinematographic spectrum and the result of a simultaneously taken acceleration record are compared for the case of a 10-knot wind. The strong rise of the spectrum computed from the accelerometer record in the low-frequency range

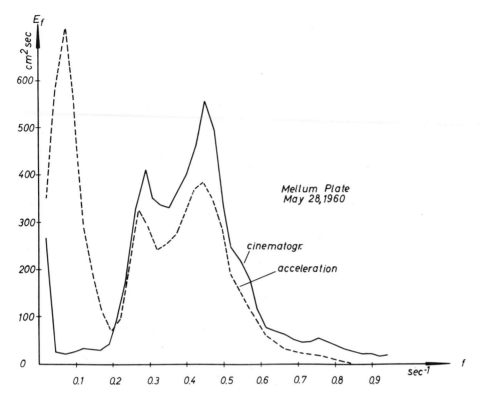

Figure 2-4-6.

is produced by "disturbances" or the partly non-vertical situation. The energy deficit at the other end of the spectrum results from the poor measuring qualities of the instrument for waves shorter than 0.8 meter when floating in a ring-shaped lifebuoy.

It was hoped that we could also get some unadulterated records of various states of sea on this occasion in order to compare them with the existing spectra formulae, the differences of which we have seen above. As the water depth near the pole at high tide ranges only to approximately 14 meters, wave components longer than about 4.5 or 5 sec period (frequency f near 0.22 resp. 0.20) are considered to be "disturbed" by the ground. It may be remarked, however, that waves longer than 10 sec period ($f = 0.1$) have been observed and also recorded at lighthouse *Mellum Plate*. The bight is open to the North Sea in the sector between westnorthwest and approximately northeast, so it should be possible to measure a nearly undisturbed fully developed wind sea for light or even moderate winds from these directions. We waited for a constant wind force 3 Beaufort of sufficient duration and fetch from westnorthwest to northnorthwest expecting a

clear wind-sea spectrum. But this record, taken under westnorthwesterly wind of 9.5 to 10 knots velocity (at 10 meters above water surface) yielded a very disappointing result insofar as the spectrum has two separate maxima. The second peak, at $f = 0.285$, may be explained as a kind of swell, although the observers have not been able to discover any "foreign" waves in the sea at the time in question.

Now, I will have to make the best of our result, and I may be allowed, nevertheless, to compare our spectrum with the so-called "theoretical" spectra for this wind velocity and fully developed sea. I think it possible to derive some conclusions though they are of minor value. For $f = 0.45$, our record is in close enough agreement with the spectra of Neumann and of Roll/Fischer in the form proposed by Burling (see Figure 2-4-1). The spectra of Darbyshire (1955), Bretschneider (1959), and the DSA II have considerably less energy in the whole high-frequency range. These differences are supposed to arise from the fact that some wave recorders do not register the high-frequency portion of the spectrum and that these measurements were used as the basic material for computing the spectral functions. On the low-frequency side, the *Mellum Plate* spectrum ends near $f = 0.15$, while all theoretical spectra except DSA II give a good deal of wave energy in this frequency section. It may be emphasized that duration and fetch of the wind were sufficient to generate a fully developed sea. There may have been abolished a small portion of the energy of the wave components longer than 4.5 sec, but since longer waves had been measured at the pole on other occasions, it is highly improbable that the energy would have been destroyed completely by ground effects had it been really present. We have no reason to assume that the water current could have abolished the comparatively long wave components. Thus, I feel compelled to presume that those theoretical spectra possibly give too high an energy density at the long-period side in this case, i.e., for 10-knots wind velocity. This

conception is supported in a certain way by the fact that some spectra have a period of maximum energy, T_{max}, at periods longer than 3.3 sec, the phase velocity of which amounts to 10 knots. Another spectrum taken at *Mellum Plate* is shown in Figure 2-4-7 together with some "theoretical" spectra for the fully arisen sea in a 15- to 16-knot wind. At the time of recording, the wind was westnorthwesterly and consequently was blowing from the open North Sea. The duration amounted to 12 hours. The fetch is estimated to have been roughly 50 nautical miles; it was thus only a little shorter than would have been required for a fully arisen sea after Pierson-Neumann-James (1955).

The most striking peculiarity of the spectrum is its lowness in total energy. The distribution of the energy density includes about the same features as the record discussed before: the energy is similar to Neumann's spectrum in the high-frequency range, and there is little or no energy at those frequencies for which the maximum energy is expected in some of the "theoretical" spectra. So far the conclusions stated before are supported.

However, the lack of total energy should be considered a reason to contemplate the possibility that a diminishing of the energy could be produced by too small a width of the wind fetch; for the geographical situation is such that land is distant about $2\frac{1}{2}$ to 5 nautical miles in all directions between true 280° and southwest. I cannot give details on the effect of a narrow wind fetch, but in any case we had better go to the open sea to take wave records.

II. Another discrepancy among the conceptions of the various authors concerns the different assumptions with regard to the growth of the total energy, that is, how it depends on the length of the fetch and on the wind duration. As far as the quantity of the total energy and not the shape of the spectrum is concerned, it is sufficient to consider any characteristic or clearly defined value of the wave height, for example, the significant wave height $\widetilde{H}_{1/3}$. Comparisons of the relations between $\widetilde{H}_{1/3}$ and the fetch (or respectively the duration), as given by several authors, were

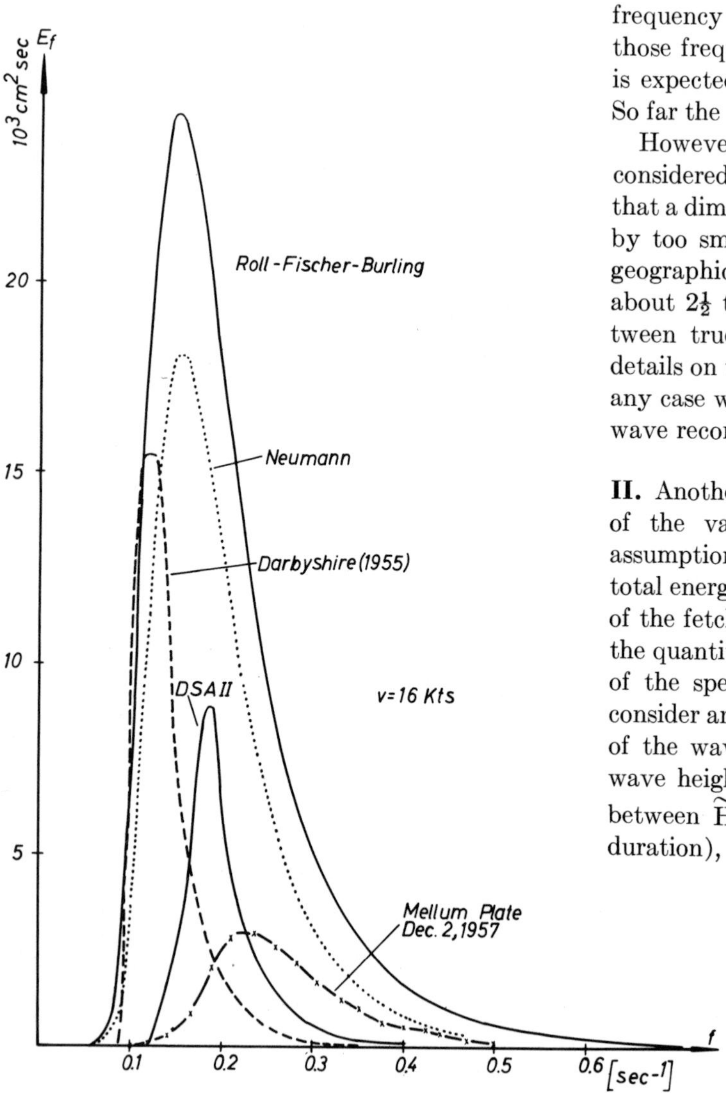

Figure 2-4-7.

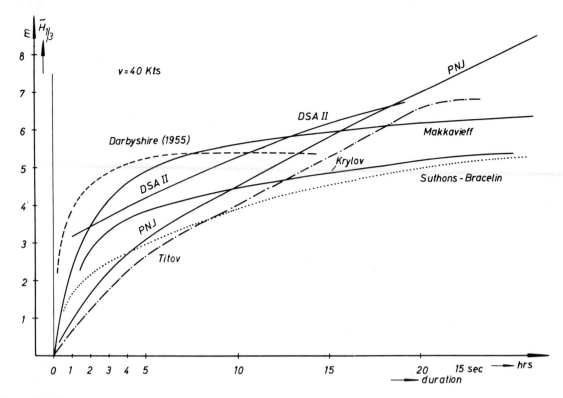

Figure 2-4-8.

published some years ago (Walden 1953/54). They can be completed today by considering also the theories for hindcasting methods that have been developed in the last years. Figure 2-4-8 gives the growth of the significant wave height $\widetilde{H}_{1/3}$ with increasing duration and Figure 2-4-9 the function between $\widetilde{H}_{1/3}$ and the fetch, both for a constant wind of 40 knots velocity. There have been plotted among others the relations given by L. F. Titov (1955). Other functions were published by J. M. Krylov (1958); he utilized relatively troublesome graphs for determining the

Figure 2-4-9.

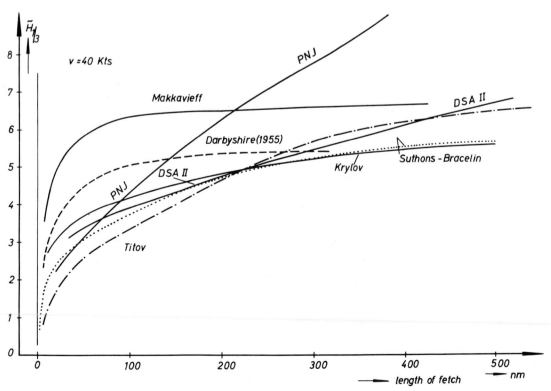

heights from the meteorological conditions. They were given in a more serviceable form by Rzeplinsky/Mercalov (1960), two other Russians. One finds also functions for the relations in question published by Djounkovski and Bojitch (1959), probably after Makkavieff, a Russian too.

The differences are partly very great in Figures 2-4-8 and 2-4-9. Concerning the effect of the fetch, Makkavieff, for example, wants only about 22 nautical miles for the generation of $\widetilde{H}_{1/3} = 5$ m, while Suthons-Bracelin state that more than 240 nautical miles are necessary to produce a similar sea. I think we are not able at present to decide which values are the correct ones in the open sea. However, in order to get a general impression of what errors could have happened, it may be mentioned here once more that the wind, even within a very short fetch, can generate a relatively high and long sea and perhaps a fully developed sea if the wind field itself is moving along in the direction of the air current or of the course of the waves and with a velocity which corresponds approximately to the speed of the wave energy. Whether the velocity of a wind field is favorable for the accumulation of wave energy or not depends very much on the proportions between wind speed and the group velocity of the wave components already generated and those to be generated in the very near future. Thus, the wind sea normally is higher and also longer at the equatorial side of the eastward-moving atmospheric depressions, ocean conditions and equal wind velocities assumed. Presumably this fact was not always taken into consideration in determining the influence of the fetch on the sea or on the spectrum, respectively. Under these circumstances, the fetches would be determined as shorter than they really are.

The assumption of Darbyshire, that a fetch of only 100 or 200 nautical miles is sufficient for the generation of a fully developed sea in any case, i.e., also in the case of gales and storms, is an interesting and perhaps a somewhat exciting statement. It may perhaps be useful to make a short estimate of whether this value of Darbyshire is plausible or not.

The transporting element of the wave energy is the waves. Let us choose a wave component of 15 sec period, which certainly is present in a fully developed storm sea and forms an important share of it. The corresponding energy moving along with the group velocity requires about 9 hours to travel a distance of 200 nautical miles. If it is

assumed — and this corresponds to the theory of Neumann — that the 15 sec waves originate as very short waves at the windward border of the fetch and gradually increase in period to 15 seconds, it will require roughly 18 hours for these waves to arrive at the lee side of a 200 nautical mile fetch. In a former statistical investigation it was shown (H. Walden, 1953/54) that, for a 30-knot wind, the wind sea is fully developed after approximately 20 hours. Also from the experience with hindcasting storm sea, it has to be considered certain that much more time (or wind duration) is necessary for the generation of the fully developed sea in a gale, storm, or even hurricane force 12.

The authors of DSA II eliminated the effect of the fetch in their formulae and apparently also in the hindcasting method. But the fetch is nevertheless taken into consideration through the manner of plotting, pursuing, and evaluating the movement of the wave trains. There is, also on principle, no doubt that the duration values can be transformed into correspondent fetch values. However, if a whole spectrum is considered and not only a single wave component, it would be desirable to take into consideration each wave component separately, because it has to be supposed that DSA II — contrary to Neumann — assumes a scheme in which all wave components, later being present in the fully developed sea, begin to arise with its full length or period from the very beginning of the wind's effect. If we adopt this conception, we should have to presume that the short wave components will reach their highest possible energy for the given wind speed within a rather short time, while, during that period of time, the longer ones can get only a small portion of the energy falling to them in their fully developed state. It follows that, for a given fetch, for example 10 nautical miles, the long components would have less time available for receiving energy from the wind than the short ones due to the different velocity of the respective energy movement. The relative portion will be smaller the longer a period is concerned. Starting, on the other hand, from a given duration, all wave components are affected by the wind during the same length of time. The schematic Figure 2-4-10 represents a comparison of these two cases: The wave components are fully developed up to the period of 6 sec; this means that the fetch is chosen just long enough so that the 6 sec-period wave component will pass through it within the given

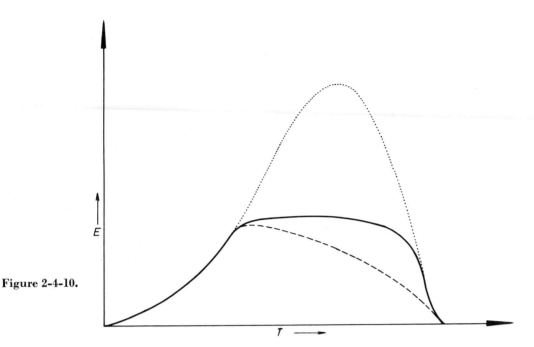

Figure 2-4-10.

time of duration. The dashed curve in the long-period area represents schematically the energy distribution if the limiting element is the length of the fetch, while the fully drawn line relates to a confined wind duration. It is evident that, if one wishes to determine the relation between fetch and duration effects on the sea without computing the influence of each single component, the error will be small if one of the longest wave components expected in the fully developed sea is considered as being equal for the two kinds of limitation (duration and fetch).

This question is dealt with here in such detail because it has been discussed in Hamburg with Mr. J. Piest and Dr. K. Hasselmann rather thoroughly and some initial misunderstandings had to be cleared up.

In order to complete Figure 2-4-9, I computed the fetch values for the DSA II, utilizing a period of 18 sec as the relating quantity. The resulting function is to be found among the other curves in Figure 2-4-9.

A clean wind sea — not disturbed by any swell — occurs very seldom in the open ocean, and usable cases for empirical investigations are rare. It is, moreover, difficult to estimate the length of a fetch on the weather map. Some meteorological or even synoptical experience is desirable.

It may be easier, in many cases, to determine the wind duration. However, differences of similar quantity and corresponding discrepancies will

also be found with regard to the relations between the wind duration and the properties of the wind sea (Figure 2-4-8) given by the various authors. Makkavieff, for example, for a 40-knot wind, expects a significant wave height of 4.5 meters after 3.7 hours, while Suthons-Bracelin demand 14.5 hours for the generation of an equally high sea.

Darbyshire did not publish a function of how the total energy or the spectrum will grow with wind duration or time. The longest period in Darbyshire's spectrum of the fully developed sea for winds of 40 knots is about 18 sec. If we use it for comparison, we can compute the durations from the fetch given in the formula. The result is interesting insofar as the duration values are extremely small compared with the other functions plotted in Figure 2-4-8.

III. The problem of how the wave energy is increasing has been touched on before. The distribution of this energy over the frequency band in the non-fully developed state of the sea may be of special importance in forecasting the swell. According to the plausible theory of energy dispersion on the decay distance given by Pierson-Neumann-James (1955), one will never find a wave or a wave component in the swell that had not existed in the wind sea before — leaving aside some exceptions of minor significance.

There is first the hypothesis of Pierson-Neumann-James (1955), which assumes that the wave components are generated one after the other in the succession of increasing periods or wave lengths. It follows from this supposition that the spectrum of a non-fully developed sea possesses a sharp "cut-off" at the longest wave component, the generation of which was just possible under the given circumstances, that are the fetch or duration conditions. Pierson-Neumann-James have smoothed out the too sharp break themselves by introducing some additional assumptions.

The physical side of these developments was explained as the result of the wave-breaking effects in the sea. Anyone who observes the sea as it becomes higher and longer will get the impression that the growth of the sea is accomplished by the perpetual new formation of ever longer waves.

In principle, however, the increase of the wave energy is thought to be brought about otherwise. It is the opinion of the authors of DSA II, Gelci, Cazalé, and Vassal, that all wave components that later will exist in the spectrum of the fully developed sea get some energy from the very beginning of the wind effect and that all wave components will grow simultaneously. Figure 2-4-11 represents the alteration of the spectrum DSA II, here depending on the duration of a 20-knot wind. One recognizes the combination of a quickly grown portion in the short-period band, which increases afterwards very slowly, and another part in the band of the longer periods, which develops rapidly with time. The period of maximum energy no longer shifts as soon as the duration has become greater than approximately 3 hours. I think this latter fact to be an unreal feature of the concept; for one can take it for granted that the apparent period and then also the period of

Figure 2-4-11.

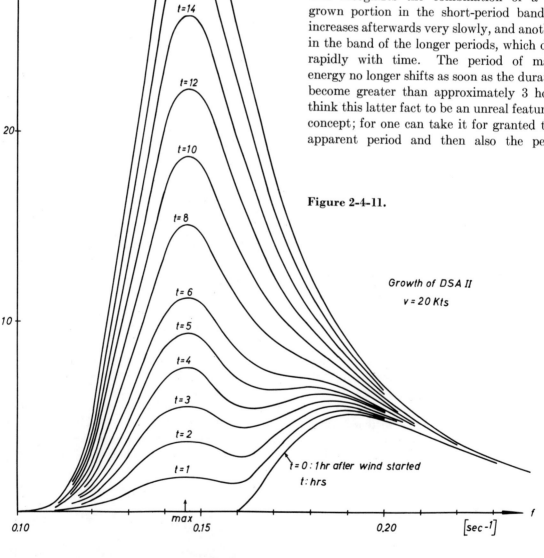

maximum energy become longer with increasing duration.

Also, K. Hasselmann (1960) holds the view that wind energy is transferred to all components of the later fully arisen spectrum simultaneously and that in the case of a fully developed sea even energy is transmitted from low frequencies to high frequencies "in analogy to the nonlinear cascade-process of turbulence." One is not able, in his opinion, to perceive visually the low frequency energy shares because the correspondent waves are very flat and hidden by the superposing shorter waves of greater height. I think these problems will be dealt with in the session on nonlinear aspects of the spectrum.

There have also been plotted (Figure 2-4-12) a sequence of spectra after C. L. Bretschneider (1959). The curves give the properties of the spectrum for a 20-knot wind when the wind duration t amounts to 6, 12, 18, 24, 66.4, and 204.5 hrs. For $t = 66.4$ hours the correlation coefficient becomes zero, which is considered to be characteristic of a fully arisen sea. But choosing the highest possible value of F_2 (including the wind velocity v and the average period $\tilde{T}$) one gets $t = 204.5$ hours, a very high duration indeed.

Bretschneider's spectra do not have an abrupt "cut-off" at the low frequency end. In the whole low frequency range the energy density is zero as long as the duration is below a certain minimum time value, but then it slowly grows with continuing steady wind. On the whole, a portion of the wave energy (density) is assumed to shift gradually from high to low frequencies. It is a surprising feature of this conception that the energy in the high frequency region decreases with increasing wind duration. A physical explanation of this interesting phenomenon possibly may be found by considering the fact that the phase velocity of the long waves and the speed of the water particles at the surface of the respective crests is high compared with the wind, so that the conditions for the

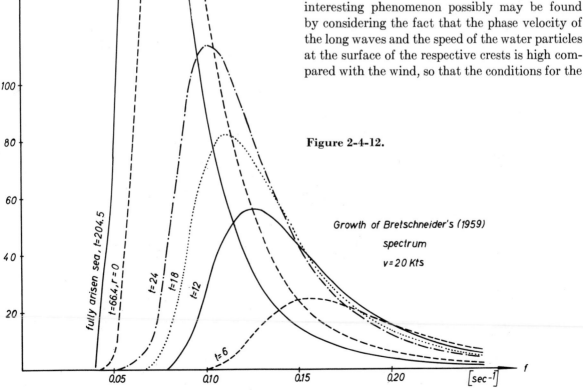

Figure 2-4-12.

Growth of Bretschneider's (1959)

spectrum

v=20 Kts

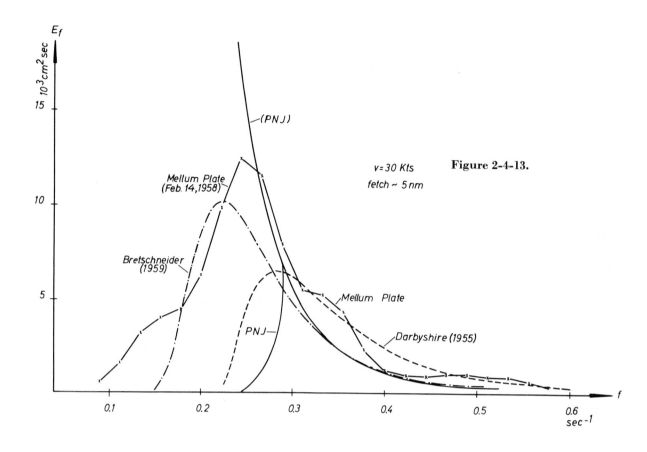

Figure 2-4-13.

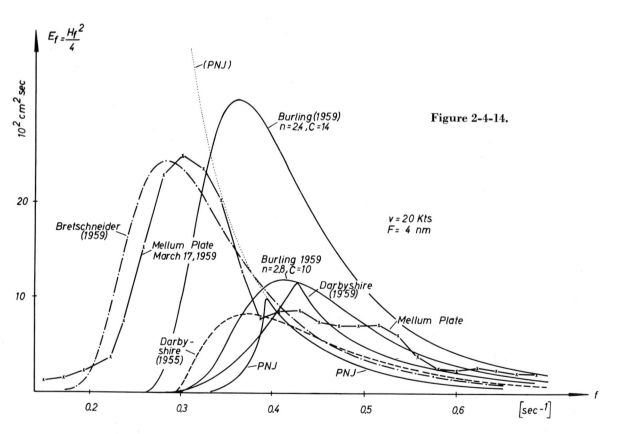

Figure 2-4-14.

generation of short waves may become less favorable.

Figure 2-4-15 shows which way Darbyshire's spectrum will grow with increasing fetch.

Can we draw any conclusion from the spectra taken at *Mellum Plate* lighthouse concerning the manner of how the spectrum grows or how the wave energy is distributed during the various phases of the generation of a wind sea?

Due to the immense amount of work necessary for the evaluation of a cinematographic record, there are only two spectra of a non-fully developed sea available at this time, which are suitable for a comparison with deep water spectra.

The one record has been taken in southwesterly wind of about 30 knots. The fetch amounted to

approximately 5 nautical miles in this direction. The air was 0.3° Centigrade colder than the water. The spectrum has been inscribed in Figure 2-4-3, where it can be compared with the spectra for the fully developed sea in a 30-knot wind. We also have marked the "cut-off" after Pierson-Neumann-James (1955) as it has to be assumed for the given data. There is, on the other hand, no indication that any wave energy of account existed in the band, in which the maximum values of energy are supposed to form in the fully developed sea.

A comparison of the recording result with some "theoretical" spectra for the fetch of 5 nautical miles is given in Figure 2-4-13. The corresponding DSA II-curve cannot be considered, as a fetch limitation was not taken into account by the authors. A reduction from the lowest duration value, one hour, would give more than 20 nautical miles. Concerning Darbyshire (1955, fetch = 5 nautical miles), there is a distinct difference in the low frequency range. The actual *Mellum Plate* spectrum coincides rather well with the "theoretical" one of Neumann (1953) over a wide range of the high frequency region. However, there is no "cut-off". The weather situation over the North Sea was such that swell was not likely to have entered the sea area near *Mellum Plate* except perhaps a small portion for wave components longer than 5 sec. Thus, most of the energy in the spectrum longer than about 2.9 sec has to be considered a real wind sea share.

The other record in question was taken in an easterly wind of 20 to 20.5 knots velocity. The fetch was 4 nautical miles long, and the air was also 0.3° Centigrade colder than the water. It is not quite certain, in this case, whether a weak swell could have entered the *Mellum Plate* environs. This spectrum has been inscribed in Figure 2-4-2, so that a comparison with the fully developed spectra for a 20-knot wind is possible. We again find coincidence with Neumann's spectrum in the high frequency region, but a steep "cut-off" does not come out. Also in this case there was a considerable quantity of energy present at the low frequency side to the frequency where the "cut-off" should have been expected

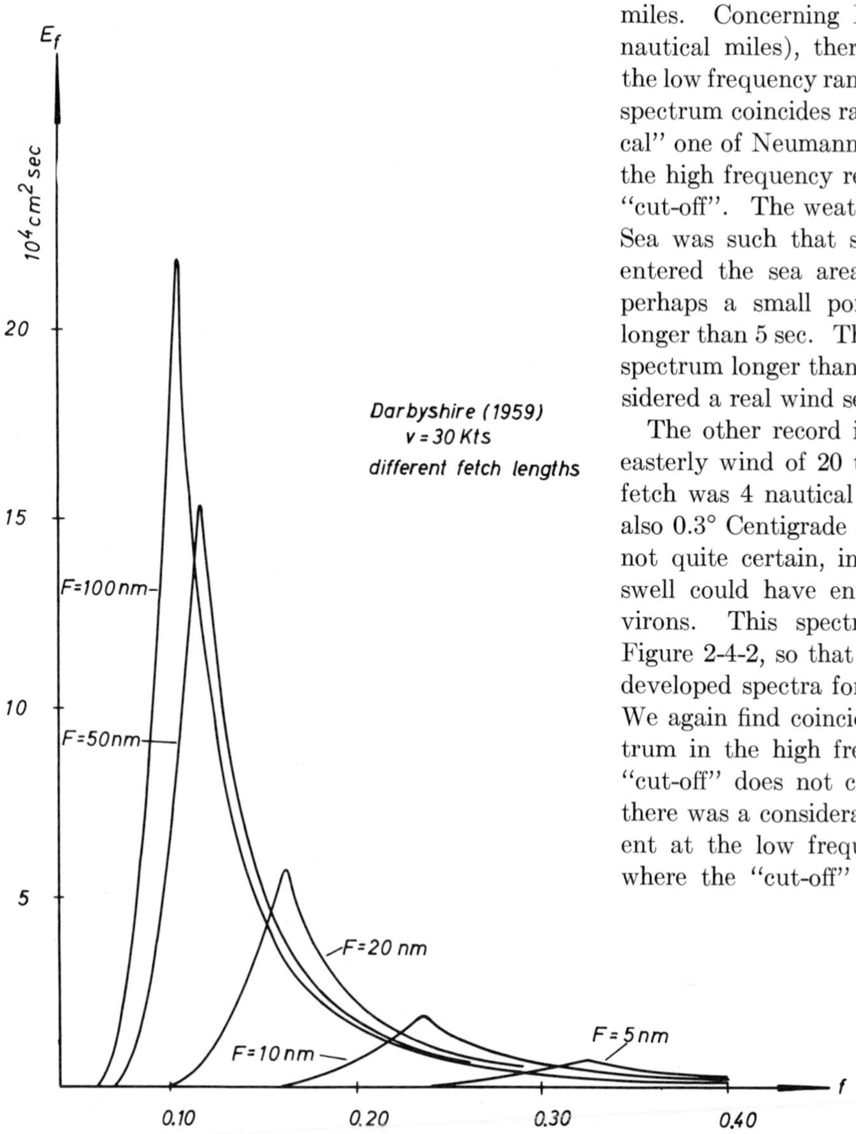

Darbyshire (1959)
v = 30 Kts
different fetch lengths

Figure 2-4-15.

after Pierson-Neumann-James (1955). The recorded energy distribution shows a minimum in that band for which some authors expect the energy maximum in the fully arisen sea.

A diagram (Figure 2-4-14) representing the comparison of various spectra for the wind velocity $v = 20$ knots and for the fetch length $F = 4$ nautical miles has been supplemented by the spectra after R. W. Burling (1959). As Burling stated his formulae for rather short fetches of about 1500 meters, it may be considered risky to extrapolate the spectra to fetch values approximately four times as great as Burling's fetches. However, it could be of some interest for comparative purposes.

In order to comprehend all his recorded spectra, Burling varies the two quantities "n" and "C" within certain limits. The diagram shows two curves after Burling, giving the spectra for rather extreme values of the quantities n and C. For $n = 2.8$; $C = 10$, Burling's spectrum lies close to that of Darbyshire (1959), but the total energy is higher after Burling. The curve for $n = 2.4$ and $C = 14$ gives very high spectral densities over a great section of frequencies.

The fact that neither of the *Mellum Plate* records in question gives any substantial energy (density) for low frequencies may support the conception of a successive, or at least partly successive, rather than a simultaneous generation of all the various wave components. This impression is strengthened by looking at the spectra at short fetches given by R. W. Burling (1959); they all fall down rather steeply at their low frequency side.

IV. Although the four records mentioned above, taken at *Mellum Plate* lighthouse, give some hints with regard to the distribution of the energy density, they are not appropriate to use in reaching a decision as to which of the so-called "theoretical" spectra is the correct one. It is strange that the authors of the various hindcasting methods nearly always find that their data agree well with the properties of the sea in consideration, even though the differences between the diagrams or spectra are so immense (as shown in the figure before). Perhaps, as supposed by W. J. Pierson (1959), it is not possible to find a single spectrum formula that is uniformly valid for all wind velocities. This view may be correct, but, in my opinion, the discrepancies ought to be very much smaller than they are. I also believe that the properties of the sea or of the waves do not depend

(or depend very little) on the geographical situation of the part of the ocean, except as they are influenced by the water depth, the fetch and — to a certain degree — the temperature difference between air and water.

For practical purposes, finding out the real relations between wind data and sea is very important. To know the properties of the spectrum in the wind sea is of special significance for forecasting swell. And, while forecasts of the wind sea have to be based on meteorological predictions or predicted weather maps, the swell and its development are in great part forecast by means of the laws which determine the behavior of the waves in their own element, *i.e.*, in the water. In the calm regions of the earth we should be able to forecast, frequently a week in advance, the swell and the corresponding surf at the coasts.

Because it is important to get a precise and more reliable prediction of the sea, wind sea and swell, it is still necessary to take as many wave records as possible, to publish the results, and to compare them with each other. For this we have to go to the open sea as we did in the aforementioned observations at *Mellum Plate* lighthouse. We need recording instruments that can be used in deep water to measure the *entire* spectrum, so that a fully valid analysis will be possible.

I regret that my contribution has been to a high degree critical or even negative. I think there should be an agreement which aims at making comparable all measurements and evaluations. A special committee should propose the steps to be taken to this end. It also would be its task to find means to collect all measurements in order to improve the possibilities of comparing the records or their results.

REFERENCES

Bracelin, P. (1952): *Observing, Forecasting and Reporting Ocean Waves and Surf.* Nav. Wea. Serv., Memo. 147/52.

Bretschneider, C. L. (1959): *Wind Variability and Wave Spectra for Wind-Generated Gravity Waves.* Beach Erosion Board, Tech. Memo. 118.

Burling, R. W. (1959): "The Spectrum of Waves at Short Fetches." *Dt. Hydrogr. Z.*, **12:** 45–64 and 96–117.

Darbyshire, J. (1955): "An Investigation of Storm Waves in the North Atlantic Ocean." *Proc. R. Soc.*, A, **230:** 560–569.

Darbyshire, J. (1956): "An Investigation into the Generation of Waves When the Fetch of the Wind is Less than 100 Miles." *Quart. Journ. R. Soc.*, vol. 82, No. 354.

Darbyshire, J. (1959): "A Further Investigation of Wind-Generated Waves." *Dt. Hydrogr. Z.*, **12**: 7–13.

Djounkovski, N. N., and P. K. Bojitch (1959): *La houle et son action sur les côtes et les ouvrages côtiers.* Paris, 1959.

Gelci, R., H. Cazalé, et J. Vassal (1957): *Prévision de la houle, la méthode de densités spectro-angulaire.* Extrait du Bulletin d'Information du Comité Central d'Océanographie . . . . . . IX, 8.

Hasselmann, K. (1960): "Grundgleichungen der Seegangsvoraussage," *Schiffstechnik* **7**: 191–195.

Krylov, J. M. (1958): *Statistical Theory and the Computation of Ocean Wind Waves,* Part 2, GOIN Nr. 42/1958 (in Russian).

Lang, A. (1960): *Über die Entwicklung von Beschleunigungsschreibern für Seegangsmessungen.* Deutsch. Wetterdienst, Seewetteramt, Einzelveröff. Nr. 24.

Neumann, G. (1953): *On Ocean Wave Spectra and A New Method of Forecasting Wind-Generated Sea.* Beach Erosion Board, Tech. Memo. 43.

Pierson, Jr., W. J., and W. Marks (1952): "The Power Spectrum Analysis of Ocean Wave Records." *Trans. Am. Geophys. Union* **33**: No. 6.

Pierson, Jr., W. J., G. Neumann, and R. W. Jame (1955): *Practical Methods for Observing and Forecasting Ocean Waves by Means of Wave Spectra and Statistics.* U. S. Navy Hydr. Off. Publ. No. 603.

Roll, H. U., und G. Fischer (1956): "Eine kritische Bemerkung zum Neumann-Spektrum des Seeganges." *Dt. Hydrogr. Z.*, **9**: 9–14.

Rzeplinsky, G. V., and V. G. Mercalov (1960): "Nomograms for the Computation of the Wave Periods and Height in Deep Sea from the Atmospheric Pressure Gradients." *Trudy/Moskva* **54**: 61–66.

Titov, L. F. (1955): *Wind Waves on the Oceans and Seas,* Leningrad (in Russian).

Walden, H. (1953/54): "Die Wellenhöhe neu angefachter Windsee nach Beobachtungen atlantischer Wetterschiffe und des Fischereischutzbootes 'Meerkatze'." *Ann. Meteorol.* **6**: 296–304.

DISCUSSION I

Dr. Hicks (prepared comment): Dr. Walden portrays clearly the unanimous disagreement among the different "theoretical" wave spectra and properly emphasizes the great need for good wind-wave measurements on the open sea. I should like to emphasize one aspect of his argument and ask two questions. As he shows, there is little agreement as to the shape of the energy spectrum. In addition, it should be recognized that in order to determine this shape, instruments must be developed that measure with an equal percentage of error the spectral energy density near the peak (at frequency f_0) of the spectrum and at say $\frac{1}{2}f_0$ and $2f_0$, where the energy density may be smaller by a factor of 30 or more. Because of its linearity over a wide dynamic range, the CSL wave probe[1] could achieve this accuracy in measuring *small* gravity waves.

My first question concerns accelerometer measurements of wave characteristics. What is the source of the "disturbances" that interfere with the low frequency wave data, and how much can they be reduced? I hope that this point will be taken up in one of the discussions. The second question is this: should not oceanographers, like other physical scientists, reserve the adjective "theoretical" for describing equations and arguments that are directly connected with known principles? The adjective is, instead, now usually used as a synonym for "non-experimental," with the implication that one man's "theoretical" guess is as good as another's.

Dr. Walden (prepared reply to Dr. Hicks): As to the first question, the "disturbances" that interfere with the low frequency wave data originate from the fact that the ability of the accelerometers used is limited. The German accelerometers record values down to only about $\frac{1}{100}$ g. This is not sensitive enough to override the inaccuracies

---

[1] Whittenbury, Huber, and Newell, "Instrument for Measuring Water Waves," *R.S.I.* **30**: 674–676, 1959.

which are present in every measurement of any instrument. There is also the problem of not being able to measure the true vertical accelerations because of the movements of the buoy (see M. J. Tucker, *Deep-Sea Research 1959*, Vol. 5, pp. 185–192). In my opinion, an improvement in the accelerometer records could be obtained mainly by increasing the "accuracy" (ability to measure small accelerations) of the instruments used.

On the second question, some of the so-called "theoretical" spectra are based partly on observations and partly on theoretical considerations; they are, consequently, intermediate between "empirical" and "theoretical." In my opinion, it is not correct to call them "theoretical" (but without quotation marks) only because they are expressed in the form of a complicated mathematical equation. I fully agree with the comments of Professor Hicks and especially of Dr. Phillips, the latter given informally.

Dr. Hasselmann (prepared comment): A common feature of all the empirical forecasting formulae that have been suggested so far is the restriction to an idealized wind field which can be described by two parameters, the wind velocity and the fetch or duration. From the point of view of practical wave forecasting this probably represents the severest limitation of the present formulae and is probably also one of the reasons why the individual formulae differ so strongly, since the assumed idealized conditions are rarely encountered in practice.

An empirical approach to the problem of wave forecasting will undoubtedly be necessary until further progress has been made in the development of an exact theory. However, the difficulties encountered in an exact theory are of quite a different nature from those implied by the present empirical approach.

In fact, from a theoretical viewpoint there is no more difficulty in determining the wave spectrum for an arbitrary wind field with arbitrary, nonstationary boundaries than for the two-parametrical wind fields assumed in the empirical formula.

The basis of an exact theory of wave spectra must clearly be the equation for the energy balance of the spectrum:

$$\frac{\partial F}{\partial t}(\mathbf{k}; \mathbf{x}, t) + \mathbf{v} \cdot \nabla_\mathbf{x} F(\mathbf{k}; \mathbf{x}, t) = L(\mathbf{k}; \mathbf{x}, t), \quad (1)$$

where $F(\mathbf{k}; \mathbf{x}, t)$ is the energy spectrum in terms of wave-number $\mathbf{k}$, dependent in general on the posi-

tion in the ocean $\mathbf{x}$ and time t, $\mathbf{v} \cdot \nabla_\mathbf{x} F$ is the divergence of the convective energy flux $\mathbf{v} \cdot F$ (with $\mathbf{v}$ = group velocity = $\frac{1}{2}\sqrt{g/k}$ $(\mathbf{k}/k)$), and $L(\mathbf{k}; \mathbf{x}, t)$ is the total rate of change of the spectrum due to the generating, dissipating, and nonlinear processes in the sea.

If $L(\mathbf{k}; \mathbf{x}, t)$ is known as a function of the spectrum and the local wind conditions, there is no great difficulty in solving (1), with appropriate boundary and initial conditions, for an arbitrary given wind field. The real difficulty is, of course, that the terms entering in $L(k; x, t)$ are not yet known well enough to solve (1) exactly, and it is toward this problem that current theoretical work is being directed.

However, it would probably be much more fruitful, from both a theoretical and a practical point of view, if more effort from the empirical side were concentrated on filling this theoretical gap rather than trying to predict the spectrum directly from the wind conditions without the help of the energy equation. A reasonable guess at L, based perhaps partly on theoretical results, partly on observations, would enable wave forecasting for arbitrary wind conditions as given by weather maps, from idealized two-parameter fields to wandering cyclones.

The question of the influence of fetch, duration, moving, and non-uniform wind fields, etc., would be solved automatically by the computer integrating the differential equation.

Deviations between observed and predicted spectra or new theoretical insights into the physical processes involved would then lead to successive improvement of the first estimate of L, and at the same time to mutual stimulation of the empirical and theoretical approach.

The method would have to be based on a digital computer rather than on charts, which makes it more complicated (though not necessarily longer) than the present methods, but this lies in the nature of the problem and is unavoidable if the limitations involved in projecting the manifold of all possible wind fields $\mathbf{U}(\mathbf{x}, t)$ on to two scalar parameters are to be overcome.

Mr. Gelci (prepared comment): These three authors (Drs. Pierson and Neumann and Dr. Walden) agree to point out the considerable discrepancies between various spectra presently proposed. It is the opinion of DSA II users, that these discrepancies come from the complex structure of actual wind fields. The mere consideration of meteorological charts generally leads to over-

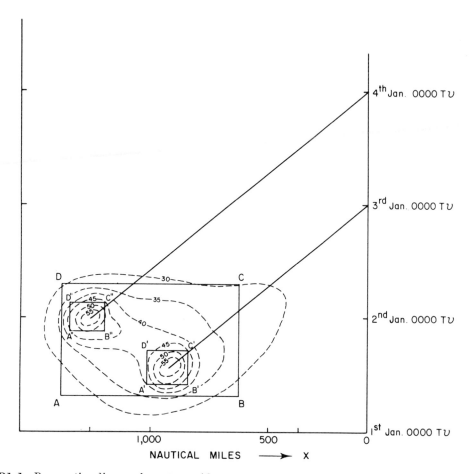

Figure 2-4D1-1, *Propagation diagram for a storm with an average wind of 40 knots.*

simplification. For example: a rectangular generating area, with constant, uniform winds in the open ocean is but an abstraction. The definition of the fetch is not rigorous, except perhaps when the wind blows from the land toward the sea. So it is very likely that the results of many workers were obtained under different meteorological conditions. Use of propagation diagrams allows a correct analysis of these conditions.

Let us consider, for instance, the case of a generating area of great dimensions, associated with a large atmospheric depression, in which the average wind is 40 knots. In reality, some isolated observations may be of 55 knots, although the greater number are from 30 to 35 knots. A propagation diagram, corresponding to this generating area, will show isotachs of strong winds, more or less circular, surrounded by a "background" of medium winds. Experience shows that every isotach of strong winds may be associated with the production of a long swell with a period $T \# W/3$ (W being the value of the strong wind). Thus, in the case of Figure 2-4D1-1, an 18-second swell will ar-

rive on the 3rd of January at 0000 GMT, and another 18-second swell will arrive on the 4th of January at 0000 GMT.

The importance of the strongest winds is, therefore, greater than that of moderate ones. The following examples are very frequent:

1-28-53 at Casablanca	$H_{\frac{1}{10}} \# 2m50$	$T \# 15$ sec
11-26-53 at Casablanca	$\# 3m50$	$T \# 15$ sec
11-10-56 at Casablanca	$\# 3m50$	$17 < T < 20$ sec
11-12-56 at Dakar	$\# 2m50$	$18 < T < 19$ sec
2- 8-57 at Casablanca	$\# 4m50$	$T \# 19$ sec
3-10-57 at Casablanca	$\# 4$ m	$14 < T < 18$ sec
4-27-57 at Casablanca	$\# 3m50$	$T \# 16$ sec
9-24-57 by 37°N 14°W	$\# 3m50$	$T \# 16$ sec
11-11-60 at St. Jean de Luz	important height, value not specified	$T = 19.3$ sec

Is it possible to hindcast such values by the PNJ method? And what winds must be used in the PNJ diagrams?

(a) We may consider the rectangle $ABCD$ as the generating area (in the space x, t) and enter the diagrams with a medium wind of 40 knots.

(b) We may also consider the two small generating areas $A'B'C'D'$ and $A''B''C''D''$, with a wind of 55 knots.

In other words, we may consider a large area and medium winds, or a small area and strong winds.

(c) It would be possible to imagine a composite utilization of PNJ diagrams, accounting for the variation of wind with time and distance, but such a procedure would need a new hypothesis, and this has not been indicated by the authors.

In order to analyze the first two procedures, it is convenient to consider Figure 2-4D1-2, deduced from PNJ diagrams. The time t, during which the wind is acting, is represented on the abscissa, and the wind W is represented on the ordinate. In the plane t, W, upper periods T_u (broken lines) are represented as a function of a wind W blowing during a time t. The points located at the lower right of the solid line represent fully arisen seas.

According to this diagram, winds of 40 knots or more do not generate components of more than 18 seconds, unless they have excessive durations. For instance, a wind with an actual value of 50 knots has never been observed to blow more than 24 hours — thus, *a fortiori*, for 50 hours — as could be expected according to the diagram. For weaker winds, the requested durations are likely. For instance, it often happens that a wind of 35 knots blows for more than 30 hours, and this duration would seem to be sufficient to raise components of 18 seconds and more. Thus, it seems possible, a priori, to "hindfind" long components with the medium winds and great durations. However, experience very frequently shows that weak or moderate winds, though blowing very long, cannot generate periods of 18 seconds or more.

Definite examples are, for Casablanca:

November 22 and 23, 1953
March 21, 1957
September 29 and 30, 1956
January 1st, 1956.

In conclusion, the PNJ method in its present form does not agree with observations in the case of strong winds (more than 40 to 45 knots). This is the opinion of Dr. Walden as expressed in a recent paper. It should be noted that these strong winds have the greatest importance for the production of swell.

As we have just seen, propagation diagrams

Figure 2-4D1-2. *Generation of Spectral components as a function of wind speed and duration.*

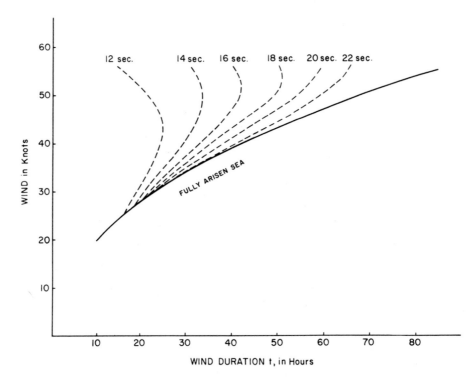

lead to a consideration of a medium-scale turbulence of the wind, which cannot be neglected. It is also likely that the small-scale turbulence of the wind is partly responsible for the disagreement between investigators. Considering this, let us remark that air-sea temperature difference characterizes the stability of the superficial air layer, thus its turbulence.

It would be very interesting to compare the spectra of waves produced by monsoon winds and those of waves produced by polar flows.

Another fault in the PNJ method lies in the fact that crosswinds and headwinds are not taken into consideration, whereas propagation diagrams take account of the decay under the action of such winds. Several recent works of Dr. Walden deal with the influence of linear increasing of wind with space or time. Such research tends to account for wind fields that are actually encountered.

It would be of some interest, of course, if very recent methods of prediction were tried by numerous applications. But the results so obtained would have but a relative value, for in any subjective technique the influence of the human calculator is predominant. The determination of the fetches and durations would certainly be questioned, so that no clear conclusion would appear. The automatism of the calculations involve either propagation diagrams or the use of an electronic computer.

The prediction of swell in narrow and/or shallow seas, such as the English Channel and the North Sea, is delicate as a result of friction and refraction that introduce a selected decay of long components. Trial applications of the DSA II technique in the neighborhood of Mont St. Michel (West Channel) did not yield satisfactory results. This leads us to state that wind-sea spectra are very different depending on whether open seas or coastal seas are concerned. This is also the opinion of Dr. Darbyshire and Dr. Walden.

DISCUSSION 2

Dr. Bretschneider (prepared comment on papers by Darbyshire, Walden, and Pierson and Neumann): I believe that there is much value in each of these papers, although I may not necessarily be in agreement with the complete context in each case. There are certain conflicts among the various papers that impede total agreement. I think it would be in order for me to include my own paper in this discussion. There are certain aspects of my paper, relevant to this conflict, that have been of some concern to me. I am also taking the liberty to discuss a paper by Dr. Burling (1959) which he so kindly sent me several weeks ago.

I believe that there are two distinct aspects to the problem, each of which will be discussed separately and then jointly. The first aspect is wave spectra, including the shape, energy density, total energy, etc. The second aspect is the generation parameters, including wind speed and direction, fetch length, wind duration, storm movements, among other factors.

I think it would be a splendid idea, as Drs. Pierson and Neumann said, if a number of wave spectra were computed by the methods used by the different people engaged in this problem, all using the same wave data. This certainly would bring to light a number of interesting factors. The question to be resolved is, what is the proper method for computing wave spectra? Perhaps there are several methods equally suitable, but I believe that the proper method must take into account the final purposes for which the results are to be used. One of the difficulties in comparing the various wave spectra is that wind speed, fetch length, etc., are included as parameters of the wave spectrum. When the same wind and fetch data are used, there appear to be tremendous differences among the various so-called theoretical wave spectra. Much of this difference is the reflection of the differences in the forecasting relations and procedures. I prefer to treat a wave spectrum in terms of its own characteristic parameters and then relate these wave spectral parameters to the wave generation parameters. In this way the two distinct aspects of the problem can be handled separately. This is the method that Dr. Darbyshire, and also Dr. Burling have used. The Neumann spectrum includes the wave generation parameter in the initial derivation, but these can be eliminated from the wave spectrum, as pointed out in my paper.

Let us consider now what I mean by the wave

spectral parameters. In my paper I suggested that one-dimensional linear wave spectra of the exponential type might be written as:

$$S_{H^2}(f) = S_{H^2}(f_0)(f/f_0)^{-m} e^{(-m/n)[(f/f_0)^{-n}-1]} \quad (1)$$

Where $S_{H^2}(f_0)$ represents the peak of the spectrum, f_0 is the corresponding frequency. $S_{H^2}(f)$ is related to the energy density $W(f)$ as used by Burling according to $S_{H^2}(f) = 8W(f)$. I am not sure whether or not equation 1 can represent the Darbyshire spectrum by proper selections of m and n, except perhaps as an approximation. The spectral parameters given by equation 1 are $S_{H^2}(f_0), f_0, m$ and n, and if such spectra exist, these parameters must be related to the wind-fetch-duration generation parameters.

The area under the curve of $S_{H^2}(f)$ is equal to the mean square wave height and is obtained from:

$$\overline{H^2} = \int_{-\infty}^{0} S_{H^2}(f)\, df \quad (2)$$

whence

$$\overline{H^2} = f_0 \cdot S_{H^2}(f_0)K \quad (3)$$

where K is a constant in terms of m and n as follows:

$$K = e^{m/n} \frac{1}{m-1} \left[\frac{n}{m}\right]^{\left(\frac{m-1}{n}\right)} \Gamma\left(1 + \frac{m-1}{n}\right) \quad (4)$$

where the Gamma Function is

$$\Gamma(X) = \int_0^{\infty} \mu^{x-1} e^{-\mu}\, d\mu, \quad x > 0 \quad (5)$$

In the following material it will be noted that

$$S\eta^2(f/f_0) = \frac{S_{H^2}(f)}{S_{H^2}(f_0)} = \frac{W(f)}{W(f_0)} \quad (6)$$

Equation 3 states that the area under the spectrum is proportional to the product of the peak of the spectrum $S_{H^2}(f_0)$ and its corresponding

frequency $f_0 \cdot K$ depends entirely on the selection of m and n; f^{-m} is proportional to the high-frequency components of the spectrum; and m and n together determine the entire shape of the spectrum. For the Neumann spectrum, $m = 6$ and $n = 2$; and for the general form of my spectra, $m = 9$ to 5 and $n = 4$. According to Burling (1959), his data fit best the relationship corresponding to equation 1, when $m = 5.5$ and $n = 7$ to 9. For an earlier spectrum of Darbyshire (1952), $m = 4$ and $n = 2$. Perhaps additional values of m and n appear in other literature, but from the above, it is seen that m is from 4 to 9 and n from 2 to 9. The following table for K has been prepared from equation 4 for various combinations of n and m.

It will be seen that $K = 0.856$ for the Neumann spectrum, $K = 0.974$ for the Roll-Fischer spectrum, $K = 1.158$ for the 1952 Darbyshire spectrum, and $K = 0.469$ to 0.698 for the Bretschneider spectra. According to the text of Burling, K should be between 0.467 and 0.512, for very short fetches.

For my paper I had made a comparison of the Neumann spectrum $m = 6$, $n = 2$ with my spectrum for $m = 5$, $n = 4$. There is a lot of similarity between these two spectra. In an earlier report (Beach Erosion Board T.M. 118) I showed that either of the above two spectra fitted equally well the data from SWOP (Chase, et al., 1957). An improvement on the comparison with the spectrum for $m = 5$, $n = 4$ can be made if one considers the data from a composite wave spectrum, as outlined in my paper. Treating the data from SWOP as that of a composite wave spectrum, I prepared Figure 2-4D2-1 using $m = 5$ and $n = 4$. This figure 2-4D2-1 shows the primary component at $f/f_0 = 1.0$, and a secondary component at $f/f_0 = 1.75$. This secondary component could be the result of second harmonics from the fundamental or primary component because it

TABLE I

VALUES OF K FOR VARIOUS COMBINATIONS OF m AND n

n	\(m\)							
	3	4	5	5.5	6	7	8	9
2	1.499	1.158	0.974	0.911	0.856	0.772	0.709	0.659
3	1.126	0.948	0.796	0.742	0.697	0.633	0.582	0.542
4	1.090	0.833	0.698	0.651	0.612	0.551	0.506	0.469
5	0.995	0.758	0.633	0.589	0.553	0.497	0.451	0.420
6			0.586	0.546	0.492	0.459	0.419	0.388
7			0.552	0.512	0.479	0.429	0.392	0.362
8			0.524	0.496	0.454	0.407	0.370	0.342
9			0.500	0.467	0.434	0.387	0.353	0.326

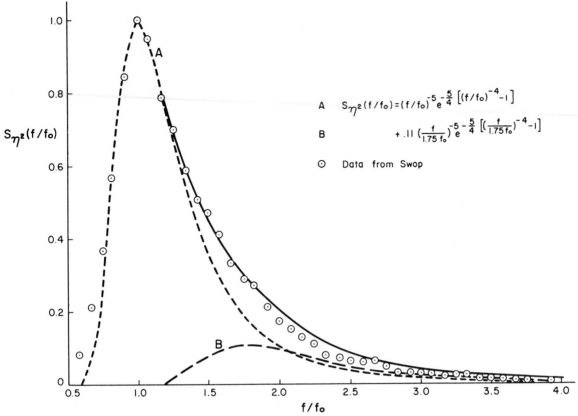

Figure 2-4D2-1. *Composite wave spectrum.*

has not yet been proven that the peak of the second harmonic components would necessarily be at $f/f_0 = 2.0$. Perhaps the secondary component is the result of local chop. The interpretation given in Figure 2-4D2-1 is not necessarily the best, since some other combinations of m and n might be more suitable for this particular spectrum. However, I do believe that this particular computed spectrum is of the composite form, otherwise almost entirely linear. It can be shown by use of Stokes' second order wave theory that the waves comprising this spectrum are of relatively low steepness; any second order and higher terms are insignificant.

Dr. Walden has presented some interesting findings, but as I mentioned before, it is rather difficult to compare wave spectra when wind speed and fetch are included. I have taken a particular fancy to Figures 2-4-7 and 2-4-13 of article one by Dr. Walden. From his Figure 2-4-7, there is a peak value of $E_f = 3.2 \times 10^3$ cm² sec and $f = 0.225$ sec − 1. Using these values and $m = 5$, $n = 4$, I computed a spectrum according to equation 1. The results are shown in Figure 2-4D2-2 of this discussion. In this case, there is

exceptionally good agreement. Figure 2-4-13 of the paper by Dr. Walden represents a composite wave spectrum similar to that discussed in my paper. Several attempts have been made to find the individual spectra resulting in the composite spectra using $m = 5$ and $n = 4$. The results are shown in Figure 2-4D2-3 of this discussion. I believe that some other combination of m and n can be found that would reproduce the results of the data better.

Using the 23 wave spectra records of Burling (1959), I have computed $K = 0.354$ with a standard deviation of 0.05, or about 14 per cent of the mean $K = 0.354$. There are various combinations of m and n which give $K = 0.354$; one of which is $m = 5.5$ and $n = 22$. Other values of m and n for $K = 0.354$ are $m = 7$, $n = 11$; $m = 8$, $n = 9$; and $m = 9$, $n = 7.5$, and other combinations. The combination of m and n for the Burling data ($K = 0.354$) should be such that the entire shape of the spectrum is best represented. Figure 2-4D2-4 shows various wave spectra for different values of m and n, together with averages of the data from Burling (1959). (Averages were determined by linear interpretations for f/f_0 at 0.05

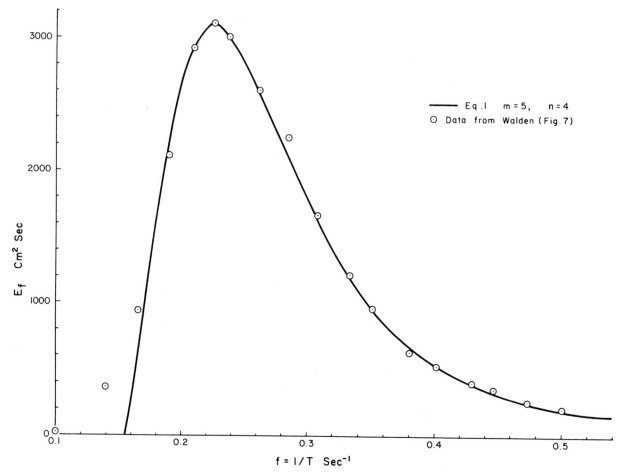

Figure 2-4D2-2. *Comparison of a computed wave spectrum.*

Figure 2-4D2-3. *Composite wave spectrum.*

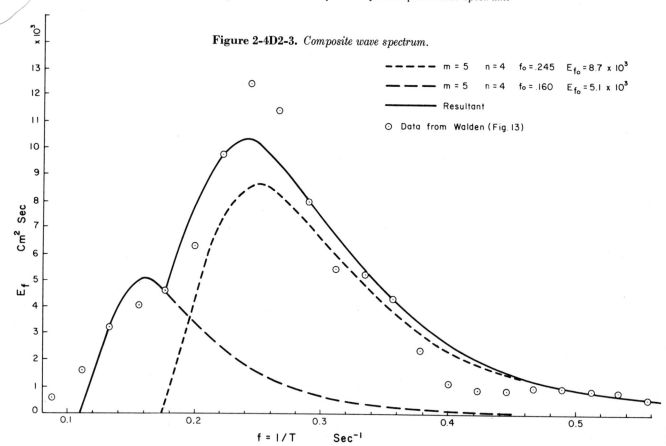

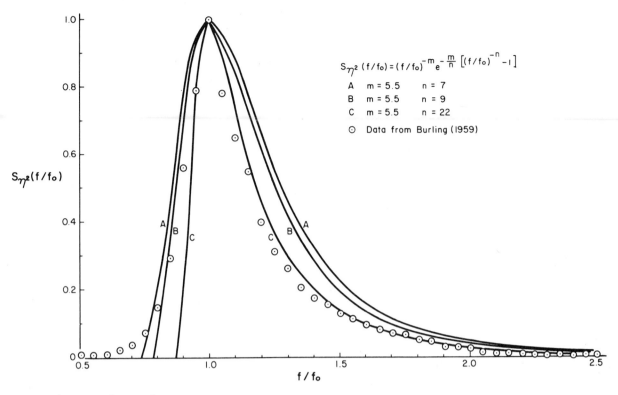

Figure 2-4D2-4. *Computed wave spectrum.*

Figure 2-4D2-5. *Darbyshire wave spectra.*

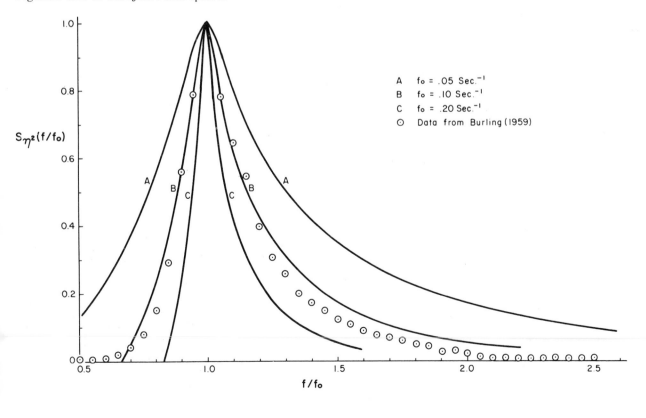

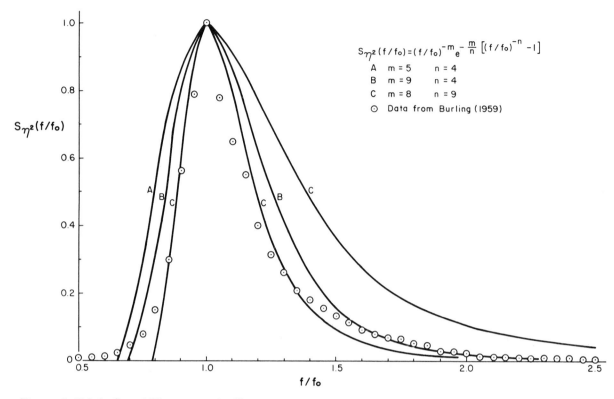

$$S_{\eta^2}(f/f_0) = (f/f_0)^{-m} e^{-\frac{m}{n}\left[(f/f_0)^{-n} - 1\right]}$$

A   m = 5   n = 4
B   m = 9   n = 4
C   m = 8   n = 9
⊙   Data from Burling (1959)

Figure 2-4D2-6. *Several Wave spectra for K = 0.354.*

increments). It is seen that none of the curves are especially good fits. In fact, if one selects $m = 8$, and $n = 9$, one obtains a much better fit as shown in Figure 2-4D2-6, but $m = 8$ and $n = 9$ are not necessarily the best selection.

The wave spectra equation given by Dr. Darbyshire, in terms of $f - f_0$ can be transformed into a family of spectra in terms of $S_{H^2}(f)/S_{H^2}(f_0)$ versus f/f_0 for various values of f_0. When this operation is performed, one obtains a set of curves as shown in Figure 2-4D2-5. Perhaps these relations might each be represented according to equation 1 with proper selections of m and n, at least approximately. The data of Burling (1959) are also shown in Figure 2-4D2-5. I became very curious when I noted that these data (mean value of $f_0 = 0.8$) fitted quite well the Darbyshire spectrum for f_0 between 0.1 and 0.2.

Now in regard to the general form of the wave spectra presented in my paper, I am not particularly satisfied with the assumption of linear regression between H and T^2. A recent paper by Gumbel (1959) presents a solution of the joint distribution function in which the two marginal distribution functions correspond to the Rayleigh distribution used in my derivation. Whereas I assumed linear regression, the relationship of

Gumbel does not result in linear regression equations, but the range of correlation coefficient is $|\rho| = 1/\pi$. However, I believe that more is involved than the joint distribution function for two Rayleigh type marginal distribution functions. Figure 2-4D2-6 shows the extremes of my wave spectra. The very early stages of generation are given for $m = 9$ and $n = 4$ and the fully developed sea for $m = 5$ and $n = 4$. The fit with the data of Burling (1959) for $m = 9$ and $n = 4$ is still not satisfactory. A better fit is given for $m = 8$ and $n = 9$. I am inclined to believe that the marginal distribution functions change during the process of wave generation. For this reason, I believe that the linear wave spectrum should be of the form given by equation 1, where both m and n change during generation. Perhaps also one set of values of m and n apply for $f > f_0$ and another set for $f < f_0$, and this should be investigated. Various combinations of m and n can be obtained from Table I for a particular value of K. The proper combination of m and n can be estimated by curve fitting or by use of statistical moments. In the latter respect, I would like to say that the spectral function can be treated in essentially the same manner as a probability distribution function for frequency. The energy density then becomes a weight factor analogous to the probability density, which is also a weight factor. Using energy density as a weight factor, one could compute moments which would be used to obtain a Gamma type energy density function analogous to the Gamma type distribution function (for wave-period variability), such as was presented by Putz (1952).

The remaining part of this discussion applies to the wave-generation parameters, for it is these parameters which must be related accurately to the wave spectral parameters. As I mentioned before, there are four important wave spectral parameters, $S_H{}^2(f_0)$ or $W(f_0)$, f_0, m, and n. The wave generation parameters have been discussed splendidly in the paper by Drs. Pierson and Neumann, and I agree with them that this is the field wherein much difficulty exists. The main difficulty is the establishment of the proper wind-fetch-duration generation parameters, or the interpretation of the meteorology. Aside from the effects of atmospheric stability on sea surface stresses, the three most important generation factors are wind speed, wind duration, and fetch length. It is of great importance to attach proper interpretations and evaluations of these factors. For example, Dr. Darbyshire states that the waves cease to grow after a fetch of about 200 miles has been reached. He has data for fetches of up to 2000 miles and sufficient wind duration to support this conclusion, but his conclusion is based on his own interpretation of fetch length and wind duration. I do not believe that his interpretation of fetch length can be the same as my interpretation. As Drs. Pierson and Neumann have stated, the waves should be no different from one ocean to another or from one side of the ocean to another side.

I believe that the problem of delineating fetch and wind duration can be solved only by some standard technique applicable to most situations. For a number of years now I have been advocating use of the "Graphical Method of Wave Forecasting" originally proposed by Wilson (1955). This method is mechanical, requiring the determination of a space-time wind field, and much of the subjectiveness of wave forecasting is removed. I would like to emphasize that this graphical procedure removes the subjectiveness of wave forecasting, and that any one of ten wave forecasters should obtain identical answers using the same forecasting relations. We can assume at present that all wave forecasting relations are not com-pletely correct, but by use of the graphical procedures, these forecasting relations can be corrected. The graphical method of wave forecasting can be adapted to any method of wave forecasting, i.e., the significant wave method or the wave spectra method. Once the significant wave method and also the wave spectra method have been adjusted so that they adapt to the graphical procedures, then one should obtain reliable forecasts from either method. Incidentally, the graphical procedures can be applied numerically with the use of a high speed computer.

REFERENCES

Bretschneider, C. L. (1959): *Wave Variability and Wave Spectra for Wind-Generated Gravity Waves.* Beach Erosion Board, Tech. Memo. 118, 192 pp.

Burling, R. W. (1959): "The Spectrum of Waves at Short Fetches." *Dt. Hydrogr. Z.* Band 12, Heft 2, 45–117.

Chase, J. L., J. Cote, W. Marks, E. Mehr, W. J. Pierson, Jr., F. C. Ronne, G. Stephenson, R. C. Vetter, and R. G. Walden (1957): *The Directional Spectrum of a Wind Generated Sea as Determined from Data obtained from the Stereo Wave Observation Project (SWOP).* New York University, Technical Report.

Darbyshire, J. (1952): "The Generation of Waves by Wind." *Proc. R. Soc.*, A 215, 299–328.

Gumbel, E. J. (1960): "Bivariate Exponential Distributions." *Jour. of American Statistical Association*, **55**: 698–707.

Wilson, B. W. (1955): *Graphical Approach to the Forecasting of Waves in Moving Fetches.* Beach Erosion Board, Tech. Memo. 73, 31 pp.

Dr. Hicks (prepared comment): Let me first outline the basis for my research philosophy. No research near Urbana, Illinois, could qualify me as a deep-water oceanographer. Yet I suspect that our studies of small waves, free from the rigorous conditions encountered in measuring large ocean waves, enable us to see more clearly than do professional oceanographers a few of the limitations of traditional methods of studying wave generation. When we consider the difficulties experienced in making and analyzing measurements of small waves, we find that the same or, indeed, much greater difficulties could be expected in measurements of comparable scope concerning ocean waves.

Whatever the origin of our research philosophy may have been, I do wish to emphasize at the outset that research on small wind waves is useful and important far beyond its immediate use and importance as a subject of scientific curiosity. I can dismiss the wide-ranging practical applications of knowledge of small wind waves by merely mentioning the words "radar" and "sonar," and then assert that research on small waves should also be recognized as an important part of the study of wind waves of all sizes, a study which is the concern of this conference.

I shall now assume what I shall partially demonstrate later, namely, that the characteristics of the generation by the wind of small waves are similar in their nature to the characteristics of the generation of the larger waves by the wind. If this assumption is true, then any well-considered measurements of small wind waves certainly will yield information of value concerning the larger waves. The experimenter also finds many other advantages in the study of small wind waves. Measurements are very fast because the time scale is shorter, by a factor of up to 100. The great speed of measurement not only permits the rapid acquisition of data but also permits real-time measurements of such important quantities as, for example, that of the wave energy contained in a narrow frequency range by the use of a band-pass filter with rms averaging device and suitable recording. Such real-time measurements are valuable when we are studying phenomena that are not well understood, like the generation of wind waves. Real-time measurement of wave energy in specific frequency bands also makes it possible later to do an extensive analysis of the data by digital machines, including estimates of errors; this is possible because much of the calculation has, in effect, already been done by the analogue devices in the field. These remarks apply to the type of measurements that we made of the waves and would apply to corresponding measurements of the wind characteristics.

Not only are measurements of small wind waves faster, they are generally also more accurate and simpler than those required for ocean waves. The equipment need not, for example, withstand the attack of salt water and large waves. Simplicity and speed of measurement make it possible for the experimenter to approach the design of his experiment with greater flexibility. One instance is the suggestion by Dr. George Newell of the cir-

cuitry for our capacitance probe measurements, which provides linear sensing of wave elevation over a very wide dynamic range. This principle once having been demonstrated for small waves, it can of course be considered for measuring large waves as well.

There is also an advantage in studies of *naturally* occurring small wind waves as compared to the study of small wind waves generated in a wind-wave tunnel. The most important single fact concerning wind-wave generation, and one that is almost if not quite ignored, is the variability of the wind vector $\vec{V}$, in direction and magnitude with position and time. It is not worthwhile to try to reproduce this variability in a tunnel, mainly because the variability has never been adequately documented. Because of the variability of $\vec{V}$, ordinary methods of characterization of the wind-wave interaction, either in measurement or theory, are inadequate. As an example, I cite the incomplete criterion that we used for steadiness of the wind-wave systems that we studied. We compared the fast fluctuations of the wave energy in an octave-wide frequency band with the slow drift of the wave energy, if any, over the duration of the recorded sample. When the drift for a given sample of record was less than one-half of the indicated fluctuations during the sample, we accepted the sample for analysis as corresponding to "steady" wind and wave conditions. In effect, therefore, we were applying a certain condition to the *duration* of the wind. Indeed, when we analyzed the wave data, we assumed implicitly that the waves had been generated by long-duration winds in all cases. Though our results are, I think, of some value, this rather cavalier approach to the variability of the wind with time certainly represents an imperfection of our experimental and analytical techniques.

The problem of characterizing or even recognizing wind variability may be brought home in another way. Suppose that we are interested in measuring, at 20 individual points and with a statistical uncertainty of 10 per cent, a spectrum whose maximum occurs at 2 cycles per second. For this purpose we would need a sample of about 1000 seconds duration. The spectral energy density is approximately proportional to the cube of the wind speed. Suppose now that we want to represent the effect of the wind speed by merely specifying average wind speed instead of the $\frac{1}{3}$ root of the average cubed wind speed. Replacing one average by the other gives an error that is less than 20 per cent of the wind speed only if the wind speed variation is less than 100 per cent, on the average, throughout this sample of 1000 seconds duration. How often has this sort of criterion been established in wind-wave studies?

The difficulties that we have outlined characterize the study of large wind waves as well as of small wind waves. If oceanographers continue to study only large wind waves, however, their progress toward gaining a deep understanding of the process will continue to be slow or at least very expensive.

Fortunately, the process of generation of small wind waves offers at the very least a *naturally occurring model of the variability of the wind and of the waves it generates*, which may be used to test our theoretical description of such processes and the suitability of our experimental tools. The generation of small wind waves probably is also, as I postulated earlier, *a naturally occurring dynamical model of the wind and wave interaction in the larger scale processes on the ocean.* In addition to (gF/V^2), there is only one dimensionless ratio that, at first sight, has different values for small and large gravity waves, and may affect their generation, namely, the ratio of the frequency at the maximum of the wave spectrum and the frequency (13.5 cps) of the slowest capillary-gravity waves. We expect capillary-gravity waves to be generated in a different fashion than gravity waves, but for small gravity waves of frequency less than say 5 cps, there is as yet no clear indication that their processes of generation by the wind waves are not dynamically similar to those of the larger gravity waves. If careful studies show that still other dimensionless ratios are relevant (such as, for example, the ratio of correlation times of wind and of waves), then these ratios must be considered for gravity waves of *all* sizes, but we still have not lost dynamical similarity until it is found that the range of any characteristic dimensionless ratio is necessarily different for wave generation on the ocean and, say, on small lakes.

For several reasons then, I earnestly recommend careful and thorough studies of small gravity waves for all those interested in understanding the generation by the wind of gravity waves of all frequencies.

Dr. Kinsman (prepared comment): These remarks do not respond directly to any one paper; they are free associations stimulated by all the papers and discussions. I have three points I wish to mention. They concern calibration, reduced-information statistics, and sampling variability. I would also like to plead for greater precision of expression.

Pierson and Neumann remark that, "In the study of waves no instrument that could be considered a primary standard of calibration exists." It must be obvious to all of us that no existing device for measuring waves is calibrated in the strict sense of the term, i.e., in the sense that it has been compared in all relevant aspects with a standard at least one order of magnitude more accurate and precise than the device being calibrated. This is not to say that we are totally ignorant of the behavior of our instruments. Actually, we know a great deal about them, but this kind of knowledge is conceptually quite different from calibration. A carefully drawn distinction reinforced by the use of two separate words would reduce the muddle.

Devising any instrument adequate to measure waves is difficult. One has the feeling that each investigator selected his instrument not because it was perfectly suited to his purposes but because its characteristics, so far as he knew them, were less repulsive to him than those of the rejected instruments. Elliptical statements such as: "The instrument was calibrated by means of so and so. The results were satisfactory," arouse more skepticism than conviction. In the first place, the reader knows that he has never been able to calibrate his own instruments in any strict sense, and in the second, he has usually considered and rejected similar instruments as unsatisfactory. The reader is unlikely to reverse his judgment without very strong persuasion. The rhetoric becomes more forceful when a detailed account of the "calibration" procedure is given, together with the resulting numbers, manipulations, and conclusions.

Each wave instrument stamps the wave record with its own peculiar signature. Until we know how these signatures are related, comparisons of results from different instruments must have a strong aura of unreality. It seems to me that one of the first things we must do is attach a precise, commonly agreed upon, operational meaning to the term "calibration" as applied to wave-measuring instruments. If at the same time we can agree on some other term in order to distinguish it from calibration in the strict sense, so much the better.

Another fundamental matter that should be tidied up soon is the question of which reduced information measures are most appropriate for various purposes. I believe that most of us would agree that waves are best viewed as a random process. This view commits us to the joint distribution function as the most complete piece of information we could have about the process. Unfortunately, the process is so complex that it is practically unobtainable and, even if we had it, too cumbersome to use. We must be content with reduced-information measures related to the joint distribution function.

Really remarkable results have come from the assumption that ocean waves are sometimes describable as a stationary Gaussian process. Were this strictly true, a knowledge of the spectrum would be sufficient, just as a knowledge of the variance is sufficient to specify an ordinary, normal, mean-zero distribution. We cannot rest content with this assumption much longer. Successful as it may be in an engineering sense, it is insufficient for the deeper insight into the process that we require.

Various reduced-information statistics should be developed systematically on a variety of assumptions. Too often we seem to get our reduced-information measures quite accidentally because they happen to exist. We could do better by carefully shaping them for our purposes, but we should not expend all our effort on stationary processes.

Reduced-information statistics alone are not enough. One must be able to measure them, and the distributions governing their sampling fluctuations must be discovered. Although we set a difficult task, it is vital because we can never be secure in our physical interpretations of what we observe so long as the sampling distributions re-

main unknown. Those we know deserve more respect. For instance, the chi-square distribution offered in 1949 by Tukey as a useful approximation for sample spectra estimates now masquerades as an unqualified chi-square distribution in at least one report published in 1960.

My quarrel here is not with the shifts and approximations forced upon us in our attempts to come to grips with physical reality. It is with the careless handling of words, which is sometimes associated with incompletely formed concepts. The entropy of any language in active use tends to increase. Concepts become more and more difficult to express exactly, and nice distinctions become impossible. Surely it is one of the first duties of a scholar to combat this degradation — at least within his own field. If a name is applied to a concept, then the concept should be completely operational in the commonly accepted sense of the name. Some years ago in formulating a problem I used a symbol that looked vaguely like a tensor, so I began to call it a tensor. A mathematician pulled me up short with "It doesn't operate like a tensor. You will mislead and confuse if you use that word. If you call it a tensor, everyone has a right to expect it to behave in all respects like one. Call it something else." I cannot believe that this is captious purism. The ability to conceive, distinguish, and communicate is the very essence of thought. If we do not conserve and improve the fundamental tool of language, much of our best effort will be dissipated in heated argument and pointless misunderstanding.

BRUCE L. HICKS

F I V E

ESTIMATION OF THE SPECTRUM FUNCTION

FOR SMALL WIND WAVES*

ABSTRACT

In studies of wave spectra at the Coordinated Science Laboratory, values of mean square energy e_m in octave-wide frequency bands were obtained in "real time" measurements through the use of analogue devices. *Illiac*, the University of Illinois digital computer, was then used to effect a least squares fit to an integral of a parameterized spectrum function $\phi_c(\lambda_n)$ and to estimate the probable errors of the parameters λ_n. The CSL data cover the ranges

$$0.15 \leq V \leq 10.2 \text{ m/sec}, \quad 5 \leq F \leq 625 \text{ m},$$
$$0.5 \leq f \leq 16 \text{ cps},$$

where V, F, and f are the average wind speed, average fetch, and wave frequency, respectively. A similar analysis was made of Burling's data, which cover a smaller range but more accurately.

The least squares calculation of the values of the parameters λ_n and their probable errors ν_n affords an objective basis for comparing the two sets of data with each other and with data from other sources, for estimating the uncertainty of derived quantities, such as the rms wave elevation, and for specifying for the first time the effect of

wind speed and fetch upon the energy spectra of small waves on the water over a large range of each independent variable.

DETAILS AND DESCRIPTION

My discussion of the conference paper by Pierson and Neumann was based in part upon our experience at CSL in measuring and analyzing systems of small wind waves. Although these studies were only one step toward a rational study of wind waves, they have yielded new, quantitative scientific information.

The results that I shall now discuss support two statements about wind wave research: (1) It is possible to gain more data, faster, and of better accuracy and scope by studying small wind waves than by studying large ones. (Note, for example, the $10^6 : 1$ range of values of the spectral energy density derived from our wave measurements.) (2) There does exist one method of analyzing objectively the errors made in describing a stochastic geophysical process by a parameterized function.

Our analysis covered both our own data and those of other investigators. I have, therefore, summarized in Table 1 the measurements of small wind waves that we analyzed. I should like to point especially to the much broader range of variation of the field variables in our measurements,

---

* Originally presented during the session on Recent Measurements and Analysis Techniques.

TABLE 1

MEASUREMENTS OF SMALL WIND WAVES

	V m/sec	F m	f sec^{-1}.
Roll (1951)	0.8–15	0.2–40	~2–20
Burling (1955)	5–9	400–1350	0.4–1.9
Cox (1958)	3–12	2.1	~2–200
Kinsman (1960)	4–8	1700–3000	0.8–2.1
Hicks (1958–61)	0.2–10	5–600	0.5–16

and to some extent in those of Roll, than in those of the other investigators. This broad range is necessary when we are trying to characterize with some certainty the gross features of wind-wave spectra as functions of wind speed and fetch. In the future, now that these gross features have been fairly well established, it will also be appropriate to measure a few points on the spectrum rather accurately.

Roll's early and very illuminating experiments yield values of the dominant frequencies of the waves but no detailed spectral information. Burling and Kinsman derived wave spectra from their records of wave elevation. Burling measured 463 values of the spectral energy density. Cox carefully measured the slope spectrum, and by assuming linear supposition of the waves, we derived the elevation spectra from his data. This transformation is subject to some question, of course. In the CSL studies we measured the energy contained in octave-wide frequency bands and derived the values of the spectral energy density from 273 of these wide band measurements. The origins of the data we shall discuss are thus rather varied, and I think it is of some interest to compare them in more than one way.

The basis for the analysis of our data and those of Burling and, less directly, of all the small-wave data, lies in the following equations:

$$\begin{cases} \phi_1 \doteq b_1 V^{r_1} F^{s_1} f^{t_1} & f \leq f_0 \\ \phi_2 = b_2 V^{r_2} F^{s_2} f^{t_2} & f > f_0 \end{cases} \quad (1)$$

In these equations V and F are the average wind speed and the average fetch, f is the frequency, f_0 is the frequency corresponding to the largest value of the spectral energy density, and ϕ_1 and ϕ_2 are spectral energy density values on the low-frequency and high-frequency sides of the spectrum relative to f_0. The frequency f_0 at the top of the spectrum is related to V and F by the equation

$$b_1 V^{r_1} F^{s_1} f_0^{t_1} = b_2 V^{r_2} F^{s_2} f_0^{t_2} \quad (2)$$

We are thus representing the energy spectrum of small wind waves by an eight-parameter function, which is flexible enough to fit existing data well, yet simple enough to facilitate a rather varied interpretation of the results. We realize, of course, that the spectrum is not this sharply peaked, but it seems to us more important to study the general form of the spectrum than just its curvature near the peak of the spectrum. Our definition of spectral energy density corresponds to the following equation for the mean-square wave elevation:

$$\xi_{\text{rms}}^2 = \int_0^\infty \phi \, df \quad (3)$$

The principal part of our analysis of the CSL data and of Burling's data consisted of two parts. First, we made a least squares fit of the above parameterized functions to the experimental data in a form appropriate to each set of data in turn. This calculation was carried out on the digital computer *Illiac* of the University of Illinois. The results for the CSL and Burling data are shown in Table 2a.

The second part of our analysis, which is indeed closely related to the first part, permitted an estimate of the probable error in determining each of these parameters for each of the two sets of data. Our procedure has been described in detail elsewhere. We chose ten subsets of each set of data by random picking with replacement and made least squares fits to each of these subsets. The resulting distribution of values of the parameters allowed us to compute probable errors. Without going into detail, we may say that this procedure[1] gives an upper limit to the probable errors caused by almost every source of error that we have been able to conceive of, including the lack of flexibility of the parameterized functions that we chose and any departure from the assumption that only the average wind speed and average fetch affect the wave growth. The computed probable errors are also given in Table 2a.

On the whole, Burling's data are much more self-consistent internally than ours, but this must be balanced against the smaller range of his data. Notice, however, that his value of t_1 exhibits a probable error not much different from our corresponding value. In comparing the values of the other parameters it is perhaps most important to

---

[1] Professor Tukey's comments on this procedure (cf. p. 349 of these proceedings) are useful.

TABLE 2a
FINAL BEST VALUES OF THE EIGHT PARAMETERS — DATA OF BURLING AND OF CSL

Source	$\log_{10} b_1$	$\log_{10} b_2$	r_1	s_1	r_2	s_2	t_1	t_2
Burling (Eq. 6, M-91) 10 b	−9.398a ±0.033	−3.086a ±0.019	2.832 ±0.065	1.798 ±0.020	0.000 ±0.023	0.003 ±0.012	6.562 ±0.290	−5.584 ±0.041
Hicks (Eq. 5, M-90) 1.5 b	−10.14a ±0.10	−3.14a ±0.23	1.79 ±0.16	2.01 ±0.07	0.48 ±0.14	−0.18 ±0.05	1.27 ±0.22	−4.54 ±0.14

a (m, sec units);   b (Height of anemometer above the mean water level (meters)

note the agreement for the parameter s_1, which measures the sensitivity of the spectrum to fetch; the agreement for the coefficient $\log b_2$, which measures the size of the waves generated on the high-frequency side of the spectrum; and the very complete evidence for saturation on this side of the spectrum, as shown by the small values of r_2 and s_2. We view the determination of the exponents r_2 and s_2 as giving the first quantitative support for saturation of the spectra of small wind waves on the high-frequency side.

In Table 2b we give estimates of the same parameters derived where possible for the other sources of data on small wind waves.

The simple form we assumed for the spectrum function allows us easily to study the dimensional implications of the least-squares results. For the CSL data ($\xi_{rms}g/V^2$) and (g/f_0V) are, with good accuracy, representable as functions only of (gF/V^2), but this is not the case for the values derived from Burling's spectral energy data. On the other hand, the combination ($f_0^2\xi_{rms}/g$) is nearly constant for both Burling's data and ours. The probable errors of the relevant constants can be derived from the probable errors given in Table 2a.

In Figures 2-5-1 and 2-5-2 we compare the different sets of data in a third way. By way of introduction we may point out that the two most important characteristics of a wave spectrum are the area under the spectral curve, which we may represent by ξ_{rms}^2, and the frequency f_0 at the top of the spectrum. The parameter ξ_{rms} is plotted in Figure 2-5-1 as a function of V and F for each

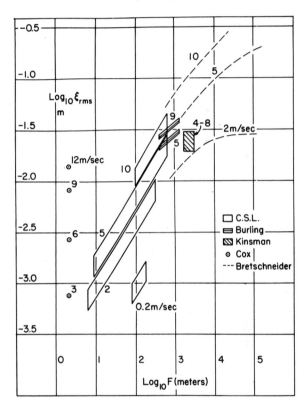

Figure 2-5-1. *The r.m.s. elevation of small wind waves.*

of the available sets of data. The CSL data run from the high-frequency data of Cox, represented by the circles, to the low-frequency data of Kinsman, Burling, and Bretschneider.[2] The data of

[2]Adapted by Wilson.

TABLE 2b
VALUES OF THE PARAMETERS DERIVED FROM OTHER SOURCES

Source	$\log_{10} b_1$	$\log_{10} b_2$	r_1	s_1	r_2	s_2	t_1	t_2
Cox 0.13 b	—	∼−1.3a	∼0.9	—	∼0	—	—	∼−6
Kinsman 1.25 b	—	−3.88a	—	—	∼0 ± 0.05	∼0 ± 0.06	—	−4.5

a (m, sec units)   b Height of anemometer above the mean water level (meters)

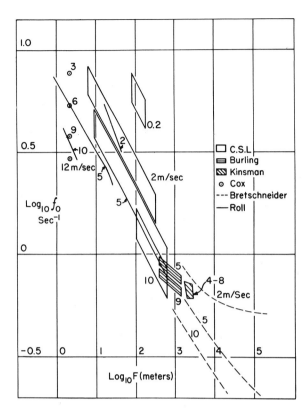

Figure 2-5-2. *The frequency f_0 for small wind waves.*

our error analysis. The vertical heights of the blocks representing the CSL data and also the Burling data are equal to twice the corresponding probable errors of $\log_{10}\xi_{rms}$ and of $\log_{10} f_0$. These probable errors and the corresponding errors of any other quantities related to the spectral energy density in a known way can be calculated directly, though not without some hard work, from the probable errors given in Table 2a. Without this information on probable errors we should have very little basis for drawing conclusions as to the amount of agreement or disagreement among our data, Burling's data, and those of other investigators. With such error information we can begin to distinguish between statistical variations of the wave properties and differences in the experimental conditions.

In Figure 2-5-3 we present a similar plot for the spectral energy density, and here only our data, those of Burling, and one curve derived from Cox are represented. The error limits are given again. Burling's data agree with the CSL data in general position although the slope, particularly on the low-frequency side of the spectrum, is quite different. The agreement between the data of Cox and those of CSL is surprisingly good in spite of the uncertainty of the transformation from slope to amplitude spectrum.

Cox and CSL agree well except at the higher wind speeds, where possibly the transformation from slope spectrum to amplitude spectrum may be at fault. Only CSL data appear to be available at wind speeds much below 1 m/sec. We have extrapolated Bretschneider's correlation of wave data down toward the small-wave region that is of interest to us, and it is seen to agree quite well with the data on small wind waves. Kinsman's data in the rectangle appear to be low. Agreement between Burling and CSL data is good in magnitude, though not in trend.

When we look at the corresponding plot for the frequency f_0 as a function of F in Figure 2-5-2, our conclusions can be very similar. Kinsman's data now seem to fall in line with those of Burling and may not be in disagreement with Bretschneider's data. The old data of Roll are in striking agreement with those of Cox and also, at the lowest wind speeds, with the CSL data, in spite of the uncertainty in translating Roll's specification of predominant period into our specification of f_0 and the aforementioned uncertainty in calculating elevation spectra from Cox's slope spectra.

In both figures we wish to emphasize the usefulness of the indications of probable error that we have been able to put on the plots as a result of

Figure 2-5-3. *Energy spectra of small wind waves.*

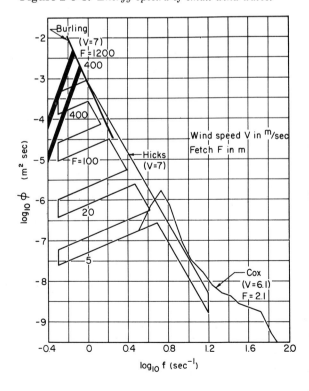

We may conclude that, as compared to our small knowledge of the generation of small wind waves in 1954, we now can predict the spectrum and the characteristics derived from it, with a degree of accuracy that can be estimated, throughout the range from $\frac{1}{2}$ to 16 cps, over a range of wind speeds from less than 1 m/sec to 10 m/sec, and over a range of fetches from less than 10 m to about 2000 m.

The success of the correlations I have presented assure us again of nature's regularity; the imperfections of our understanding should warn us that we must seek to account fully for the temporal and spatial variability of the processes of wave generation.

ACKNOWLEDGEMENT

This work was supported by a Tri-Services Contract, U. S. Department of Defense.

REFERENCES

Burling, R. W. (1955): "*Wind Generation of Waves on Water*." Ph. D. Thesis, Imperial College of Science and Technology, University of London.

Hicks, B. L. (1960a): *The Generation of Small Water Waves by the Wind, Part I. Comparison of Data from Different Sources*. Coordinated Science Laboratory, Report M-86.

Hicks, B. L., and E. A. Huber (1960): *Part II. CSL Wide-Band Data*. Coordinated Science Laboratory, Report M-87.

Hicks, B. L., and C. W. Mendel (1960): *Part III. Final Reduction of CSL Data*. Coordinated Science Laboratory, Report M-90.

Hicks, B. L. (1960b): *Part IV. Final Reduction of Burling's Data and Comparison with Other Data*. Coordinated Science Laboratory, Report M-91.

Hicks, B. L. (1960c): *The Energy Spectra of Small Wind Waves*. Coordinated Science Laboratory, Report M-92.

Roll, H. U. (1951): "Neue Messungen zur Entstehung von Wasserwellen durch Wind." *Ann. Met.* (Hamburg) **4:** 269–286, 1951.

Cox, C. S. (1958): "Measurements of Slopes of High-frequency Wind Waves." *J. Marine Research*, Sears Foundation **16:** 199–225.

Kinsman, Blair (1960): *Surface Waves at Short Fetches and Low Wind Speeds — A Field Study*, Technical Report XIX, Chesapeake Bay Institute, The John Hopkins University.

Wilson, Basil W. (1960): *Deep Water Wave Generation by Moving Fetches of Variable Wind*, Technical Report No. 206-1, Texas A and M Research Foundation.

DISCUSSION

Dr. Pierson: If I understand your parameterization correctly, if you plot the spectrum on a linear frequency and a linear spectral scale and if this is f_0, your result would suggest that the front part of the spectrum looks like a linear increase from $f = 0$ to f_0 over the range 0 to f_0 and for $f < f_0$. Is that correct?

Dr. Hicks: No, it is linear on a logarithmic plot on both sides.

Dr. Pierson: You have f^t (where $t \cong 1$).

Dr. Hicks: Yes. You are asking about our particular data and not the function. Reduction of our data led to a very small logarithmic slope for $f < f_0$. There may have been something peculiar about our experimental conditions, but I have not identified any such peculiarity.

Dr. Pierson: Have you done any spectral analysis that estimates the energy in equal frequency intervals instead of by decades?

Dr. Hicks: Our original estimates were for octave-wide frequency bands. We then performed the deconvolution. The least squares method permitted us to find what slope best fitted the data.

Dr. Pierson: I have never been able to understand how you handle the possibility of a spectrum that essentially has spectral values of zero over a certain range below the peak. I suggest that that might be the source of this apparent inconsistency.

Dr. Hicks: I am not sure that there is a connection between your understanding and the way we did it. I think we were able to handle this situation of large slope as well as any other in the process of deconvolution.

R. GELCI
P. CHAVY

SIX

TECHNICAL ASPECTS OF

NUMERICAL FORECASTING OF SWELL*

INTRODUCTION

A proposal for forecasting the state of the sea numerically was outlined in January 1960.

Because of the size of the model adopted, there appeared to be a need for many changes and improvements.

It is not intended here to describe in detail the outline of the program presently being tried. First of all, such a description would impose a strain on the reader; besides, this program has not yet been completely polished. Nevertheless, because of the general nature of the research to which it has led up to now, it may be of interest to some specialists.

THE GRID SYSTEM

The grid system used is rectangular and consists of 1000 squares, 25 × 40 (Figure 2-6-1). The height of the swell is calculated for each of these 1000 squares, then printed in decimeters by means of an ordinary teletype.

This process makes it possible to transmit directly without the intermediate need of the facsimile.

---

* Presented separately. Included here because of relationship to one-dimensional spectrum problems.

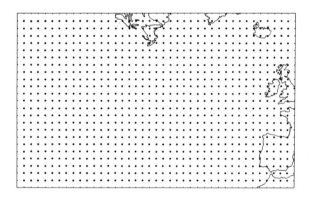

Figure 2-6-1.

Because of the characteristics of the teletype and the scale of the maps used, we have had to choose a rectangular instead of a square grid ($a = 87$, $b = 90$ nautical miles, approximately).

It was necessary to discard the broken-line grid initially in use. The recurrence relationships of the computation program became particularly complicated when this grid system was used. There was an advantage, however, in that most of the squares in that grid system corresponded to points located at sea.

It should be noted, however, that the grid system presently in use was used on the map in such a way as to cover as many of the swell generating regions of the North Atlantic as possible while avoiding land.

The use of oblique grids might lead to an even better adjustment to the problem. The advection formulas that we shall discuss in the next paragraph would not be appreciably modified. This improvement would require a slightly more complicated printing program; this step will be taken later.

PLANE PROPAGATION

Let us recall the propagation equation

$$\frac{d\rho}{dt} = -\vec{V} \operatorname{grad} \rho \qquad (1)$$

or

$$\Delta\rho = -(\vec{V} \operatorname{grad} \rho)\Delta t \qquad (2)$$

where ρ is the angular spectral density (dsa) of the energy waves of period T and direction θ, and V is the group velocity of these waves. This equation is rigorously valid for only an infinitely small time interval.

Let us assume that, at the instant $t - \Delta t$ (where $\Delta t = 3$ hours), the dsa are respectively $\rho_M \rho_P \rho_Q \rho_R$ for points M, P, Q, R.

Moreover, let us consider the vector $\vec{AM} = \vec{V}\Delta t$, whose end point is M. At instant t, dsa at point M is equal to dsa at point A for instant $t - \Delta t$. However, we know only $\rho_M \rho_P \rho_Q \rho_R$, but not ρ_A.

Our first approximation is to interpolate linearly between points MPQ (Figure 2-6-2). Thus we find

$$\Delta\rho = (\rho_P - \rho_M)\frac{V_x\Delta t}{a} + (\rho_Q - \rho_M)\frac{V_y\Delta t}{b}, \qquad (3)$$

Figure 2-6-2.

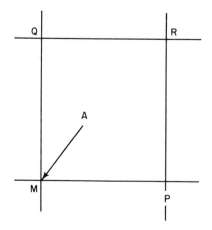

where Vx and Vy are the components of V along the north and south axes of the grid system; a and b are the distances between the "meshes."

In the case where A is inside triangle QPR, a different equation must be used (Figure 2-6-3):

$$\Delta\rho = (\rho_P - \rho_M)\frac{V_x\Delta t}{a} + (\rho_Q - \rho_M)\frac{V_y\Delta t}{b}$$
$$- (\rho_P + \rho_Q - \rho_R - \rho_M)\left(\frac{V_x\Delta t}{a} + \frac{V_y\Delta t}{b} - s\right) \qquad (4)$$

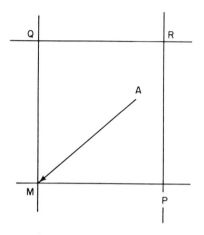

Figure 2-6-3.

BREAKUP INTO SPECTROANGULAR COMPONENTS

The components of the swell total 64(4 spectral bands and 16 directions). Figure 2-6-4 shows points A relative to the components of the first quadrant. An increase in the number of spectral components would have been preferred.

Moreover, the large dimensions of the grid system would also require an increase in the number of directions. Nevertheless, the model presently being experimented with is only a prototype.

The programming for a model with more than 64 components is not much more complicated; it will be taken into consideration. The wind direction is also broken down into 16 directions, a number that seems quite sufficient.

SPHERICAL PROPAGATION

Up to this point we have assumed linear propagation along the straight lines of the map in use.

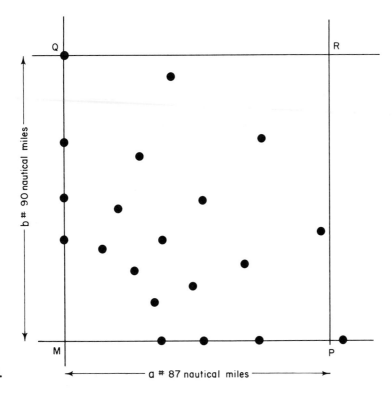

Figure 2-6-4.

In fact, we should assume orthodromic propagation. Nevertheless, the error is unacceptable.

However, if we selected a grid system of greater dimensions, we would have to bear this in mind. This is possible provided we expand in the notion of direction.

Let us consider a great circle R on the earth, which is called the reference circle. Consider Points $D1, D'1, D2, D'2 \ldots Dn, D'n$, which are diametrically opposed in pairs and equidistant along R (Figure 2-6-5). Let us consider a Point M on the sea surface, located outside R, as well as the great circles:

$$C1 = D1MD'1$$

$$C2 = D2MD'2$$

$$\overline{Cn = DnMD'n}$$

These n circles define an angular dissociation at Point M. This breakup is equidistant if M is one of the poles of R. In general, however, it is not equidistant. When M is close to R, the n circles especially tend to blend into one another.

We shall agree that all waves converging toward the same point Di have the same direction i. This being the case, let us consider the grids $MPQR \ldots$ of the sea surface which, at time

$t - \Delta t$ have a dsa of $\rho_M \rho_P \rho_Q \ldots$ (relative to the component of period T and direction i).

Let us further consider the great circle Ci, which goes through M, and let us take on this circle a Point A such that $AM = gT/4\pi$ (group velocity of the component under consideration).

Figure 2-6-5.

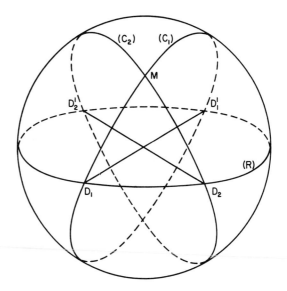

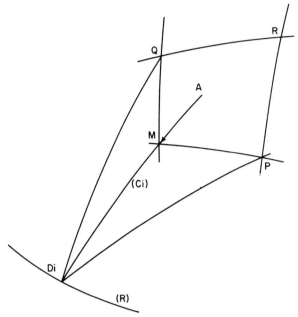

Figure 2-6-6.

The dsa at M at time T is equal to the dsa at A at time T_A. We will then calculate ρ_A as a function of $\rho_M \rho_P \rho_Q \rho_R \ldots$ (Figure 2-6-6). However, this time the interpolation formula will depend also on grid M under consideration. This particular propagation type cannot yet be considered because of the complication it would entail in the programming. Nevertheless, it would be absolutely necessary to tackle this problem when we have a grid system of large dimensions.

THE GROWTH

Equations 3 or 4 used for propagation are then completed so as to take into account the influence of wind, which increases or decreases the dsa.

We must write

$$\frac{d\rho}{dt} = -\overrightarrow{V} \text{ grad } \rho + \eta, \qquad (5)$$

this being the angular spectral growth (csa).

We have adopted for η a simple linear formula

$$\eta = (G - \rho)F, \qquad (6)$$

where G and F are functions of:

Period T of the component under consideration.

The wind speed W.

The angular difference $/\theta - \omega/$ between the direction of the component and the wind direction.

For an observer whose velocity is equal to the group velocity of the component, this equation leads to an exponential variation of ρ,

$$\rho = G(1 - e^{-ft}) \text{ or, if } \rho_0 > G$$

$$\rho - G = (\rho_0 - G)e^{-F(t - t_0)}$$

Equation 6 has the advantage of being easily adapted for a computer; it also simultaneously condenses growth and decay according to the values of the parameters T, W, and $/\theta - \omega/$. This requires knowing F and G for all possible values of these parameters. Hence,

> 4 possible values for T
> > 7, 10, 14, 20
> 9 possible values for $/\theta - \omega/$
> > 0 to 8 in a wind rose of 16 points
> 13 possible values for W
> > from 10 to 70 knots by increments of 5 knots,

altogether, 936 constants.

The values of G (corresponding to the fully-arisen sea) are obtained from equations published earlier.

The values of F were deduced so as to make the exponential growth and the bilinear growth as close as possible (Figure 2-6-7).

Figure 2-6-7.

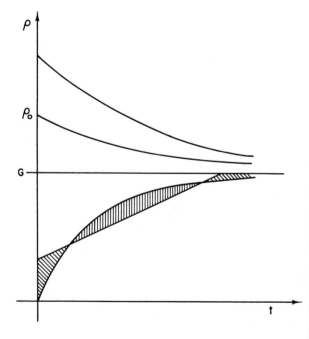

THE ELEMENTARY OPERATIONS

The elementary operations are propagation and growth. We have seen that there are 64 tables of 1000 dsa, each one of these tables corresponding to a value of period T and direction θ.

On each of these tables we begin by carrying out the propagation (which is nothing but a translation $\vec{V}\Delta t$, $\vec{V}$ being the group velocity of the component). Then for each grid we treat the new dsa ρ' (after the propagation) with the wind, which is found at the corresponding grid of the wind table.

Starting with T, θ, W (wind velocity), ω (wind azimuth), we deduce $/\theta - \omega/$, then F and G, and finally η (angular spectral growth). We then need only to calculate the sum $\rho + \eta$ in order to get the final value of dsa.

Since these two operations are carried out for each of the 1000 grids, we then add the 64 dsa's corresponding to the same grid, i.e., $\sum\limits_{T} \sum\limits_{\theta} \rho$.

The height of the swell for each grid is then given by the equation

$$H_{1/10} = 3,2 \sqrt{\sum\limits_{T} \sum\limits_{\theta} \rho},$$

where $H_{1/10}$ is the mean height of the highest one-tenth of the waves (in decimeters); ρ is the dsa in centijoules/cm².

The need for a third elementary operation will be considered at a future time; i.e., interferential breaking which would, for each step, require the consideration of the 64 dsa's for a same grid. From this we would deduce the eventual decrease of each dsa due to breaking by interference.

PROGRAMMING

The programming consists of 5 parts:

1. A sub-program of "wind arrangement," which enables us to put in the computer the speed and direction of the wind relative to each of the 1000 grids. It is necessary to analyze first, for each grid and every 3 hours (in practice, every 6 hours), the variation of the wind at sea level. This manual analysis, done first on the observed charts, then on the forecast charts, is evidently time-consuming (requiring several hours). The results of this analysis are then transcribed on perforated tape, which is fed into the computer.

2. A sub-program for computing certain constants which depend on the component being considered (for example, the constants of advection).

3. A sub-program for computing a table of 1000 dsa's. The 1000 dsa's of a component are subjected to the two elementary operations: propagation and growth.

4. A sub-program of output which adds, first, the 64 dsa's of the same grid, deduces the amplitude $H_{1/10}$, and prints it on teletype; 1000 values of $H_{1/10}$ are thus printed.

5. Finally, a sub-program of organization which governs the entries, the outputs, and the cycles of all preceding sub-programs.

The over-all program consists of a large number of elementary orders. Its operation on a daily basis requires about one-half hour (not taking into account the time required for analyzing the charts).

DISCUSSION

Comments concerning all papers in Session II.

Mr. Farmer: My remarks are rather general. Without considering the directional spectrum, the four papers presented in this session point out the problems we face and the differences that exist in our methods and results. The papers by Darbyshire and Bretschneider illustrate the completely different approach used in arriving at an expression for the energy spectrum, and, more significantly, they illustrate the very marked differences in the spectra that have been proposed. Walden presents a general comparison of the various proposed spectra and has included some observations from the German Bight. Walden also points out that for the average wave forecasting problem where one does not require an accurate spectrum there is still far too much disagreement among the several spectra available. One would suspect that the use of measured data analyzed to give energy spectra would be the most reliable. Darbyshire's spectrum is the only one to have been obtained in this manner; yet considerable disagreement seems to exist concerning some of its properties.

Neumann and Pierson in discussing certain known and unknown properties of the wave spectrum offer us a qualitative analysis of our results to date. Briefly, they have discussed our observational and instrumental techniques, the problems associated with defining the meteorological conditions and the methods of analysis, and how variations in these procedures might be expected to contribute to the diversity of our results.

The authors point out the wide range and type of instruments presently in use. This, of course, is necessary as no one instrument is suitable for all conditions. It is, however, the accuracy of the instrument under the conditions in which it is used that is of concern to us. Different measurement principles are used in the various wave-measuring instruments, and each instrument has its own characteristic frequency response. Interpretation of the data obtained from the different sources could be assisted if there were available a systematic comparison of these instruments. In the past, attempts were made to compare the results of ship-borne wave recorders installed on the *Atlantis* and another ship and those on the *Atlantis* and a wave pole. These tests were very limited as only low seas existed at the time of the tests. With the availability of *Splashnik*, I believe some very effective tests could now be made. Tests between *Splashnik* and the SBWR can readily be made under normal open-sea conditions. At a fixed platform, say Stage I of the USN Mine Defense Laboratory, a resistance wire recorder, *Splashnik*, a pressure recorder, and an inverted echo sounder could all be tested. The latter instrument should be included in these tests in view of its possible use from a submarine.

A more difficult problem stressed by Neumann and Pierson is that of a suitable definition of the meteorological conditions, i.e., fetch, duration, and wind speed, and their effect on the wave spectrum. It is pointed out in reference to the several forecasting methods, which in turn reflect different concepts in fetch and duration *vs.* wind speed, that "it is possible to propose various experiments that would, one by one, concentrate on these differences and resolve the conflicts. . . ." An experiment in progress to ascertain the effect of fetch is described. It is interesting to note that some difficulties have arisen in specifying fetch length because of operations near the New York Bight. If this experiment is to be clearly definitive, as it is hoped to be, then the proper site must be selected and sufficient time allowed so that the desired data can be obtained. Clearly defined fetches should be obtainable off the east coast of the U.S., but these sites will become rather restricted if observations in or across the Gulf Stream are to be avoided. The main current of the stream could be encountered in approximately 150 miles in a southeast direction from the New Jersey Coast.

The authors do not say how many ships will be available to make the observations in this experiment. If only one ship is available, then it would appear that the experiment may be severely restricted because of the need for very long durations, or the need to make numerous corrections for variations in wind speed and direction by means which are also not well known. Take for example the 26-knot wind with observations at 31, 85, 180, and 270 miles. Approximately 17 hours are required to develop the sea. If we assume one-half hour observations and a ship speed of 15 knots, then it will require a minimum of 20 hours additional time to complete the observations. To obtain sufficient data to verify the fetch dependence, the higher wind speeds of at least 30 knots must also be used, and the higher the wind speed, the more excessive the duration requirements become for the observations. It is true that useful information would be obtained if a single ship took only one or two observations at the extreme fetches, but for the experiment as proposed it would appear that at least two ships are required.

The experiments proposed by the authors will certainly add to our knowledge. I believe they also show our need for more truly synoptic wave data, which could be obtained if more of the North Atlantic weather ships were instrumented with the SBWR.

Mr. Schule: With regard to the problem of using the *Splashnik* to study the variation in the spectrum with fetch, I can endorse Mr. Farmer's remarks about the difficulty of doing this with one ship. At the Hydrographic Office we have been cooperating with New York University on this problem, and so far we have been able to find only two promising cases. The problem was made more difficult by the fact that the ship was at sea and therefore had to measure the spectrum for the longest fetch first. In one case the wind held quite steadily for the entire experiment, but in the other a slight wind shift was observed nearshore, which will probably detract from the validity of the data.

Dr. Pierson: I think that Dr. Farmer's remarks are quite correct. It would be nice if we had six or seven ships all in a line, all properly equipped, and all taking observations at the same time. What we did was try to accomplish something with available equipment. You don't have to fill in a particular wind speed at one time. You can fill in various parts of that table (in our paper) at different times as long as you can keep a good close watch of the meteorological situation. There is a question as to shoal water. It is a question whether the wind was off Long Island or off the New Jersey coast. The other set was a well-defined offshore wind for various fetch values.

Dr. Darbyshire: In Dr. Walden's paper he used only my 1955 spectrum and not the 1959 one. He has to some extent rectified that now. I strongly suspect though that he has used the deep sea spectrum. As his observations are in the North Sea, he should have used my shallow water spectrum. That was published also in 1959. Admittedly, he could not possibly have put in the innovations I suggested yesterday because they are too recent. He also mentioned my assumption of the saturation effects after 100 miles, but in the North Sea, with all due respect, it is not an assumption, it is an observation. I showed those slides yesterday. It might have appeared that there were only a few points on them, but they were the means of 3,000 observations.

Dr. Walden: I will try to give a short reply. We have two records of fully developed seas. The wind was from the northwest, and the wind force was so weak that we thought that the effect of the bottom would be slight. Two other spectra given here were for a very short fetch, so again the effect of the bottom would have been small.

Dr. Dorrestein: I would like to close this discussion with a few words. It is obvious that there are many discrepancies and differences of opinion among various workers. Some points may have been clarified. The final conclusions of this conference are yet to be made. I think we can say that we know very little about one-dimensional spectra as long as so many reasonably intelligent scientists can disagree with one another on so many points. We have been able to find certain laws only with a large margin of uncertainty. Because of this vagueness, we know hardly anything about several secondary effects: lapse rates, bottom depths, currents, etc.

I can repeat two main themes developed by Dr. Deacon for future research. We need better and more systematically planned observations and measurements in the field and on a model scale; and we need closer integration of theorists and experimentalists in formulating problems and their possible solutions so that the theorists can give more guidance in the planning of observations and in the design of experiments.

TWO-DIMENSIONAL

SPECTRA

G. E. R. DEACON

CHAIRMAN

M. S. LONGUET-HIGGINS

D. E. CARTWRIGHT

N. D. SMITH

O N E

OBSERVATIONS OF THE DIRECTIONAL SPECTRUM OF SEA WAVES

USING THE MOTIONS OF A FLOATING BUOY

ABSTRACT

The vertical acceleration of a floating buoy, and the two angles of pitching and rolling, can be used to determine the first five Fourier coefficients $(a_0, a_1, b_1, a_2, b_2)$ of the angular distribution of energy in each band of frequency.

From these coefficients can be found a weighted average of the directional spectrum with respect to the horizontal azimuth ϕ, and also certain useful parameters: the total spectral density $(C_{11}[\sigma])$, the mean direction of the energy $(\overline{\phi})$, the angular spread of the energy (ψ), and a parameter indicating the shape of the distribution $(I_{\min}/a_0)$.

Five complete records were analysed, corresponding to local wind speeds that ranged from 8 to 23 knots. The record with the highest wind speed (Record No. 5) fortunately corresponded to a very simple weather situation, with a well-defined fetch and constant wind direction. In this record it was found that at the higher frequencies the total spectral density tended to Phillips's limiting law, proportional to $(frequency)^{-5}$. The angular spread of the spectrum increased with the frequency. At low frequencies it approximated the "resonance" angle $\sec^{-1}(U/c)$, where U and c denote wind speed and wave speed respectively. At intermediate frequencies the angular spread was somewhat less than the resonance angle, owing probably to the growth of the waves by shear-flow instability. At the highest frequencies the angular width was again increased, owing probably to nonlinear effects.

The parameters of the spectrum were consistent with an angular distribution proportional to $\cos^{2s}(\tfrac{1}{2}\phi)$, where the parameter s varies markedly with frequency. Thus s decreases from about 4 at low frequencies to less than 1 at high frequencies. The parameters of the spectrum did not fit a "square-topped" distribution of energy so well, much less a distribution with two narrow directional bands of energy. However, the possibility of a mildly "bimodal" spectrum cannot be entirely ruled out.

The atmospheric pressure fluctuations at the sea surface were also recorded. These were generally of an order of magnitude smaller than those assumed by Phillips (1957) to exist in a turbulent air stream. Moreover, the recorded pressure fluctuations can be attributed mostly to the aerodynamic pressure changes produced by the flow of the air over the waves, together with the hydrostatic pressure changes due to the vertical displacement of the buoy. The pressure fluctuations were consistent with the cosine-power law for the angular distribution, stated above.

INTRODUCTION

The question of how the energy in sea waves is distributed with regard to direction of propagation is not only essential from the point of view of the wave forecaster, but is also of great interest because it throws light on the processes of wave generation. Very few determinations of the complete two-dimensional spectrum have been attempted. Among those hitherto published we may mention Barber's (1954) technique using an array of wave height recorders, and also the analysis of aerial stereophotographs described in the SWOP report (Chase *et al.*, 1957; Cote *et al.*, 1960). In the present paper we propose to describe some results obtained by a different method, which makes use of the recorded motions of a free-floating buoy. The method was first suggested by Barber (1946) and was developed by Longuet-Higgins (1946, 1955); the observations have been made at the National Institute of Oceanography since 1955. Simultaneously with the motions of the buoy, we have recorded the atmospheric pressure fluctuations close to the sea surface. Our present object is to describe the method and the results and to discuss them in the light of recent theories of the generation of water waves by wind.

THEORY OF THE METHOD

To a first approximation, a floating object may be regarded as performing small oscillations about a fixed point, with horizontal co-ordinates x, y and vertical co-ordinate z (measured upwards). Further, for waves sufficiently long compared with its diameter, a floating buoy will tend to have the same vertical and horizontal displacements as a particle in a free wave, and to take up the same orientation as the free surface.[1] Hence, if the motions of the buoy (i.e., vertical displacement and angles of pitching and rolling) can be recorded we shall have available the quantities

---

[1] Later on, calibrated response factors, appropriate to each wave length and frequency, are used.

$$\zeta, \frac{\partial \zeta}{\partial x}, \frac{\partial \zeta}{\partial y} \qquad (1)$$

as functions of time, where $\zeta(x, y, t)$ denotes the elevation of the free surface.

As a representation of the sea surface we may take the stochastic integral

$$\zeta = \mathcal{R} \int \int e^{i(\mathbf{k}\cdot\mathbf{x} - \sigma t)} \, d\mathbf{A}(k), \qquad (2)$$

where $\mathbf{x} = (x, y)$ and $\mathbf{k} = (k \cos \phi, k \sin \phi)$ represents a vector wave-number. To a first approximation the frequency σ satisfies the well-known relation for waves on deep water:

$$\sigma^2 = gk. \qquad (3)$$

The directional spectrum $F(\sigma, \phi)$ of the waves is defined by

$$F(\sigma, \phi) = \frac{\overline{\frac{1}{2}d\mathbf{A} \, d\mathbf{A}^*}}{d\sigma \, d\phi} \qquad (4)$$

(where a star denotes the complex conjugate, and a bar denotes the mean value). In other words, $F(\sigma, \phi)d\sigma \, d\phi$ is the contribution to the mean-square value of ζ arising from wave elements which lie in the infinitesimal ranges of frequency and direction $(\sigma, \sigma + d\sigma)$ and $(\phi, \phi + d\phi)$.[2]

Suppose then that the three quantities of (1) are denoted by ξ_1, ξ_2, ξ_3. We have

$$\left. \begin{aligned} \xi_1 &= \mathcal{R} \int \int e^{i(\mathbf{k}\cdot\mathbf{x} - \sigma t)} d\mathbf{A} \\[2mm] \xi_2 &= \mathcal{R} \int \int ik \cos \phi \, e^{i(\mathbf{k}\cdot\mathbf{x} - \sigma t)} d\mathbf{A} \\[2mm] \xi_3 &= \mathcal{R} \int \int ik \sin \phi \, e^{i(\mathbf{k}\cdot\mathbf{x} - \sigma t)} d\mathbf{A} \end{aligned} \right\} \qquad (5)$$

By numerical methods or otherwise we may form the co-spectra C_{ij} and the quadrature-spectra Q_{ij} of any pair of quantities ξ_i and ξ_j. From the definitions we have

$$\left. \begin{aligned} C_{11} &= \int_0^{2\pi} F(\sigma, \phi)d\phi \\[2mm] C_{22} &= \int_0^{2\pi} k^2 \cos^2 \phi \, F(\sigma, \phi)d\phi \\[2mm] C_{33} &= \int_0^{2\pi} k^2 \sin^2 \phi \, F(\sigma, \phi)d\phi \end{aligned} \right\} \qquad (6)$$

---

[2] In terms of the two-dimensional spectrum $E(\mathbf{k})$ used in Longuet-Higgins (1957) we have $F = k \dfrac{dk}{d\sigma} E = \dfrac{2k^2}{\sigma} E$.

and

$$C_{23} = \int_0^{2\pi} k^2 \cos \phi \sin \phi \; F(\sigma, \phi) d\phi$$

$$Q_{12} = \int_0^{2\pi} k \cos \phi \; F(\sigma, \phi) d\phi \quad \Bigg\} \quad (7)$$

$$Q_{13} = \int_0^{2\pi} k \sin \phi \; F(\sigma, \phi) d\phi$$

each of the above six quantities being a function of σ. The right-hand sides are clearly related to the Fourier coefficients

$$a_n + ib_n = \frac{1}{\pi} \int_0^{2\pi} e^{n i \phi} F(\sigma, \phi) d\phi \qquad (8)$$

of the spectrum $F(\sigma, \phi)$, and in fact

$$a_0 = \frac{1}{\pi} C_n$$

$$a_1 = \frac{1}{\pi k} Q_{12}, \quad b_1 = \frac{1}{\pi k} Q_{13} \quad \Bigg\} \quad (9)$$

$$a_2 = \frac{1}{\pi k^2} (C_{22} - C_{33}), \quad b_2 = \frac{2}{\pi k^2} C_{23}$$

We can therefore obtain from the motions of the buoy, *the first five Fourier coefficients* of the angular distribution of energy and thus the first five terms of the series

$$F(\sigma, \phi) = \tfrac{1}{2} a_0 + (a_1 \cos \phi + b_1 \sin \phi)$$
$$+ (a_2 \cos 2\phi + b_2 \sin 2\phi)$$
$$+ \dots . \qquad (10)$$

From ζ, $\partial \zeta / \partial x$, and $\partial \zeta / \partial y$ it is not possible to get higher coefficients, but more terms could be obtained if quantities such as $\partial^2 \zeta / \partial x^2$, $\partial^2 \zeta / \partial x \, \partial y$, etc., could be measured.[3]

What then can be done with this amount of information? In the first place we can form the partial Fourier sum

$$F_1(\sigma, \phi) = \tfrac{1}{2} a_0 + (a_1 \cos \phi + b_1 \sin \phi)$$
$$+ (a_2 \cos 2\phi + b_2 \sin 2\phi). \qquad (11)$$

This may be a fair approximation to the infinite series (Equation 10) provided that terms of higher order are relatively small. On the other hand, substitution for a_0, a_1, b_1, a_2, b_2 in Equation 11 shows that

---

[3] An experimental program to measure the second derivatives of ζ is in progress.

$$F_1(\sigma, \phi) = \frac{1}{2\pi} \int_0^{2\pi} F(\sigma, \phi') W_1(\phi' - \phi) d\phi' \qquad (12)$$

where

$$W_1 = 1 + 2 \cos (\phi' - \phi) + 2 \cos 2(\phi' - \phi)$$
$$= \frac{\sin \frac{5}{2}(\phi' - \phi)}{\sin \frac{1}{2}(\phi' - \phi)} \qquad (13)$$

In other words, the partial sum $F_1(\sigma, \phi)$ is the smoothed average of the actual distribution $F(\sigma, \phi)$ by the weighting function $W_1(\phi' - \phi)$. Since W_1 can be negative, it is possible that F_1 may be negative too, whereas $F(\sigma, \phi)$ itself is essentially positive. One may therefore prefer, as in the present paper, to take an alternative approximation to $F(\sigma, \phi)$, namely

$$F_3(\sigma, \phi) = \tfrac{1}{2} a_0 + \tfrac{2}{3}(a_1 \cos \phi + b_1 \sin \phi)$$
$$+ \tfrac{1}{6}(a_2 \cos 2\phi + b_2 \sin 2\phi) \qquad (14)$$

which corresponds to the weighted average of $F(\sigma, \phi)$ by the weighting function

$$W_3 = 1 + \tfrac{4}{3} \cos (\phi' - \phi) + \tfrac{1}{3} \cos 2(\phi' - \phi)$$
$$= \tfrac{8}{3} \cos^4 \tfrac{1}{2}(\phi' - \phi) \qquad (15)$$

W_3 is not only non-negative but is also a decreasing function of $|\phi' - \phi|$. Other weighting functions are of course possible; which particular function one chooses is to some extent a matter of taste, since each of the averages $F_i(\sigma, \phi)$ is a weighted average of each of the others.

Apart from the weighted averages just mentioned, the first five coefficients a_0, a_1, b_1, a_2, b_2 can be used to provide some useful and significant parameters of the spectrum $F(\sigma, \phi)$. The simplest of these is a_0 itself, which measures the total energy per unit of frequency, summed over all possible directions.

Second, as a measure of the directional properties at each frequency we may define the two angles ϕ_1 and ϕ_2 which "best" fit the distribution, in the following sense. Consider the integral

$$I = \frac{1}{2\pi} \int_0^{2\pi} 16 \sin^2 \frac{\phi - \phi_1}{2} \sin^2 \frac{\phi - \phi_2}{2} \; F(\sigma, \phi) d\phi$$
$$(16)$$

where ϕ_1 and ϕ_2 are any angles. I may easily be expressed in terms of ϕ_1, ϕ_2 and the five known coefficients a_0, a_1, b_1, a_2, b_2. We now choose ϕ_1 and ϕ_2 so as to make I a minimum.

This definition is clearly appropriate in the extreme case when swell is coming from two direc-

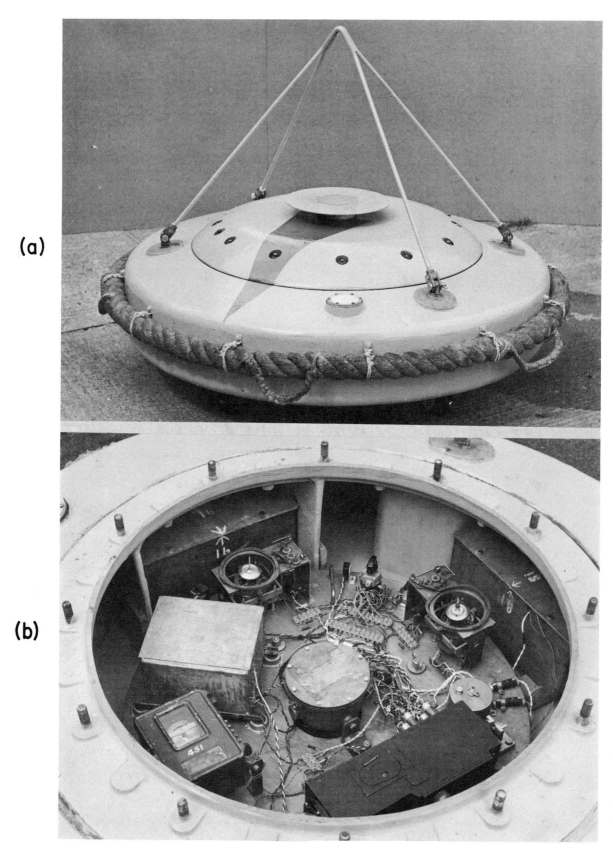

Figure 3-1-1. (a) *Exterior view of the wave recording buoy;*
(b) *The instrument panel.*

tions only, say α_1 and α_2. For then $I/a_0 = 0$ only if ϕ_1, ϕ_2 coincide with α_1, α_2; if ϕ_1, ϕ_2 do not coincide with α_1, α_2, then I/a_0 is positive, since there is a positive contribution to the integral at $\phi = \alpha_1$, α_2, and the integrand is never negative.

In a more general case, when $F(\sigma, \phi)$ has a continuous distribution, the two "best" angles ϕ_1, ϕ_2 still have a useful significance. For if the spectrum is not too broad, the mean value

$$\overline{\phi} = \tfrac{1}{2}(\phi_1 + \phi_2) \qquad (17)$$

approximates the mean direction of energy in the spectrum, and the half-difference

$$\psi = \tfrac{1}{2}|\phi_1 - \phi_2| \qquad (18)$$

is a measure of the angular width of the spectrum. It is shown in the Appendix that ψ is approximately equal to the r.m.s. angular deviation of the energy from the mean direction.

Last, if $I_{\min}$ is the minimum value of I (corresponding to the two "best" angles ϕ_1 and ϕ_2), then $I_{\min}/a_0$ is an indicator of the *shape* of the distribution $F(\sigma, \phi)$. For example, very small values of $I_{\min}/a_0$ would indicate that the energy was concentrated near two directions α_1, α_2 at most. In the Appendix it is shown that in general $I_{\min}/a_0$ is related to the fourth moment of the angular distribution of energy about the mean.

Formulae for calculating ϕ_1, ϕ_2, and $I_{\min}/a_0$ in terms of the known coefficients a_0, a_1, b_1, a_2, b_2 are given in the Appendix.

APPARATUS

A general view of the buoy is shown in Figure 3-1-1. The frame is an aluminium alloy casting, of horizontal diameter 5'6'', which when loaded floats in water up to the top of the vertical rim. It is surrounded by a stout hemp fender. The four-legged hoisting gear is secured at the base by four steel pins, which can quickly be removed. Inside the buoy (Figure 3-1-1(b)) can be seen the instrument panel. In the center is an accelerometer of a design similar to that used in the shipborne wave recorder (Tucker, 1952, 1956). The working part of the accelerometer is mounted on gymbals so that it tends to take up an orientation in line with the vector acceleration plus gravity. Since the water surface also tends to do just this, the accelerometer remains practically fixed relative to the buoy.

The electrical output from the accelerometer is integrated twice electronically before being re-

corded. (The integrating circuits are contained in the metal box nearest the accelerometer.) All recording was done by the 12-channel galvanometer-recording camera seen in the foreground.

Two gyroscopes for measuring angles of pitch and roll can be seen on the far side of the instrument board. Each is center-seeking with a time constant of about 6 minutes. The other instruments on the panel are time switches for making time marks on the record and for automatic operation of the equipment over predetermined intervals. The batteries are seen surrounding the instrument panel.

To record atmospheric pressure a very sensitive condenser-type microbarograph was built very similar to that described, for example, by Baird and Banwell (1948). For modifications to the interior design and to the accompanying electronic circuits we are indebted to Mr. R. Dobson and Mr. M. J. Tucker. The microbarograph and its electronics were situated in the lid of the buoy (see Figure 3-1-1(a)) and access to the atmosphere was through 12 small orifices (diameter 0.04 inch). To prevent sea water from blocking the instrument, a series of precautions was taken: the openings were raised 2.4 inches above the surface of the buoy (Figure 3-1-1(a)); the orifices themselves were surrounded by small heating elements (dissipating 5 watts per coil) so as to evaporate any spray blocking the passages (the time taken to clear any hole was a fraction of a second); the passages to the microbarograph were designed so that liquid penetrating the orifices was drained off into a drip-can beneath the instrument; and last, the passages were surrounded by dessicators. Together these arrangements proved effective.

To keep the buoy in a constant alignment relative to the wind, a drogue and pellet were attached, as in Figure 3-1-2. So far as could be judged from visual observation, the orientation of the buoy remained quite constant during any period of observation.

Figure 3-1-2. *Arrangement for aligning the buoy with the wind.*

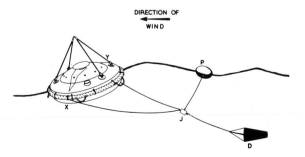

DIRECTION OF
WIND

Both the microbarograph and the integrated acceleration possessed phase and amplitude characteristics dependent upon frequency, which were measured in the laboratory. The buoy itself, because of its finite dimensions, had a varying response at the higher frequencies. Calibration of the heaving and pitching motions of the buoy relative to the elevation and slope of the waves in the absence of the buoy was carried out for us in the 1200-ft. wave tank at the Ship Hydrodynamics Laboratory (National Physical Laboratory). The calibrations covered the range $2.1 < \sigma < 4.5$ radians/sec. and indicated a "resonance" at around $\sigma = 4.0$ radians/sec. in both heave and pitch. However, because of the high damping, the amplitude response factors did not differ much from unity whenever $\sigma \geq 3.5$ radians/sec. All the response factors have been allowed for in the subsequent determination of the frequency spectra.

TREATMENT OF THE DATA

Out of 16 records obtained during 1955 and 1956, 5 were selected as being apparently free of faults over continuous stretches of time lasting 12 minutes or more. The corresponding positions, dates, and times, together with local wind speeds and directions as measured by the ship's anemometer, are given below in Table 1. It will be seen that conditions ranged from light winds (8 knots) to a fairly constant wind of force 6 (23 knots); this was near the limit for safe launching and recovery of the buoy. Charts showing the synoptic weather situations at about the times of recording are shown in Figure 3-1-3.

A typical record of the outputs from the two gyroscopes, the accelerometer (after integration), and the microbarograph is reproduced in Figure 3-1-4. Each of the four traces was digitised (manually) at intervals of approximately 0.5 sec., so that the records, 12–17 minutes long, contained about 2,000 sets of readings each. These were

stored on punched cards. The computation of the co-spectra and quadrature-spectra, which was carried out on the *Deuce* at the Royal Aircraft Establishment at Farnborough, was similar to that described by Blackman and Tukey (1958). A standard program computed the mean variance and auto- and cross-correlations of two given series of observations, with a total number of "lags" between 57 and 66. Another program was then used to compute the Fourier sine- and cosine-transforms, and the result was smoothed by consecutive weighting factors $\frac{1}{4}, \frac{1}{2}, \frac{1}{4}$.

The numerical results showed that the spectral density dropped to negligible values beyond $\sigma = 5$ radians/sec. confirming that the sampling interval was small enough not to introduce "aliasing" difficulties. Full calculations, however, were made only up to $\sigma = 4$ radians/sec., owing to the response characteristics of the buoy.

Finally, to allow for "noise" introduced by errors in reading the traces, a small constant was subtracted from each auto-spectrum. The errors were easily estimated by repeating a few digital conversions and corresponded to a standard error of about $1\frac{1}{2}$ units in 1,000 (about 0.2 mm. of the original film record).

Consideration was given to possible correction of the spectra for nonlinear effects. Tick (1958) has estimated the second-order correction to a uni-directional spectrum to allow for nonlinear terms in the boundary conditions at the free surface. The correction consists mainly of a superposed spectrum, largest in the region of frequencies double those of the largest waves. A rough calculation of the correction to $C_{11}(\sigma)$ for Record No. 5 (corresponding to the steepest waves) showed it to be small—about 10 per cent of C_{11} at $\sigma = 2$ to 3 radians/sec. Such corrections were therefore ignored. The corrections for non-verticality of the accelerometer (Tucker, 1959) were appreciable only at low frequencies, for $\sigma < 0.4$ radians/sec., and similarly for the second-order corrections to slope. Since these corrections are

TABLE 1

DATA CONCERNING WAVE RECORDS

	Number of record	Date	Time (G.M.T.)	Position		Wind speed and direction (ship's anemometer)
Cruise I	1	31.5.55	0915-0935	41°08′N	14°37′W	19 kts. from 340°
	2	31.5.55	1435-1455	41°08′N	14°37′W	14 kts. from 350°
	3	3.6.55	0910-0930	39°16′N	11°53′W	17 kts. from 320°
Cruise II	4	30.10.56	1450-1510	50°58′N	12°15′W	8 kts. from 080°
	5	1.11.56	1525-1545	50°19′N	11°54′W	23 kts. from 065°

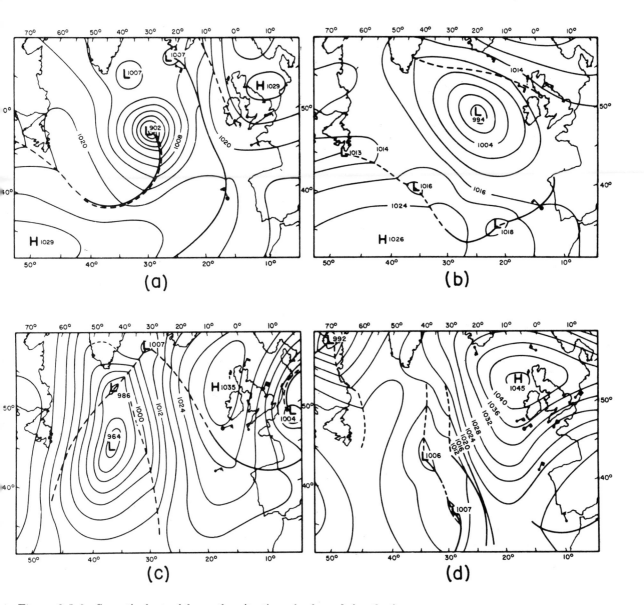

Figure 3-1-3. *Synoptic charts of the weather situation a few hours before the times of recording.   The position of the ship is marked by a full circle ● .*

    (a) **0001**   G.M.T., **31.5.55;**
    (b) **0001**   G.M.T., **3.6.55;**
    (c) **0001**   G.M.T., **30.10.56;**
    (d) **0001**   G.M.T., **1.11.56;**

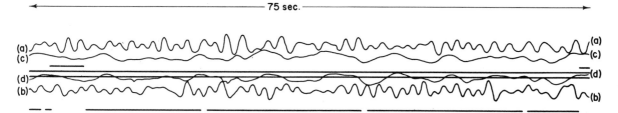

Figure 3-1-4. *A typical length of film record, showing the traces of the four measured quantities:*

    (a) *angle of pitch;*
    (b) *angle of roll;*
    (c) *twice-integrated vertical acceleration;*
    (d) *atmospheric pressure.*

PERCENTAGE OF
ORDINATES

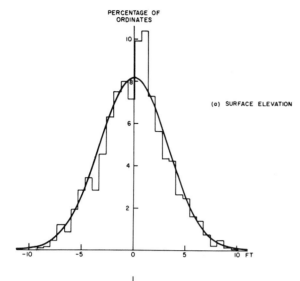

(a) SURFACE ELEVATION

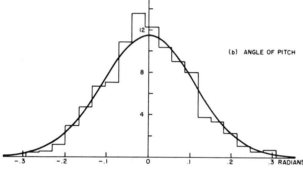

(b) ANGLE OF PITCH

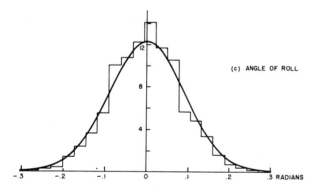

(c) ANGLE OF ROLL

Figure 3-1-5. *Histograms of the film traces, for record No. 5 (wind speed 23 knots).*
(a) Heave; (b) Pitch; (c) Roll.

proportional to the square of the first-order spectra, they must be even smaller for records other than No. 5. They were not investigated further.

A further indication of the linearity of the waves was afforded by a comparison of the observed distributions of height and slope with the theoretical Gaussian distributions. The histograms for Record 5 (the highest wind speed) are shown in Figure 3-1-5. Visually the data fit the Gaussian curves fairly well, though a χ^2-test based on the total number of observations (2,000) in each record does in fact give probabilities well below the 1 per cent significance level in each case.

RESULTS

The total variances of the wave elevation ζ and of the two components of slope $\partial\zeta/\partial x$, $\partial\zeta/\partial y$, in the frequency range $0.4 \leq \sigma \leq 4.0$ radians/sec., are listed in Table 2.

In only one case, Record No. 5, were the waves sufficiently free from external swell for the wave height to be directly related to the local wind speed. In that case the wind speed was $V = 23$ knots over a well-defined fetch of 300 miles. The observed r.m.s. elevation of 2.6 ft. may be compared with the value 2.8 ft. given by the empirical formula $\sqrt{\{0.121(V/10)^5\}}$ of Pierson, Neumann and James (1955) and 2.2 ft. given by the formula $0.00405V^2$ of Darbyshire (1959).

The variances of the surface slopes, which depend chiefly upon the shorter waves, have been plotted against local wind speed in Figure 3-1-6. As was found by Cox and Munk (1954, 1956), the variances increase about proportionally to the wind speed. However, the actual values for the total variance are only about 20 per cent of those suggested by Cox and Munk's optical method (0.053 radians^2 at 10 m/sec.). This presumably is because most of the slope variance is contributed by waves of frequency σ greater than 4.0 radians/sec.

TABLE 2
VARIANCES OF WAVE HEIGHTS AND SLOPES

Number of record	Wave height (ft²)	Angle of roll (deg² x 10²)	Angle of pitch (deg² x 10²)	Total angle (deg² x 10²)	Ratio of angular variances
1	1.92	2.80	3.25	6.1	1.16
2	2.09	2.34	3.65	6.0	1.56
3	2.33	1.95	3.83	5.8	1.97
4	2.03	1.82	2.24	4.1	1.23
5	6.58	4.19	7.81	12.0	1.86

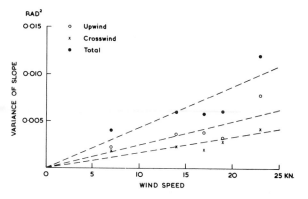

Figure 3-1-6. *Variances of surface slope:*
(a) up-wind; (b) cross-wind; (c) total.

The frequency spectra of the surface elevation (regardless of direction) are shown in Figure 3-1-7 (i) to (v). Both the scales are logarithmic. In each of the figures a straight line has been inserted corresponding to Phillips' (1958a) limiting spectrum[1]

$$C_{11}(\sigma) = Cg^2\sigma^{-5}, \qquad (19)$$

---

[1] Phillips' (1958a) uses $\Phi(\sigma)$, equivalent to $\frac{1}{2} C_{11}(\sigma)$.

with the constant $C = 14.8 \times 10^{-3}$ chosen to fit Burling's (1955) data. It will be seen that the nearest approach to this spectrum is in Record 5, corresponding to the highest wind speed.

We come now to the directional properties of the spectra. For each of the five records, the "smoothed" spectra $F_3(\sigma, \phi)$, defined by equation (15), have been computed, and these are shown in Figure 3-1-8.

The weather charts in Figure 3-1-3 show that the mean directions in each frequency band do in fact correspond fairly closely to the directions of the winds expected to generate the waves ($\phi = 0$ corresponds to the local wind. In Records 1, 2, and 4, and to a lesser extent in Record 3 there is some change in the mean direction with frequency. In Record 5 the mean direction is practically constant between $\sigma = 0.6$ and 3.6, and this corresponded to a situation in which the wind was in a steady direction from the ENE with little possibility of interfering swell. On the other hand, in Records 1 and 2 there is evidence of secondary maxima in the spectrum (necessarily smoothed out by the weighting function W_3), which can be shown to correspond to swell from different wind systems.

Figure 3-1-7. *Frequency spectra of surface elevation.*

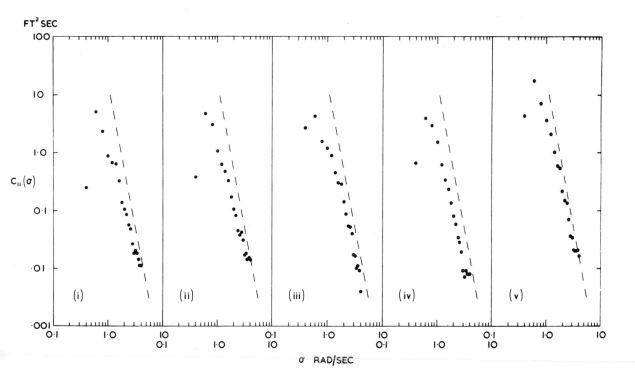

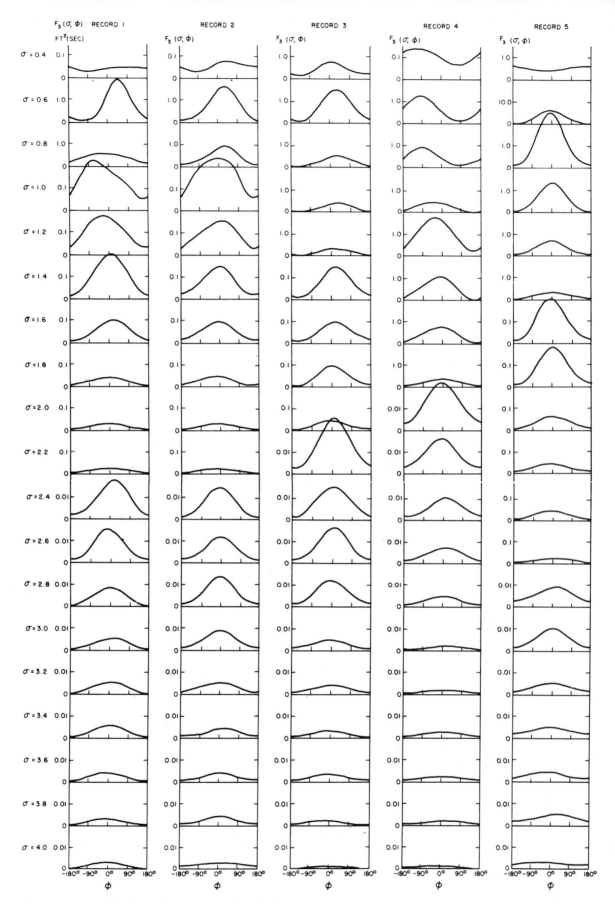

Figure 3-1-8. *Smoothed estimates of the directional spectrum.*
[*Note added in proof: In Record 4, σ = 1·2 r_σ 1·8, the vertical scale shoud be 0.1*]

ANGULAR WIDTH OF THE SPECTRUM

The angle ψ defined in Section 2 has been plotted in Figure 3-1-9 as a function of the ratio U_1/c, where U_1 is the reference wind velocity, defined on page 123, and $c = g/\sigma$ is the speed of the waves of frequency σ. Only those data from Records 3 and 5 have been used in which the wind direction was practically constant over the region of wave generation.

If we neglect the two observations at $\sigma = 0.4$, which may be influenced by external swell, it appears that the angle ψ increases as the ratio U_1/c increases; in other words, that the angular width of the spectrum increases with the ratio of wind speed to wave speed.

The curves inserted in Figure 3-1-9 are discussed below (page 124).

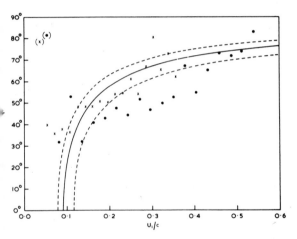

Figure 3-1-9. *Observations of the angular width* ψ. $\times$ = *Record 3;* $\bullet$ = *Record 5.*

COMPARISON WITH THE SWOP RESULTS

An exact comparison with the results obtained by the stereographic method of Chase *et al.* (1957) is not possible, since an instantaneous stereophotograph does not in principle distinguish opposite directions in the spectrum. Hence, the stereographic method is unable, without some further assumption, to yield the coefficients a_n, b_n corresponding to *odd* harmonics of the angular distribution of energy. In face of this situation, Chase *et al.* have assumed $F(\sigma, \phi)$ to be zero when ϕ differs by more than 90 degrees from the wind direction — an assumption which we prefer not to make. It follows that any comparison of our data

with the SWOP data must be carried out through the harmonics a_n, b_n of *even* order.

One suitable parameter for this purpose can be defined as follows. Let

$$m_2(\sigma, \phi') = \int_0^{2\pi} \sin^2(\phi - \phi') F(\sigma, \phi)d\phi \qquad (20)$$

denote the second moment of the distribution of energy about the direction ϕ'. In terms of the Fourier coefficients,

$$m_2(\sigma, \phi') \propto a_0 - (a_2 \cos 2\phi' + b_2 \sin 2\phi') \qquad (21)$$

The maximum and minimum values of this function are $a_0 \pm \sqrt{a_2^2 + b_2^2}$, and they occur in two pairs of directions, mutually at right angles. A measure of the angular spread of the spectrum in the frequency band $(\sigma, \sigma + d\sigma)$ is, therefore,

$$\gamma(\sigma) = \left[\frac{(m_2)_{\min}}{(m_2)_{\max}}\right]^{1/2} = \left[\frac{a_0 - \sqrt{a_2^2 + b_2^2}}{a_0 + \sqrt{a_2^2 + b_2^2}}\right]^{1/2} \qquad (22)$$

When the spectrum is narrow, it can be shown that $\gamma(\sigma)$ is almost equal to the r.m.s. angular deviation of energy in the spectrum.

To fit the SWOP data, Chase *et al.* have suggested the empirical formula

$$F(\sigma, \phi) = P(\sigma) \times \begin{cases} 1 + [0.50 + 0.82Q(\sigma)] \cos 2\phi \\ \qquad\qquad + 0.32Q(\sigma) \cos 4\phi, \\ \qquad\qquad\qquad |\phi| < \dfrac{\pi}{2}, \quad (23) \\ \\ 0, \quad |\phi| > \dfrac{\pi}{2}, \end{cases}$$

where

$$Q(\sigma) = e^{-1/2(\sigma V/g)^4} \qquad (24)$$

and $P(\sigma)$ is another function of σ and V only. According to this formula we should have

$$a_2 = 0.25 + 0.41Q(\sigma), \quad b_2 = 0, \qquad (25)$$

and so

$$\gamma(\sigma) = \left[\frac{0.75 - 0.41Q(\sigma)}{1.25 + 0.41Q(\sigma)}\right]^{1/2} \qquad (26)$$

The theoretical curve is shown in Figure 3-1-10 together with our observed results. It will be seen that our results are not inconsistent with the SWOP curve.

SHAPE OF THE SPECTRUM

It was seen in Section 2 above that an indicator of the shape of the spectrum is the ratio $I_{\min}/a_0$.

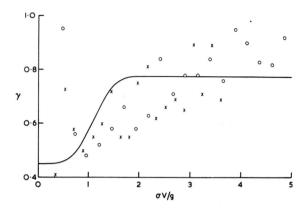

Figure 3-1-10. *Observations of ψ (σ), compared with the SWOP curve. $\times$ = Record 3; $\bullet$ = Record 5.*

In Figure 3-1-11 this ratio has been plotted against the corresponding angular half-width ψ for the two Records 3 and 5 for which the wind system was simplest (from this point of view greater weight should be given to Record 5, the data for which are indicated by circles).

For comparison, we have plotted in the same figure the values of I_{min}/a_0 and ψ corresponding to some very simple distributions.

Figure 3-1-11. *$I_{min}./a_o$ plotted against ψ. $\times$ = Record 3; $\bullet$ = Record 5.*

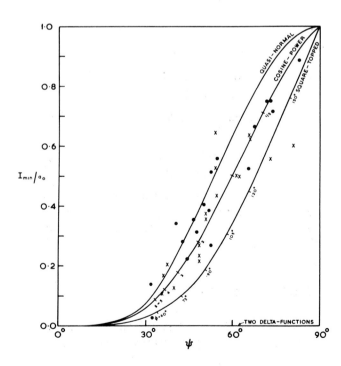

(1) The line drawn along the ψ-axis corresponds to an idealised distribution consisting of (at most) two narrow bands of long-crested waves:

$$F(\sigma, \phi) \propto \delta(\phi - \alpha_1) + \delta(\phi - \alpha_2). \quad (27)$$

For such a distribution we have seen that I_{min}/a_0 vanishes.

(2) The lowest of the three curves corresponds to a "square-topped" angular distribution of given width $2\phi_0$:

$$F(\sigma, \phi) \propto \begin{cases} 1, & |\phi| < \phi_0 \\ 0, & |\phi| > \phi_0 \end{cases} \quad (28)$$

(The given values of ϕ_0 are indicated along the curve.)

(3) The middle continuous curve corresponds to the cosine-power distribution

$$F(\sigma, \phi) \propto (1 + \cos \phi)^s \propto \cos^{2s}(\tfrac{1}{2}\phi) \quad (29)$$

for which

$$\frac{a_n}{a_0} = \frac{s(s - 1) \ldots (s - n + 1)}{(s + 1)(s + 2) \ldots (s + n)} \quad (30)$$

(The value of the parameter s is indicated along the curve.) When $s = 0$, then the distribution is independent of ϕ, and as s increases, the distributions become more and more concentrated about the mean direction $\phi = 0$. When s is large, the distributions are approximately normal, with angular variance equal to $(2/s)$ radians².

Figure 3-1-12. *Closest values of the parameter s corresponding to the plotted points of Fig. 3-1-11 (data from Record 5).*

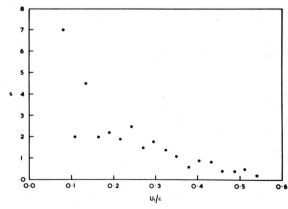

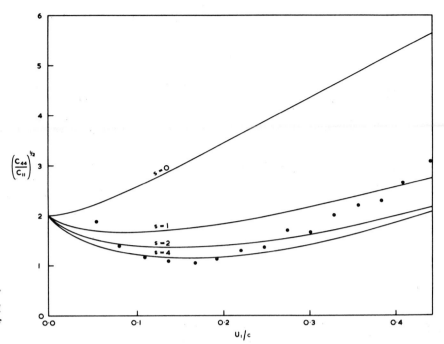

Figure 3-1-13. *Values of* $(C_{44}/C_{11})^{1/2}$, *giving ratio of spectral densities of pressure (in ft. of air) and surface elevation.*

(4) The upper continuous curve corresponds to the "quasi-normal" distribution

$$F(\sigma, \phi) \propto e^{-2\Delta^{-2} \sin^2 \phi/2} \qquad (31)$$

which when Δ is small also approximates a normal distribution. For this distribution it is found that

$$\frac{a_n}{a_0} = \frac{I_n(\Delta^{-2})}{I_0(\Delta^{-2})} \qquad (32)$$

where $I_n(z)$ is the Bessel function of imaginary argument.

Of the four laws considered, it appears that the cosine-power (28) is the best fit to the observations. For each observation, a corresponding value of s may be allotted by taking the point on the "cosine-power" curve nearest to the observation. The values of s so obtained have been plotted in Figure 3-1-12 against the value of U_1/c for each observation. It will be seen that in general s is a decreasing function of U_1/c.

THE PRESSURE FLUCTUATIONS

From the typical length of record shown in Figure 3-1-4 it will be seen that the trace of atmospheric pressure has a general tendency to follow the trace of surface elevation; and when the spectra of the pressure fluctuations were computed

they were found to be very similar in general to the spectra of surface elevation. Figure 3-1-13 gives the *ratio* of the spectral density of pressure (units are feet of air) to the spectral density of surface elevation in the typical case of Record 5. The theoretical curves drawn in the same figure are based on the discussion given below.

DISCUSSION OF RESULTS

We propose now to discuss our results relating to the angular distribution of energy in the light of what is known or conjectured about the processes of wave generation by wind.

In the first place, we need some estimate of the wind profile. Observations at sea (Roll, 1948; Hay, 1955) appear to support a logarithmic form for the mean wind velocity U, in conditions of neutral stability:

$$U = U_1 \log_e \left(\frac{z}{z_0}\right) \qquad (33)$$

where U_1 and z_0 are constants. We have

$$U_1 = \frac{U_*}{K} \qquad (34)$$

where U_* is the friction velocity ($= \sqrt{\tau_0/\rho_a}$) and K is von Karman's constant ($\doteq 0.41$). U_* may, in turn, be expressed in terms of the "anemometer wind speed" U_a by

$$U_*^2 = c_D U_a^2, \tag{35}$$

where c_D is a drag coefficient. Sheppard (1958) quotes the empirical formula

$$c_D = (0.08 + 0.00114 U_a) \times 10^{-3},$$
$$U_a \text{ in cm/sec.} \tag{36}$$

U_a will be identified with the measured wind speed V, so that

$$U_1 = \frac{c_D^{1/2}}{K} U_a \tag{37}$$

is of order $V/10$.

On dimensional grounds, Charnock (1955) has suggested that

$$z_0 = \frac{U_*^2}{ga} \tag{38}$$

where a is a constant. Not all observations give a consistent value of a, but Hay's (1955) data support a value of around 13 (see Ellison, 1956). Miles (1957) has introduced the parameter

$$\Omega = \frac{gz_0}{U_1^2} = \frac{gz_0 K^2}{U_*^2} = \frac{K^2}{a}, \tag{39}$$

whose value is thus about 1.3×10^{-2}; but it may well vary by a factor of 2. Since surface waves of length $2\pi/k$ must travel with almost the free-wave velocity $c = (g/k)^{1/2}$, it follows that (33) can be written

$$\frac{U}{c} = \frac{U_1}{c} \log_e \left(\frac{kz}{\Omega(U_1/c)^2} \right), \tag{40}$$

the right-hand side being a function only of kz, U_1/c, and Ω.

THE RESONANCE ANGLE

At the present time, two kinds of mechanism for the transfer of energy to water waves from the atmosphere are under active discussion. On the one hand, the effect of pressure fluctuations (associated with atmospheric turbulence) acting on the surface of the water has been considered by Phillips (1957, 1958b). According to Phillips' original hypothesis, the spectrum of the water surface in the principal stage of development would be given by[1]

---

[1] Phillips' $\Phi(k, t)$ is equivalent to $2F(\sigma, \phi) \dfrac{d\sigma \, d\phi}{k \, dk \, d\phi}$, that is to say, to $(g/\sigma k)F$. Our $\Pi(\mathbf{k}, t)$ is the same as his.

$$F(\sigma, \phi) = \frac{k^2 \sigma t}{2(g\rho_w)^2} \int_0^\infty \Pi(\mathbf{k}, \tau)$$
$$\cos \left[\left(\frac{U \cos \phi}{c} - 1 \right) \sigma\tau \right] d\tau, \tag{41}$$

where t denotes the time since the wind started to blow, $\Pi(\mathbf{k}, \tau)$ is the pressure spectrum, defined by Phillips, and U is the "convection velocity" of the eddies of wavenumber $\mathbf{k}$. This velocity is probably not very different from the mean wind speed at a height above the surface of order $2\pi/k$. Phillips pointed out that if the pressure spectrum is reasonably isotropic, the integral on the right-hand side of (41) is likely to be greatest when

$$U \cos \phi = c \tag{42}$$

in other words, when the component of the wind velocity in the direction of propagation is just equal to the wave speed. This may be called the resonance condition, and the corresponding angle

$$\phi = \sec^{-1} \frac{U}{c} \tag{43}$$

may be called the resonance angle.

Let us assume that the convection velocity, as defined by Phillips (1957), can be identified with the mean velocity U at a height $z = 2\pi/k$. Writing $kz = 2\pi$ in Equation (9.40), we have

$$\phi = \sec^{-1} \left[\frac{U_1}{c} \left(\log \frac{2\pi}{\Omega} - 2 \log \frac{U_1}{c} \right) \right] \tag{44}$$

If we were to take the velocity at a different height, say π/k, this would be equivalent to a change in the assumed value of Ω by a factor 2.

We have calculated the angle ϕ corresponding to (43) taking, for definiteness, $\Omega = 1.3 \times 10^{-2}$; the result is indicated by the full curve in Figure 3-1-9. The lower broken curve shows the effect of taking a value of Ω five times greater than this, and the upper curve the effect of taking Ω five times less.

Two conclusions are obvious. In the first place, the value of the resonance angle ϕ depends only slightly on the parameters of the logarithmic profile, and second, the angle ψ does indeed show a trend similar to the resonance angle.

On the other hand, Miles (1957, 1959) has considered the growth of an air-water interfacial disturbance as an instability in the shearing flow of the air, or rather, of the combined air-water system. An input of energy into the waves is brought about (according to this model) by a coupling of the surface pressure fluctuations to the already existing waves. Assuming that the airflow may be treated as a small perturbation of the mean wind profile (so that the perturbed potential satisfies the Orr-Sommerfeld equation) and that the mean profile is logarithmic, Miles has computed values for the rate of growth of the waves which are in substantial agreement with observation.

More recently (1960) Miles has combined his mechanism with that of Phillips, in such a way that the turbulent pressure fluctuations in the airstream appear as the means of initiating the waves, which are then augmented by the instability of the shear flow. Thus, in place of (41) Miles proposes a more general equation (4.5a)[1] which we rewrite as follows:

$$F(\sigma, \phi) = \frac{k^2 \sigma t}{2(g\rho_w)^2} \, \mathcal{F}(MT) \int_0^\infty \Pi(\mathbf{k}, t)$$
$$\cos\left[\left(\frac{U \cos \phi}{c} - 1\right) \sigma t\right] dt, \quad (45)$$

where

$$M = \frac{\rho_a}{\rho_w}\left(\frac{U_1 \cos \phi}{c}\right)^2 \frac{U_1}{c} \beta,$$
$$(46)$$
$$T = \frac{gt}{U_1}$$

and

$$\mathcal{F}(MT) = \frac{e^{MT} - 1}{MT} \quad (47)$$

Here β is a dimensionless coefficient which has been computed by Miles (1959). For small values of T, and so for small values of MT, the function $\mathcal{F}(MT)$ tends to 1, and equation (45) tends to (41). Initially, therefore, the Phillips spectrum is applicable. However, as t increases, MT may become large, and $\mathcal{F}(MT)$ exponentially large. In that case, if (45) is still valid, the function $\mathcal{F}(MT)$ represents a factor by which the original spectrum F is distorted. Since M depends upon the direction of propagation ϕ, so also does $\mathcal{F}(MT)$.

Using Miles' values of β, and taking as before $\Omega = 1.3 \times 10^{-2}$, we have computed M as a function of ϕ for various values of U_1/c (see Figure 3-1-14). From this graph it is fairly simple to compute $\mathcal{F}(MT)$ for any given record, if T is known. For Record 5, for example, we have taken

$$U_a = 23\mathrm{kn} = 1,180 \text{ cm/sec}$$

---

[1] Compare Phillips (1960).

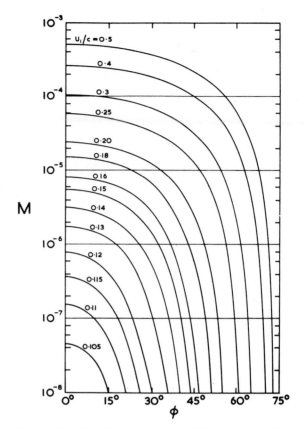

Figure 3-1-14. *M as a function of the angle ϕ, (taking $\Omega = 1.3 \times 10^{-2}$).*

$$c_D = (0.08 + 0.00114U_a) \times 10^{-3}$$
$$= 2.15 \times 10^{-3}$$

$$U_1 = \frac{c_D^{1/2}}{K} U_a = 134 \text{ cm/sec}$$

$$\frac{U_1}{c} = \frac{\sigma U_1}{g} = 0.136\sigma \quad (\sigma \text{ in radians/sec})$$

According to the weather charts, the length of time since the wind began to blow was about 45 hours. However, the fetch L being limited to 300 miles, the spectrum at the lower frequencies is limited by fetch. We have taken $t \leq L \div$ group velocity $= 2\sigma L/g$, and so

$$T = \frac{gt}{U_1} = \min\left\{\begin{array}{l} 0.72 \times 10^5 \sigma \\ 1.28 \times 10^5 \end{array}\right.$$

With these values, the factor $\mathcal{F}(MT)$ is as shown in Figure 3-1-15.

The most striking feature of the figure is the very large amplification factors involved, especially at the higher frequencies. These, however, need not be taken literally, for we saw in Section 5

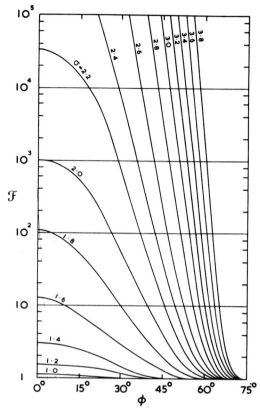

Figure 3-1-15. *Curves of the distortion factor $\mathcal{F}$ as a function of angle ϕ, for Record No. 5.*

that at the higher frequencies ($\sigma > 2.0$ radians/sec) the total spectrum approaches Phillips' equilibrium law; this indicates that nonlinear effects associated with breaking of the waves are predominant, and a linear theory would no longer apply. Nevertheless, at some of the lower frequencies ($1.3 < \sigma < 2.0$) it would appear that the effect of Miles' coupled mechanism would be to narrow somewhat the angular distribution of energy. Referring again to Figure 3-1-9, we have apparent confirmation of this, since in the range $0.15 < U_1/c < 0.4$ (i.e., $1.1 < \sigma < 3.0$) the angular width of the spectrum for Record 5 is somewhat less than the resonance angle.

On this interpretation then, the sequence of events would be as follows: in the first stage of development of the waves, exemplified by the range $\sigma < 1.1$ in Record 5, the waves are due mainly to uncoupled turbulent pressure fluctuations in the air. At a later stage, exemplified by the range $1.3 < \sigma < 2.0$, the shear-flow instability mechanism takes over, and this has the effect of reducing the r.m.s. angular width of the spectrum in any given frequency band from the value indi-

cated by the resonance angle. Finally the spectrum is limited by breaking of the waves, and it would appear from Figure 3-1-9 that there is some associated broadening of the directional spectrum. This also can be understood from Figure 3-1-15, for if $\mathcal{F}$ is limited by nonlinear effects to a certain value, say 10^3, it will be seen that the higher the frequency the broader is the angular spread of $\mathcal{F}$. This is quite apart from any broadening of the spectrum that may be due to breaking and other nonlinear effects.

INTERPRETATION OF THE PRESSURE FLUCTUATIONS

In his original paper (1957) Phillips assumed a value for the m.s. turbulent pressure fluctuations in the air equal to

$$\overline{p^2} = 9 \times 10^{-2} \rho_a^2 U_a^4 \qquad (48)$$

where U_a denotes anemometer wind speed. This is equivalent to

$$\overline{\left(\frac{p}{g\rho_a}\right)^2} = \frac{0.09 U_a^4}{g^2} \qquad (49)$$

In Table 3 the above value is compared with the mean-square values actually observed in Records 1–5. The comparison confirms what had been suspected by both Phillips (1958b) and Miles (1960), namely that the pressure fluctuations are generally smaller than those originally assumed in Phillips (1957).

TABLE 3
VARIANCES OF THE ATMOSPHERIC PRESSURE
FLUCTUATIONS

Record No.	U_a (ft./sec.)	$\dfrac{0.09 U_a^4}{g^2}$ (ft.²)	$\overline{\left(\dfrac{p}{g\rho_a}\right)^2}$ (ft.²)
1	32	91	7.3
2	24	29	8.2
3	29	62	5.2
4	14	3	9.8
5	39	203	13.1

Moreover, we shall now show that a substantial part of the observed pressure fluctuations can be attributed simply to the flow of air over the undulating surface of the sea.

In Miles' (1957, 1959) model the aerodynamical pressure exerted on a sinusoidal boundary

$$\zeta = \mathcal{R}ae^{i(kx - \sigma t)} \qquad (50)$$

by an airstream in the direction of wave propagation has the form

$$p = \mathcal{R}(\alpha + i\beta)\rho_a U_1^2 \, k\zeta, \qquad (51)$$

where α and β are real, non-dimensional quantities depending on the wind profile. To (51) we must add the static pressure term $-g\rho_a\zeta$. Thus, the total pressure measured by an apparatus floating in the surface is

$$p = \mathcal{R}\left\{-g\rho_a\zeta\left[1 - (\alpha + i\beta)\left(\frac{U_1}{c}\right)^2\right]\right\} \quad (52)$$

The phase lag χ of the pressure relative to the surface depression $-\zeta$ is given by

$$\chi = \tan^{-1}\frac{\beta(U_1/c)^2}{1 - \alpha(U_1/c)^2} \qquad (53)$$

From the numerical values given by Miles (1959) for the logarithmic profile we have computed χ (see Figure 3-1-16)[1]. It appears that over the range $0 < U_1/c < 0.5$ the phase-angle does not exceed 0.35, $= \cos^{-1}(0.94)$. Hence, the amplitude of the pressure fluctuation is due almost entirely to the in-phase component of the pressure:

$$\left|\frac{p}{g\rho_a\zeta}\right| \doteq 1 - \alpha\left(\frac{U_1}{c}\right)^2, \qquad (54)$$

with an error of at most 6 per cent.

---

[1] Miles' Figure 6 gives the angle $\tan^{-1}(-\beta/\alpha)$.

Figure 3-1-16. *The theoretical phase-angle χ between the surface depression, on Miles's shear-flow model.*

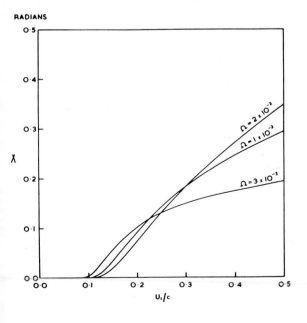

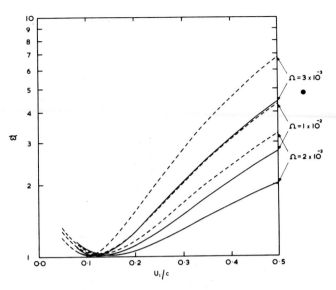

Figure 3-1-17. *The theoretical in-phase component of the pressure: ——— according to Miles (1959); ------ approximation from Brooke Benjamin (1959).*

We have computed the right-hand side of (54) (denoted by ϖ) from the numerical values given by Miles (1959), and the results are shown in Figure 3-1-17 for representative values of Ω. It will be seen that ϖ has a minimum at around $U_1/c = 0.11$, that is, at around $U_a/c = 1$.

The behaviour of ϖ can be understood if we consider the well-known Kelvin-Helmholtz model in which the wind profile is assumed to be vertical: the velocity U is constant. In that case (see Lamb, 1932, p. 370) it is easily found that

$$\varpi = 1 + [(U/c) - 1]^2 \qquad (55)$$

which is clearly a minimum when $U = c$, that is to say, when the wind speed just equals the phase velocity of the waves.

More generally, Brooke-Benjamin (1959) has shown that an approximation to the in-phase component of the pressure is given by

$$\varpi_1 = 1 + \int_0^\infty [(U/c) - 1]^2 \, e^{k\eta} d(k\eta) \qquad (56)$$

(we have added the statical term), where η is a co-ordinate orthogonal to the free surface. On substituting for U from Equation (40) and replacing z by η, we find on evaluating the integral

$$\varpi_1 = 1 + \frac{\pi^2}{6}\left(\frac{U_1}{c}\right)^2 + \left[\frac{U_1}{c}\log_e \frac{\gamma\Omega U_1^2}{c^2} + 1\right]^2 \quad (57)$$

where $\gamma = \exp(0.5772\ldots)$. The curves for ϖ_1 have been plotted in Figure 3-1-17 for comparison with Miles' numerical results. It will be seen that ϖ_1 somewhat exceeds ϖ but that the general behaviour of ϖ and ϖ_1 is very similar.

Consider now the more general case of a sine-wave travelling at an arbitrary angle ϕ relative to the wind. By Squire's theorem (cf. Lin, 1955, C. 3), the component of the wind parallel to the crests has no effect on the pressure perturbations, which may thus be calculated as though the mean wind-field were equal to $U\cos\phi$ in the direction of wave propagation. Returning to (40), we see that the effective wind profile $U\cos\phi$ remains logarithmic; but to maintain the *form* of the results the parameter Ω must be multiplied by $\sec^2\phi$. Since the dependence of ϖ upon ϕ cannot be readily expressed analytically,[1] we use as an approximation Equation (57), generalised to arbitrary directions of propagation; that is to say

$$\varpi \doteq 1 + \frac{\pi^2}{6}\left(\frac{U_1\cos\phi}{c}\right)^2$$
$$+ \left[\frac{U_1\cos\phi}{c}\log\frac{\gamma\Omega U_1^2}{c^2} + 1\right]^2 . \quad (58)$$

Let the right-hand side of (58) be denoted by $\varpi(\sigma, \phi)$. We see that the spectrum of the pressure (in square feet of air) is then

$$C_{44}(\sigma) = \int_0^{2\pi} \varpi^2 F(\sigma, \phi)\,d\phi; \quad (59)$$

and since ϖ^2 involves only the fourth power of $\cos\phi$, $C_{44}(\sigma)$ may be expressed in terms of the coefficients a_n, b_n up to $n = 4$. On division by

$$C_{11}(\sigma) = \int_0^{2\pi} F(\sigma, \phi)\,d\phi = \pi a_0, \quad (60)$$

we have the ratio C_{44}/C_{11} in terms of a_n/a_0 and b_n/a_0 up to $n = 4$. In particular for a symmetrical spectrum ($b_n = 0$) we find

$$\frac{C_{44}}{C_{11}} = 4 + 8P\frac{a_1}{a_0} + (4P^2 + 2Q^2)\left(1 + \frac{a_2}{a_0}\right)$$

---

[1] And in any case the numerical values of α and β may be sensitive to actual departures from the logarithmic wind profile.

$$+ P(P^2 + Q^2)\left(3\frac{a_1}{a_0} + \frac{a_3}{a_0}\right)$$
$$+ \frac{1}{8}(P^2 + Q^2)^2\left(3 + 4\frac{a_2}{a_0} + \frac{a_4}{a_0}\right) \quad (61)$$

where

$$P = \frac{U_1}{c}\log\frac{\gamma\Omega U_1^2}{c^2}, \quad Q = \frac{\pi^2}{6}\left(\frac{U_1}{c}\right)^2 \quad (62)$$

The curves drawn in Figure 3-1-14 illustrate the ratio $(C_{44}/C_{11})^{1/2}$ computed for the cosine-law spectrum (29). The (constant) values of U_1 and Ω are those appropriate to the data of Record 5. It appears that the behaviour of the observations (a minimum at around $U_1/c = 0.11$), corresponds quite well with the behaviour of the theoretical curves. It should be borne in mind that at larger values of U_1/c the theoretical curves may be somewhat high, since ϖ_1 generally exceeds ϖ. Nevertheless, there is qualitative agreement even in this part of the range of U_1/c. Moreover, there is a tendency for the equivalent value of s to diminish with U_1/c, as shown independently in Figure 3-1-13.

From this comparison it appears that the greater part of the pressure fluctuations at the surface are simply the aerodynamical pressure changes due to the flow of air over the undulating surface, together with the statical pressure changes arising from the buoy's vertical displacement.

Confirmation is provided by considering the phase differences between the pressure and the surface elevation. If the pressure fluctuations were due only to uncoupled turbulence, there would be no definite phase relation between p and ζ. If, however, the pressure fluctuations are due mainly to the local shear flow and not to the turbulence, then from Figure 3-1-16 we expect the phase-differences between p and $-\zeta$ to be small.

Owing to uncertainties in the phase calibrations of the microbarograph, the accelerometer and its integrating circuit, and of the heaving motion of the buoy, the phases could be determined only to within about 10 degrees for $\sigma < 3.0$, and within wider limits at higher frequencies. The estimated phase differences are shown in Table 4.

It will be seen that over the most energetic part of the spectrum, p and ζ are about 180 degrees out of phase. (However, for $\sigma > 3.0$ the angles cannot be relied upon.) From this evidence it would seem that more than 90 per cent of pressure spectrum is coupled to the waves, and less than 10 per cent is associated directly with turbulence.

TABLE 4
PHASE LAG OF PRESSURE BEHIND WAVE HEIGHT
(RECORD 5)

σ (radians/sec.)	Phase lag on film	Instrumental corrections	Corrected phase lag
0.4	214°	−50°	164°
0.6	220	−36	184
0.8	210	−30	180
1.0	209	−26	183
1.2	207	−24	183
1.4	207	−23	184
1.6	210	−22	188
1.8	202	−22	180
2.0	205	−22	183
2.2	206	−22	184
2.4	213	−22	191
2.6	211	−22	189
2.8	197	−23	174
3.0	230	−23	207
3.2	224	−22	202
3.4	221	−13	208
3.6	222	+14	236
3.8	221	38	259
4.0	225	86	311

It appears then that the mean-square pressure fluctuations originally assumed by Phillips may be in error by a factor of the order of 10^2. This would invalidate Phillips' formulae (1957, p. 442) for the mean-square surface displacement after time t. On the other hand, we have seen that over much of the spectrum Miles' instability mechanism is probably responsible for much of the wave growth. If Miles' more general expression for the wave spectrum (Equation 45) is used, a reduction in the estimated turbulent pressure fluctuations by the amount indicated is not inconsistent with the observed wave spectrum.

APPENDIX: *Calculation of the "Best" Angles*

It is shown in Longuet-Higgins (1955) that to minimise the integral of Equation (16) in this paper, the angles ϕ_1 and ϕ_2 must be roots of the quadratic

$$S_0 e^{2i\phi} - S_1 e^{i\phi} + S_2 = 0 \qquad (63)$$

whose coefficients S_0, S_1, S_2 satisfy

$$\left.\begin{aligned}
(a_0 - I)S_0 - (a_1 + ib_1)S_1 + (a_2 + ib_2)S_2 &= 0 \\
(a_1 - ib_1)S_0 - a_0 S_1 + (a_1 + ib_1)S_2 &= 0 \\
(a_2 - ib_2)S_0 - (a_1 + ib_1)S_1 + (a_0 - I)S_2 &= 0
\end{aligned}\right\} \quad (64)$$

The value of I is found from the condition that the simultaneous equations (64) shall be consistent, that is, that the determinant of the coefficients shall vanish. Thus,

$$\Delta_0 I^2 - 2\Delta_1 I + \Delta_2 = 0 \qquad (65)$$

where Δ_N denotes the determinant

$$\Delta_N = \begin{vmatrix}
a_0 & a_1 + ib_1 & \cdots & a_N + ib_N \\
a_1 - ib_1 & a_0 & & a_{N-1} + ib_{N-1} \\
\cdot & \cdot & & \cdot \\
\cdot & \cdot & & \cdot \\
\cdot & \cdot & & \cdot \\
a_N - ib_N & a_{N-1} - ib_{N-1} & \cdots & a_0
\end{vmatrix} \qquad (66)$$

The lower root of (65) gives the minimum value of I.

In terms of real quantities we have

$$I = \frac{1}{a_0}[(a_0^2 - a_1^2 - b_1^2) - \sqrt{(\mathscr{P}^2 + \mathscr{Q}^2)}], \quad (67)$$

where

$$\begin{aligned}
\mathscr{P} &= a_0 a_2 - a_1^2 + b_1^2 \\
\mathscr{Q} &= a_0 a_2 - 2a_1 b_1
\end{aligned} \qquad (68)$$

and so

$$a_0 - I = \frac{1}{a_0}[(a_1^2 + b_1^2) + \sqrt{(\mathscr{P}^2 + \mathscr{Q}^2)}]. \quad (69)$$

To find ϕ_1 and ϕ_2 we note that in Equations (63) and (64) only the ratios $S_0 : S_1 : S_2$ are relevant. So we may take S_1 to be real, and then the first and third of Equations (64) show that S_0 and S_2 are conjugate complex quantities. So writing

$$S_0 : S_1 : S_2 = e^{-i\vartheta} : r : e^{i\vartheta}, \qquad (70)$$

we have

$$\left.\begin{aligned}
(a_0 - I + a_2)\cos\vartheta - b_2\sin\vartheta - a_1 r &= 0 \\
b_2\cos\vartheta - (a_0 - I - a_1)\sin\vartheta - b_1 r &= 0
\end{aligned}\right\}, \quad (71)$$

and so

$$\frac{\cos\vartheta}{X} = \frac{\sin\vartheta}{Y} = \frac{r}{Z}, \qquad (72)$$

where

$$\left.\begin{aligned}
X &= (a_0 - I)a_1 - (a_1 a_2 + b_1 b_2) \\
Y &= (a_0 - I)b_1 - (a_1 b_2 - a_2 b_1) \\
Z &= (a_0 - I)^2 - (a_2^2 + b_2^2)
\end{aligned}\right\} \quad (73)$$

or

$$\cos \vartheta = \frac{X}{\sqrt{(X^2 + Y^2)}}, \quad \sin \vartheta = \frac{Y}{\sqrt{(X^2 + Y^2)}},$$

$$r = \frac{Z}{\sqrt{(X^2 + Y^2)}} \qquad (74)$$

From (63) and (70), the product of the roots is given by

$$e^{i(\phi_1 + \phi_2)} = \frac{S_2}{S_0} = e^{-2i\vartheta}. \qquad (75)$$

Thus,

$$\bar{\phi} = \tfrac{1}{2}(\phi_1 + \phi_2) = \vartheta, \qquad (76)$$

where ϑ is given by (74). Further,

$$\phi_1, \phi_2 = \vartheta \pm \chi, \qquad (77)$$

where from (63)

$$e^{i\chi} - r + e^{i\chi} = 0 \qquad (78)$$

or

$$\cos \chi = \frac{1}{2} r = \frac{\tfrac{1}{2}Z}{\sqrt{(X^2 + Y^2)}}. \qquad (79)$$

This is the required general expression.

A Symmetrical Spectrum

The most interesting special case is when the spectrum is symmetrical about one particular direction, say $\phi = 0$. Then b_1 and b_2 are both zero, and Equation (67) reduces to

$$I = \frac{1}{a_0} [(a_0^2 - a_1^2) - |a_0 a_2 - a_1^2|]. \qquad (80)$$

Two cases now arise, corresponding to whether $(a_0 a_2 - a_1^2)$ is positive or negative. Examples may be given of both. Thus, if $F(\sigma, \phi)$ consists of two equal delta functions at $\phi = 0$ and π (corresponding to "standing" waves), then

$$a_0 : a_1 : a_2 = 1 : 0 : 1 \qquad (81)$$

and so

$$(a_0 a_2 - a_1^2) > 0 \qquad (82)$$

If, on the other hand, $F(\sigma, \phi)$ consists of two delta functions at arbitrary angles $\phi = \pm \alpha$ on either side of the mean direction, we have

$$a_0 : a_1 : a_2 = 1 : \cos \alpha : \cos 2\alpha \qquad (83)$$

and so

$$(a_0 a_2 - a_1^2) \propto -\sin^2 \alpha < 0. \qquad (84)$$

In all the practical cases met in this paper we have $(a_0 a_2 - a_1^2) < 0$, and so from (80)

$$I = \frac{1}{a_0} (a_0^2 - 2a_1^2 + a_0 a_2). \qquad (85)$$

The formulae for $\bar{\phi}$ and χ then reduce simply to

$$\bar{\phi} = 0, \quad \chi = \cos^{-1} \frac{a_1}{a_0}. \qquad (86)$$

Interpretation of χ and I_{min}/a_0

From (86),

$$\sin^2 \frac{1}{2} \psi = \frac{1}{2} (1 - \cos \psi) = \frac{a_0 - a_1}{2a_0}. \qquad (87)$$

But on expressing a_0 and a_1 as Fourier coefficients, we have

$$a_0 - a_1 = \frac{1}{\pi} \int_0^{2\pi} (1 - \cos \phi) F(\sigma, \phi) \, d\phi$$

$$= \frac{1}{\pi} \int_0^{2\pi} 2 \sin^2 \frac{1}{2} \phi \, F(\sigma, \phi) \, d\phi \qquad (88)$$

Suppose now that the distribution $F(\sigma, \phi)$ is fairly narrow, that is to say that the direction of most of the energy is not widely different from the mean direction. Then in (88) $\sin \frac{1}{2} \phi$ may be replaced by $\frac{1}{2} \phi$; and if we define the rth angular moment of the distribution by

$$m_r = \int_0^{2\pi} \phi^r F(\sigma, \phi) d\phi \qquad (89)$$

it is apparent that

$$a_0 - a_1 \doteq \frac{1}{2\pi} m_2. \qquad (90)$$

But also

$$a_0 = \frac{1}{\pi} m_0 \qquad (91)$$

so from (87)

$$\sin^2 \tfrac{1}{2} \psi = \frac{m_2}{4m_0}. \qquad (92)$$

But this is small by hypothesis so the l.h.s. can be replaced by $\frac{1}{4}\psi^2$. Hence,

$$\psi^2 \doteq \frac{m_2}{m_0} \qquad (93)$$

In other words ψ equals the r.m.s. angular deviation of energy from the mean direction.

In a similar way we have from (85)

$$Ia_0 = a_0^2 - 2a_1^2 + a_0 a_2$$

$$= \frac{1}{\pi^2} \int\int \left[1 - 2\cos\phi\cos\phi' \right.$$
$$\left. + \frac{1}{2}(\cos 2\phi + \cos 2\phi') \right]$$
$$\times F(\sigma, \phi)F(\sigma, \phi')d\phi \, d\phi'$$
$$= \frac{4}{\pi^2} \int\int \left(\sin^2\frac{1}{2}\phi - \sin^2\frac{1}{2}\phi' \right)^2$$
$$F(\sigma, \phi)F(\sigma, \phi')d\phi \, d\phi' \quad (94)$$

an exact formula. Again, if the energy is not too broadly distributed in direction, then

$$Ia_0 \doteqdot \frac{1}{4\pi^2} \int\int (\phi^2 - \phi'^2)^2 F(\sigma, \phi)F(\sigma, \phi')d\phi \, d\phi'$$
$$= \frac{1}{2\pi^2}(m_0 m_4 - m_2^2) \quad (95)$$

Hence,

$$\frac{I}{a_0} \doteqdot \frac{m_0 m_4 - m_2^2}{m_0^2} \quad (96)$$

However, since (96) involves the fourth moment m_4 this approximation will generally be less accurate than (92), which involves only m_0 and m_2.

For very narrow spectra the ratio

$$\frac{2I}{a_0 \psi^4} \doteqdot \frac{m_0 m_4 - m_2^2}{m_2^2} \quad (97)$$

is an indicator of the "peakedness" of the energy distribution with regard to direction. Thus, for a normal distribution of energy with regard to ϕ this ratio takes the value 2; for a "square-topped" distribution it is $\frac{4}{5}$; and for two isolated delta-functions it is theoretically zero. However, for most forms of $F(\sigma, \phi)$ the approximation (97) will be accurate to within 10 per cent only if ψ is less than about 30 degrees.

* * *

ACKNOWLEDGMENTS

We would like to acknowledge our debt to the Ship Hydrodynamics Laboratory, Feltham, for calibrating the motions of the buoy; to the Royal Aircraft Establishment, Farnborough, for allowing us generous use of their *Deuce* computer; and to many members of the National Institute of Oceanography. In particular, the design and construction of the buoy itself, apart from the instruments, were carried out by Mr. F. E. Pierce. We are indebted to the Captain and crew of R.R.S. Discovery II for expert handling of both the ship and the buoy in rough weather. Finally we are grateful to Dr. O. M. Phillips, Professor J. W. Miles and Professor L. N. Howard for useful discussions based on a preliminary report.

REFERENCES

Baird, H. F., and C. J. Banwell (1940): "Recording of Air Pressure Oscillations Associated with Microseisms at Christchurch." *N.Z.J.Sci. Tech.*, **21** B: 314–329.

Barber, N. F. (1946). *Measurements of Sea Conditions by the Motion of a Floating Buoy.* Admiralty Res. Lab. Report 103.40/N.2/W, Teddington (bound as one of *Four Theoretical Notes on the Estimation of Sea Conditions*, by M. S. Longuet-Higgins and N. F. Barber, 1946).

Barber, N. F. (1954): "Finding the Direction of Travel of Sea Waves." *Nature*, **174**: 1048–1050.

Barber, N. F., and D. Doyle (1956): "A Method of Recording the Direction of Travel of Ocean Swell." *Deep-Sea Res.*, **3**: 206–213.

Blackman, R. B., and J. W. Tukey (1958): *The Measurement of Power Spectra.* Dover Publ., New York, 190 pp.

Brooke-Benjamin, T. (1959): "Shearing Flow Over a Wavy Boundary." *J. Fl. Mech.*, **6**: 161–205.

Burling, R. W. (1955): "Wind Generation of Waves on Water." Ph.D. Thesis, University of London.

Charnock, H. (1955): "Wind Stress on a Water Surface." *Quart. J. Roy. Met. Soc.*, **81**: 639–642.

Chase, J., *et al.* (1957): *The Directional Spectrum of a Wind-Generated Sea as Determined from Data Obtained by the Stereo Wave Observation Project.* New York U., Coll. Eng. Report, July, 1957.

Cote, L. J., *et al.* (1960): (title as in preceding reference). *Met. Pap.*, New York U., Coll. Eng. **2**: No. 6.

Cox, C., and W. Munk (1954): "Statistics of the Sea Surface Derived from Sun Glitter." *J. Mar. Res.*, **13**: 198–227.

Cox, C., and W. Munk (1956): "Slopes of the Sea Surface Deduced from Photographs of Sun Glitter." *Bull. Scripps Inst. Oceanogr.*, **6**: 401–488.

Darbyshire, J. (1959): "A Further Investigation of Wind-Generated Gravity Waves." *Deut. Hydr. Zeitschr.*, **12**: 1–13.

Ellison, T. H. (1956): "Atmospheric Turbulence." *Surveys in Mechanics*, Cambridge U. P., pp. 400–430.

Hay, J. S. (1955): "Some Observations of Air Flow Over the Sea." *Quart. J. Roy. Met. Soc.*, **81**: 307–319.

Lamb, H. (1932): *Hydrodynamics* (6th ed.), Dover Publ., New York.

Longuet-Higgins, M. S. (1946): *Measurement of Sea Conditions by the Motion of a Floating Buoy. Detection of Predominant Groups of Swell.* Admiralty Res. Lab. Report 103.40/N5.

Longuet-Higgins, M. S. (1955): "Bounds for the Integral of a Non-Negative Function in Terms of its Fourier Coefficients." *Proc. Camb. Phil. Soc.*, **51**: 590–603.

Longuet-Higgins, M. S. (1957): "The Statistical Analysis of a Random, Moving Surface." *Phil. Trans. Roy. Soc.*, A, **249**: 321–387.

Miles, J. W. (1957): "On the Generation of Surface Waves by Shear Flows." *J. Fl. Mech.*, **3**: 185–204.

Miles, J. W. (1959): "On the Generation of Surface Waves by Shear Flows," (Part 2). *J. Fl. Mech.*, **6**: 568–582.

Miles, J. W. (1960): "On the Generation of Surface Waves by Turbulent Shear Flows." *J. Fl. Mech.*, **7**: 469–478.

Phillips, O. M. (1957): "On the Generation of Waves by Turbulent Wind." *J. Fl. Mech.*, **2**: 417–445.

Phillips, O. M. (1958a): "The Equilibrium Range in the Spectrum of Wind-Generated Waves." *J. Fl. Mech.*, **4**: 426–434.

Phillips, O. M. (1958b): "On Some Properties of the Spectrum of Wind-Generated Ocean Waves." *J. Mar. Res.*, **16**: 231–245.

Phillips, O. M. (1960): "Resonance Phenomena in Gravity Waves." *Proc. Am. Math. Soc. Symposium on Hydrodynamic Instability and Related Problems, New York, April, 1960.* pp. 91–103.

Lin, C. C. (1955): *The Theory of Hydrodynamic Stability.* Cambridge U. P., 155 pp.

Pierson, W. J., G. Neumann and R. W. James (1955): *Practical Methods for Observing and Forecasting Ocean Waves by Means of Wave Spectra and Statistics.* U. S. Navy Hydrogr. Off. Pub. 603, 284 + xx pp.

Roll, H. U. (1948): "Wassernahes Windprofil und Wellen auf dem Wattenmeer." *Ann. Met.*, **1**: 139–151.

Sheppard, P. A. (1958): "Transfer Across the Earth's Surface and Through the Air Above." *Quart. J. Roy. Met. Soc.*, **84**: 205–224.

Tick. L. J. (1958): *A Non-Linear Model of Gravity Waves 1.* New York U., Coll. of Eng. Tech. Report 10.

Tucker, M. J. (1952): "A Wave-Recorder for Use in Ships." *Nature*, **170**: 657–659

Tucker, M. J. (1956): "A Shipborne Wave Recorder." *Trans. Instn. Naval Architects*, **98**: 236–250.

Tucker, M. J. (1959): "The Accuracy of Wave Measurements Made with Vertical Accelerometers." *Deep-Sea Res.*, **5**: 185–192.

DISCUSSION

Dr. Hasselmann: I should like to congratulate the authors for their most interesting and original measurements. On one point, however, I feel there may be some danger of a misunderstanding.

The high correlation observed between the pressure p and the surface elevation ζ implies a small correlation between p and the normal surface velocity $\dot{\zeta}$, as ζ and $\dot{\zeta}$ are orthogonal random variables. Unfortunately, it is the small mean product $\overline{p\dot{\zeta}}$, i.e., the work done by the pressure forces, which determines the rate of wave growth, and only the spectral analysis of this term can yield direct insight into the mechanism of wave generation by pressure forces. The authors, however, restricted their analysis to the mean prod-

uct $\overline{p\zeta}$, apparently because the instrumental error was too great to determine $\overline{p\dot{\zeta}}$ with sufficient accuracy. As a result the information gained from the pressure measurements, though interesting in itself, is irrelevant to the question of wave generation.

Nor do the pressure measurements alone yield *indirect* evidence as to whether an internal instability mechanism or external turbulent pressure fluctuations are responsible for wave growth.

The fact that Miles' instability theory predicts $\overline{p\zeta}$ correctly does not imply that $\overline{p\dot{\zeta}}$ is also predicted correctly, since all models, if worth considering at all (e.g., the Kelvin-Helmholtz model, Jeffries sheltering theory, etc.), give reasonably correct results for the first order term $\overline{p\zeta}$ but can differ considerably in the crucial second order term $\overline{p\dot{\zeta}}$.

Furthermore, the fact that the observed mean square turbulent pressure fluctuations $\overline{p_t^2}$ are considerably smaller than originally assumed by Phillips does not imply that the resulting wave growth is also correspondingly smaller than Phillips' original estimate, as Phillips' derivation of the rate of wave growth from $\overline{p_t^2}$ was based on an incorrect assumption. This can best be seen by writing Phillips' formula for the wave growth in a different form.

If the three-dimensional spectrum of the turbulent pressure fluctuations $\overset{\wedge}{\pi}(\mathbf{k}, \omega)$ in $\mathbf{k} \times \omega$-space is introduced, Phillips' formula becomes simply

$$E(\mathbf{k}) = \frac{\pi k t}{\rho^2 g} \overset{\wedge}{\pi}(\mathbf{k}, - \sigma), \qquad (98)$$

where $E(\mathbf{k})$ is Longuet-Higgins (1957) spectrum and $\sigma = \sqrt{gk}$. According to Equation (98), the growth of $E(\mathbf{k})$ is determined by the spectral density of the pressure fluctuations on the "resonance surface" $\omega + \sqrt{gk} = 0$ in $\mathbf{k} \times \omega$-space, corresponding to pressure fluctuations $dP(\mathbf{k}, - \sigma)$ exp $[i(\mathbf{kx}) - i\sigma t]$ in resonance with free gravity waves. Now the pressure fluctuations $dP(\mathbf{k}, \omega)$ exp $[i(\mathbf{kx}) + i\omega t]$ will generally have phase velocities in wind direction approximately equal to the "local convection velocity" $U(k)$. In other words, the spectral density $\overset{\wedge}{\pi}(\mathbf{k}, \omega)$ will be concentrated mainly around the "local convection surface" $\omega + kU \cos \phi = 0$, where ϕ is the angle between $\mathbf{k}$ and the wind direction. We shall, therefore, expect the spectral density $\overset{\wedge}{\pi}(\mathbf{k}, - \sigma)$ in Equation (1) to have a maximum on the curve of intersection of the "resonance" and "local convection" surfaces, i.e., for wave-numbers corresponding to free gravity waves with phase velocities equal to the wind velocity (see Figure 3-D-1). Phillips, however, assumed that the pressure fluctuations corresponding to these very low wave-numbers would be negligible (except for very light winds) and that $\overset{\wedge}{\pi}(\mathbf{k}, - \sigma)$ is appreciable only in the region of small wave-numbers well away from the "local convection" surface, corresponding to phase velocities considerably smaller than the wind velocity. In the derivation following, Phillips then equated a differential time scale with an integral time scale, arguing that both would be of the same order of magnitude. Although the assumption appeared reasonable in Phillips' formulation,

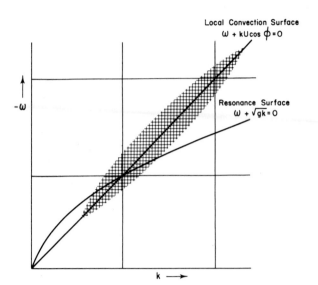

Figure 3-D-1. *Local convection and resonance curves for fixed ϕ, $U(k)$ constant (Kelvin-Helmholtz model).*

it can now immediately be seen that it is in fact incorrect, the two time scales describing completely independent properties of the pressure spectrum. The integral time scale determines in effect the pressure density $\overset{\wedge}{\pi}(\mathbf{k}, - \sigma)$ away from the "local convection" surface and is thus a measure of the *spread* of $\overset{\wedge}{\pi}(\mathbf{k}, \omega)$ on both sides of the maximal surface, i.e., of the degree to which Taylor's hypothesis (that fluctuating components can be considered as "frozen waves" being convected by the local mean velocity) does *not* hold. The differential time scale, on the other hand, is simply the fluctuation period of a point on the "local convection" surface as seen from a system moving with the phase velocity of the corresponding point with the same wave number on the "resonance" surface. As a characteristic time scale it is thus based on Taylor's hypothesis and is independent of the degree of accuracy of the hypothesis.

The order of magnitude of wave generation by turbulent pressure fluctuations is thus still an open question. It appears probable that the mechanism will be effectively mainly, if at all, for longer waves moving with phase velocities approximately equal to the wind velocity. This view is supported by the fact that despite the small instability of these waves (for waves with phase velocities greater than the wind velocity most instability theories predict damping rather than instability), the observed fully-developed spectra always show a pronounced peak for wave-numbers corresponding to these waves. However, the energy loss of long waves is small, so that only relatively small generating forces need be involved and further observations will be necessary in order to determine the relative importance of the two proposed generating mechanisms in this wave-number region. For shorter waves, the expected increase in instability and decrease in turbulent-pressure excitation, together with the observed strongly exponential growth of shorter waves as discussed by Phillips in the session on one-dimensional spectra all point to the predominance of an instability mechanism.

It should be emphasized, however, that our concepts of wave generation by pressure forces are still based entirely on indirect arguments and that it has not yet been possible to obtain further hints as to which generating mechanism is most effective for which wave-number region by direct pressure measurements. This, of course, does not imply that the pressure measurements described by the authors are not valuable and will not perhaps later yield a useful estimate of the order of magnitude of Phillips' pressure term, for example, when more is known about the distribution of the three-dimensional pressure spectrum.

Dr. Longuet-Higgins (in reply to Dr. Hasselmann's comments): We are grateful to Dr. Hasselmann for clarifying certain points in our paper. We agree that the approximations involved in the later part of Phillips' 1957 paper cannot be relied upon and hence that the observed low value for the turbulent pressure fluctuations are not themselves conclusive evidence against the turbulence theory. However, our reasons for thinking that shear-flow instability is responsible for the greater part of the wave energy are based not so much on the pressure fluctuations but on the observed angular distribution of energy, as discussed in Section IX of our paper (on pp. 124–126). The pressure measurements in Section X are quoted only as being *consistent* with this hypothesis.

We would like to emphasize that Phillips' expression for the spectrum (our Equation 41) and Miles' corresponding expression (our Equation 45) do not depend for their validity upon the approximations discussed by Dr. Hasselmann; in (41) there is no approximation involving the equality of integral and differential time-scales. Nevertheless, it is still probable that the integral in (41) is a maximum with regard to ϕ, when $\cos \phi = c/U$. Hence, the discussion in Section IX of our paper is not affected.

Certainly we would like to have measured $\overline{p\dot{\zeta}}$; but the accuracy of our observations did not allow us to do this except to verify that it was reasonably small.

A claim to have measured $\overline{p\dot{\zeta}}$ directly was made by A. G. Kolesnikov at the Helsinki meeting of the U.G.G.I. last August. We have not seen the details of Kolesnikov's work.

Dr. Phillips: The stability analysis should, I think, provide us with estimates of these two quantities. Certainly $\overline{p\dot{\zeta}}$ is the one you would really like to know from the point of view of wave generation. However, if the other quantities given by the stability analysis and the experiments indicate that this is about the right order of magnitude, isn't it reasonable to say that this fact alone, although not a direct confirmation, gives us reason to believe that this is on the right track?

Dr. Barber: I only have to say how much I admire the way in which this is being put into practice and brought to a working state. My own experiments lead me to appreciate the great difference between thinking of ways in which an experiment might be done and actually doing it.

In the discussion it does strike me — and this was an outcome of some comments by Dr. Cartwright on my own paper — that the buoy can determine the number of waves of a particular frequency. Of course, we know what the wave number is, or at least we think we do; but it would be nice if the buoy actually did measure the wave number and I rather think it does.

Dr. Longuet-Higgins: Yes. One of the things that we did was to see whether the frequency wave number relationship, as measured by the buoy's motion, was in agreement with the theoretical relation

$$\sigma^2 = gk$$

In the case of a continuous spectrum the relation analogous to this is

$$C_{22} + C_{33} = k^2 C_{11}$$

So the ratio

$$k = \frac{g}{\sigma^2} \left(\frac{C_{22} + C_{33}}{C_{11}} \right)^{1/2}$$

equals unity. We calculated this ratio and I would have shown it, if the paper had not been rather long already. I have left it until the dis-

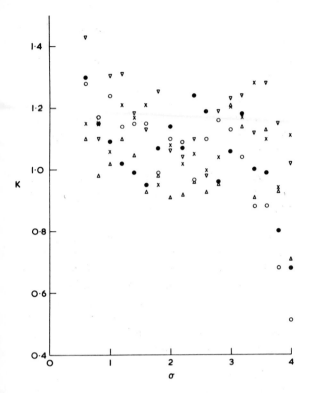

Figure 3-D-2. *A plot of* $k = [(C_{22} + C_{33})/C/11]^{1/2} g/\sigma$ *as a function of* σ.

cussion (Figure 3-D-2). We found the usual expected statistical scatter, but it is the scatter about a mean value which is a little greater than one — perhaps 1.1 — and there is some odd behavior at very high frequencies which makes us rather skeptical of our calibrations in that region. I think it is probably the calibration that is in error because the buoy has a natural response curve, which was measured as I mentioned. It varies very rapidly in the neighborhood of its natural resonance, which is just about at σ equals 4.0.

Dr. Pierson: I think we all recognize that this is a very interesting and valuable contribution to the study of the actual sea surface. May I compliment Dr. Longuet-Higgins and his fine group of co-workers in this area?

I cannot resist the temptation to compare some of these results with those of SWOP in a little more detail. I think the first principle we have to recognize is that of the invariance of the difficulty. It turns out to be about as difficult to obtain meaningful results by these procedures as it was by a stereophotogrammetric technique. We both encountered a high attenuation in the amount of data that was taken and the amount of data that was finally reduced and analyzed.

In the end we had one good set of data. Dr.

Longuet-Higgins ended up with two good sets of data. So we now have three directional spectra, one by stereo and two by his methods. There is the problem of calibration. We could not get a wave pole record to agree with the stereo results. The ship-borne recorder was properly calibrated against a directional spectrum for a ship underway in such a sea, which is a major accomplishment that Mr. Cartwright told us about yesterday.

This is quite important to the naval architect. We find that the pressure sensor of the shipboard recorder behaves as if it were $2\frac{1}{2}$ times deeper than it actually is in the water.

There is another interesting problem. The question of the possibility of the double peak, as a function of θ for high frequencies has not been resolved by this analysis nor was it resolved in our data. We might ask ourselves how it could be resolved. What kind of experiment or set of observations would have to be carried out? Here we would have to pay a great deal more attention to sampling variability. In Dr. Longuet-Higgins' report to us I missed the confidence interval, or something akin to it, in the charts. I think they would be quite important.

Scatter may or may not be comparable to the confidence interval that you would compute from theoretical grounds if possible. I don't know how it would be done from these data. If possible, it would be helpful to see whether the scatter exceeded or fell within the estimates that you might expect due to sampling variability.

The question of the double peaked function of θ as opposed to the single peak, is a very interesting and very important one for many applications and in particular for forecasting swell correctly.

My feeling is that it will be necessary to go to much higher resolution; but a complicated buoy system is required to get the desired resolution. I submit to you that in this particular case stereo has advantages, and we can go to an increased amount of resolution for the even harmonics. Of course, the disadvantages of stereo are that the nonlinear features of the surface as a function of X and Y observed at a fixed instant of time may be far more severe than the nonlinear effects that are encountered in the integrated response of a buoy. This makes the analysis much more complicated.

Is the actual wave length shorter or longer than the theoretical?

Dr. Longuet-Higgins: The ratios were greater than one, so the waves appeared a little shorter than suggested by linear theory.

Dr. Pierson: The last point is that it is quite likely that we would learn a great deal more by combining the two methods than we would by using either one alone.

The described method of analysis, even for the low frequencies in the spectrum, yields the result that some portion of the spectrum as a function of direction is travelling opposite to the wind, or at an angle greater than 90 degrees to the wind. I would ask, does Dr. Longuet-Higgins really believe that this is the case?

Dr. Longuet-Higgins: We have estimated confidence limits for the one-dimensional spectrum. The plotted points have a 95 per cent probability of lying within 20 per cent of their actual values.

As for the question of energy travelling at angles of more than 90 degrees to the wind, our observations, of course, cannot really determine this question rigorously because we have only two harmonics.

I myself have an open mind on this question, and I certainly would not like to assert dogmatically that there is no energy going at angles of more than 90 degrees from the wind. My reasons for this are that I think that nonlinear mechanisms, such as the breaking of the waves and the tertiary wave interactions, may contribute something.

Dr. Pierson: Do you think that we made a serious mistake in assuming that the major part of the spectrum was contained within 90 degrees of the wind direction?

Dr. Longuet-Higgins: I am not saying that you made a serious mistake. All I am saying is that I have an open mind on the question.

Dr. Cox: I would like to say that I consider this work a monumental undertaking, which is giving people who are working in the field of waves a profound sense of admiration for the work at N.I.O. Has anyone measured the coherency between the pressure fluctuations and the wave amplitudes? This will give some information on the turbulent characteristics of the pressure fluctuations.

Dr. Cartwright: I did measure the coherency on one set of data. It was certainly high — about 0.8, but it should be less than 1 theoretically.

N. F. BARBER

T W O

THE DIRECTIONAL RESOLVING POWER

OF AN ARRAY OF WAVE DETECTORS

INTRODUCTION

It is desirable to be able to distinguish waves both by their different wave numbers and by their different directions of travel even when they are present simultaneously in a complicated sea.

The orientation of wave crests can, of course, be seen if a photograph of the sea surface is taken from a considerable height by a camera pointing vertically downwards. The sun should preferably be at a low elevation. The different wave numbers and orientations in such a photograph can be revealed conveniently by a simple process of optical diffraction. Unfortunately, one cannot know precisely how the varying density in the photograph is related to water slope or water elevation, so this diffraction method has very limited application. More recently it has been suggested that a diffraction process directly from the sea surface, using radio waves of suitable wavelengths, may provide an effective means of analysing waves. This, however, is the subject of another session of the conference.

I wish to discuss here the systems that require measurements of water elevation or water slope to be made at a variety of points on the sea, and that then deduce the directional wave spectrum through the correlogram or correlation coefficients. Except when the measurements are made by stereophotography, it is usually practicable to record the waves only at a quite small number of points on the sea. This small number of points necessarily limits the accuracy with which the directional spectrum can be found. The purpose of this paper is to find the directional resolving power of any array of measuring points.

It is now well accepted that the directional power spectrum can very conveniently be found through the use of the correlogram or correlation coefficients. A brief justification of this attack will be given, however. The paper then goes on to discuss the directional resolving power of an array of measuring points with reference to particular examples.

THE CORRELOGRAM AND POWER SPECTRUM

Surface Waves: The complicated pattern of waves that is observed under wind is being thought of as the superposition of many long-crested wave trains. Actually, it is only when the slopes of the water surface are all very small that simple wave trains tend to have a sinusoidal profile and can be regarded as combining their motions by simple addition. It is not entirely correct to apply such an analysis to wind driven waves, but it is at least a first approach to the problem.

137

If the slopes of the water surface are sufficiently small, the surface elevation η caused by a long-crested wave train is a sinusoidal function of the horizontal coordinates x and y and of the time t.

$$\eta(x, y, t) = a \cos 2\pi (l\,x + my + ft + \alpha) \quad (1)$$

The frequency f is the number of wave cycles executed per unit of time at any fixed position. The quantities l and m are the numbers of wave cycles displayed per unit of distance in the coordinate direction x and y at any instant of time. Although one's natural mental picture of a wave is that of a sinusoidal pattern advancing with time, it is clear from the formula that the quantities l and m are quite analogous to f and could be called "space frequencies." In a Fourier treatment too it is desirable to avoid patterns that move and change, so in what follows the reader is invited to think of the pattern of elevation as displayed explicitly in three dimensions, perhaps with x and y horizontal and t vertical. The pattern of elevation produced by a wave train then becomes a sinusoidal distribution in these three dimensions with wave crests represented by planes whose inclination to the t axis shows their velocity of travel. The changing pattern of elevations in a complicated sea becomes a fixed distribution in these three coordinates. The technique of analysis aims to represent this complicated pattern as the sum of sinusoids in three dimensions each characterised by its three "frequencies" along the xy and t axes.

It is true, of course, that the three frequencies l, m, and f tend to be linked by the wave equation governing surface waves, but the effect of this will be considered at a later stage.

As for the more usual concepts of wavelength and wave direction, it can readily be shown that the number of cycles per unit of distance in a horizontal direction normal to the crests is k

$$k = (l^2 + m^2)^{1/2} \quad (2)$$

This is the reciprocal of the wavelength. Also the ratios l/k, m/k are the direction cosines of the wave normal in the xy plane, so the direction of wave travel θ is expressed by

$$l = k \cos \theta \quad m = k \sin \theta \quad (3)$$

The Power Spectrum: If one were informed of the surface elevations over all a region of sea extending from 0 to A in the x direction and 0 to B in the y direction and during a time span 0 to C, one could, in principle at least, express this three-dimensional distribution as the sum of three dimensional sinusoids each representing an elementary wave train.

$$\eta(xyt) = \sum_{-\infty}^{u=\infty} \sum_{-\infty}^{v=\infty} \sum_{-\infty}^{w=\infty} \mathbf{A}_{uvw}$$
$$\exp i2\pi \left[\frac{ux}{A} + \frac{vy}{B} + \frac{wt}{C} \right] \quad (4)$$

The symbols uvw denote integers, positive or negative, and the quantities $u/A, v/B, w/C$ are the possible values of the sinusoidal frequencies l, m, f in this Fourier series. Complex notation has been used for preference, but since η is real, one might ignore the imaginary parts and write the typical term as a real sinusoid.

$$|A|_{uvw} \cos 2\pi \left[\frac{ux}{A} + \frac{vy}{B} + \frac{wt}{c} + \alpha_{uvw} \right] \quad (5)$$

where $|A|$ is the modulus and α is the argument of the complex amplitude $\mathbf{A}$.

This Fourier expression is an exact representation of the observed elevations in the sample of waves. It is not, however, what is needed. The theory of "noise" suggests that in the representation of any such sample, each coefficient $\mathbf{A}$ is best regarded as a random choice from some normal gaussian family of complex numbers, so that in another wave sample having the same extensions A, B, C and taken in the same "sea state" the new values of the complex amplitudes $\mathbf{A}$ would all be different from those in the first sample. In assessing the wave state, one ought to ignore such details as are accidental to the particular sample and look for some statistic that is common to all samples. This statistic is the variance or mean square modulus of the family from which each coefficient $\mathbf{A}$ is drawn.

We, therefore, aim to assess this variance and to show how it depends upon the values of the "frequencies" l, m, and f. It may be remarked that the squared modulus of any coefficient $\mathbf{A}$ in the Fourier series is closely connected with the energy or power of the wave train that the sinusoid represents. Consequently the three-dimensional distribution of variance, using as coordinates the frequencies l, m, and f, is usually called the "power spectrum." This power spectrum rather than the Fourier spectrum is the right way to summarize the frequency characteristics of a random process.

The Correlogram: To find the variance one might contemplate recording a large number of different samples of waves and making a Fourier analysis of each. The amplitude of any one sinusoid would be different in each, and one could assess the variance as the mean squared modulus of these different values of the amplitude. It would be found to vary, perhaps slowly, with the three frequencies of the sinusoids.

Alternatively, one might contemplate taking a single extensive sample and finding the Fourier series to represent it. Because A, B, and C are large, the frequency differences between adjacent sinusoids in the series would then be very small, being $1/A$, $1/B$, and $1/C$. One could, therefore, suppose that the amplitudes **A** of sinusoids having frequencies in a reasonably small range of u, v, w were all drawn from families with a very similar variance. The mean-squared modulus of this group of amplitudes would then be a good estimate of the variance in the vicinity of those values of frequency.

These methods would be very laborious. A more satisfactory method would involve first making a "convolution" of the original wave data. The convolution theorem is so necessary in this and later arguments that a formal statement of it is made in the Appendix. In the present case the use of a Fourier series to represent the wave data implies the assumption that outside the sample the wave pattern repeats itself at intervals A on the x range, B on the y range, and C on the t range. To be consistent one may make the same assumption in forming the convolution. The appropriate formula for it is

$$\rho(X,Y,\tau) = \frac{1}{ABC} \int_0^{x=A} \int_0^{y=B} \int_0^{t=C} \eta(xyt)$$
$$\eta(x+X, y+Y, t+\tau)dx\,dy\,dt \quad (6)$$

The convolution ρ is the mean product of pairs of elevations η differing by given intervals x, y, τ in the coordinates x, y, and t. Of course, ρ varies with the chosen values x, y, and τ.

The convolution theorem states that this convolution is represented by the following Fourier series, which should be compared with that given for the elevation

$$\rho(X,Y,\tau) = \sum_{-\infty}^{u=\infty} \sum_{-\infty}^{v=\infty} \sum_{-\infty}^{w=\infty} |A|_{uvw}^2 \exp i2\pi \left[\frac{uX}{A} + \frac{vY}{B} + \frac{w\tau}{c} \right] \quad (7)$$

The difference is that the amplitudes in this new series are the squared moduli of the amplitudes

in the series for η. This suggests that the convolution is a step towards finding the variance or "power."

It may be remarked that the convolution is a somewhat simpler function than the wave data from which it is derived. Because the amplitudes in its Fourier series are all real and positive, the sinusoids tend to combine to give large, positive values to ρ near to the origin of x, y, and τ. At large values of x, y, and τ the sinusoids tend to interfere and lead to small positive or negative values of ρ.

Some technique is needed to provide a mean value of all the amplitudes $|A|_{uvw}^2$ that occur in each fairly small range of u, v, and w. This can be achieved very simply. One merely takes note of the large values of ρ occurring in the vicinity of its origin and ignores the small values of ρ that occur at large values of X, Y, and τ. One also ignores the repetitions of ρ that occur at intervals A, B, and C on the X, Y, and τ coordinates. In effect, one is multiplying the convolution ρ by a factor, say $g(X, Y, \tau)$, that is unity at small values of X, Y, and τ and is zero at all large values. By the convolution theorem it follows at once that the spectrum of this modified convolution is a smoothed version of the set of discrete powers $|A|_{uvw}^2$. At any values of frequency l, m, f, it is the average of all the values $|A|_{uvw}^2$ appropriate to frequencies w/A, v/B, w/C near to l, m and f. But this average is just what is needed as an estimate of the variance or power.

It will be appreciated that the foregoing process is effective in giving an estimate of variance and leads also to a great saving of labour. One need only calculate the convolution values for intervals X, Y, and τ that are relatively small, much smaller than the ranges A, B, and C of the wave sample. The result is a relatively simple distribution in x, y, and τ, for which it is relatively easy to calculate the power spectrum as its three-dimensional Fourier transform.

The formal statement of the argument follows most easily if one writes the expansion of ρ a little differently:

$$\rho(X,Y,\tau) = \int_{-\infty}^{\infty} \int_{-\infty}^{\infty} \int_{-\infty}^{\infty} R(lmf)$$
$$\exp i2\pi(lX + mY + f\tau)dl\,dm\,df \quad (8)$$

Comparing this with the Fourier series for ρ, it is seen that R must be a set of delta functions occurring at frequencies u/A, v/B, w/C. Each delta function has an integrated value equal to the corresponding amplitude $|A|^2_{uvw}$. Consequently, R has the nature of a power density. Also if the last equation is abbreviated to the statement ·

$$\rho(X, Y, \tau) \quad \textit{has the transform} \quad R(l, m, f) \quad (9)$$

and if $\mathcal{G}(l, m, f)$ is the spectrum of the masking function $g(X, Y, \tau)$,

$$g(X, Y, \tau) \quad \textit{has the transform} \quad \mathcal{G}(l, m, f) \quad (10)$$

Then for the modified convolution $\rho \cdot g$ it follows from the convolution theorem that

$$\rho(X, Y, \tau) \cdot g(X, Y, \tau) \quad \textit{has the transform} \quad E(lmf)$$

where

$$E(lmf) = \int_{-\infty}^{\infty} \int_{-\infty}^{\infty} \int_{-\infty}^{\infty} R(l_0 m_0 f_0) g(l - l_0,$$
$$m - m_0, f - f_0) dl_0 \, dm_0 \, df_0 \quad (11)$$

Since the integral of $\mathcal{G}$ is unity, being equal to $g(000)$, the last integral is a weighted average of R in the vicinity of each value l, m, f. It has, like R, the nature of a power density on a three-dimensional plot against $l, m,$ and f, and is an approximation to the power spectrum.

Instability: Since R is composed of discrete delta functions at intervals $1/A$, $1/B$, $1/C$ on the scales of $l, m,$ and f, only a finite number of them is included by the averaging function $\mathcal{G}$. The resulting average will not, therefore, be an exact measure of the power density but will be subject to sampling error. If, for instance, the function $\mathcal{G}$ includes 400 delta functions in R, the probable error of the mean will be about 5 per cent. This is called "instability" and shows itself as erratic variations in the power spectrum. The instability can be made less by giving $\mathcal{G}$ a wider spread. Since $\mathcal{G}$ is the transform of the "masking" function g, this effect is brought about by making g narrower, thereby paying attention to a yet smaller zone of the convolution near its origin. The danger in this technique is that one may smooth out real variations in the power spectrum. This sort of error obviously arises if g is so restricted that significantly large values of the convolution occur in the region that is being ignored. The better remedy is to use a more extensive sample of wave data; if trial shows that almost all the significant values of the convolution appear to be included in a zone extending $\pm\frac{1}{2}a$, $\pm\frac{1}{2}b$, $\pm\frac{1}{2}c$ in X, Y, τ about the origin, then for 5 percent stability the sample size should make ABC/abc greater than 400.

The word "correlogram" is sometimes used for the convolution of the wave sample. It is perhaps better to restrict this term to the ideal, limiting form to which the convolution tends when the wave sample is very large. The correlogram then has no errors of sampling, and its spectrum or Fourier transform is the true power spectrum of the waves.

The Wave Equation: In what has gone before, the power spectrum has been regarded as a three-dimensional plot using the frequencies l, m, f as coordinates, just as the wave sample or the convolution of the sample were regarded as three-dimensional distributions in coordinates x, y, t or X, Y, τ, respectively. Wave theory shows, however, that the velocity of advance of a wave train is related to its wave length. In the analysis of a complicated sea one may therefore expect to find little power associated with wave trains whose frequencies do not conform or nearly conform to the wave equation

$$2\pi f^2 = g_1(l^2 + m^2)^{1/2} \quad (12)$$

where g_1 is here the acceleration of gravity. This formula defines a surface in the l, m, f plot, a parabola with the f axis as the tangent at its vertex and rotated about that axis. Power tends to concentrate on this surface, so a display of power in three dimensions is not necessary in the study of sea waves. Only two coordinates need to be used. Probably l and m are the most convenient pair. If l and m are plotted at right angles, each point on the plot represents a possible wave train, while the direction and distance of the point from the origin display respectively the direction from which the wave is coming and the reciprocal of its wave length. The frequency f can, of course, be inferred from the wave length on the assumption that the frequency is inherently positive.

This simplification will be referred to in connection with particular practical methods of wave survey.

PRACTICAL SIMPLIFICATIONS

The preceding arguments dealt with an ideal case, where waves had been observed continuously over large ranges in both space and time. Such extensive and complete data are not essential to a good analysis.

Ergodic Property: Equation (1), for instance, shows

each value of the convolution as being derived from an average extending over large ranges in all three variables, x, y, and τ. There is reason to expect, however, that waves will have an ergodic property, by which an average over a sufficient range in any one or any two of the variables will tend to the same value as an average taken over all three. This opens the way to a variety of different practical methods of assessing the correlogram. One may, for example, use an array of relatively few wave detectors and observe their outputs over a sufficiently long period of time. Estimates of correlation are then gotten by a time average, and the array itself need spread only far enough to include all distances X or Y at which the correlogram need be calculated. On the other hand, the SWOP project used a stereo-photograph of the sea surface to give an observation of water elevation over a wide area of sea. Estimates of correlation were then found by a space average in x and y. Or again, if it were possible to record the profile of the sea on long lines at a variety of orientations, the correlation values could be based on averages over the long lines.

Measurement at Discrete Times: It is not essential for the observations to extend continuously over the ranges of space and time. Suppose, for instance, that the outputs of an array of wave detectors were recorded not continuously but only at instants separated by a small fixed interval, τ_0. Correlations could then be calculated only at time intervals that were multiples of τ_0. Intervening values of correlation would not be known and would have to be treated as zero. The effect is the same as if the true complete correlogram had been multiplied by a factor that consisted of a series of equal delta functions at instants 0, $\pm\tau_0$, $\pm 2\tau_0$, etc. Consequently, where the set of discrete values of the correlogram is transformed to find the power spectrum, the result is not the true power spectrum but a convolution between the true power spectrum and the Fourier transform of the series of delta functions. This latter is itself a series of delta functions lying at frequencies 0, $\pm 1/\tau_0$, $\pm 2/\tau_0$, etc. The result can be thought of as the superposition of many copies of the true power spectrum with their origins placed at 0, $\pm 1/\tau_0$, $\pm 2/\tau_0$, etc. In general this seems likely to be very confusing, but in certain circumstances it is easily interpreted. Suppose for instance that it is known beforehand that no waves are present

with frequencies greater than $\pm 1/2\tau_0$. The multiple images of the true spectrum do not then overlap: that centered on frequency $1/\tau_0$ cannot extend beyond $1/2\tau_0$ to $3/2\tau_0$, that centered on frequency $-1/\tau_0$ cannot extend outside $-3/2\tau_0$ to $-1/2\tau_0$, and so on. The portion of the transform lying between $\pm 1/2\tau_0$ is therefore the true power spectrum, and the repetitions that occur at higher frequencies can be ignored. In short, it is sufficient to observe the waves at discrete, equally-spaced instants provided that the interval is not greater than half the period of the shortest wave element directed by the instruments.

Measurement at Discrete Positions: Similarly, it is not essential to observe waves at every point over an area of sea. Wave detectors set in the form of a T (a modified Mills cross) are an example of this technique. If the shortest waves that are being studied have a wave length L, it is sufficient to set wave detectors at equal intervals $\frac{1}{2}L$ along the x axis (both negative and positive branches) and at equal intervals $\frac{1}{2}L$ along the positive part of the y axis. There should be enough detectors for the array to extend from the origin to distances sufficient to include all significant values of the correlogram. If there are N instruments in each of the three arms and one at the origin, $3N + 1$ in all, it can be seen that different pairs of detectors can be chosen to provide all space intervals xy in a complete square array

$$\left.\begin{array}{l} X = \frac{1}{2}L \cdot p \\ Y = \frac{1}{2}L \cdot q \end{array}\right\} \; p, q \text{ integers ranging } -N \text{ to } +N \quad (13)$$

Correlations at only these positions are calculated and used in making a transformation to the spectrum. It is as if the true complete correlogram had been multiplied by a set of delta functions, with p and q extending to infinity. The transform, of this set, is another square set of delta functions at frequency values l, m equal to $(0, 0)$, $(0, \pm 2/L)$, $(\pm 2/L, 0)$, and so on. The transform of the set of measured values of the correlogram is the sum of a series of images of the true power spectrum with the origins shifted to these positions on the plot of space frequency. But so long as the true spectrum does not extend beyond values of space frequency l and m equal to $\pm 1/L$, there is no overlapping or confusion. This condition is met, of course, if L is the wave length of the shortest wave being studied. It is worth remarking that L does not need to be the shortest wave length that the instruments are actually detecting, for such waves can be excluded from the calculation because of their higher frequency in time. Thus the wave data are usually recorded at time intervals of less than half the period of the shortest waves that are being *detected* by the instruments, but the space interval L needs only be made less than half the wave length of the shortest wave that it is proposed to *study*.

It is also worth remarking that it is the *correlogram* that must be detected at equal space intervals. The actual wave measuring instruments do not need to form a regular array. For instance, in a very simple one-dimensional array one may place detectors in a straight line at successive intervals $\frac{1}{2}L$, $\frac{3}{2} \cdot L$, L. From different pairs of detectors one may estimate correlations at the regular array of space intervals,

$$0, \tfrac{1}{2}L, L, \tfrac{3}{2}L, 2L, \tfrac{5}{2}L, 3L$$

The advantage of the irregular array is that it uses only four instruments, whereas a regular array of the same length would require seven.

Persistence: No two wave records taken at different places or different times are the same, but it is expected that the correlogram of the waves will vary only slowly with time or position on the sea. One outcome of this is that it should be possible to build up a picture of the correlogram in a piecemeal manner. One should be able to use two detectors separated by some space interval X_1, Y_1, to find the value of the correlation at this distance and then place them at a new interval X_2, Y_2 to find the new correlation. This would be done at a sufficient number of different intervals for the combined values to present a picture of the correlogram. It is not essential, in other words, for all values of the correlogram to be obtained from wave records all taken simultaneously. This process would allow the correlogram and power spectrum to be found by only two detectors, but of course, one must have reason to think that the "wave state" is not changing during the succession of measurements.

Line Arrays: A two-dimensional array, such as the Mills cross or its modifications, calls for a large number of detectors. In studying sea waves, however, little is lost by restricting the detectors to a single line, and the economy in detectors is considerable. It is possible to use a line array in studying sea waves because the wave frequency and the wave length have a definite relation. Although three frequencies, that is l, m, and f have been quoted as characterising a wave train, these are related by the expression

$$2\pi f^2 = g_1(l^2 + m^2)^{1/2} \qquad (14)$$

A line of detectors along the x axis serves to distinguish waves by the space frequency l, and the frequency f can be found from the history of the signals. Consequently the frequency m can be inferred, and the wave direction can be deduced. The only ambiguity is in the sign of m; that is, one cannot usually decide from which side of the line the waves are coming. In a number of situations this question can be answered on physical grounds. If, for instance, the line of detectors is approximately at right angles to the wind, it is improbable that any of the wave trains produced by the wind would be approaching the array from the downwind side. The very simple one-dimensional array mentioned in the previous section is therefore not irrelevant to the study of sea waves.

Figure 3-2-1. *Spectral representation for a line array.*

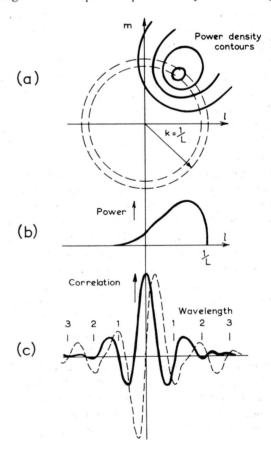

The use of a line array is illustrated in Figure 3-2-1. The full contours in (a) indicate the directional power spectrum of the waves using as coordinates the space frequencies l and m. When the waves are being observed by an array of detectors, it is possible to restrict attention to waves with some narrow range of time frequency near to f. In the directional spectrum such waves correspond to points lying in a narrow annular zone of radius k (the reciprocal of the corresponding wave length). An array of detectors along the x axis studies the power spectrum as it appears when projected on to the l axis. When the power in the annular zone is projected on to the axis it amounts to a power distribution shown in curve (b). The Fourier transform of this curve is the plot of correlations for intervals X parallel to the x axis and is sketched in (c), the full line representing the cosine transform that is the "in phase" correlation, and the broken line representing the sine transform that is the "quadrature" correlation.

In practice, one would go through this process in reverse, selecting wave signals of frequency f from the detectors on the x axis, calculating the correlations for the various intervals X that the array presents, and so finding the curves in (c). These would then be transferred to give curve (b). Finally, this curve would be interpreted into an angular distribution of power around the annulus in the directional spectrum. It should be noted that the projection of (a) into (b) involves some foreshortening. Curve (b) must be multiplied by $\sin \theta$ or $(1 - l^2/k^2)^{1/2}$ in estimating the power density per unit angle of direction in (a).

The Over-all Dimensions of an Array: The array should be extensive enough to allow the correlogram to be calculated at all its important central values. Evidently, the desirable size of the array depends on the nature of the waves that are being studied. In wind-driven waves, for instance, it is likely that correlogram values will become negligible at separations greater than $1\frac{1}{2}$ wave lengths in the cross-wind direction. This calls for only a relatively short array. Long swells coming from a generating area that subtends perhaps 10 degrees at the receiving station can be expected to show significant correlations at intervals up to 5 wave lengths along a line parallel to the wave crests. This calls for a very extensive array if such swells are to be picked out from a background of waves of similar frequency coming from other directions. Some possible simplifications in studying long

swell will be mentioned, however, in the next section.

The correlogram persists for greater distances along the wind direction or along the direction of travel of the swell. In the case of wind waves one may expect the correlogram to persist for 3 or 4 wave lengths. For long swells it is almost entirely controlled by the width of the frequency band; if the reciprocal wave lengths in the swell range from $0.9k$ to $1.1k$, where $1/k$ is the mean wave length, the correlogram may be expected to persist for about 10 wave lengths in the direction of travel. It seems better, therefore, to arrange a line array to lie across the line of travel rather than along it.

The Observation of Swell: If it can be expected that only one swell is present with the particular wave frequency that is being studied, a very simple directional arrangement is possible. This uses only two detectors at a separation rather less than half the wave length appropriate to the selected frequency. The correlation between the two wave signals will be high, and the argument of the correlation (that is the phase difference of the wave signals) indicates the direction of travel in an obvious way. Since long swell is refracted, even in quite deep water, it is worth remarking that if one can find a locality in which the underwater contours are straight and parallel, and if the detectors are set upon a line parallel to the contours, the phase difference is unaffected by the refraction; and the direction in deep water can be calculated as if no refraction or change in wave length had been produced by the shoaling water.

This technique presumes, however, that there are no waves of the same period as the swell coming from local storms and in particular that the swell is not being reflected or scattered from nearby shores. It seems possible, however, to modify the technique to avoid the interference such scattered reflections would cause. Scattered waves will have a fairly broad range of direction, and their correlogram would not be expected to persist as far as, say, 3 wave lengths. Then if one uses a line of three wave detectors, the second and third being set at 3 and $3\frac{1}{2}$ wave lengths from the first, the correlations between these detectors and the first one would be due almost entirely to the swell. The difference in argument of the correlations is then the phase difference of the swell for a displacement of half a wave length along the line, and the direction of travel of swell may be inferred as before.

SOME SIMPLE ARRAYS

The previous sections have discussed ideal systems that are sufficiently extensive to find the true directional spectrum. Very often one must be content to use systems of only a few detectors. This section considers how one may foretell the limited ability of such systems to distinguish the directions of different wavetrains.

Analysis: Although the array may present only a very few space intervals at which one may calculate the correlation, one may adopt an analysis on the same lines as that which would be used for an ideal system. In forming the convolution there is in principle no difficulty in introducing a great variety of time delays τ, because each wave record is very extensive in time. The only space intervals, however, are those few intervals that are presented by the various pairs of detectors, say

$$(0, 0), (X_1, Y_1), (X_2, Y_2), \text{ etc.} \quad (15)$$

Thinking of the three-dimensional convolution in X, Y, and τ, it is evident that one can only calculate its values along a number of tracks that are straight lines parallel to the τ axis. The values along a typical track $X_1 Y_1 \tau$ are gotten from the signals of two detectors that happen to lie at a separation $X_1 Y_1$ and these values are often called the "lag correlogram" of the wave signals from these two instruments. The assembly of all the "lag correlograms" from the various pairs of instruments is all that is known about the three-dimensional convolution.

One proceeds to make a three dimensional Fourier transform of the convolution. In doing so, all the unknown values of the convolution have to be treated as zero. The first step is to transform in time. This amounts to making a time transform of each "lag correlogram." Thus the transform of a typical "lag correlogram" $\rho(X, Y, \tau)$ can be calculated as

$$\int_{-\infty}^{\infty} \rho(X, Y, \tau) \exp(-i2\pi f \tau) \, d\tau$$
$$= P(X, Y, f) - iQ(X, Y, f) \quad (16)$$

Here P is the cosine transform, and Q is the sine transform of the lag correlogram. They are, of course, functions of the time frequency f.

Having made the transforms of all the lag correlograms, one may select any frequency f_0 and from the assembly of P, Q values make a transform to find how the power at this frequency f_0 is distributed with the space frequencies l and m.

Such a transform is

$$\int_{-\infty}^{\infty} \int_{-\infty}^{\infty} [P(X, Y, f_0) - iQ(X, Y, f_0)]$$
$$\exp[-i2\pi(lx + mY)] \, dX \, dY \quad (17)$$

Because the P, Q functions have to be treated as zero at all X, Y values except those that the array presents, this integral turns into a summation. Here one treats the PQ quantities as delta functions whose X, Y integrals are the values previously calculated. The summation is

$$\sum_{-N}^{n=N} [P(X_n Y_n f_0) - iQ(X_n Y_n f_0)]$$
$$\exp[-i2\pi(lX_n + mY_n)] \quad (18)$$

This can be expressed as real sinusoids in l and m; the convolution has diametral symmetry

$$\rho(X, Y, \tau) = \rho(-X, -Y, -\tau) \quad (19)$$

so the time transforms also have symmetry

$$P(X_n, Y_n, f_0) = P(-X_n, -Y_n, f_0)$$
$$Q(X_n, Y_n, f_0) = -Q(-X_n -Y_n, f_0) \quad (20)$$

The summation becomes

$$\sum_{-N}^{n=N} \{P(X_n, Y_n, f_0) \cos 2\pi(lX_n + mY_n)$$
$$- Q(X_n, Y_n, f_0) \sin 2\pi(X_n + mY_n)\} \quad (21)$$

This suggests that at the specified frequency f_0 power is distributed over the whole l, m plane in the three-dimensional spectrum. One knows from the wave equation that the distribution cannot be correct; at the selected frequency f_0 wave power should be associated only with points whose l, m values place them on a circle of radius k_0 corresponding to the frequency f_0. Indeed, with a sufficiently extensive array, say a Mills cross, the sinusoids in the above summation would tend to combine into a distribution that showed power being restricted to the periphery of this circle. The more elementary array usually fails to show this restriction of power to the right radial distance k_0. What is one to do in this case? One answer would be to calculate the summation only for points on the circle, writing

$$l = k_0 \cos \theta \quad m = k_0 \sin \theta, \quad (22)$$

where θ is the wave direction. The resulting curve of values could then be taken to represent the way in which wave power is dependent on direction. Since the total power (per unit range of f near frequency f_0) that is incident from all directions is the known quantity $P(0, 0, f_0)$ gotten from the lag correlogram of any single instrument, the ordinates of the curve could be scaled to represent power density per unit angle θ .for all directions θ.

This approach does not, however, make the best use of the information inherent in the wave equation governing sea waves. The present treatment of the P, Q values is applicable, however, in such studies as radioastronomy, where the radio wave length measured in the horizontal plane is not uniquely related to frequency. It will, therefore, be pursued briefly in connection with some simple arrays. A treatment that is more suitable for sea wave analysis is described below in the subsection "Making better use of the wave equation."

Directional Resolving Power: It is important to be able to estimate before the array is built what the directional resolving power of any array will be. There is quite a simple graphical way of doing this. The theoretical argument will be given first, and then it will be illustrated by reference to various simple arrays.

When an array of wave detectors presents a set of space intervals $(0,0)$, (X_1, Y_1), (X_2, Y_2), etc., the three-dimensional convolution in X, Y, τ can be calculated only at these particular space intervals. Values of the convolution at other space intervals are undetermined and have to be treated as zero. It is, therefore, as if the true convolution $\rho(X, Y, \tau)$ had been multiplied by a factor $g(X, Y)$ that was zero everywhere except at the values $(0,0)$, (X, Y), etc., where it was a set of unit delta functions. A transform is therefore being made not of the true convolution ρ but of the product $\rho \cdot g$. The result is, therefore, not the true power spectrum $E(lmf)$ but its convolution with the transform of the factor g, say $\mathcal{G}(lm)$. The formal expression for the result is

$$\int_{-\infty}^{\infty} \int_{-\infty}^{\infty} E(l_0 m_0 f)\mathcal{G}(l - l_0, m - m_0)dl_0 \, dm_0 \quad (23)$$

It is as if each elementary value of E had spread out in the l, m plane into a pattern like $\mathcal{G}$. The sum of all these patterns is the spectrum that would be gotten by calculation from the wave data given by the array, a blurred picture of the true spectrum. This point of view is a useful one; if one supposes that the array is set to examine a single wave train defined in direction and wave length by the space frequencies l_0, m_0, the routine processing of the wave data will suggest that wave power is not associated only with the point l_0, m_0

in the spectrum, but spreads over a range of l, m values around l_0, m_0. The pattern of power distribution is the function $\mathcal{G}(l - l_0, m - m_0)$. Evidently this function $\mathcal{G}$ is characteristic of the array and indicates its deficiencies in resolution. If the function $\mathcal{G}$ has a wide spread, the array evidently has a poor resolving power, and the picture of the power spectrum that can be derived from such an array would be very blurred. The question of the resolving power of any proposed array is, therefore, answered by calculating the function $\mathcal{G}$.

Now the factor $g(X, Y)$ is a set of unit delta functions at points $(0, 0)$, (X_1, Y_1), (X_2, Y_2), etc., including the negative intervals $(-X_1, -Y_1)$, $(-X_2, -Y_2)$, etc. Its transform is

$$\mathcal{G}(lm) = \int_{-\infty}^{\infty} \int_{-\infty}^{\infty} g(X, Y)$$
$$\exp -i2\pi(lX + mY)dX \, dY \quad (24)$$
$$= 1 + 2\cos 2\pi(lX_1 + mY_1)$$
$$+ 2\cos 2\pi(lX_2 + mY_2) + \text{etc.}$$

The function $\mathcal{G}$ is, therefore, a sum of sinusoids and can be quite readily constructed graphically. The process will be illustrated for some simple arrays.

Three Detectors in a Triangle: Suppose three detectors are set in a triangle whose sides are the space intervals X_1, Y_1, X_2, Y_2 and X_3, Y_3. The function $\mathcal{G}$ is then

$$\mathcal{G}(lm) = 1 + 2\cos 2\pi(lX_1 + mY_1)$$
$$+ 2\cos 2\pi(lX_2 + mY_2) \quad (25)$$
$$+ 2\cos 2\pi(lX_3 + mY_3).$$

In the l, m plane (supposing l and m axes taken parallel to the x and y axes) the sinusoids have crest lines at right angles to the directions that separate the appropriate pairs of detectors, and their wave lengths in the l, m plane are the reciprocals of the distance separating the detectors. For each sinusoid one may readily draw parallel lines that are its contours at values of ± 1 and ± 2. This is detailed enough for the present purpose. If the contours for all three sinusoids are drawn on one sheet, they can readily be added (together with the unity term) to give contours of the function $\mathcal{G}$. This is illustrated in Figure 3-2-2. The set of three detectors is shown in (a), and the corresponding function $\mathcal{G}$ is shown in (b). In this case the function $\mathcal{G}$ is a repetitive pattern, the large values at the origin being repeated regularly over the l, m plane.

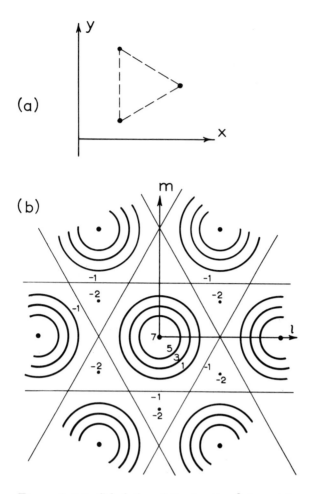

Figure 3-2-2. *Calculation of the function $\mathcal{G}$ for a triangular array.*

circle. One would pay attention only to the values of the pattern occurring at points on this circle. The fact that the $\mathcal{G}$ pattern shows large values of power not only at l_0, m_0 but at other points around this circle is an indication of the inability of the array to decide the direction of the waves. The values of $\mathcal{G}$ around this circle may be plotted as a curve against direction angle to show the "directional spread pattern." One may repeat this procedure for a variety of different values l_0, m_0, that is for waves of different wave lengths and directions. It is not necessary, of course, to redraw the $\mathcal{G}$ pattern each time. One merely takes the $\mathcal{G}$ pattern and draws on it circles of appropriate radius k_0 with their centers displaced in any desired direction. $\mathcal{G}$ values along these circles are read off and plotted as "spread patterns." Various conclusions can at once be drawn. Because the $\mathcal{G}$ pattern is far from having circular symmetry, the "spread patterns," even for waves of a prescribed wave length, will be noticeably different for waves travelling in different directions. If the array is used to study very long waves, the appropriate circle will be of small radius, and large $\mathcal{G}$ values may occur everywhere upon it, indicating a wide "spread pattern" and a poor directional resolution. If the array is used to study short waves, the appropriate circle will have

Figure 3-2-3. *Calculation of the function $\mathcal{G}$ for a single wave train using a triangular array.*

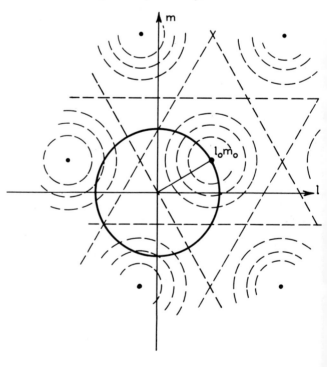

Now if the array of three detectors is set to examine a single wave train characterised by space frequencies l_0, m_0, the true power spectrum is merely a delta function of power density occurring at l_0, m_0 as in Figure 3-2-3. The analysis of the wave records from the array would not represent this spectrum as it really is but would interpret the power as spreading out into a pattern like function $\mathcal{G}$ with its origin set at the point l_0, m_0. This $\mathcal{G}$ pattern is represented by contours of broken lines in Figure 3-2-3. Of course the examination of the wave data would show that the waves had a quite well defined frequency, and in studying sea waves one could ignore waves suggested by the $\mathcal{G}$ pattern that were too long or too short. Indeed, one need only consider waves having a space frequency k_0 that corresponds to the observed time frequency f_0. In the spectrum such waves would be represented by points on a circle of radius k_0 that is sketched in Figure 3-2-3 as a full a large radius and may be large enough to encounter one or more of the other peaks in the repetitive $\mathcal{G}$ pattern. The spread pattern will then show two or more large peaks, and there will be ambiguity in deducing the direction of such waves. A triangular array of detectors is probably at its best in examining waves of wave length about twice the length of its sides, and for "all round" looking an equilateral triangle is best.

It will be observed that some negative values occur in the $\mathcal{G}$ pattern and in the spread patterns. The method of analysis discussed here could lead to power spectra showing occasional negative values. This should not be regarded as a defect. Errors are present everywhere in the spectrum deduced from the array, and errors that make themselves obvious are to be welcomed rather than avoided.

Four Detectors in a "Star": Figure 3-2-4(a) pictures four detectors in a symmetrical star. Six different intervals are present, so the $\mathcal{G}$ function is now the sum of six sinusoids. It has been constructed graphically and is pictured in Figure 3-2-4(b). The pattern is again repetitive, but the individual peaks are more sharply defined. Figure 3-2-4 shows the circle drawn for a wave travelling in a direction parallel to one of the legs of the star and having a wave length twice the length of the leg. The "spread pattern" around this circle of direction is shown in Figure 3-2-5 as a full line. For comparison the spread pattern that would be gotten by three detectors in an equilateral triangle for a wave directed parallel to one side and having a wave length twice the length of that side is shown as a broken line. Evidently the four detectors give a narrower directional spread and are better able to resolve wave directions.

Making Better Use of the Wave Equation: The use that has been made of the wave equation so far is not so effective as it might be. The situation is that from the mechanics of waves we know that at any selected frequency f_0, power must be restricted to points in the l, m plane on the periphery of a circle of radius k_0 corresponding to f_0. If it were possible to evaluate the correlogram for all space intervals, the power spectrum at the selected frequency f_0 would be composed of a very large number of sinusoids, one corresponding to each point in the correlogram, and they would in fact combine to show the power as being zero everywhere except on the circle. Actually we know the

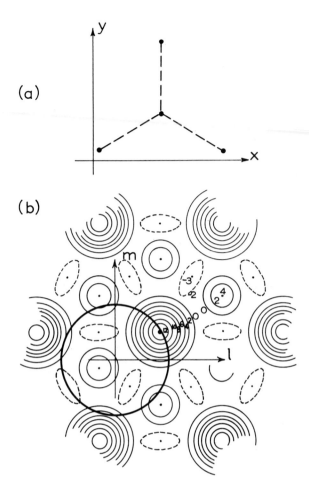

Figure 3-2-4. *Calculation of the function $\mathcal{G}$ for a four-detector symmetrical array.*

value of only a few sinusoids. When these alone are used, the power appears to spread over all wave lengths and directions. Consequently we know *something* about the missing sinusoids; they must be such as to make the power zero everywhere except on the k_0 circle. It seems certain that if we could use the information gotten from the array to create a power spectrum having power only at points on the k_0 circle, the estimate of power distribution on the k_0 circle itself would be improved.

Figure 3-2-5. *Spread pattern of the function $\mathcal{G}$ for three and four detector arrays for specified wave trains.*

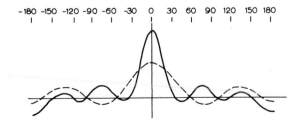

This may be done as follows. Whatever may be the distribution of power around the k_0 circle, say $E(\theta)$ per unit angle at direction θ, it may be expressed as a Fourier series

$$2\pi E(\theta) = A_0 + A_1 \cos \theta + A_2 \cos 2\theta + \ldots$$
$$+ B_1 \sin \theta + B_2 \sin 2\theta + \ldots \quad (26)$$

It is true that all the terms of this series except the first show negative as well as positive values. Such distribution could not by itself represent any realizable wave pattern. However, the expansion is a purely formal one made merely for a mathematical purpose, and in any actual case the sum of the series would everywhere be positive.

Now this power spectrum is the transform of some correlogram. It will be recalled that the transformation from correlogram to power spectrum was thought of in two stages. It was suggested that the wave correlogram $\rho(xy\tau)$ should first be transformed in time τ to give a function $(P + iQ)$ that depended on X, Y, and f and that at any selected frequency f_0 this function (or the set of discrete values representing it) should be transformed in space to give the power distribution $E(l, m, f_0)$ at the selected f_0. For the purpose of the present discussion one need only return to the half-way stage and ask what is the function $(P + iQ)$ whose space transform is the power spectrum that has been called $E(\theta)$.

To answer this, it is more convenient to use polar space coordinates rather than the rectangular ones x, y. These polar coordinates will be written as D, θ, where

$$x = D \cos \theta \quad y = D \sin \theta \quad (27)$$

Then it can readily be shown that the space transform of $E(\theta)$ is

$$P + iQ = \sum_0^{n = \infty} \iota^n [A_n \cos n\theta + B_n \sin n\theta]$$
$$J_n(2\pi k_0 D) \quad (28)$$

It is the sum of a number of patterns, one corresponding to each term of the Fourier series for $E(\theta)$. The writer finds it helpful to visualize these patterns, but it is not essential to do so. The point is that when the "lag correlograms" of the wave records are transformed in time τ, they give a limited number of values of the function $(P + iQ)$ corresponding to various values of the space intervals. From these measured values of $(P + iQ)$ it should be possible by the last equation to deduce at least the early members of the series A_0, A_1, B_1, etc. These estimated values can

then be used to build up $E(\theta)$ or an approximation to it. The advantage of this process is that one is certainly producing a power spectrum in which power appears only on the circle representing permissible wave lengths.

To illustrate this process, consider an equilateral triangle of three detectors (side D) that observes a swell travelling in a direction parallel to one of the legs, $\theta = 0$, and having a wave length twice as long as that leg, $k_0 = 1/2D$. The wave signals at these two detectors will differ in phase by 180 degrees while the other detector pairs, $\theta = \pm 120$ degrees, will show wave signals differing in phase by ± 90 degrees. Of course at zero separation there is phase agreement. Then it can be seen that apart from a normalizing factor, the $P + iQ$ values at these various intervals will be

$$\begin{aligned}
&\text{Separation } (0, 0), &&P + iQ = 1 \\
&\text{Separation } (D, 0), &&P + iQ = -1 \\
&\text{Separation } (D, 120°), &&P + iQ = -i \\
&\text{Separation } (D, -120°), &&P + iQ = -i
\end{aligned} \quad (29)$$

Equating these values to the general expression for $P + iQ$ at these separations leads to the relations

$$1 = A_0 J_0(0)$$
$$-1 = A_0 J_0(\pi) - A_2 J_2(\pi) + A_4 J_4(\pi)$$
$$- A_6 J_6(\pi) + \ldots$$
$$0 = A_0 J_0(\pi) + \tfrac{1}{2} A_2 J_2(\pi) - \tfrac{1}{2} A_4 J_4(\pi)$$
$$- A_6 J_6(\pi) + \ldots$$
$$0 = A_1 J_1(\pi) - A_3 J_3(\pi)$$
$$+ A_5 J_5(\pi) + \ldots \quad (30)$$
$$-1 = -\tfrac{1}{2} A_1 J_1(\pi) - A_3 J_3(\pi)$$
$$- \tfrac{1}{2} A_5 J_5(\pi) + \ldots$$
$$0 = \frac{\sqrt{3}}{2} B_2 J_2(\pi) + \frac{\sqrt{3}}{2} B_4 J_4(\pi) + 0 + \ldots$$
$$0 = \frac{\sqrt{3}}{2} B_1 J_1(\pi) + 0 - \frac{\sqrt{3}}{2} B_5 J_5(\pi) + \ldots$$

At the particular wave length being considered the J functions have arguments equal to π, and their values are

$$\begin{aligned}
&J_0(0) = 1, &&J_0(\pi) = -0.31, \\
&J_1(\pi) = 0.28, &&J_2(\pi) = 0.48 \\
&J_3(\pi) = 0.33, &&J_4(\pi) = 0.15, \\
&J_5(\pi) = 0.05, &&J_6(\pi) = 0.012
\end{aligned} \quad (31)$$

One would expect these seven equations to allow seven of the Fourier coefficients to be calculated, but there are some difficulties. Coefficient B_3 does not appear at all, owing to the particular form of the array, and so is indeterminate. More seriously, all the high-order coefficients enter the equations, so the ones of low order cannot be evaluated without assuming that the ones of higher order are negligible. However, by ignoring the coefficients of the fourth, fifth, seventh, and higher orders, the lower order coefficients are estimated to be

$$A_0 = 1.0, \quad A_1 = 2.4, \quad A_2 = 1.4$$
$$A_3 = 2.0, \quad A_6 = 2.0, \quad B_1 = 0, \qquad (32)$$
$$B_2 = 0.$$

The distribution of power around the k_0 circle, therefore, is estimated to be

$$\begin{aligned} 2\pi E(\theta) = 1 &+ 2.4 \cos\theta + 1.4\cos 2\theta \\ &+ 2.0 \cos 3\theta + 2.0 \cos 6\theta \end{aligned} \qquad (33)$$

This curve is drawn in Figure 3-2-6(a). For comparison the power curve estimated by the previous methods is also shown, as a broken line. There is no appreciable difference between them at the central peak that corresponds to the true direction of the wave, but the peaks that previously appeared at 130 degrees to the true direction have been much reduced. Apparently, the present technique is an improvement on the one indicated in Figure 3-2-3.

The technique can be applied to any simple array of detectors, and the array need not be a

Figure 3-2-6. *Directional spread of power for a triangular array calculated by two methods.*

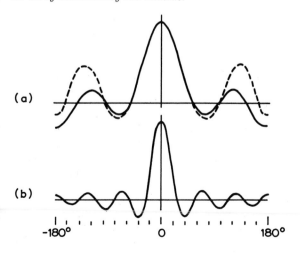

(a)

(b)

-180°   0   180°

symmetrical one. For example, in the case of four detectors in a star, thirteen equations would appear, from which one would aim to find thirteen of the Fourier coefficients for the power distribution on the k_0 circle.

Negative Power: Negative values of power can appear in the estimated spectrum. This is likely to happen when the array is not sufficiently extensive to measure the correlogram adequately. One may merely ignore negative values as being errors, but it seems likely that some use can be made of them. They appear because certain sinusoidal components in the spectrum have not been determined by the array and have therefore been omitted in estimating its form. But it is clear that these missing components must be such as to cancel the impossible negative powers. Therefore, one should be able to guess something about their values and in doing so improve the power estimate.

Negative values, for instance, appear in the curve of Figure 3-2-6(a). This curve was obtained by ignoring the values of A_4, A_5, B_4, and B_5. The equations show that one may introduce an arbitrary A_4 provided that an additional A_2 value is also introduced subject to the relation

$$\frac{A_4}{A_2} = \frac{0.15}{0.48} \qquad (34)$$

One may also introduce an arbitrary A_5 so long as an additional A_1 is introduced subject to the relation

$$\frac{A_5}{A_1} = \frac{-0.28}{0.05} \qquad (35)$$

Trial suggests that both A_4 and A_5 might be given the value of 2.0 and B_4 and B_5 left as zero. Then the series become

$$\begin{aligned} 2\pi E(\theta) = 1 &+ 2.1 \cos\theta + 2.0 \cos 2\theta \\ &+ 2.0 \cos 3\theta \\ &+ 2.0 \cos 4\theta + 2.0 \cos 5\theta \\ &+ 2.0 \cos 6\theta \end{aligned} \qquad (36)$$

The new curve is plotted in Figure 3-2-6(b). It shows an obvious improvement in the spread pattern. When negative estimates of power appear, it seems that they can help to improve the estimate of the power distribution. Although the methods used in this illustration are rather subjective, attention is drawn to a quite systematic method that was developed by M. S.

Longuet-Higgins to serve a similar purpose and may perhaps be modified to suit the present purpose. ("Bounds for the integral of a non-negative function in terms of its Fourier coefficients." *Proc. Cam. Phil. Soc.* 51, 590–603, 1955).

APPENDIX

The Convolution Theorem Summarized: Any function $u(x)$ and its Fourier transform $U(l)$ are related by the equations

$$u(x) = \int_{-\infty}^{\infty} U(l) \exp i2\pi lx \, dl \qquad \text{(a)}$$
$$\qquad\qquad\qquad\qquad\qquad\qquad\qquad (37)$$
$$U(l) = \int_{-\infty}^{\infty} u(x) \exp -i2\pi lx \, dx \qquad \text{(b)}$$

These will be abbreviated to the statement

$$u(x) \quad has\ the\ transform \quad U(l) \qquad (38)$$

Similarly one may suppose there is another function $v(x)$ and its transform $V(l)$

$$v(x) \quad has\ the\ transform \quad V(l) \qquad (39)$$

These four functions may in general all have complex values though the variables x and l are real. One may then consider the conjugate forms gotten by changing the sign of i. Equations (37a and b) will still be true if the sign of i is changed on each side. When i is not explicitly shown, as in $u(x)$, the fact that the conjugate form is being used will be indicated by an asterisk as in $u^*(x)$.

Then using equations of the type (37a), it is evident that

$$u^*(x) \cdot v(x) = \int_{-\infty}^{\infty} U^*(p) \exp -i2\pi px \, dp$$
$$\int_{-\infty}^{\infty} V(q) \exp i2\pi qx \, dq \quad (40)$$

where, of course, p and q represent the different

values in the two integrals. Rearranging this expression and writing $q - p$ as l, gives

$$u^*(x) \cdot v(x) =$$
$$\int_{-\infty}^{\infty} \exp i2\pi lx \, dl \int_{-\infty}^{\infty} U^*(p)V(l + p)dp \quad (41)$$

On comparing the form of this equation with that of Equation (37a), it is evident that

$u^*(x)v(x)$ *has the transform*

$$\int_{-\infty}^{\infty} U^*(p)V(l + p)dp \quad (42)$$

The last integral is called a convolution of the functions U and V. In a similar way, using equations like 37(b), it may be shown that

$$\int_{-\infty}^{\infty} u^*(x)v(x + X)dx \quad has\ the\ transform$$
$$U^*(l) \cdot U(l) \quad (43)$$

This integral is the convolution of u and v.

Certain forms of the theorem are of use in the previous text. If u is a real function such as a record of wave elevation, Equation (43) shows that its convolution has a transform that is the squared modulus of the transform of u.

On the other hand, if $u(x)$ and $v(x)$ are both real, their transforms have conjugate symmetry in that

$$U^*(l) = U(-l) \quad (44)$$

Then from Equation (42) the product of u and v has a transform that is the convolution of their separate transforms:

$u(x)v(x)$ *has the transform*

$$\int_{-\infty}^{\infty} U(p)V(l - p)dp \quad (45)$$

This relates to the conversion of the correlogram into the power spectrum when the correlogram has been multiplied by some factor.

A PLEA FOR THE RECTANGULAR LAG WINDOW

An experimental time series is always of limited duration. It is well understood that its power spectrum does not bear too detailed an examination. The most rapid variations of power with frequency are mere accidental characters of that particular experimental sample. One needs to smooth the spectrum by some averaging factor in order to cut down the accidental variations while leaving the broader features that would be common to the spectra of all samples.

The power spectrum is found as the Fourier transform of the correlogram, and to smooth the spectrum one weights the correlogram by a factor that is zero at large lag intervals but rises to unity at zero. The use of such a factor or *lag window* has the pleasant advantage of reducing the numerical computation while it improves the final power estimate.

Three possible lag windows are pictured in Figure 3-3-1(a). They have been chosen so as to be equally effective in reducing the accidental detail. The criterion is that they have the same maximum value (unity) and the same integral of their squared values. It should be noted that it is only in those parts of the spectrum where the power varies quite slowly with frequency that the best stability is achieved. Narrow peaks of power in the spectrum will still show large variations from sample to sample in spite of the use of the lag window.

These lag windows automatically produce averaging factors or *spectral windows* that smooth the power spectrum. Their forms are shown in Figure 3-3-1(b). The spectral window is the Fourier transform of the lag window. Of course, a spectral window not only cuts down the accidental detail but also smooths, and may to some extent obscure, the significant details of the spectrum. Since all the spectral windows in Figure 3-3-1(b) are equally effective in suppressing accidental detail, one must decide which window will confuse the true spectrum least. There is probably little to choose between them in those parts of the spectrum where they best reduce the accidental detail, for this occurs where the spectrum is very smooth and uniform and would be well represented by any of the windows. If, however, the true spectrum contains sharp peaks, each of these spreads out into a pattern like the spectral window. The broad spectral window with numerous side lobes therefore seems to be the least desirable of those illustrated. Consequently one avoids using the rectangular lag window that produces it.

But in some experimental work a quite different situation can arise. In radio astronomy, or in studies of ocean surface waves or seismic waves, one is interested not only in waves of different frequency but in their wave length and direction of travel. These last two features can be interpreted in terms of frequencies in space or the

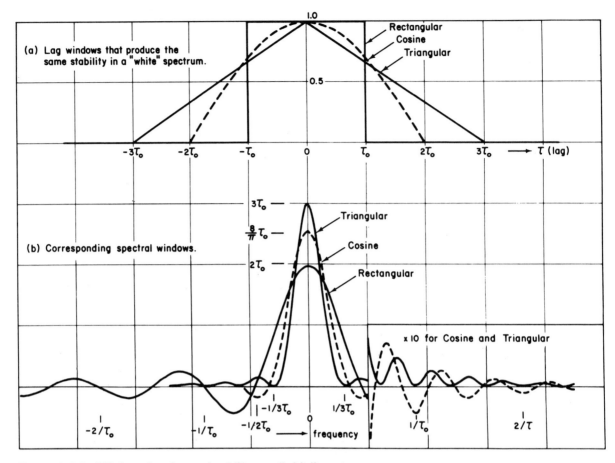

Figure 3-3-1. *Windows that give equal stability to a "white" spectrum.*

number of cycles of the wave per unit space interval along rectangular space axes. The directional power spectrum (which shows how power is distributed over the range of space frequencies) is obtained as the transform of the space correlogram of the waves. Thus, two detectors may be placed at some short separation D along the x axis; after the signals are filtered (or some other means is used to restrict attention to waves near to some prescribed frequency in time), they may be correlated by forming a time average of their product. This correlation is the value of the space correlogram for the interval D in the x direction. Using other detectors, one may in the same way find values of the space correlogram at intervals $2D$, $3D$, etc., in the x direction. In many cases it is desirable to make the intervals extend also in the y direction (at right angles to x).

To get the directional spectrum it is also necessary to measure "quadrature" correlations, obtained by delaying one of the signals by $\frac{1}{4}$ cycle in time. This, however, is incidental to the present argument. The important point is that these cor-

relation values are obtained by a time average and that good stability in the correlation and consequently in the directional spectrum can be gotten by making the averaging time sufficiently long. One, therefore, is in the position of being able to find stable correlation values at some limited number of space intervals. The limitation to the size of the space intervals is not imposed in an effort to produce stability but is imposed by practical limitations on the number of detectors that can be used, or by limitations on the over-all dimensions of the array.

Thinking of one space dimension only, one can suppose that stable correlation values have been found for space intervals 0, D, $2D \ldots ND$. These values also indicate the correlations at negative intervals $-D$, $-2D \ldots -ND$ since the co-correlation is an even function and the quadrature correlation is an odd function of the space interval. One has good measurements, therefore, of the space correlogram between $-ND$ and ND. Correlations at larger intervals are unknown, and in calculating the directional power spectrum these are usually treated as being zero. Practical limitations, therefore, have produced a lag window limiting the correlogram to the range $\pm ND$ in space.

What shall be done with the measured correlations? If they are transformed without further change, this is analogous to using a rectangular "lag window." Would it perhaps give a less confused spectrum if the correlations were to be given a cosine or a triangular weighting by analogy with the "lag windows" that seemed better for the time series discussed at first?

The basis for comparison is now rather different. The known correlations extend between $\pm x_0$ in space ($x_0 = ND$), and the spatial "lag windows" are all limited to this length. Three possible forms are illustrated in Figure 3-3-2(a). The corresponding "spectral windows" are pictured in Figure 3-3-2(b), where the horizontal coordinate is now the space frequency or cycles of the wave per unit distance. Which of these spectral windows will least confuse the spectrum? Opinions appear to differ. Some radio astronomers are quite happy to use the rectangular window and some

prefer to taper the correlogram. These choices are implicit even when the measuring technique does not develop the space correlogram explicitly. If for instance one has antennae at positions x, $x + D$, $x + 2D$, ... $x + ND$, one usually adds the output signals, say V_0, V_1, ... V_N and measures the power or mean square of the combined signal. Evidently this can be written

$$\text{Power} = \text{mean square } \sum_0^N V_n$$

$$= \text{mean of } \sum_0^N \sum_0^N V_n V_m \tag{1}$$

The measured power is therefore the sum of many mean squares and mean products of different pairs of signals. But the mean product $V_n V_m$ is evidently the correlation from detectors separated by a distance $(n - m)D$. With this uniform array of detectors there are $(N + 1)$ mean squares, each of which corresponds to the correlation at zero space interval. Similarly there are $2N$ products between signals from detectors at an interval D, so it is as if the correlations at inter-

Figure 3-3-2. *Windows at choice when the correlogram is stable but is curtailed to lags* $\pm x_0$.

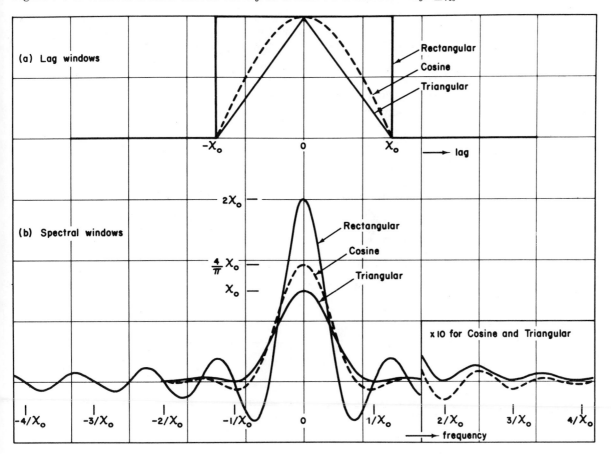

val D and at interval $-D$ are added with weighting N. As the interval increases, the weighting falls till correlations at intervals ND and $-ND$ are present with only unit weighting. Thus the uniform array of detectors implies a triangular lag window.

On the other hand, some systems measure the mean product of the signals from two different sets of antennae, and these systems are easily arranged to give equal weight to all space intervals. Therefore, they achieve a rectangular "lag window."

In spite of the numerous side lobes in its spectral window, I am inclined to think that the rectangular lag window is the best of all windows of equal over-all width. When stability is not in question, it would be a mistake to reject it without thought. I go on to list its properties.

PROPERTIES OF THE RECTANGULAR LAG WINDOW

1. The rectangular lag window is one of the few lag windows that can sometimes lead to an exact representation of the power spectrum. This is easily seen as follows: one may meet cases in which the correlogram is really zero outside some range of lag $\pm x_0$. Thus, cutting it short at these points does not change it at all. But if one goes further and introduces weightings other than unity within this range, the correlogram and its spectrum are both changed. It is sometimes thought desirable to use spectral windows that are entirely positive. It is easy to show, then, that

the associated lag windows may have value unity at the origin but must be less than unity everywhere else. Positive spectral windows can never represent the spectrum exactly, no matter how broad and simple the spectrum may be (unless it is perfectly flat).

2. The spectrum resulting from a rectangular lag window has an error whose square, averaged over the whole spectrum, is smaller than that of the spectrum produced by any other lag window of the same width. This has been pointed out by Arsac (1955). It is a valid argument in favour of the rectangular lag window if one is dealing with spectra that contain no very narrow peaks. Figure 3-3-3 shows that the rectangular window gives a quite good representation of a triangular power distribution whose over-all width is only twice that of the spectral window between its first zeros. The representation given by the cosine lag window is noticeably worse.

3. The rectangular lag window can occasionally lead to negative estimates of power in some regions of the spectrum. This is a virtue not a defect. The spectrum is likely to be full of errors whatever lag window we use. With a rectangular lag window it has been seen that the mean square error is less than for any other window of equal width. When some errors distinguish themselves by leading to impossible negative values of energy, we may merely ignore all negative values and get a spectrum whose error is smaller than before.

But the point can be carried further. When negative values arise through the use of a rec-

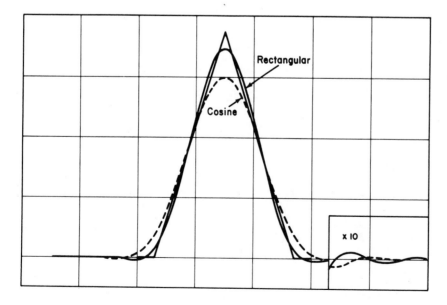

Figure 3-3-3. *Representations of a triangular power distribution.*

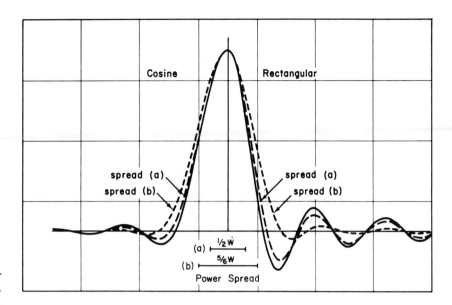

Figure 3-3-4. *Patterns representing narrow spreads of power.*

tangular lag window, it is because the correlogram really has appreciable values outside the selected range $\pm x_0$, and these have been ignored. The presence of negative values in the spectrum tells something about these unknown values of the correlogram; they must be such as to annul all its negative values. This use of negatives to delineate the spectrum more exactly has been developed by M. S. Longuet-Higgins.

4. When the spectrum has narrow peaks of power, they are more readily recognised with the rectangular lag window whose central peak is higher and whose pattern of side lobes is distinctive. The distinction between true delta functions and power peaks with a quite small spread in frequency is most easily detected with the rectangular lag window. Figure 3-3-4 compares in this respect the rectangular lag window (on the right) with the cosine (on the left). With increasing spread of power the changes in the pattern given by the

rectangular lag window are more obvious. The curves illustrate true power spread uniformly over widths of 0 (a delta function) and $\frac{1}{2}W$ and $\frac{5}{6}W$, where W is the width of the (rectangular) spectral window between its first zeros. Actually W is $1/x_0$, where $\pm x_0$ is the over-all length of the correlogram window. Curves have been drawn to the same peak height, but the cosine window would of course give smaller peaks than would the rectangular window (see Figure 3-3-2).

REFERENCES

Arsac, J. "Transmissions des fréquences spatiales dans les systèmes recepteurs d'ondes courtes." *Optica Acta* II (1955), 112.

Longuet-Higgins, M. S. "Bounds for the integral of a non-negative function in terms of its Fourier harmonics." *Proc. Cam. Phil. Soc.* LI (1955) 590–603.

DISCUSSION

Mr. Cartwright: In Figure 3-3-1(b) the power distribution, when it is projected on the l axis, will tend to have singularities or high peaks at the limits $\pm l/L$ if there is appreciable power in waves travelling approximately along the line of detectors. The effect will be very marked if the wind is blowing along the line of detectors. Does this

not explain the tendency of the correlogram to persist for large distances down wind? The power peak will be broader and the correlogram less persistent if the waves have a wide angular spread. As I see it, it is mainly the angular spread of the waves that controls the persistence of the correlogram down wind, but in the paper this persistence is attributed to the narrowness of the frequency band that has been selected.

I can see that the directional resolving power of an array deteriorates as one uses it to examine longer waves, but I do not agree that it loses all directional properties for very long waves. If the detectors are sufficiently accurate, the differences of their outputs are measures of the slopes of the water surface. The buoy that we have been using measures the elevation and two slopes at a point on the water, and from it we can deduce the first five Fourier coefficients in the angular distribution of wave power at any selected frequency.

Dr. Barber: Mr. Cartwright's first comment summarizes the situation well. The projected power will certainly tend to peak sharply at the limiting value of l, and the higher and narrower this peak, the more persistent the correlogram will be. I think that there are two ways in which the peak can be made wider. If the waves have a large angular spread, the power will spread into smaller values of l so the peak will have a gentler slope on that side. On the other hand, a fairly wide frequency band will mean that power is being projected from an annulus rather than a ring, and the projected power will then fall away more gently toward the limiting value of l. Both angular spread and frequency spread seem able to affect the down-wind correlogram. With narrow frequency bands, I must agree that the angular spread may have the largest effect.

I agree fully with the second comment too. The triangle of detectors that Dr. W. H. Munk has used at the Scripp's Institution has served to give directions of swell of very low frequency and long wave length. The correlations between three detectors (at a selected frequency) give seven numbers, and in general one would expect them to serve to find seven characteristics of the angular distribution of power. With very long waves, however, it appears that they serve only to find six characteristics, and only six characteristics could be found even with a more complicated array.

The reason is as follows: correlations between detectors provide the space correlogram (or its values at certain points). The "in phase" correlations refer to a correlogram made up of sinusoids, each of which corresponds to a wave train in the sea but takes its positive maximum value at the space origin (x, y = zero). This correlogram is an even function and could be expressed by

the formula

$$\rho_1 = a + bx^2 + cxy + dy^2$$
$$+ \text{ etc. (even powers)} \quad (1)$$

Arrays of small extent (relative to the wave length) can observe the correlogram only near to the xy origin. Here the correlogram is fully described by the four coefficients a, b, c, and d. Actually, three detectors provide only four "in phase" correlation values, so even for long waves these are all meaningful.

The "quadrature" correlations, obtained by delaying one signal of any pair by a quarter cycle, refer to a correlogram made up of sinusoids that all take zero values at the origin. This space correlogram is an odd function and could be expressed by the formula

$$\rho_2 = px + qy + \text{ etc. (odd powers)} \quad (2)$$

Near its origin it is fully described by only two coefficients. Actually, the three detectors provide three values of quadrature correlation. Evidently they cannot be independent when the waves are very long. One can readily show that they tend to add up to zero.

I conclude that no array can determine more than six directional characteristics of long waves. I understand that the buoy used by Dr. Cartwright determines five. The extra one given by the triangular array is a measure of the wave length or wave number at the selected frequency.

Mr. Cartwright: I feel uneasy about Dr. Barber's deduction that a small array can measure no more than six coefficients of the space correlogram. Taking for instance the real correlogram which is even, if one can measure values near to the origin with sufficient accuracy to estimate by differences the second derivatives, getting the coefficients of x^2, xy, and y^2, surely somewhat greater accuracy will allow one to estimate fourth derivatives and get the coefficients of x^4, x^3y, x^2y^2, xy^3, and y^4. Similarly in the imaginary correlogram one should, by greater accuracy, be able to find the third derivative and estimate the coefficients for x^3, x^2y, xy^2, and y^3.

The point is of particular interest to me because I have in view a system of flat buoys attached to a common rigid frame, designed to obtain coefficients of a higher order than are provided by our present wave-measuring buoy. This system will measure the first differences of slopes, which approximate the second derivatives of the elevation.

Dr. Barber: I agree with Mr. Cartwright. The information that a small array can give depends upon what we assume it can measure.

With instruments that measure elevation one has the feeling that he will fail to detect any difference between signals given by instruments that are very close together. When this happens, a small array observes only the elevation at a point and loses all its directional properties.

This need not happen. One might use very sensitive differential pressure instruments or measure water slopes, as is done with the N.I.O. buoy. If a small system is able to detect the elevation and the two gradients of elevation, it provides six parameters of the power distribution. I think it is true that the N.I.O. buoy measures wave length in addition to the five Fourier coefficients.

The next stage would be a small system that would, in addition, measure the curvatures and twist of the water surface. These are due in part to the third and fourth order Fourier coefficients, and such a system would give information about them. I think this is what Mr. Cartwright has in mind with his new buoy.

Dr. Longuet-Higgins: Dr. Barber's contribution seems to me to be an attractive account of Fourier analysis and linear detector theory, in which many different points of view are brought together. I particularly like the author's derivation of the sensitivity patterns corresponding to various simple arrays.

Some Isolated Remarks: Under the heading "persistence" the author points out that if sea conditions are not rapidly changing, then the correlations may be evaluated successively and not simultaneously. I would add that this procedure may be advantageous from the point of view of reducing statistical errors, since it increases the number of degrees of freedom in an over-all estimate of the spectrum.

On the subject of "line arrays" the author suggests that it is improbable that any wave energy would be approaching the array from the down-wind side. However, various nonlinear effects may produce appreciable energy traveling in the opposite sense; as do, for example, the tertiary wave interactions, which were mentioned by Dr. Phillips, and will be discussed in this after-

noon's session. Breaking of the waves may also contribute some appreciable energy.

At the end of his paper the author hints that the analysis of a paper of mine (to which he refers) might perhaps be modified in order to improve an estimate of the spectrum derived from only a limited number of harmonics. Perhaps I ought to give an opinion on this.

Briefly, the method referred to is applicable in a situation where we are given, experimentally, certain Fourier coefficients of a function $f(\theta)$ defined in $0 \leqslant \theta \leqslant 2\pi$, and we know that $f(\theta)$ is non-negative. The method was first applied to measurements from the pitch-and-roll buoy, where we know, for example, a_0, a_1, b_1, a_2, b_2, and where $f(\theta)$ is simply the energy-density $f(k, \theta)$. It is also applicable when we have a line array of detectors with pairs of spacings $X, 2X, 3X \text{---} NX$, where X is less than half a wave length. For then, as the author has shown, we have the first $2N + 1$ Fourier coefficients related to the projection of $[f(k, \theta) + f(k, -\theta)]$ on the line of the array. However, in the more general case when the detectors are not all in one line, the situation appears from the author's paper to be more complicated. For the author has shown that $P + iQ$ is given by an *infinite* series of harmonic components and the Fourier coefficients are found by truncating the series at some arbitrary point and then solving the equation. So the estimates of the coefficients are themselves approximations, containing errors of the same order of magnitude as those that we are trying to eliminate by the introduction of further harmonics. I doubt whether my method could cope with this.

Dr. Tick: The paper by Professor Barber is a most interesting application of some of the ideas of antenna theory to the determination of the directional spectrum from a set of wave recorders in space. Unfortunately, the paper is exceedingly concise, and since my knowledge of antenna theory is all but non-existent I do not feel able to comment on the "meat" of the paper. However, this dinner does have an "appetizer" of an elementary exposition of random processes as they apply to wave studies. I shall restrict my comments to that.

Professor Barber states that it is not strictly correct to think of waves as a superposition of many long-crested wave trains unless the slopes are small. Let me point out that Fourier's theorem is true for all integrable functions and that the spectral representation theorem states that *any* stationary random process can be represented as a superposition of complex exponentials with uncorrelated coefficients. It may not be the case that the coefficients are statistically independent, but they are uncorrelated.

I doubt if **A**'s are best regarded as coming from a Gaussian family of complex numbers. There is a tendency among many geophysicists to regard all stationary processes as Gaussian. In fact the nonlinear hydrodynamic equations indicate that Gaussian processes are only an approximation.

Professor Barber says that since the "intervening values of correlation [are] not known, [they] would have to be treated as zero." This is not the case. The intervening values are filled in by interpolation.

Dr. Barber: In regard to Dr. Tick's discussion, I think some of the difficulties here are somewhat my fault in that I tried to omit as many equations as I could. Partly this allows me to be a little woolly. The sort of mathematics that I do here is all pictorial, as you see, so I was trying to draw it pictorially in the paper to avoid putting in those horrible things with triple integrals, and so on. As a matter of fact, I don't believe equations until I can see a picture of why they work, and then I believe them.

I intend the meaning that if wave slopes are small, the sinusoids obtained by the Fourier Transformation correspond to trains of gravity waves propagating with a velocity appropriate to their wave number, but that it would not be correct to apply this simple interpretation to the sinusoids gotten by a Fourier analysis of waves of finite slope. Thus, the "second-order" components of the spectrum as derived by Dr. Tick do not, I imagine, correspond to wave trains that could propagate away from the disturbed region of sea and be encountered elsewhere as short-period swell.

I agree that most geophysicists like to think that their variables are Gaussian rather than near-Gaussian. When one is able to take account of nonlinear behaviour, as Dr. Tick has done, it is of course a valuable advance. Yet the problems of geophysics are always abstractions from the real world, and one has to be content with abstractions that are tractable. Perhaps Dr. Tick will suggest some text where the statistics of a non-Gaussian variable are discussed.

I assume that it is profitless to interpolate between discrete values of a function if the properties of a function are unknown. I go on to show that if the spectrum is band-limited, it may be calculated exactly from the known discrete values of the function. In making this argument, I assume that the transform of a set of equal delta functions equally spaced is itself a set of delta functions equally spaced. Are these assumptions incorrect?

The discussion of practical methods assumes that the waves have ergodic properties, and at the start I try to show why it is that this assumption makes the practical problem simpler.

The whole paper is merely my own way of looking at the problems of direction finding. I aimed to start from the ground up, and I do not call upon any accepted body of "antenna theory." Readers of the second half would therefore be wise to show the same healthy scepticism that Dr. Tick has shown in reading the first half. Since the mathematical arguments I make all have a pictorial form, I hope to make the paper more readable by omitting most of the equations.

Dr. Munk: I will be very brief. We would appreciate showing you some of the results obtained with our triple station. We now have approximately a hundred consecutive and high-quality direction spectra as a result of work done by Frank Snodgrass, Gaylord Miller, and me for more years than I would like to admit to this audience. I notice that Dr. Longuet-Higgins' paper also had three authors and that it refers to weather maps dated 1955–56. I think there is some similarity in difficulty between the two investigations. Looking back to operation SWOP, maybe we can consider the difficulty as proportional to the number of authors.

The method we used is the one that Dr. Barber has mentioned briefly. Three wave recorders were located in a depth of 100 meters of water, measuring bottom pressure against time, using Frank Snodgrass's vibrotron. The triangle was 1,000 feet on its side. The output of the pressure transducers was in fact a frequency modulated signal, which was counted by electronic counters in the laboratory and immediately recorded in digital form. We took an average of 10,000 numbers per day for 100 days.

As I say, we have obtained 100 consecutive daily spectra. For each day we would separate our spectrum into 100 frequency bands with roughly 60 degrees of freedom. For each of those we would

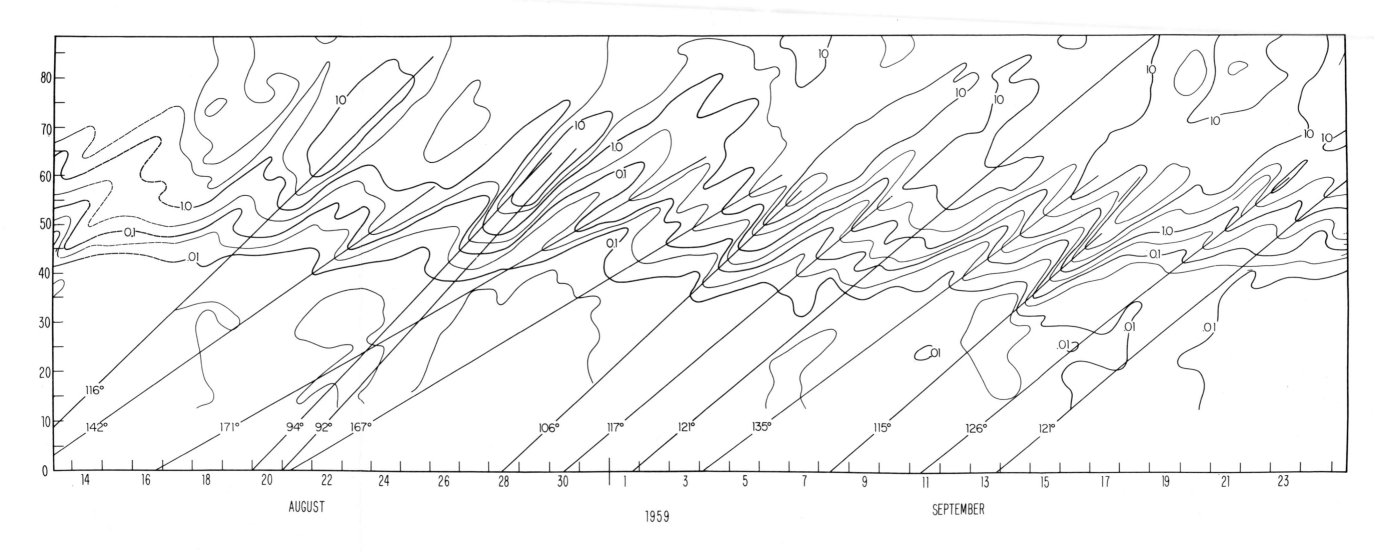

Figure 3-3D-1. *Contours of equal power density, E(f, t), on a frequency-time plot. The contours are at equal intervals of log E(f, t). Heavy contours correspond to .01, 0.1, 1.0, and 10 cm²/cpks. On the time axis the ticks designate midnight GCT. The ridge lines correspond to the dispersive arrivals from a single source, and their slope is inversely proportional to the distance from the source. For each ridge line we have marked the great circle distance in degrees.*

obtain 7 independent numbers, namely, the 7 correlation functions that Dr. Barber mentioned.

The main difference between this work and the other two efforts to get directional spectra (Longuet-Higgins' and SWOP) is that we deliberately emphasized the low-frequency shoulder of the spectrum — the swell. It is a different problem in many ways from measuring the angular distribution of a locally generated sea.

Figure 3-3D-1 is a contour diagram, dated in 1959 and extending over a period of two months. It shows frequency and contours of power density obtained from a daily spectrum. The heavy lines differ by a factor of ten in energy density. In one area we have, corresponding to about 80 cycles per kilosecond (about 12-second waves) an energy density 1,000 times on the average above that in another area where we are dealing with something like 30-second waves.

So we are dealing with a low-frequency shoulder of the wave spectrum. What is characteristic is that superimposed on this steep hill going from the low frequencies to the local sea are very pronounced ridge lines that, on the average, rise 100 times above background. They are very clear. There is no doubt, generally, of how they need to be contoured. They represent the arrival of dispersive signals much as was shown by Barber years ago at N.I.O. in a slightly different display.

The theory predicts that those should be straight ridges, and they are remarkably straight. The theory predicts that in this kind of display the slope is proportional to the inverse distance and the intercept at the zero axis is equal to the time of origin.

We have in this particular chart something like 12 outstanding arrivals. For each of those we could put down a number giving the angular distance (the angle subtended at the center of the earth) and the time of origin. Nothing has been said about direction so far.

We have gotten lower frequencies than anyone else has managed to get by this kind of effort. We do get waves up to 28, 29, and 30 seconds, first showing up on these ridge lines before they disappear about a week later. So one can get extremely low frequencies with this kind of instrumentation.

The distances generally are of the order of 120 degrees subtended at the center of the earth and our array faced towards the south, southwest, and west.

The chief surprise is that there were two cases where the distance was appreciably longer than the others. When the distances are computed, they are of the order of 180 degrees. In other words, they indicate an origin from the other side of the world.

The only possible route is a great circle through the window between Australia and Antarctica, which gives you an unimpeded oceanic view to the Antipole somewhere near Kerguelen Island.

Now, the direction was obtained by the method mentioned by Dr. Barber. We first tried something very akin to what Dr. Longuet-Higgins discussed (with differences I have no time to go into), and found in most instances, particularly on top of the ridges, that the results did not differ very appreciably from what you would expect from a single, narrow source. This is not a surprising result since we are working a long distance from storm centers. This being the case, we made a synthesis by finding the most prominent single source (in the least-square sense), and the numbers that cover this frequency time-diagram show the best point sources consistent with each time and each frequency band. We have at least one criterion of success. We can say that our point source solution has eliminated a given fraction of the energy. In some instances this fraction is 0.9. So one feels that this most simple-minded method is a quite satisfactory procedure.

At the low frequency end, we begin to see the effects of refraction in the sense that one would expect, with the waves turning parallel to shore. The question immediately arises of whether these long arrivals come from the right direction. They do.

I have since had some weather maps from the French Weather Service, which indicate that there were three heavy storms during the time we recorded, and the two arrivals correspond very nicely to two of these. The third checked on hindsight. I think there is no question that we have been able to detect swell from very severe storms halfway around the earth.

There are two more interesting features I would like to mention. One is that following the heavy ridge lines there is a general decay of energy. In principle there are two possible causes. It could be the arrival of wave energy from a decaying storm, or it could be the scattered arrival of wave energy from a short-lived storm. Scattered in the sense that it is scattered by coast lines all around the world and by islands.

I am almost sure that the second is the more

reasonable interpretation of the data, and it would appear that the Pacific Basin has a sort of reverberation time of about one week for the long swell. Some of the energy is reflected on the sides — not very much — so that from heavy arrivals you are down to a noise level after five or six or ten reflections at the boundaries.

This indicates a rather surprisingly small reflection from the coast line, and one thing we have learned is that it really would have been possible to make a quite sensible analysis with two instruments only, since reflection from shore is a somewhat minor factor if one is concerned with picking up the heaviest storms.

We are now convinced that our system is the simplest method of obtaining day-to-day directional spectra. This agreement is not unanimous along these lines; Longuet-Higgins feels that their procedure is the most promising and Pierson bets on SWOP.

NONLINEAR ASPECTS OF

THE SPECTRUM

CARL ECKART

CHAIRMAN

LEO JOSEPH TICK

O N E

NONLINEAR PROBABILITY MODELS OF OCEAN WAVES*

INTRODUCTION

The past decade has seen a tremendous expansion in the use of random-process models for the study of ocean waves. In fact, the concept which is the subject of this conference — ocean-wave spectra — becomes richest when viewed as part of random-process theory.† The expansion in use is due to the considerable success in understanding, description, and prediction which followed the early applications. Since many of the pioneers are present at this conference, since there is some lack of general agreement as to history, and since there are enough controversial points to be raised on technical aspects, I shall avoid that topic.

The earliest approaches involved little more than the assumption (often implicit) that the time series observed was a finite segment of a realization (sample function) of a stationary process. Later, hydrodynamics was formally introduced by having the space-time process satisfy some relevant differential equations. It manifested

this attribute by reducing the dimensionality of the spectrum. That is to say, in the long-crested case, the two-dimensional surface process has a one-dimensional spectrum. To complete the description of the process a Gaussian assumption was made about the probability structure. Although it seems to me that this was mainly for convenience, many of the deductions from this model were found to be in reasonable agreement with nature. A number of papers were written on distributions of various properties of this model, like crests and other geometrically interesting characteristics.

Most of this development was centered about the stationary process, which was potential and satisfied the linearized free-surface and pressure equations, with pressure equal to a constant. More recently, in the study of the problems of wave generation (not stationary in time but stationary in space), the condition of constant pressure was removed and an assumed random atmospheric pressure field inserted. The inadequacies of these models are well known to most of you (even better than to me). The fashion today in many areas of mechanics is toward nonlinear models. It is in this direction that some investigators (including the author) have moved to alleviate the above-mentioned inadequacies. Apart from fashion, it is essential that our models contain some nonlinearity. In wave studies, as in many areas of applied fluid mechanics, it is of

* The research reported in this paper was supported by the David Taylor Model Basin, Geophysics Branch, Office of Naval Research, and Bureau of Ships under Contracts Nonr-285(17), Nonr-285(03), and NObs-72018. Reproduction in whole or in part for any purpose of the United States government is permitted.

† In some areas of applications this was not recognized — to the later discomfort of some of the original appliers.

extreme interest to know the mechanism by which energy entering into the system is changed in character, distributed, and dissipated. In essence, how are the frequencies changed? Such change is possible only in a nonlinear system.

In this paper I shall discuss mainly, with criticism, my own small efforts in the construction of nonlinear, stationary random models of waves. The emphasis will be as much (if not more) methodological as substantive. (If research is to be expended in this direction, it would be well to appreciate in advance the analytical problems that arise due to the interaction between the nonlinear and probability elements of the problem.) The particular models that I shall discuss are those for long-crested waves with infinite and finite depth. Originally I had hoped to discuss the short-crested case, but the results in this direction are too meager to present at this time.

NONLINEAR EQUATIONS AND PERTURBATIONS

In a great many problems of mathematical physics in which the describing equations are nonlinear, there is a known linearization which gives reasonably good results. These linearizations are often made by assuming that some parameter in the system is small in the usual circumstances and truncating an expansion in this parameter after the linear terms. In gravity water waves theory the resulting equations after such an expansion are referred to as the "theory of small oscillations." If the resulting linear theory is good, it is natural to expect that taking the next (quadratic) term in the expansion would constitute an improvement. Since the linear theory is good, one may also expect that a few terms of the series will extract most of the information present in the original equations. The procedure of finding an approximate equation set is called, of course, the perturbation method. The equations that were used in the linear random theory were obtained in this way, and as they proved very useful, it was natural to consider an "improvement" by obtaining the next (quadratic) term in the perturbation expansion.

QUADRATIC PROCESS IN INFINITE DEPTH, INFINITE CREST CASE

The procedure outlined above was carried out in

Reference (2), page 173, for the infinite depth, infinite crest case. The development given there will not be repeated here. It is enough to give the result. The linear plus quadratic expression (in spectral terms) for the free surface process at a fixed point is given by

$$\eta(t) = \eta^{(1)} + \frac{1}{g}\eta^{(2)}(t) \qquad (1)$$

where

$$\eta^{(1)}(t) = \int e^{-i\omega t}d\xi(\omega) \qquad (2)$$

$$\eta^{(2)}(t) = \int\int e^{-i(\omega+\omega')t}Q(\omega,\omega')d\xi(\omega)d\xi(\omega') \qquad (3)$$

and

$$Q(\omega,\omega') = -[sgn(\omega)sgn(\omega')]\frac{||\omega|\omega + |\omega'|\omega'|}{2} \qquad (4)$$

The $d\xi(\omega)$ are the random coefficients, and

$$E|d\xi(\omega)|^2 = s^{(1)}(\omega)d\omega$$

where $s(\omega)$ is the spectral density. The only probability assumption made to get $(1) - (4)$ is that the processes were jointly stationary in space and time. The spectra are of great interest, but in order to obtain them for Equation (1), further assumptions must be made about the probability structure, as expressions of the form

$$E[d\xi(\alpha)d\xi(\beta)d\xi(\gamma)]$$

and

$$E[d\xi(\alpha)d\xi(\beta)d\xi(\gamma)d\xi(\sigma)]$$

need to be evaluated. Since the linear model with the Gaussian assumption was in fair agreement with observations,* it was natural to make this assumption about $\eta^{(1)}(t)$. The spectral density of $\eta(t)$ is then

$$\text{spec. of } \eta(t) = s^{(1)}(\omega)$$
$$+ \frac{1}{g^2}\int_{-\infty}^{\infty}\frac{[|\omega - \lambda|(\omega - \lambda) + |\lambda|\lambda]^2}{2}$$
$$s^{(1)}(\omega - \lambda)s^{(1)}(\lambda)d\lambda \qquad (5)$$
$$= s^{(1)}(\omega) + \left(\frac{1}{g^2}\right)s^{(2)}(\omega)$$

[Notice that Equation (5) is *exactly* the spectral density of $\eta(t)$. No order statements are made about (5).] For the perturbation procedure to be

---

* Certainly to the extent of applicability of linear, potential motion.

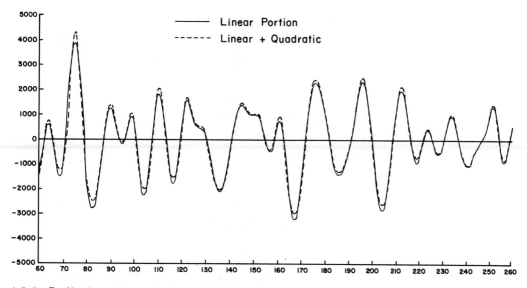

Figure 4-1-1. *Realization of the quadratic model for infinite depth.*

useful, $\eta^{(2)}/g$ must in some sense be smaller than $\eta^{(1)}$. As a result of the Gaussian assumption, the average value of cross products of $\eta^{(1)}$ and $\eta^{(2)}$ is zero. Therefore, the correction to the spectrum of $s^{(1)}(\omega)$ due to $\eta^{(2)}$ could be small. This is borne out by numerous calculations. At least two conclusions are possible. One is the method is not good or that the linear equations are the best that can be done with potential flow. The second is that the Gaussian assumption is not sufficiently accurate to be used with a more refined (quadratic) theory. My personal view is that the latter is true. Some study is under way to determine methods of inferring the third moment structure of $\eta^{(1)}(t)$ if the model $(1) - (4)$ is assumed to be correct. However, such analyses require the proper development (e.g., estimates and computation programs) of what Tukey has termed bispectral estimation procedures. (The bi-spectrum is the Fourier transform of the third moment function.)

So far we have given the model only in spectral terms. It is also possible to write Equation (3) as a quadratic operation on $\eta^{(1)}$. This is

$$\eta^{(2)}(t) = \tfrac{1}{2}\eta^{(1)}\eta^{(1)}_{tt} - \tfrac{1}{2}\mu^{(1)}\mu^{(1)}_{tt}$$
$$+ \frac{1}{2\pi}\int_{-\infty}^{\infty}\frac{\mu^{(1)}_{\tau\tau}(\tau)\eta^{(1)}(\tau) - \mu^{(1)}(\tau)\eta^{(1)}_{\tau\tau}(\tau)}{(\tau - t)}\,d\tau \quad (6)$$

where the subscripts refer to derivatives and

$$\mu^{(1)}(t) = \frac{1}{\pi}\int_{-\infty}^{\infty}\frac{\eta^{(1)}(\tau)}{\tau - t}\,d\tau$$
$$= \int_{-\infty}^{\infty}e^{-i\omega t}(-i\ sgn\ \omega)d\xi(\omega) \quad (7)$$

is the Hilbert transform (conjugate process) of $\eta^{(1)}$. It should be recalled that the Hilbert transform operation shifts the phase of each frequency component by 90 degrees. (It is like a derivative without the change in amplitude.) The effect of at least the first term of the right-hand side of Equation (6) is to increase the peak and flatten the troughs of $\eta^{(1)}$. (The coordinate system used in Reference [2] has z directed positive downward.) Using Equation (6), a realization of the random process $\eta(t)$ was constructed. Starting with normal (Gaussian) deviates, a realization of $\eta^{(1)}(t)$ was constructed with a spectrum roughly of the form $k\omega^4 e^{-\alpha\omega^2}$. The time scale was chosen so that the peak corresponds to a 15-second wave. The requisite Hilbert transforms and derivatives were taken. The computational details can be found in Reference [5]. The results are given in Figure 4-1-1. The scaling is such that the variance is about 22 (ft)². The effect of the quadratic correction is to sharpen the high crests and to flatten the troughs. The correction is in the desired direction. Even though the correction in the spectral density is very small, the change in the profile is observable. Loosely speaking, the energy character is not changed by the quadratic (plus Gaussian) correction, but the motion character is.

FINITE DEPTH, INFINITE CREST CASE

With a procedure exactly like that used in Reference [2], but for a depth of h, the analogous result (Reference [4]) for the free surface is

$$\eta(t) = \eta^{(1)} + \frac{1}{g}\eta^{(2)}(t) \qquad (8)$$

where

$$\eta^{(2)}(t) = \iint e^{-it(\omega+\omega')}Q_h(\omega,\omega')d\xi(\omega)d\xi(\omega') \qquad (9)$$

The kernel Q_h is given by

$$Q_h(\omega,\omega') = \frac{1}{2}\frac{|kk'|kk'}{\omega\omega'} - \frac{\omega\omega'}{2} - \frac{(\omega+\omega')^2}{2}$$

$$+ \frac{(\omega+\omega')^2\left[\frac{|kk'|kk'}{\omega\omega'} + \frac{1}{2}\omega\omega' + \frac{\omega k'^4 + \omega'k^4}{2\omega\omega'(\omega+\omega')} - \frac{(\omega+\omega')^2}{2}\right]}{(|k|k + |k'|k')\tanh\left[d^2(|k|k + |k'|k')\right] - (\omega+\omega')^2} \qquad (10)$$

where

$$d^2 = \frac{h}{g} \qquad (11)$$

and $k = k(\omega)$, $k' = k(\omega')$, is defined as the solution to the equation

$$\omega^2 = k^2\tanh d^2k^2 \qquad (12)$$

The sign of k is the same as the sign of ω. The last term of Q_h in Equation (10) is due to the quadratic correction to the potential function, and the rest are due to the quadratic term in Bernoulli's equation. The limit of $\tanh ax$ as $a \to \infty$, is the signum function $sgn\ x$. As $d \to \infty$, $k \to \omega$, and it can be easily shown that $Q_h(\omega,\omega') \to Q(\omega,\omega')$. The convergence, however, is not uniform. The nature of Q_h is quite different from Q for $(d\omega)^2$ small, (i.e., <1.3). Along the coordinate axis there are lines of singularities,* whereas Q is finite. This is an aspect of the non-uniformity of convergence. Along the line $\omega = -\omega'$, Q_h is not zero if ω is finite, while it is zero for Q. It is a pair of ω, ω' in the vicinity of this line which gives rise to the low-frequency contributions to the spectrum from the quadratic terms. Therefore, we can expect a large difference in the low-frequency part of $s^{(2)}(\omega)$ for finite depth. The spectrum of $\eta(t)$ for a Gaussian assumption on $\eta^{(1)}$ is

$$s^{(1)}(\omega)$$

$$+ 2\int_{-\infty}^{\infty}Q_h^2(\omega-\lambda,\lambda)s^{(1)}(\omega-\lambda)s^{(1)}(\lambda)d\lambda \qquad (13)$$

The limit of Equation (13) may or may not equal

---

* The singularities cause no problem since they are an artifact. In order for the potential function to exist

$$s(\omega) = 0(\omega^2) \quad \text{as} \quad \omega \to 0.$$

that of Equation (5) as $d \to \infty$, depending on the characteristics of $s^{(1)}(\omega)$. That is, it depends on whether the properties of $s^{(1)}$ "smooth" out the non-uniformities of Q_h^2. Notice also that $Q_h \to Q$ as ω and ω' grow larger, which is saying only that small waves are not affected by the bottom.

Some calculations of Equation (13) were made assuming $s^{(1)}(\omega) = C\omega^4 e^{-6\omega}$ for $\omega < 2$, and zero for $\omega > 2$. The scale was chosen so that the variance was $2(\text{ft})^2$. The results for $(1/g^2)s^{(2)}(\omega)$ are given in Figure 4-1-2 for $d = 1$, 1.2, 1.5, and 2. The linear spectrum $s^{(1)}(\omega)$ is also plotted there. The effect of the bottom decreases very rapidly as the water gets deeper. The $s^{(1)}(\omega)$ used has some energy at very low frequencies, so it is of interest to determine whether the low-frequency energy of $s^{(2)}(\omega)$ comes from the lows of $s^{(1)}$ or interaction of the highs. In Figure 4-1-3 we have calculated the family of $s^{(2)}(\omega)$ for the same type of $s^{(1)}$ as in Figure 4-1-2 but made equal to zero for $\omega < 0.10$, 0.18, 0.34, and 0.50. Thus we see that a considerable amount of the low-frequency energy of $s^{(2)}$ comes from the higher frequencies of $s^{(1)}$. It should also be remembered that part of the reason for the reduction in $s^{(2)}$ for the 0.34 and 0.5 cutoff is that there is a substantial reduction in the total energy in $s^{(1)}$.

The reduction in pressure spectrum of the quadratic portion depends on

$$\frac{\cosh^2\left[-(|k|k + |k'|k')(z-h)/g\right]}{\cosh^2\left[(|k|k + |k'|k')h/g\right]} \qquad (14)$$

The low-frequency portion of $s^{(2)}$ is attenuated with depth like low frequencies. Even with the Gaussian assumption the quadratic effect is quite large for shallow water. (Without this assumption it would be much larger.) Therefore, one should be quite wary of interpreting any very low-frequency peaks in the spectra of measurements made in shallow water as indications of low-frequency energy external to the system. It is probable that certain bi-spectral analyses will help in such interpretations. We are attempting to construct a realization similar to that given in

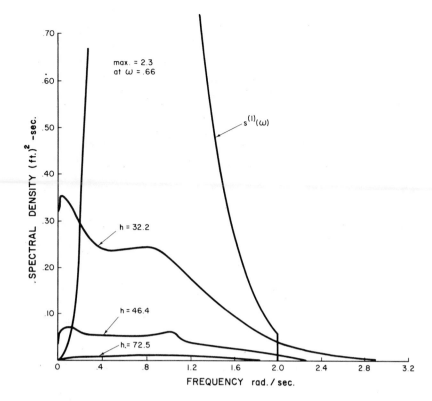

Figure 4-1-2. $s^{(2)}(\omega)$ *for varying depth* $h = 32.2,\, 4.64,\, 72.5$ *ft.*

Figure 4-1-3. *Effect on* $s^{(2)}(\omega)$ *of removing energy from low frequency part of* $s^{(1)}(\omega)$ *i.e.,* $s^{(2)}(\omega) = 0$ *for* $\omega < \omega_0 \cdot h = 32.2$ *ft.*

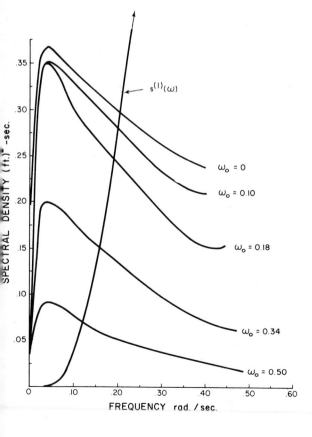

Figure 4-1-1, but for a finite depth. However, the analytical work is quite difficult.

SOME METHODOLOGICAL OBSERVATIONS

If we are going to treat the nonlinear equations describing waves by perturbation methods* to derive random models, then certain methodological issues are raised. It will be seen that many of these are glamorized versions of the comparatively simple problem of approximating a function of one variable.

Random perturbation solutions are of the form

$$\sum_{n=1}^{\infty} \int \dots \int e^{i(\omega_1 + \dots + \omega_n)\,t} Q_n(\omega_1, \dots, \omega_n) \left[\prod_{k=1}^{n} d\rho(\omega_k) \right] \quad (15)$$

in the spectral domain, and of the form

$$\sum_{n=1}^{\infty} \int \dots \int q_n(t - \tau_1, \dots, t - \tau_n) \left[\prod_{k=1}^{n} X(\tau_k) \right] \quad (16)$$

in the time domain, where q_n is the n-fold Fourier transform of Q_n, and

$$X(t) = \int e^{i\omega t}\, d\rho(\omega) \quad (17)$$

---

* I see no other approach that offers much competition as yet.

would be the linear solution. The forms (15) and (16) are very reminiscent of polynomial expansions, and they have been called "polynomial functionals" by N. Wiener in Reference [6]. There are the elements of a theorem floating around (but not completely proved yet) that any stationary random process can be represented in this way. Furthermore, and I feel sure that it can also be proved, there is another that states that under suitable restrictions and not unreasonable ones (from an applied viewpoint) the $\rho(\omega)$ may be a brownian motion (Wiener), hence Gaussian process. Therefore, $X(t)$ is also a Gaussian process. From these two (potential) theorems one could get a degree of confidence in using solutions of the form (15 and 16). I am not saying that the Q's generated by a perturbation expansion are necessarily those that go with previously cited "theorems." However, there is a good chance that they are. What is perhaps more relevant is that it is unlikely that Q's from the perturbation expansion is the set that generates the solution starting from a *Gaussian linear term*. So far these are mathematical (like existence) statements as distinct from practical (problem-solving) statements. Given that we feel (15 and 16) is a tractable *type* of solution, the most essential question in a given problem is what is the upper limit of the summation? Mathematically it is infinite, but practically it had better be small; otherwise, the whole notion is academic (i.e., useless). Here we see that the problem is conceptually identical with that of polynomial approximation. Suppose one has a function defined explicitly or implicitly (by an equation), which is to be approximated over an interval by a polynomial of a given order. The most obvious choice is to evaluate the truncated Taylor expansion. In this case the coefficients have meaning and are the derivatives. What assurance does one have that this produces a good fit? First, there is the Weierstrass theorem that any reasonable function can be fitted arbitrarily closely by a polynomial (of unstated degree) and Taylor's theorem that a regular function has an expansion. Still for a *given* degree of polynomial are we getting a good fit? There are other methods of fitting the polynomial; some are least-squares and mini-max (Chebycheff), both of which are global and will give a more "useful" fit. However, the coefficients generated are artifacts of the fitting procedure and have no intuitive meaning.

A perturbation process gives not only a poly-nomial functional type of representation but also a method of obtaining the Q's (the "coefficients"). But given a representation of a fixed order, how does one choose the Q's *and* the probability structure of $X(t)$ so that the fit is good according to some criterion? Even though the Gaussian assumption may ultimately (for a sufficiently high-degree system) give a good fit, the analytic expression may be entirely too unwieldy. So far I have answered no questions and raised enough for many, many years of hard work.

The forms (15) and (16) have begun to receive considerable attention, particularly at the Research Laboratory of Electronics, M.I.T. Discussions can be found in References [3] and [6] and particularly in [1]. The purpose in the latter reference is the use of Equation (16) to describe a general time invariant system with $X(t)$ as the input. In Reference [3] a simple procedure is given to estimate Q when the system is quadratic. When one has decided on a set of Q's as being adequate, the next methodological problem is to find some of the probability characteristics of the process knowing the characteristics of $X(t)$. In the general case this can be very complex. However, there is a circumstance that makes for considerable simplification. This is when the nonlinear operations are instantaneous and operations involving multiple time points are linear in nature. This is not as unlikely as it may seem, for the situation treated under *Nonlinear Equations and Perturbations* above of precisely this nature. This is easily seen by form (6). The nonlinear operations are products, and they occur at the same time. There is a theorem which states that any (reasonable) operator may be built up from sandwiches of linear and nonlinear instantaneous layers. Again this is a useful observation only if the sandwich doesn't become a Dagwood (for those who remember the Bumsteads). It does say that one should make this kind of an approximation to ease the next stage in the analysis.

CONCLUSION

The volume of effort expended on nonlinear random wave models will certainly increase. In spite of my own efforts in this direction, I would suggest that other linearizations, based perhaps on other equations, be examined before it is decided that linear theory is inadequate. For example, we might consider non-potential flow more vigorously or the Lagrangian system of coordinates, though the analytical problems of nonlinear models are extremely difficult.

* * *

ACKNOWLEDGEMENTS

The computing of the spectra in the finite depth case was done by Mrs. Marilyn Golub, and I am most pleased to acknowledge her painstaking assistance. I am also indebted to Professor Walter Munk for a quiet six weeks in the summer of 1960, during which some important mistakes in the early stages of part of the research reported here were discovered and (I hope) corrected.

REFERENCES

1. George, D. A., *Continuous Non-Linear Systems*, M.I.T., Research Laboratory of Electronics, Report 355, 1959.

2. Tick, L. J., "A Non-Linear Random Model of Gravity Waves I," *Journal of Math. and Mech.*, viii: No. 5, 1959.

3. Tick, L. J., "Estimations of the Transfer Function of a Quadratic System." *Technometrics*, iii, No. 4, 1961.

4. Tick, L. J., "A Non-Linear Random Model of Gravity Waves II: Finite Depth Case." Unpublished manuscript, 1961.

5. Tick, L. J., and G. Radin, "A Non-Linear Random Model of Gravity Waves III: Construction of a Realization." Unpublished manuscript, 1960.

6. Wiener, N., *Non-Linear Problems in Random Theory*. Technology Press, 1958.

TWO

THE DYNAMICS OF RANDOM FINITE AMPLITUDE GRAVITY WAVES

ABSTRACT

This paper presents some recent results concerning properties of a random wave field, which cannot be described in terms of infinitesimal wave theory. A number of topics are discussed: (a) the establishment of an equilibrium or saturation range of the spectrum, (b) the mean vorticity and turbulence generated in the water by surface waves in a real fluid, (c) the second-order distortion of the wave profiles and the third-order resonant energy transfer among wave components, (d) the skewness of the surface displacement, and (e) a new method of setting up the dynamical equations in closed form for irrotational water motion. The aim is to provide a basis for the evaluation of the respective roles of the various nonlinear effects that can occur.

INTRODUCTION

The first purpose in this paper is analytical. It is to describe a number of separate phenomena associated with nonlinear effects in a field of random gravity waves. The second involves a synthesis of these phenomena to evaluate the roles played by each of them in determining the structure and dynamical behaviour of wind-generated ocean waves. I do not intend to consider any particular aspect of the subject in exhaustive detail, but to attempt to show where nonlinear effects are important and what their influence is likely to be. Some of the topics that I will cover have been considered in detail elsewhere, and some are presented here for the first time. In no case, however, will I indulge in much detailed analysis, but I will try to indicate how the results were obtained, to make them physically plausible without an enveloping cloud of mathematical analytics, and to show their significance. I hope that the performance justifies the promise.

Let us first of all recall some of the nonlinear effects that present themselves in a single train of waves moving in one direction, which have been known for many years. In a deep inviscid fluid, to the first order, a train of sinusoidal waves moves without distortion at its appropriate phase speed $(g/k)^{1/2}$, where g is the gravitational acceleration and $k = 2\pi/\lambda$ is the wave number. At the second order, the first nonlinear effect appears as a slight distortion of the wave profile: the crests of the waves become slightly sharper and the troughs shallower. In other words, a second harmonic is generated whose amplitude is fixed relative to that of the primary wave and which moves at the same speed as the primary wave. At the third order, a new effect appears: the phase speed of the wave increases by the amount $\frac{1}{2}k^2a^2(g/k)^{1/2}$, where a is the amplitude of the primary wave. We will see later that this well-known effect is a special case resulting from a type of dynamical interaction which does not appear at the second order and which is capable of continually transferring energy from one Fourier component of the wave field to another. But perhaps the most dramatic non-linear phenomenon is the formation of sharp crests on the waves when the wave slope ka becomes sufficiently large. This motion is not described accurately by approximations to any finite order based on perturbation of a first-order system, but involves a new consideration — the stability of the water surface. In the limiting configuration the downward acceleration of fluid elements at the wave crests is equal to the gravitational accelera-tion g in standing waves or $\frac{1}{2}g$ in progressive waves, and if the wave system requires a particle acceleration greater than this, the free surface becomes unstable, and the crests detach.

In the case of a random sea, described by a con-tinuous spectrum, we will find counterparts of each of these three effects being manifest in differ-ent and sometimes unsuspected ways. In some respects the simplest, and certainly the most strik-ing, effect is concerned with the stability of the free surface and the existence of the equilibrium or saturation range of the wave spectrum.

THE EQUILIBRIUM RANGE

In the generation of waves by wind, if the fetch and duration are sufficiently large, the wave crests tend to become sharper, and abrupt changes in surface slope develop. Some crests may be unable to maintain their attachment, becoming unstable and degenerating to whitecaps. The appearance of sharp crests among the waves sug-gests that, in the two-dimensional wave-number spectrum $\Phi(\mathbf{k})$, the behaviour at large k must be determined by the physical parameters that govern the stability and the limiting configura-tions of the wave crests. An obvious relevant parameter is g, and a careful examination of the physical processes involved in the stability (Phil-lips, 1958) suggests that this is the only one aside from the wave-number k. We are therefore led to the conclusion that in a wind-generated wave system the form of $\Phi(\mathbf{k})$ at large wave numbers must be determined by the parameters g and k, and similarly the frequency spectrum $\Psi(\omega)$ of the surface displacement at a fixed point is, at high frequencies, determined by g and ω alone. On dimensional grounds, therefore, we must have

$$\Psi(\omega) = \beta g^2 \omega^{-5} \qquad (1)$$

$$\Phi(\mathbf{k}) = f(\alpha)k^{-4} \qquad (2)$$

for large values of ω and k, where β is a dimension-less absolute constant and $f(\alpha)$ is a dimensionless function specifying the directional distribution of the large wave-number components.

It is interesting to note that these expressions are independent of the fetch and wind speed, since

Figure 4-2-1. *Observations from SWOP and Burling. (a) The frequency spectrum $\Phi(\omega)$ from the SWOP wave-pole data. (The solid curve represents the equilibrium range spectrum $\Phi(\omega) \sim 7.4 \times 10^{-3}g^2\omega^{-5}$.)*

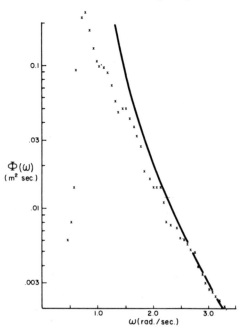

(b) Spectra of wind-generated waves measured by Burling (1955). (The cluster of lines on the left are representa-tive of the spectra at low frequencies for which equilib-rium has not been attained. On the right the curves merge over the equilibrium range, and the broken lines indicate the extreme measured values of $\Phi(\omega)$ at each frequency ω. The crosses represent the mean observed value at each ω, and the heavy line the relation $\Phi(\omega) = \alpha g^2 \omega^{-5}$ with $\alpha = 7.4 \times 10^{-3}$.)

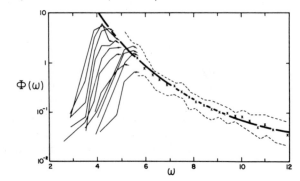

these quantities are not directly relevant to the surface stability. They are involved only indirectly in the requirement that they be large enough for the equilibrium or saturation values of the spectra to be attained. An implicit requirement also is that the wind speed not be so great that the wave crests are significantly disturbed by the wind. We might observe too that the prospects of obtaining Equation (1) or (2) from a perturbation analysis are not good, since for even a single wave train such methods are inadequate to describe the limiting configuration governed by surface stability.

There is a good deal of experimental evidence now available that generally supports the relations (1) and (2). Figure 4-2-1 shows the results of measurements by Burling (1955) at short fetches and from the Stereo-Wave Observation Project (1957) in the open ocean for the frequency spectrum $\Psi(\omega)$. The asymptotic behaviour of both spectra for large ω agrees well with Equation (1) (the constant β being 7.4×10^{-3}) despite the very different conditions of generation. More recent evidence can be found in the measurements of Cox (1958), Hicks and Huber (1960), and Kinsman (1960). Figure 4-2-2 shows the two-dimensional spectrum $\Phi(\mathbf{k})$ from the SWOP data, integrated over all directions α of a fixed scalar wave number and then weighted by k^4. At large k, this function approaches a constant value, in accord with the prediction (2).

Figure 4-2-2. *The approach to an equilibrium range $\Phi(\mathbf{k}) \sim k^{-4}$ at high wave-numbers of the two-dimensional instantaneous spectrum.*

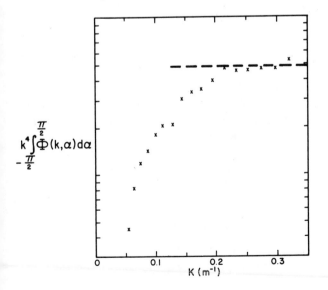

THE VORTICITY FIELD INDUCED BY THE WAVE MOTION

In first-order wave theory the assumption is usually made that the water motion is irrotational. However, when higher-order effects are to be considered, this assumption may be made only with great caution. In a most important paper, Longuet-Higgins (1953) showed that in a real fluid of finite but small viscosity, a second order vorticity field diffuses inwards from the free surface and the bottom, ultimately affecting the entire motion. A consequence of this vorticity field is a non-zero mean velocity distribution in the fluid and a mass transport velocity that is different from the value derived by Stokes (1847) for potential flow. When the fluid viscosity is vanishingly small, the vertical gradient of the mass transport velocity is independent of the viscosity and is exactly twice the value given by Stokes. These findings are of the first importance for wave theory; they are an example of the singular nature of the viscous perturbation to the flow, since taking the limit $\nu \to 0$ in the solution to the full Navier-Stokes equations gives a different result from solving the equations with $\nu = 0$.

Longuet-Higgins' predictions have been well verified experimentally by Vincent and Ruellan (1957), Russel and Osorio (1958), and by Longuet-Higgins himself (1960), and there is no doubt of their experimental as well as theoretical significance.

In geophysical wave motions, where the wave components travel in different directions, the vorticity field would be expected to become convoluted in a random manner. In other words, we would expect the water motion to be turbulent. Even in the absence of wind stresses or currents this turbulence would be maintained by a balance between the rate of generation of the straining motions associated with the waves and the rate of viscous dissipation. It is likely that Longuet-Higgins' results will remain valid even under these conditions, since they are independent of the small molecular viscosity and presumably also independent of a small eddy viscosity. As far as the oscillatory properties of the wave motion are concerned, it can be shown (Phillips, 1961b) that the weak turbulent field has a third-order effect if the wave Reynolds number $R_\lambda = c\lambda/\nu$ is large and results in an attenuation of the type

$$a(t) = a(t_0)\{1 + R_\lambda^{-1}a^2(t_0)k^2 n(t - t_0)\}^{-1/2} \quad (3)$$

where $a(t)$ is the wave amplitude at time t, $k = 2\pi/\lambda$ is the wave number, and n the wave frequency. In physical terms the mechanism is that the turbulence draws energy from the wave motion by the straining process and dissipates it through viscosity. Although this attenuation is a third-order effect, it is a small one; the wave amplitude is reduced to $1/\sqrt{2}$ of its original value in

$$\theta_a = \frac{R_\lambda}{2\pi} \{a(t_0)k\}^{-2} \text{ wave periods} \qquad (4)$$

The presence of the factor R_λ implies that the attenuation time is large compared with the time scale of other third-order processes (as described in the next section), so that it appears to be physically meaningful to carry the assumption of potential flow to the third order in describing the oscillatory properties of the wave field, provided we keep this slow attenuation in mind. However, one would hesitate to use any approximation higher than this.

THE DYNAMICAL INTERACTIONS AMONG WAVE COMPONENTS

We therefore assume, for the purposes of making approximations to the third order, that the water motion is irrotational. If x, y represent co-ordinates in the horizontal plane, and z is taken vertically upwards, the fluid velocity $\mathbf{q}$ is given by

$$\mathbf{q} = \left(\frac{\partial\phi}{\partial x}, \frac{\partial\phi}{\partial y}, \frac{\partial\phi}{\partial z}\right)$$

where

$$\frac{\partial^2\phi}{\partial x^2} + \frac{\partial^2\phi}{\partial y^2} + \frac{\partial^2\phi}{\partial z^2} = 0 \qquad (5)$$

The kinematic surface boundary condition to the motion is

$$\left(\frac{\partial\phi}{\partial z}\right)_\xi = \frac{D\xi}{Dt} = \frac{\partial\xi}{\partial t} + (\nabla\phi)_\xi \cdot \nabla\xi \qquad (6)$$

where $\xi(x, y, t)$ represents the surface displacement and the horizontal gradient operator

$$\nabla = \left(\frac{\partial}{\partial x}, \frac{\partial}{\partial y}\right) \qquad (7)$$

Equation (6) can be expressed in terms of w, the vertical component of the fluid velocity and $\mathbf{u}$, the horizontal (vectorial) component as

$$w_\xi = \dot{\xi} + \mathbf{u}_\xi \cdot \nabla\xi \qquad (8)$$

If the surface pressure is constant (we neglect here any influence of the wind), Bernoulli's equation gives the dynamical surface boundary condition

$$\dot{\phi}_\xi + \tfrac{1}{2}q_\xi^2 + g\xi = 0 \qquad (9)$$

These are the basic equations to describe the wave motion. The equation of motion, Laplace's equation (5), is almost trivial, but the difficulty arises from the nonlinear boundary conditions (equations 8 and 9) that are specified on the surface $z = \xi(x, y, t)$, which is an unknown, and, in general, random function of position and time.

If the surface displacement is represented as the generalised Fourier transform

$$\xi(x, y, t) = \int B(\mathbf{k}, t)e^{i\mathbf{k}\cdot\mathbf{x}}d\mathbf{k} \qquad (10)$$

where $\mathbf{k}$ is a two-dimensional wave-number vector and the integration is over the entire $\mathbf{k}$ plane, the velocity potential ϕ can be eliminated from the basic equation (5), (8), and (9) by the usual expansion techniques, giving a dynamical equation for the transform $B(\mathbf{k}, t)$ correct to the third order. It is of the form (Phillips, 1960)

$$B''(\mathbf{k}) + gkB(\mathbf{k})$$
$$= k \int [H_1(\mathbf{k}, \mathbf{k}_1)B''(\mathbf{k} - \mathbf{k}_1)B(\mathbf{k}_1)$$
$$+ H_2(\mathbf{k}, \mathbf{k}_1)B'(\mathbf{k} - \mathbf{k}_1)B'(\mathbf{k}_1)]d\mathbf{k}_1$$
$$+ k \iint \{H_3(\mathbf{k}, \mathbf{k}_1, \mathbf{k}_2)B''(\mathbf{k} - \mathbf{k}_1 - \mathbf{k}_2) \quad (11)$$
$$B(\mathbf{k}_1)B(\mathbf{k}_2)$$
$$+ H_4(\mathbf{k}, \mathbf{k}_1, \mathbf{k}_2)B'(\mathbf{k} - \mathbf{k}_1 - \mathbf{k}_2)$$
$$B'(\mathbf{k}_1)B(\mathbf{k}_2)\}d\mathbf{k}_1\,d\mathbf{k}_2$$

where $H_1, \ldots, H_4$ are algebraic functions of the variables specified.

Solutions to Equation (11) can be found by the usual expansion technique by substituting

$$B(\mathbf{k}) = B_1(\mathbf{k}) + B_2(\mathbf{k}) + B_3(\mathbf{k}) + \ldots \quad (12)$$

where $B_1(\mathbf{k})$ is a solution to the linearised equation [with the right-hand side of (11) neglected], $B_1(\mathbf{k}) + B_2(\mathbf{k})$ the solution with the second-order terms [the single integral of (11)] retained, $B_1(\mathbf{k}) + B_2(\mathbf{k}) + B_3(\mathbf{k})$ the solution to third-order, and so on if desired.

Clearly

$$B_1(\mathbf{k}, t) = \alpha(\mathbf{k})e^{i(\mathbf{k}\cdot\mathbf{x} - nt)} \qquad (13)$$

where $n = (gk)^{1/2}$ is the solution to the linearised problem; we have used the convention that the direction of propagation is in the direction of the wave-number vector $\mathbf{k}$. The second-order term B_2 arises from the interaction of pairs of first-order or primary waves and can be studied by substituting $B_1(\mathbf{k}) + B_2(\mathbf{k})$ for $B(\mathbf{k})$ in Equation (11) and neglecting terms of an order higher than the second. It is enough to consider the interaction of any two components, say $\mathbf{k}_1$ and $\mathbf{k}_2$, giving rise to components with sum and difference wave numbers $\mathbf{k}_1 \pm \mathbf{k}_2$ and sum and difference frequencies $n_1 \pm n_2$, where $n_1 = (gk_1)^{1/2}$, $n_2 = (gk_2)^{1/2}$. Under these conditions, Equation (11) simplifies to

$$\left(\frac{d^2}{dt^2} + g|\mathbf{k}_1 \pm \mathbf{k}_2|\right) B_2(\mathbf{k}_1 \pm \mathbf{k}_2, t)$$
$$= G[\alpha(\mathbf{k}_1), \alpha(\mathbf{k}_2), \mathbf{k}_1, \mathbf{k}_2] \exp\left[\pm i(n_1 \pm n_2)t\right] \quad (14)$$

where G is an algebraic function of its arguments. In mechanical terms this is the equation of a forced linear oscillator, and the solution will have the same frequency as the forcing function — in this case the sum or difference frequency $n_1 \pm n_2$. The amplitude of the oscillation is bounded unless the natural frequency of the system is equal to the frequency of the forcing function — in this case unless

$$\{g|\mathbf{k}_1 \pm \mathbf{k}_2|\}^{1/2} = n_1 \pm n_2, \quad (15)$$

where $n_1 = (gk_1)^{1/2}$, $n_2 = (gk_2)^{1/2}$. However, it can be shown (Phillips, 1960) by using some elementary algebra that no pairs of wave numbers $\mathbf{k}_1$, $\mathbf{k}_2$ satisfy the condition (15). In other words, the secondary components generated by the second-order interactions are always bounded and are, in fact, small, having amplitudes of order (slope) times the amplitude of the primary. They represent simply a distortion of the wave shape that is exactly analogous to the second-order distortion of the Stokes wave. They do not contribute to any continuing energy transfer from one component of the wave system to another. In the limiting case when one wave length is very much shorter than the other, Longuet-Higgins and Stewart (1960) show that the influence of the shorter wave upon the longer can be represented as a "radiation stress." In a random wave field the algebra becomes complicated, but the physical mechanism is identical; the second-order interactions among all possible pairs of wave numbers results in a distortion of the wave profiles but no energy transfer among the various components. This is the effect considered by Tick (1959), who

sought to interpret a secondary peak observed in the SWOP spectrum in this way.

From the point of view of the mechanics of the nonlinear wave system, then, the second-order effects are not very exciting. It is not until we consider the third-order terms that we find any profound dynamical influence. The tertiary wave components resulting from these third-order terms are generated either by the interaction of three primary (first-order) components or by a primary component interacting with a secondary. When we substitute from (12) into (11) and retain third-order terms, we find that the equation to describe the interaction of any three primary components is

$$\left(\frac{d^2}{dt^2} + g|\mathbf{k}_1 \pm \mathbf{k}_2 \pm \mathbf{k}_3|\right) B_3(\mathbf{k}_1 \pm \mathbf{k}_2 \pm \mathbf{k}_3, t)$$
$$= F \exp i(n_1 \pm n_2 \pm n_3)t \quad (16)$$

where F is a non-zero algebraic function of the amplitudes and wave numbers of the three primary waves. This equation is of the same generic type as (14), but now involves the possible sums and differences of the *three* wave numbers concerned. If the amplitude of B_3 is to grow with time as in a mechanical resonance, we require that

$$(g|\mathbf{k}_1 \pm \mathbf{k}_2 \pm \mathbf{k}_3|)^{1/2} = n_1 \pm n_2 \pm n_3 \quad (17)$$

for at least some combinations of the signs. The essential difference now emerges, for it *is* possible to find wave numbers $\mathbf{k}_1$, $\mathbf{k}_2$, $\mathbf{k}_3$ such that Equation (17) is satisfied, contrasting sharply with the second-order case. The implication of this is that for wave-number trios satisfying (17), the tertiary component formed by their interaction will grow indefinitely, or at any rate until the amplitude becomes comparable with those of the primary waves. From the dynamical point of view, energy is transferred from one component of the wave field to another, and this transfer is a continuous process. Figure 4-2-3 illustrates a particular case of this type of interaction when the primary component of wave number $\mathbf{k}_1$ interacts with the secondary component associated with $\mathbf{k}_0$ to give a growing tertiary component of wave number $2\mathbf{k}_0 - \mathbf{k}_1$. Any other wave number to any point on the crossed loop of Figure 4-2-3 will interact similarly with $\mathbf{k}_0$ to give a growing tertiary component. The time taken for the tertiary component to become comparable in amplitude with the primary is approximately the reciprocal square of the primary wave slope times the tertiary wave period (Phillips, 1960). For primary waves with

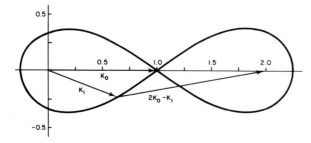

Figure 4-2-3. *The resonance loop for third-order binary interactions. (The wave-number k_1 interacts with the bound secondary component associated with k_0 to produce a developing component of wave-number $2k_0 - k_1$. The arrows represent the directions of propagation.)*

slopes of order 1/40, this interaction time is of order 1600 tertiary wave periods. On an oceanographic scale, this time is quite short — considerably shorter than the attenuation time discussed previously.

What role does this mechanism play in determining the structure of a random wave field? A detailed analysis has not yet been completed, though I understand that Dr. Hasselmann in Hamburg is working on the problem. However, we can certainly make some valuable qualitative statements of a rather general kind. In the first place, we have a mechanism for the transfer of energy from one wave component to another, or for the redistribution of energy among the components of the spectrum. If the wave spectrum has a sharp peak, then the tertiary interactions may result in making the peak broader, both in wave number (or frequency) and direction. This can be seen from Figure 4-2-4, where the shaded area represents wave numbers where the energy density is initially high. New wave-number components are generated in the outer area by the tertiary interactions, a typical one being specified by the resonance loop shown. Similarly, if there is a trough in the spectrum, or an absence of certain components, then the tertiary interactions can tend to "fill in the trough."

Besides this smoothing effect, in both magnitude and direction, these interactions are capable of other effects. If a swell of wave number k_1, say, (Figure 4-2-3) passes through a storm area in which there is considerable energy in components with wave numbers near k_0, then a tertiary wave system with wave number $2k_0 - k_1$ is generated. The wave length and direction may be significantly different from both the original swell and from the

components of the storm system. In fact, there are so many possibilities of interactions of this kind that there is danger that they may be invoked — as turbulence frequently is — to "explain" anything that we cannot readily understand!

A last comment on this type of interaction. The third-order theory of the Stokes permanent wave appears as a special case when the wave numbers k_0 and k_1 of Figure 4-2-3 coincide. A primary wave interacts with its own secondary component (the second harmonic) generating a tertiary wave of the same wave number as the primary (see Figure 4-2-4). However, the phase of the tertiary wave is found to be advanced by $\pi/2$, so that the energy transfer to the tertiary component can be, and usually is, interpreted as simply an increase in the phase velocity of the wave.

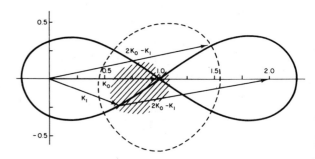

Figure 4-2-4. *The redistribution of energy by tertiary wave interactions. (If the energy density at wave-numbers lying within the shaded area is initially high, the interactions (of which a typical one is shown) redistribute the energy over a wider range of wave-numbers, enclosed by the broken line.)*

SOME "EXACT" RELATIONS

In this final section, I would like to offer a brief outline of a new method (Phillips, 1961a) of specification of the dynamics of a finite amplitude wave system. The relations are exact within the context of potential theory, but, in view of our remarks in the section above on "The vorticity field induced by the wave motion," they can be regarded as reliable only to the third order for the momentum equation, or to the fourth order in the energy equation (formed, as below, by multiplying the momentum equations by the first-order surface velocity $\dot{\xi}$). The central objective is to obtain closed expressions for the kinetic energy (and its time derivatives) of the wave motion per unit horizontal area, namely

$$\mathcal{T} = \tfrac{1}{2}\rho \int_{-\infty}^{\xi} q^2 \, dz \qquad (18)$$

These are obtained by representing the three-dimensional water motion by quantities specified on the free surface, such as the surface displacement ξ, the velocity potential at the free surface ϕ_ξ, etc. These functions depend on only two spatial variables x, y and time t. The value of this approach is that it enables us to represent higher-order effects exactly (subject to the limitations for a real fluid already mentioned) as products of first-order terms. To obtain a first approximation to such higher-order effects, only the linearised wave solution is required, and we can avoid many of the tedious expansions otherwise encountered.

The analytical details of this approach are given elsewhere (Phillips, 1961a), but for the purposes of illustration some simple examples of the type of result obtained are shown here. From Equation (18), together with the exact relations (6) and (8), it follows after some manipulation that the mean kinetic energy per unit horizontal area for a spatially homogeneous wave field is.

$$T = \tfrac{1}{2}\rho \, \overline{\phi_\xi \dot{\xi}}, \qquad (19)$$

where no approximation save that of irrotational motion has been made. The rate of change of T with time can be expressed in a number of alternative ways. Starting from

$$\dot{T} = \tfrac{1}{2}\rho \frac{d}{dt} \overline{\left(\int_{-\infty}^{\xi} q^2 \, dz \right)} \qquad (20)$$

where the overbar represents a probability or ensemble average, it can be shown that

$$\dot{T} = \rho \, \overline{\dot{\phi}_\xi \dot{\xi}} + \tfrac{1}{2}\rho \, \overline{q_\xi^2 \dot{\xi}} \qquad (21)$$

$$= \tfrac{1}{2}\rho \{ \overline{\dot{\phi}_\xi \dot{\xi}} + \overline{\phi_\xi \ddot{\xi}} + \overline{w_\xi \dot{\xi}^2} \} \qquad (22)$$

The latter expression can also be obtained by direct differentiation of Equation (19).

If we multiply the dynamic free surface condition

$$-p = \rho \dot{\phi}_\xi + \tfrac{1}{2}\rho q_\xi^2 + \rho g_\xi \qquad (23)$$

by $\dot{\xi}$ and take the ensemble average, we have

$$-\overline{p\dot{\xi}} = \rho \, \overline{\dot{\phi}_\xi \dot{\xi}} + \tfrac{1}{2}\rho \, \overline{q_\xi^2 \dot{\xi}} + \rho g \, \overline{\xi \dot{\xi}} \qquad (24)$$

which can be interpreted as an equation for the mean energy balance for a field of gravity waves.

The term on the left represents the rate of input of energy per unit area from the surface pressure fluctuations; the first two terms on the right give, from Equation (21) the rate of change of the mean kinetic energy density and the last term the rate of change of mean potential energy V per unit area, where

$$V = \tfrac{1}{2}\rho g \, \overline{\xi^2} \qquad (25)$$

Also, if we multiply (23) by the surface displacement ξ, we obtain an equation for the mean energy partition between potential and kinetic energy

$$\rho^{-1} \, \overline{p\xi} + \tfrac{1}{2} \, \overline{q_\xi^2 \xi} + g \, \overline{\xi^2} = -\overline{\dot{\phi}_\xi \xi} \qquad (26)$$

which, after a little manipulation, reduces to

$$V = T + \tfrac{1}{2}\rho \, \overline{\xi(w_\xi \dot{\xi} - \tfrac{1}{2}q_\xi^2)} - \tfrac{1}{2}\rho \, \overline{p\xi}$$
$$- \tfrac{1}{2}\rho \frac{d}{dt} \overline{(\xi\phi_\xi)} \qquad (27)$$

where T is given by Equation (19) and w_ξ is the vertical component of the fluid velocity at the free surface. Under most oceanographical situations, where the time rate of change of mean wave properties is small and the hydrostatic contribution to V (i.e., $\tfrac{1}{2}\rho \, \overline{p\xi}$) also is small, the last two terms are very small compared with the others, so that the energy difference

$$V - T = \tfrac{1}{2}\rho \, \overline{\xi(w_\xi \dot{\xi} - \tfrac{1}{2}q_\xi^2)} \qquad (28)$$

Now this energy difference appears to be of the third order, being represented as the product of three first-order quantities. This is characteristic of the way in which many higher-order effects appear. However, mean triple products are a little special, since we have a very general theorem (Phillips, 1961a) which states that in a homogeneous wave field, such triple products of first-order quantities are always of fourth or higher order in the usual parameter $\epsilon = [\overline{(\nabla\xi)^2}]^{1/2}$. The reason is that the third-order contributions always vanish identically, so that, for example, in the expression (28) the difference between the two forms of energy is in fact of the fourth order, not the third, as we would expect at first sight.

Incidentally, another application of this theorem provides an estimate of the order of magnitude of the skewness of the probability distribution of the surface displacement. The mean cube displacement, $\overline{\xi^3}$ is, according to the theorem, of fourth order, whereas $(\overline{\xi^2})^{3/2}$ is clearly of third order, so that the skewness

$$\frac{\overline{\xi^3}}{(\overline{\xi^2})^{3/2}}$$

is a first-order, dimensionless quantity, and so is of order $[\overline{(\nabla \xi)^2}]^{1/2}$. As the root mean square slope tends to zero, so does the skewness, in accord with the well-known property that in the limit of infinitesimal wave slopes, the surface displacement has a symmetric probability distribution. A direct calculation of the skewness confirms this order of magnitude result, though the detailed expression is too complicated to be of much further value in the general case. Measurements of Kinsman (1960) on the skewness of wind-generated waves are also consistent with this result.

Returning to the dynamical problem, let us take note of what we have achieved by this representation and where we can proceed. We have expressions for the energy balance involving rates of change of T and V. We also have another relation between T and V (i.e., Equation 28), so that the kinetic energy density T can be eliminated from the problem. We therefore have dynamical expressions in which the energy input is balanced by changes in $2V$ (the primary experimental observable) plus higher-order terms. The same approach can be used to derive a direct dynamical equation for $\Phi(\mathbf{k}, t)$, the surface displacement spectrum (or when multiplied by $\frac{1}{2}\rho g$, the potential spectrum). It is of a slightly more complex form but still enables the expansion methods to be postponed to a later stage in the analysis and provides a considerable simplification over the more direct method. The principal difficulty in the study of these nonlinear effects is simply the algebraic complexity, so I believe this to be a real advantage.

It will, I hope, be clear from this discussion that the analysis of nonlinear effects in a random wave field of the kind encountered in the oceans is capable of yielding a number of interesting and important results. Many of these are of the order-of-magnitude kind or serve to point out the relevant mechanisms that operate. In some respects this kind of result is the most useful. Because of its generality, it can provide insight into many of the very diverse situations encountered in nature. However, it is clear that detailed quantitative analyses of specific situations will result in still further understanding, and this next step, based on the ideas and techniques that I have tried to outline, is just beginning.

REFERENCES

Burling, R. W., *Wind Generation of Waves on Water*. Ph.D. dissertation, Imperial College, London, 1955.

Cox, Charles, *J. Mar. Res.*, XVI (1958) 199-225.

Hicks, B. L. and E. A. Huber, *The Generation of Small Water Waves by the Wind*, C. S. L. Report M-87, University of Illinois, 1960.

Kinsman, Blair, *Surface Waves at Short Fetch and Low Wind Speed — a field study*, Tech. Rep. 19, Chesapeake Bay Institute, The Johns Hopkins University, 1960.

Longuet-Higgins, M. S., *Phil. Trans. Roy. Soc.*, A, CCXLV (1953) 535-581.

Longuet-Higgins, M. S., *J. Fluid Mech.*, VIII (1960) 293-306.

Longuet-Higgins, M. S. and R. W. Stewart, *J. Fluid Mech.*, VIII (1960) 565-581.

Phillips, O. M., *J. Fluid Mech.*, IV (1958) 417-445.

Phillips, O. M., *J. Fluid Mech.*, IX (1960) 193-217.

Phillips, O. M., *J. Fluid Mech.*, XI (1961a) 143-155.

Phillips, O. M., *J. Geophys. Res.* LXVI (1961b) 2889-2893.

Russel, R. C. H. and J. D. G. Osorio, *Proc. 6th Conf. on Coastal Engineering*, 1957, 171-193. Council on Wave Research, Univ. of Calif., Berkeley, 1958.

Stereo-Wave Observation Project, *The Directional Spectrum of a Wind-generated Sea*, College of Engineering, New York University, 1957.

Stokes, G. G., *Trans. Camb. Phil. Soc.*, VIII (1847) 441-455.

Tick, L. J., *J. Math and Mech.*, VIII (1959) 643-652.

Vincent, G. and F. Ruellan, *Houille Blanche B*, XII (1957) 605-722.

DISCUSSION 1

Dr. Tick (prepared comment on paper by Dr. Phillips): This paper contains some striking and, from all appearances, quite fundamental results. Unfortunately the documentation of many of the most striking ones is to be found in as yet unpublished papers of the author. However, this serves to show that we conferees are receiving the very latest in this rapidly developing area.

I shall limit myself mostly to a discussion of the results of the sections on "the dynamical interactions among wave components" and "some 'exact' relations," since this topic most closely parallels my own interests. But first I have a few comments on some of the statements in the two preceding sections.

On page 173 reference is made to the SWOP data, which the author claims provides evidence to support certain statements. I was connected with this effort over most of its life. A careful reading of the report should convince anyone that the nature of this type of measurement technique, as well as the very large number of difficulties encountered in this particular application of the technique, has given these results a rather large component of error. It seems to me highly unsatisfactory to use these data to support or reject any *refined* conclusions.

In passing I would like to call attention to two types of inferential statements which seem not to be distinguished by some authors at this conference. They are: (1) the evidence supports the hypothesis; (2) the evidence fails to contradict the hypothesis. The first implies the second, but it also implies that the data *does* contradict the set of alternatives. In the language of statistical theory the latter statements say that the probability of error of the second kind is small. For those geophysical data which have a large variability (and thus not an empty class) the more conservative statements are in order. It was most interesting to me to read the remarks on page 173 about the lack of uniform convergence as $v \to 0$. It seems the wave equations have many such unpleasant properties. You have a similar type of effect (non-uniformity) when the depth approaches ∞.

Before taking up my major comments on section 4 (really my major confusions) I would like to clear the record on the bit of "mind reading" given on page 175. Now mind reading is at best a

hazardous occupation even for professionals. The transmission media are quite noisy, and the modulation schemes are not such as to permit easy separation of the signal from the background noise. Not in any document or public statement have I ever said that the SWOP data led me to consider nonlinear theories. (My comments about these data would preclude that.) If *any* data provided the impetus, it was those taken in a tank, and it turned out that in a later experiment with a better instrumentation setup the secondary peak was sharply reduced. Most of the nonlinearity was in the measurement system. If we remember that these were laboratory measurements, the conference will understand my skepticism about the preciseness of open sea measurements.

My reading of the fourth and fifth sections left me quite confused. This is due mostly to the scarcity of probability statements. The word "random" appears in the title of the paper and in the first paragraph. I can find very few other statements of the probability type. Since I prefer to avoid mind reading, I don't quite follow the arguments. If I go through some of the steps and make some sort of "reasonable" (to me) "fill-ins" of the probability assumptions, perhaps you will follow and clarify my own difficulties.

After the usual hydrodynamical introduction, Professor Phillips gives Equation (10). Since this is a random theory, I would guess that ξ is to be a random process. He wishes to give it a Fourier representation, so what assumptions are to be made on ξ? These assumptions will determine the probability characteristics of B, which must also be a random process. From remarks made later and his other published work I believe that Professor Phillips intends the ξ process to be spatially homogeneous. From this we know that at least B must be the derivative of a process of uncorrelated increments. The rest of the conditions to make ξ homogeneous are not known at this time. I also guess (and it is only a guess) that there is some intention on the part of the author that the ξ process be stationary in time, but I leave that aside for the moment. It is next assumed that ξ_1 corresponding to B_1 has this same property of spatial homogeneity. It is not obvious to me that it follows from the initial assumptions, and it is apparently not true about the time situation. (This point will, I hope, become clearer as I proceed.) From Equation (13) it is seen that ξ_1 is jointly stationary in space and time. This is to me an interesting result, though from a physical standpoint it is perhaps obvious. Conditions are imposed on B_2 to make ξ_2 statistically homogeneous, and $\xi_2(x, t)$ is obtained, which again is jointly stationary in space and time. This was interesting to me mostly because it showed that the joint stationary assumption that I made was superfluous. Either would have been sufficient.

At the third order things get sticky, and my confusion sets in. Now the *formalism* of the perturbation is such that the lower solutions are used to drive a linear equation. Therefore, whatever happens in linear differential equations with driving forces can happen here. In particular we can expect the counterpart of *resonance*. In fact this is precisely what happens. The condition of spatial homogeneity in ξ_2 produces a solution which is an increasing function of time. At this point, I would like to cast a skeptical eye on what has happened. Not that I doubt its formal accuracy, but rather I'd like to look more closely at the interpretation.

In linear differential equation theory when we talk about resonance, we have in mind some initial value problem, with the solution growing in time. In the present context I don't see where initial time came in or what are the initial conditions. If the process started at $-\infty$, it should be quite large by now.

Taking a different tack, suppose one wanted to have ξ jointly stationary in space and time (as I did in my own work), how would one proceed? One could impose the condition that the ξ_i's have this property. This is the way I proceeded, but I'm rapidly losing my confidence in it. Since I went only to second order, there was no conflict, but what about the next order? Suppose I tried to obtain ξ_3 which was jointly stationary in space and time. I had hoped to be able to answer this query by this time and set one of my staff to work on it. But the algebra is involved, and we have no confidence in the results to date. My guess, based on Professor Phillips' paper, is that there is no third-order stationary solution of the *type under discussion*. (These last words are crucial. I don't know about the rest of you, but I find the notion of order of a solution a less than exact one. I get the feeling that it becomes exact only when a particular method is stated.) So far

we have found that a large number of terms entering into the solution are zero. If there is any interest, I could inform you of the outcome later.

What is the point of all this? Just this: the third-order terms are growing and (from Hasselmann's paper) so are the third, fourth, fifth, etc. If there is to be a steady state, then all of this growth can't be in the same direction. I can't help thinking of an equation to which the solution is $\cos t$. To zero-th order it is a constant (nice steady state). First order is zero; second grows negatively; third, zero; fourth grows positively, etc. None of the non-zero terms after the zero-th are "stationary" yet the solution is. Since perturbation methods are a variety of power series method I wonder how much of this last mentioned artifact of the solution method is true of the wave problem. In reading some books on nonlinear mechanics I see that there is much worry about the *secular trend* and what methods exist, like perturbing the frequency or Krylov-Bougilubov, for eliminating it so that the result will be goods for long times. How much of this is relevant here? Professor Pierson's comments take up this point so I won't tarry.

Dr. Pierson (prepared comment on paper by Dr. Phillips): The purpose of these comments is to point out what appear to be a number of inconsistencies and errors in the section on "the dynamical interactions among wave components" in Dr. Phillips's paper. Some of the conclusions stated concerning the way in which the spectrum of the waves will grow due to tertiary interactions are far from substantiated by the results in the paper by Phillips (1960) on which the material in this section is based.

It is necessary to study the results in Phillips (1960) in detail before returning to some of the conclusions stated in the above mentioned section. The proper formulation of nonlinear initial value problems is quite difficult. Apparently part of the results obtained are due to the incomplete formulation of these initial value problems, and waves are produced with independent higher-order effects that are erroneously interpreted. Other parts are in error due to a failure to consider the changes that occur at third order in the frequency of a wave if its wave number is held fixed. In particular, the results given in Equations (4.16) and (5.9) of Phillips (1960) are very curious and require comment.

The problem of the interaction of two waves of

different wave numbers and direction of propagation to the third order is a difficult problem both to pose correctly and to solve. The discussion of the results given by the two equations cited above will at least provide reason to doubt Dr. Phillips' conclusions.

FORMULATION OF THE PROBLEM

Phillips (1960) has considered the nonlinear interactions of the various spectral components in a system of waves that are stationary in space but variable in time. His analysis uses a random Fourier Stieltjes representation for such a wave system, and the results turn out to be quite complex. However, the pertinent results are all based on the use of delta functions at appropriate places in the derivation. The results finally simplify to the study of the nonlinear behavior of one wave or of two interacting waves. The pressure on the free surface in the pertinent results is considered to be zero.

Phillips' results (1960) are obtained by solving second-order ordinary differential equations in the time domain for the motion of the free surface. The equations to be solved for the primary, secondary, and tertiary components are linear. The right-hand sides of these equations contain the known previously solved for nonlinear interactions of the lower-order components in the wave system. There is, however, a question as to the completeness of the equations since the effect of varying frequencies does not seem to have been taken into consideration.

These same results ought to be obtainable by the analysis of a system of three equations, namely, two first-order linear equations in the free surface and the potential function, and the potential equation. In these comments this procedure will be used because it tends to point out some of the difficulties that arise in the analysis.

The original nonlinear equations that are under study are given in Equations (1), where $\eta(x, y, t)$ is the free surface and $\phi(x, y, z, t)$ is the potential function. Subscripts denote partial differentiation.

$$g\eta - \phi_t + \tfrac{1}{2}(\phi_x^2 + \phi_y^2 + \phi_z^2) = 0$$
$$\text{at } z = \eta(x, y)$$
$$\eta_t + \phi_z = \phi_x \eta_x + \phi_y \eta_y \quad \text{at } z = \eta(x, y) \quad (1)$$
$$\phi_{xx} + \phi_{yy} + \phi_{zz} = 0 \quad \text{for } z \leqslant \eta$$

The initial conditions for such a problem would be given by

$$\eta = \eta(x, y) \quad \text{at } t = 0 \quad \text{and} \quad \frac{\partial \eta}{\partial t} = W(x, y)$$
$$\text{at } t = 0 \quad (2)$$

Such initial conditions for a nonlinear problem are difficult to pose so that they correspond to a physically realistic situation since *the initial conditions themselves tacitly involve nonlinear effects.*

Now if the problem to be solved involves just one wave, the variation in y can be omitted, and there is a way to proceed. For *two waves* of different lengths traveling in different directions, the proper procedure for the solution of Equation (1) with realistic conditions for Equation (2) is not easily obtained.

Since this analysis will be restricted to one wave, it must be noted that the wave number is fixed. However, there is no reason to expect that the frequency of response will be the same for a fixed wave number in a nonlinear problem when this frequency is compared with the frequency obtained in a linear problem.

It is necessary therefore in using a perturbation scheme to expand the frequency of response, the free surface, the potential function, and the initial conditions in a series in ϵ as follows:

$$\tau = (\omega_0 + \epsilon\omega_1 + \epsilon^2\omega_2)t$$
$$\eta(x, t) = \epsilon\eta_1(x, t) + \epsilon^2\eta_2(x, t) + \epsilon^3\eta_3(x, t)$$
$$\phi(x, z, t) = \epsilon\phi_1(x, z, t) + \epsilon^2\phi_2(x, z, t)$$
$$+ \epsilon^3\phi_3(x, z, t) \quad (3)$$
$$W(x) = \epsilon W_1(x) + \epsilon^2 W_2(x) + \epsilon^3 W_3(x)$$
$$\text{at } t = 0$$

Also ϕ must be expanded in the neighborhood of $z = 0$ in terms $z = \eta$, for example,

$$\phi_{x/t=\eta} = \epsilon\phi_{1x} + \epsilon^2(\phi_{2x} + \phi_{1xz}\eta_1)$$
$$+ \epsilon^3\left(\phi_{3x} + \phi_{2xz}\eta_1 + \phi_{1xz}\eta_2 + \phi_{1xzz}\frac{\eta_1^2}{2}\right) \quad (4)$$

For further explanation of the processes employed, see Pierson and Fife (1961), where $C = C_0 + \epsilon C_1 + \epsilon^2 C_2$ replaces $\omega_0 + \epsilon\omega_1 + \epsilon^2\omega_2$ and the derivation is somewhat different.

The first-order equations become

$$g\eta_1 - \phi_{1\tau}\omega_0 = 0 \quad \text{at } z = 0$$

$$\eta_{1\tau}\omega_0 + \phi_{1z} = 0 \quad \text{at } z = 0 \tag{5}$$

$$\phi_{1xx} + \phi_{1zz} = 0 \quad \text{for } z \leqslant 0$$

with the initial conditions that

$$\eta_1 = \eta_1(x) \quad \text{at } t = \tau = 0$$

$$W_1 = W_1(x) \quad \text{at } t = \tau = 0 \tag{6}$$

The second-order equations become

$$g\eta_2 - \phi_{2\tau}\omega_0 = \phi_{1\tau}\omega_1 + \phi_{1\tau z}\eta_1\omega_0 - \tfrac{1}{2}(\phi_{1x}^2 + \phi_{1z}^2)$$
$$\text{at } z = 0$$

$$\eta_{2\tau}\omega_0 + \phi_{2z} = -\eta_{1\tau}\omega_1 - \eta_1\phi_{1zz} + \phi_{1x}\eta_x$$
$$\text{at } z = 0 \tag{7}$$

$$\phi_{2xx} + \phi_{2zz} = 0 \qquad\qquad \text{for } z \leqslant 0$$

with the initial conditions

$$\eta_2 = \eta_2(x) \quad \text{at } t = \tau = 0$$

$$W_2 = W_2(x) \quad \text{at } t = \tau = 0 \tag{8}$$

The third-order equations become

$$g\eta_3 - \phi_{3\tau}\omega_0 = \phi_{1\tau}\omega_2 + \phi_{2\tau}\omega_1 + \phi_{1\tau z}\eta_1\omega_1$$

$$+ \phi_{2\tau z}\eta_1\omega_0 + \phi_{1\tau z}\eta_2\omega_0 + \phi_{1\tau zz}\omega_0\frac{\eta_1^2}{2}$$

$$- (\phi_{1x}\phi_{2x} + \phi_{1x}\phi_{1xz}\eta_1 + \phi_{1z}\phi_{2z}$$

$$+ \phi_{1z}\phi_{1zz}\eta_1) \tag{9}$$

$$\eta_{3\tau}\omega_0 + \phi_{3z} = -\eta_{1\tau}\omega_2 - \eta_{2\tau}\omega_1 - \phi_{2zz}\eta_1 - \phi_{1zz}\eta_2$$

$$- \phi_{1zz}\frac{\eta_1^2}{2} - \eta_{1x}\phi_{2x} - \eta_{1x}\phi_{1xz}\eta_1$$

$$- \phi_{1x}\eta_{2x}$$

$$\phi_{3xx} + \phi_{3zz} = 0$$

with the initial conditions that

$$\eta_3 = \eta_3(x) \quad \text{at } t = \tau = 0$$

$$W_3 = W_3(x) \quad \text{at } t = \tau = 0 \tag{10}$$

It is thus necessary to recognize four different problems. They are (1) the problem of finding $\eta_1(x, t)$, given $\eta_1(x)$ and $W_1(x)$ at $t = 0$; (2) the problem of finding $\eta^{(2)}(x, t) = \eta_1(x, t) + \eta_2(x, t)$, given $\eta_1(x)$, $W_1(x)$, $\eta_2(x)$, and $W_2(x)$ at $t = 0$; (3) the problem of finding $\eta^{(3)}(x, t) = \eta_1(x, t) +$ $\eta_2(x, t) + \eta_3(x, t)$, given $\eta_1(x)$, $W_1(x)$, $\eta_2(x)$, $W_2(x)$, $\eta_3(x)$, and $W_3(x)$ at $t = 0$; and (4) the problem posed by Equations (1) and (2). There does not seem to be any part of the analysis due to Phillips that is analogous to the perturbation of the frequency in the above derivation. Frequency perturbation is a standard technique in such nonlinear problems as are shown, for example, in Cunningham (1958, see pp. 140 ff.) and in the references in Pierson and Fife (1961).

By definition, for the purposes of these comments, the first-order solution to Equations (1) and (2) is $\eta^{(1)}(x, t)$, the second-order solution is $\eta^{(2)}(x, t)$, and the third-order solution is $\eta^{(3)}(x, t)$. A first-order term contains only a, a second-order term contains a^2, and a third-order term contains a^3. The frequency ω_0 is of zero order.

The actual physical situation usually provides a fairly realistic solution to Equations (1) and (2) apart from some valuable results of Longuet-Higgins (1960) on the effects of molecular viscosity and the generation of vorticity in wave motions. In solving for an approximation to reality, care must be taken to keep just that part of the nonlinear effects that is pertinent.

THE LINEAR PROBLEM

The procedures for the solution of Equations (5) and (6) are well known. Any arbitrary function can be assumed for $\eta_1(x)$ and $W_1(x)$. The linear problem therefore does not need further discussion.

THE SECOND-ORDER PROBLEM

In Equation (4.16) of Phillips (1960) a solution to Equations (5), (6), (7), and (8) is given that satisfies the following conditions:

$$\eta_1(x) = \cos kx$$

$$W_1(x) = a\omega_0 \sin kx$$

$$\eta_2(x) = 0 \tag{11}$$

$$W_2(x) = 0$$

The solution is

$$\eta^{(2)}(x,\,t) = a \cos\,(kx - \omega_0 t) + \frac{a^2 k}{2} \cos 2(kx - \omega_0 t)$$

$$+ \frac{a^2 k}{4} [\,(\sqrt{2} - 1) \cos\,(2kx + \sqrt{2}\omega_0 t)$$

$$- (\sqrt{2} + 1) \cos\,(2kx - \sqrt{2}\omega_0 t)]$$

$$\text{where } \omega_0^2 = gk. \qquad (12)$$

If, on the other hand, the initial conditions are given as

$$\eta_1(x) = a \cos kx$$

$$W_1(x) = a\omega_0 \sin kx$$

$$\eta_2(x) = \frac{a^2 k}{2} \cos 2kx \qquad (13)$$

$$W_2(x) = a^2 k \omega_0 \sin 2kx$$

at $t = 0$, the solution becomes

$$\eta^{(2)}(x,\,t) = a \cos\,(kx - \omega_0 t)$$

$$+ \frac{a^2 k}{2} \cos 2(kx - \omega_0 t) \qquad (14)$$

where $\omega_0^2 = gk$. In each case an appropriate potential function would also be obtainable. $\phi_2(x, z, t)$ is zero in the solution of Equation (13).

Now quite evidently both Equation (12) and Equation (14) are solutions that satisfy the original nonlinear equations in such a way that only third- and higher-order terms do not cancel out. However, that is not the point. The so-called free waves in Equation (12) are *solely the result of the choice that $\eta_2(x)$ and $W_2(x)$ are identically zero*. A different choice of η_2 and W_2 eliminates the free wave. If one is studying the second-order behavior of a wave with a fixed wave length, it would be appropriate to consider the formulation of the initial value problem to second order also. The free waves are thus introduced by an attempt to force a water wave to look like a sine wave to second order.

Phillips's analysis is not too realistic in a number of additional respects. The problem studied is, of course, only an approximation of the physical world, and it is instructive to inquire just how one might bring about conditions that the initial con-

ditions required by Equations (11) and (13) actually approximate.

Consider a wave tank very long and deep compared to the wave length to be generated. If a paddle is caused to oscillate at one end of the tank at a frequency ω_0, waves will propagate down the tank, and soon the whole length of the tank will have waves in it. If the end of the tank has a wave absorber, some sort of non-changing condition will be observed after a sufficient period of time. There will be present in such a tank, by definition, no frequencies with the value $\sqrt{2}\omega_0$. There may be some free waves present with the frequency $2\omega_0$ if the paddle is not properly designed, as Longuet-Higgins (1960) found in a wave tank he used.

At some time, arbitrarily set at $t = 0$, an arbitrary $x = 0$ is chosen, and the waves will satisfy Equations (13) to second order. For later times and earlier times, the free surface will look like Equation (14).

How then can one realize approximately the initial conditions given by Equation (11)? The generator must also supply a wave of amplitude $a^2 k(\sqrt{2} + 1)/4$ and frequency $\sqrt{2}\omega_0$ in comparison with the amplitude a of the wave with frequency ω_0. At the other end of the tank a way must be found to generate a wave of amplitude $a^2 k\,(\sqrt{2} - 1)/4$ going the other way. Some way to absorb this wave at what was originally the wave-generating end of the tank must also be found. If these three free waves are provided then, disregarding complications due to the fact that the frequencies are irrational, there will be portions of the tank where the initial conditions given by Equation (11) are approximately satisfied once in a while *to second order* and where the waves obey the solution given. However, the waves with the frequency $\sqrt{2}\omega_0$ do not mysteriously appear as a property of waves with a frequency, ω_0. They must be supplied independently, and there must be a source of energy for them at the appropriate frequency.

THE THIRD-ORDER PROBLEM

In Equation (5.9), Phillips (1960) gives a solution to the following initial value problem as formulated to third order by means of Equations (5) through (10).

$$\eta_1(x) = a \cos kx$$

$$W_1(x) = a\omega_0 \sin kx$$

$$\eta_2(x) = \frac{a^2 k}{2} \cos 2kx$$

$$W_2(x) = a^2 k\omega_0 \sin kx \qquad (15)$$

$$\eta_3(x) = \frac{3a^3 k^2}{8} \cos 3kx$$

$$W_3(x) = \frac{a^3 k^2 \omega_0}{2} \sin kx + \tfrac{9}{8} a^3 k^2 \omega_0 \sin 3kx$$

The solution as given by Phillips, obtained from the equations derived by him, is given by

$$\eta^{(3)}(x, t) = a \cos (kx - \omega_0 t)$$
$$+ \frac{a^3 k^2 \omega_0 t}{2} \sin (kx - \omega_0 t)$$
$$+ \frac{a^2 k}{2} \cos (2kx - \omega_0 t) \qquad (16)$$
$$+ \frac{3a^3 k^2}{8} \cos 3(kx - \omega_0 t)$$

where $\omega_0^2 = gk$

If, on the other hand, the initial conditions in Equation (15) are used to solve Equations (5) through (10), all proceeds satisfactorily. At second order, ω_1 has to be zero, but at third order, ω_2 turns out to be equal to $a^2 k^2 \omega_0/2$, and the solution to third order, apart from a constant perhaps, becomes

$$\eta^{(3)}(x, t) = a \cos \left[kx - \left(\omega_0 + \frac{a^2 k^2}{2} \omega_0 \right) t \right]$$
$$+ \frac{a^2 k}{2} \cos \left\{ 2 \left[kx - \left(\omega_0 + \frac{a^2 k^2}{2} \omega_0 \right) t \right] \right\}$$
$$+ \frac{3a^2 k^2}{8} \cos \left\{ 3 \left[kx - \left(\omega_0 + \frac{a^2 k^2}{2} \omega_0 \right) t \right] \right\}$$
$$(17)$$

It is interesting to compare the two different solutions to the initial conditions posed by Equation (15). In Equation (16) the potential energy averaged over x for a fixed positive t is mysteriously increasing with time. Where does the energy come from? Certainly not from the forcing pressure field since it is identically zero! It also does not come from some other wave in the system as there is none. In Equation (17) the result of solving Equations (9) and (10) imposes a slight increase in the wave frequency when ω_2 is deter-

mined. This eliminates the resonant condition found by Phillips by removing the forcing term with a frequency ω_0. It would seem that by the time initial conditions given by Equation (15) become appropriate, the solution given by Equation (17) would also be appropriate.

In Equation (16) the higher harmonics of the system are propagating with the zero-order phase speed, and the fundamental is outracing them. The waves will soon cease to look like anything remotely resembling reality. In Equation (17) the system propagates without a change of form, as all well-behaved, truly periodic waves ought to propagate.

It is stated that, subject to the initial conditions posed, the third-order wave of frequency ω_0 grows to an amplitude comparable with that of the primary wave of frequency ω_0 and that the frequency of the primary wave eventually becomes $\omega^* = \omega_0(1 + a^2 k^2/2)$. In Equation (17) a solution to the same initial value problem yields the result that the frequency is immediately given by ω^*. Equation (16) due to Phillips does not show that the "bound" second and third harmonics also have the same increase in frequency that Equation (17) shows. Moreover, the amplitude of the fundamental in Equation (16) is actually

$$a(1 + \tfrac{1}{4} a^4 k^4 \omega_0^2 t^2)^{1/2}$$

whereas in Equation (17) it remains equal to a.

It is again worth while to consider how close the various solutions come to approximating reality. Quite obviously, if the wave tank experiment described above is analyzed to third order, the result will be Equation (15) as the initial condition and Equation (17) as the form of the free surface.

The question arises as to how it would be possible to generate a wave system of the form given by Equation (16). This does not seem to be possible. To third order, it is not possible to generate a wave with the frequency ω_0, given by $\omega_0^2 = gk$, since the frequency is found to be $\omega^* = \omega_0(1 + a^2 k^2/2)$. It seems that the fact that the frequency of a wave at third order is not the same as the frequency at first or second order has not been considered.

It appears to this writer that Equation (16) has many internal contradictions and that it does not appear to correspond to the solution of a physically meaningful problem.

THE THIRD-ORDER PROBLEM FOR TWO INTERSECTING WAVE TRAINS

If Equations (1) and (2) are now considered, the system equivalent to Equations (5) and (6) is given by Equations (18) and (19) since the *frequency perturbation need not be specified at first order.*

$$g\eta - \phi_t = 0$$

$$\eta_t + \phi_z = 0 \qquad (18)$$

$$\phi_{xx} + \phi_{yy} + \phi_{zz} = 0$$

$$\eta_1 = \eta_1(x, y) \qquad W_1 = W_1(x, y) \qquad (19)$$

A free surface of the form

$$\eta = a \cos(l_1 x + m_1 y - \omega_1 t)$$
$$+ a_2 \cos(l_2 x + m_2 y - \omega_2 t) \quad (20)$$

for the initial conditions

$$\begin{aligned} \eta_1(x, y) &= a_1 \cos(l_1 x + m_1 y) \\ &+ a_2 \cos(l_2 x + m_2 y) \\ W_1(x, y) &= a_1 \omega_1 \sin(l_1 x + m_1 y) \\ &+ a_2 \omega_2 \sin(l_2 x + m_2 y) \end{aligned} \qquad (21)$$

and subject to the requirements that

$$\omega_1^2 = g(l_1^2 + m_1^2) = gk_1$$

and
$$\omega_2^2 = g(l_2^2 + m_2^2) = gk_2 \qquad (22)$$

will satisfy Equation (18).

The problem, however, is that of expanding Equations (1) and (2) properly in terms of one (or two) small parameters and of generalizing the frequency perturbation in Equation (3) for a problem in which two frequencies are involved. At second order, there will be no change in the two frequencies, but at third order there is reason to believe that the frequency will change. They need not, however, change in the same way that the frequency changed in the third-order, single wave problem. That is, $\omega_1^* = \omega_1(1 + a_1^2 k_1^2/2)$ and $\omega_2^* = \omega_2(1 + a_2^2 k_2^2/2)$ need not be the corrected frequencies to third order. It is quite likely that the correction to ω_1 will involve a_2 and k_2 as well as a_1 and k_1, and the correction to ω_2 will involve a_1 and k_1 as well as a_2 and k_2.

The second-order frequency correction that arises in the study of the third-order, single-wave problem eliminates an apparent resonance in the differential equations with the result that only third-order terms in the wave profile arise at third order. It is quite likely that appropriate corrections to the frequencies ω_1 and ω_2 in the analysis of the third-order problem will eliminate the forcing resonant term on the right-hand side of the third-order equations and provide a third-order solution that is solely of third order and that does not vary in amplitude with time.

The full solution and complete formulation of the third-order problem for two intersecting wave trains does not appear to have been given by Phillips. Only certain sum and difference frequencies and sum and difference vector wave numbers that arise in the linear problem are considered in the third-order analysis. By the nature of the problem, the wave numbers cannot be changed, but at third order the frequencies will change. The term that grows linearly with time due to these so-called resonance effects may well disappear when appropriate adjustments in the frequency are made.

Although the full solution has not been given, interesting problems arise as to the source of the energy that causes the wave to grow in Phillips's solution. Its source may prove to be just as elusive as the source of the energy in Equation (16).

It would seem that the physically meaningful problem in this area would be to study a process that was stationary in space but transient in time with a forcing term that would cause the linear part of the solution to grow. The questions would then arise whether or not the higher-order terms could grow fast enough to keep up with the linear terms and whether nonlinear interactions would be possible.

For these reasons the validity of Figure (4) in Phillips (1960), which is Figure (3) in his conference paper, is open to question. Figure (4) of the conference paper is thus to be doubted also, as are the statements concerning how wave spectra grow. There are many other possible mechanisms for the growth of a wave spectrum. It does not seem to be necessary to resort to third-order nonlinear interactions.

REFERENCES

Cunningham, W. J., *Introduction to Nonlinear Analysis*, New York: McGraw-Hill Book Company, 1958.

Longuet-Higgins, M. S., "Mass Transport in the Boundary Layer at a Free Oscillating Surface," *J. Fluid Mech.*, **8** (1960) 293–306.

Phillips, O. M., "On the Dynamics of Unsteady Gravity Waves of Finite Amplitude," *J. Fluid Mech.*, **9**

(Oct., 1960) Part 2.

Pierson, W. J. and P. Fife, "Some Nonlinear Properties of Long-Crested Periodic Waves with Lengths Near 2.44 Centimeters," *J. Geophys. Res.*, **66** No. 1 (1961) 163–179.

D I S C U S S I O N   2

Dr. Phillips (prepared reply to comments by Dr. Pierson): I fear that Dr. Pierson is confused about the difference between initial value problems and "steady state" problems (where we insist that the wave amplitudes are constant throughout the entire motion).

The formulation of initial value problems is not difficult but perfectly straightforward. We prescribe an initial configuration and velocity and then let the motion go; we allow nature to take her own course. The initial conditions can be chosen arbitrarily, and, of course, the subsequent motion reflects the particular ones that we choose. There is no question of the "correctness" or otherwise of the initial conditions, nor is there any question of perturbing the frequency, since we allow it to take whatever value the equations dictate. This is the method used in the paper, (Phillips, 1960), on which Dr. Pierson is commenting.

On the other hand, a "steady state" problem is frequently more difficult, as Pierson and Fife (1961) discovered. By insisting *a priori* that the wave amplitudes are time-independent, we are necessarily considering only a certain class of possible motions and, because of the restrictions already placed on the motion in a successive approximation scheme, it is necessary to make successive approximations on the frequency, etc., in order to find dynamically possible motions if they exist. Dr. Pierson's confusion apparently arises from a misunderstanding of this distinction. It is perhaps excusable since in wave dynamics a good number (but by no means all) of the interesting motions are of the "steady state" kind.

The specific difficulties and "inconsistencies" that Dr. Pierson finds can be resolved readily.

1. His discussion of the second-order problem is entirely correct. As he says (and as I stated in the paper in question), the free waves that occur in Equation (12) of his comments are a consequence of the initial conditions chosen; they play no part in the dynamical interactions and are really quite unimportant.

2. The successive approximation scheme in the initial value problem is valid only until the higher-order terms become comparable with the first-order ones. In the second-order theory, this never happens; they are always small. In the third-order theory, because of the "resonance" effect, the third-order terms grow, and, as demonstrated in the paper (Phillips, 1960), the solution given by this simple technique is valid only when

$$a^2 k^2 \omega_0 t \ll 1 \qquad (1)$$

i.e., for times small in comparison with the interaction time.

Equation (16) in Pierson's comments is therefore valid under this condition. Equation (17) is the well-known steady-state solution; for times t such that Equation (1) is satisfied, the cosine terms in Equation (17) can be expanded, and when terms of order higher than the third are discarded, we exactly recover (16). To this order, Equations (16) and (17) are identical over the time interval (1) above. In this particular case, we have an existence proof for the steady motion, and Equation (16) is a valid approximation to it, subject to Equation (1) above.

3. The amplitude of the fundamental to third order is a. The paragraphs following Equation (17) seek to infer from a third-order theory effects of fourth or higher order, which are not meaningful. The energy of the developing component, of course, comes from the primary wave; the initial decay of its amplitude is of fourth order and does not appear explicitly in a third-order analysis.

4. For two intersecting wave trains, the initial value problem shows that there is no steady-state, third-order solution in general. Is there any real reason to expect one, as Dr. Pierson insists? No existence proof of a steady solution is available in this case.

The other difficulties described are of the same

kind, so I do not think that I need comment further. Dr. Pierson's remarks provide little reason to doubt the existence of the resonant type of energy transfer from one wave number to another, though he is at perfect liberty to disbelieve it if he wishes.

[*For References:* See Dr. Pierson's comments.]

Dr. Pierson (additional prepared comment on paper by Dr. Phillips): Dr. Phillips's reply to my comments has clarified the ideas and procedures that he used in obtaining the results under discussion. Since the questions that have been brought up are rather important, perhaps I may be excused for submitting a reply to a reply.

The formulation of initial value problems is quite difficult. One must be sure that the initial values chosen are physically realizable by some natural process that will bring them about. The initial values that I chose are, of course, physically realizable by observing the steady-state solution at some instant of time. This is why they were chosen.

With reference to item 1 of Dr. Phillips' reply, if it were also stated that waves with a frequency of $\sqrt{2}\,\omega_0$ are not causally connected in any way with waves with a frequency of ω_0, then perhaps there would be no further difficulty.

As for item 2, let us pursue its line of analysis further. Let Equation (17) be expanded as follows, as suggested by Dr. Phillips:

$$\eta(x, t) = a \cos\left[(kx - \omega_0 t) - \frac{a^2 k^2 \omega_0 t}{2}\right]$$
$$+ \frac{a^2 k}{2} \cos\left[2(kx - \omega_0 t) - \frac{2a^2 k^2 \omega_0 t}{2}\right]$$
$$+ \frac{3a^3 k^2}{8} \cos\left[3(kx - \omega_0 t) - \frac{3a^2 k^2 \omega_0 t}{2}\right]$$

$$= a \cos(kx - \omega_0 t) \cos\frac{a^2 k^2 \omega_0 t}{2}$$
$$+ a \sin(kx - \omega_0 t) \sin\frac{a^2 k^2 \omega_0 t}{2}$$
$$+ \frac{a^2 k}{2} \cos 2(kx - \omega_0 t) \cos\frac{a^2 k^2 \omega_0 t}{2}$$
$$+ \frac{a^2 k}{2} \sin 2(kx - \omega_0 t) \sin\frac{a_2 k_2 \omega_0 t}{2}$$
$$+ \frac{3a^3 k^2}{8} \cos 3(kx - \omega_0 t) \cos\frac{3a^2 k^2 \omega_0 t}{2}$$
$$+ \frac{3a^3 k^2}{8} \sin 3(kx - \omega_0 t) \sin\frac{3a^2 k^2 \omega_0 t}{2}$$

$$= a \cos(kx - \omega_0 t)\left[1 - \frac{a^4 k^4 \omega_0^2 t^2}{8} + \cdots\right]$$
$$+ a \sin(kx - \omega_0 t)$$
$$\left[\frac{a^2 k^2 \omega_0 t}{2} - \frac{1}{6}\frac{a^6 k^6 \omega_0^3 t^3}{8} + \cdots\right]$$
$$+ \frac{a^2 k}{2} \cos(2(kx - \omega_0 t))$$
$$\left[1 - \frac{a^4 k^4 \omega_0^2 t^4}{8} + \cdots\right]$$
$$+ \text{other terms.} \qquad (1)$$

Terms to third order only, i.e., terms containing a, a^2, and a^3, yield Equation (16). If Dr. Phillips were to go to eighth order (or so) in his procedure, he would obtain a solution that would be more or less the equivalent of the third-order solution obtained by the frequency perturbation procedure for times for which the series expansion of the trigonometric terms is valid. Thus, even for initial value problems, the technique of frequency perturbation yields a more meaningful and more rapidly convergent solution. Equation (16), if I interpret Dr. Phillips' reply correctly, seems to be only a very poor approximation to the steady-state solution. Note that both Equations (16) and (17) satisfy the same initial conditions.

With regard to item 3, Equation (16) can be written in two forms,

$$\eta(x, t) = a \cos(kx - \omega_0 t) + \frac{a^3 k^2 \omega_0 t}{2} \sin(kx - \omega_0 t)$$
$$+ \text{other terms}$$
$$= a\left[1 + \frac{a^4 k^4 \omega_0^2 t^2}{4}\right]^{1/2}$$
$$\cos\left[kx - \omega_0 t - \tan^{-1}\frac{a^2 k^2 \omega_0 t}{2}\right]$$
$$+ \text{other terms} \qquad (2)$$

Thus, the amplitude contains a fifth-order term in the third-order solution. It may not be valid to consider the amplitude of the fundamental to be growing with time. Dr. Phillips insists that the amplitude is a, but he still refers to a developing component that arises due to the decay at fourth order of the primary wave. (Perhaps Dr. Phillips is referring to the term

$$\left[-\frac{a^5 k^4 \omega_0^2 t^2}{8} \cos(kx - \omega_0 t)\right]$$

in Equation (1) above.) One suspects even more that the problem under consideration is simply a very poor approximation to the steady-state solution.

As for item 4, the techniques used by Dr. Phillips may not be the best way to prove either the existence or the nonexistence of a steady state, third-order solution for two intersecting wave trains. There is a very good reason to expect that such a steady-state solution exists. Dr. Phillips has assumed that the initial conditions are stationary in space and that no pressures are acting on the free surface. The only way to establish initial conditions, $\eta(x, y)$ and $W(x, y)$, for such a situation under these assumptions would be to generate the waves at an infinite distance away, causing them to propagate into the region of interest and past it to infinity in the other direction. The establishment of initial conditions appropriate for observing waves at some instant in time that are stationary in space thus seems to require an infinitely long time. It is therefore quite likely that some steady-state has been established.

The resonant type of energy transfer that Dr. Phillips found in the study of two interacting wave trains arises for the same mathematical reason as the term

$$\frac{a^3 k^2 \omega_0 t}{2} \sin (kx - \omega_0 t)$$

in Equation (16). In (16) this term turns out to be merely the first term in the expansion of

$$a \sin (kx - \omega_0 t) \sin \frac{a^2 k^2 \omega_0 t}{2}$$

in a Taylor series. In the interacting wave train problem, Dr. Phillips now assumes the ability of this type of term to grow in amplitude until it is comparable to the amplitudes of the two interacting primary waves. To the contrary, it may well stop growing when it reaches an amplitude that is of third order compared to the amplitude of the two fundamental waves. Also, by means of a frequency perturbation, as discussed in my previous comments, a much more rapidly converging steady-state condition is a distinct possibility.

There is an internal inconsistency both in Dr. Phillips' original paper and in his comments. For Equation (16), it is stated that the solution is valid only for an extremely brief time after $t = 0$. If this same restriction is applied to the results for two interacting waves, the resonant component will certainly be unable to grow to an amplitude comparable to the two fundamental waves.

The point of the two figures in Dr. Phillips' conference paper was that he claims to have found a mechanism at third order that is more powerful than second-order interactions and that is capable of producing waves at new wave numbers and frequencies that will cause observable first-order changes in the wave spectrum. For example, the spectrum will fill in gaps and grow to first-order importance in regions where this interaction is possible. This I do not believe has been proved by Dr. Phillips' analysis. There is still a distinct possibility that this third-order interaction term can never be of more than third order in importance.

These difficulties and inconsistencies, as pointed out in my previous comments and as amplified in these comments, in my opinion provide quite a few reasons to doubt the existence of the resonant type of energy transfer from one wave number to another. Perhaps for these reasons others will also disbelieve along with me. I would welcome additional comments on these questions by Dr. Longuet-Higgins.

Dr. Barber (comment on papers by Mr. Tick and Dr. Phillips): I would like to understand how much reality I should attach to the waves resulting from the nonlinear interactions. May I report an observation and ask a question?

I recall standing on the shores of a lagoon about 600 meters in width. The wind was blowing away from the shore on which I stood at a speed of perhaps three meters/second, and wind waves of a period of perhaps one-half to one second were developed towards the farther shore (Figure 4-2D2-1). The water just before me was quite smooth and very shallow, and I noticed that very low waves of a period of perhaps one second were coming towards me.

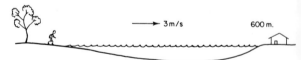

Figure 4-2D2-1.

These waves were therefore travelling in the upwind direction. I am not prepared to say what had produced them. I saw no boats. They might have been reflections from the farther shore, though so far as I recall, this was a beach, not a wall.

There may have been some obvious explanation for these waves. I only wish to ask whether waves like this might possibly have been produced by nonlinear interactions in the wind waves. In other words, do these interactions produce waves that are real in the sense that they can be created in one place and then travel like swell to another place? I see Dr. Phillips signalling that this is the case.

Dr. Longuet-Higgins (additional prepared comment on paper by Dr. Phillips): Figure 3 in Dr. Phillips' paper shows that it is possible to create waves travelling up-wind. I have been particularly struck by this result of his theory. If one has wave numbers in the ratio 1 to $2\frac{1}{4}$ travelling down-wind, the interaction gives a wave number $\frac{1}{4}$ travelling up-wind. Or in terms of wave period, two waves of period 2 seconds and 3 seconds travelling down-wind could interact to produce a real wave of period 6 seconds travelling up-wind.

K. HASSELMANN

THREE

ON THE NONLINEAR ENERGY TRANSFER IN A WAVE SPECTRUM

INTRODUCTION

The final stage of development of a wind-generated sea is probably determined largely by two nonlinear processes: (1) the dissipation of wave energy due to wave breaking, and (2) the energy flux in the wave spectrum resulting from the nonlinear interactions among different wave components. The present paper is restricted to an analysis of the second process. The nonlinear interactions are in general small and can thus be evaluated by conventional perturbation techniques. The perturbation analysis of a random sea surface to the second order has already been carried out in detail by Mr. L. J. Tick. The perturbation solutions were found to be steady, sinusoidal waves yielding a constant correction term for the wave spectrum. However, the analysis did not disclose any dynamical interactions involving energy transfer among different wave components, as these are described by perturbation equations of a higher order than the second.

By extending the perturbation equations to the third order, Dr. O. M. Phillips explained the mechanism of these interactions and examined the conditions under which energy transfer is possible between two discrete wave trains. In order to determine the energy transfer in the case of a continuous spectrum, however, the perturbation analysis has to be extended still further to the fifth order. Moreover, supplementary statis-

tical analysis of the response of an undamped oscillator to certain random forcing functions is also necessary. The final result can be interpreted in terms of quadruple interactions in which, under certain resonance conditions, energy is transferred from three "active" components controlling the transfer rate to a "passive" fourth component. The process is proportional to the fourth power of the wave slope, giving an estimated order of magnitude comparable to the magnitudes of the generating and dissipating processes in a seaway.

PERTURBATION ANALYSIS

As the derivation of the perturbation equations for a random sea surface with small mean square wave slope has been described in detail by Mr. Tick and Dr. Phillips, we can restrict ourselves here to a brief outline of the method with indications of the additional aspects encountered in extending the analysis to the fifth order.

The sea surface $z = h(x, y, t)$ is assumed to be a homogeneous random function, which can thus be represented as a Fourier sum

$$h(x, y, t) = \sum_{\mathbf{k}} H_{\mathbf{k}}(t) e^{i\mathbf{k}\cdot\mathbf{x}} \qquad (1)$$

where $\mathbf{x} = (x, y)$ and x, y, and z denote cartesian coordinates with the z-axis directed vertically upwards. Approximating Fourier-sums will be used throughout rather than exact Fourier-Stieltjes integrals as they allow a more condensed presentation of the rather complicated multiple integrals occurring later in the analysis.

In the linear approximation (denoted by a subscript 1) the equations of motion and the boundary conditions lead to the differential equation:

$$_1\ddot{H}_{\mathbf{k}}(t) + \omega_{\mathbf{k}}^2 \,_1H_{\mathbf{k}}(t) = 0 \qquad (2)$$

where $\omega_{\mathbf{k}} = \sqrt{gk}$, $k = |\mathbf{k}|$ (neglecting surface tension). The general solution is

$$_1H_{\mathbf{k}}(t) = _1H_{\mathbf{k}}^+ \, e^{-i\omega_{\mathbf{k}}t} + _1H_{\mathbf{k}}^- \, e^{i\omega_{\mathbf{k}}t}, \; _1H_{\mathbf{k}}^{\pm} \text{ const} \qquad (3)$$

so that from Equation (1)

$$_1h = \sum_{\mathbf{k}} [_1H_{\mathbf{k}}^+ \, e^{i\mathbf{k}\cdot\mathbf{x} - i\omega_{\mathbf{k}}t} + _1H_{\mathbf{k}}^- \, e^{i\mathbf{k}\cdot\mathbf{x} + i\omega_{\mathbf{k}}^- t}] \qquad (4)$$

The sign-indices denote the direction of propagation of the waves relative to the wave-number $\mathbf{k}$. As $_1h$ is real, the amplitudes satisfy the relation

$$_1H_{\mathbf{k}}^+ = (_1H_{-\mathbf{k}}^-)^* \qquad (5)$$

In the nonlinear case the amplitudes $H_{\mathbf{k}}(t)$ can be developed in a perturbation series

$$H_{\mathbf{k}}(t) = _1H_{\mathbf{k}}(t) + _2H_{\mathbf{k}}(t) + _3H_{\mathbf{k}}(t) + \cdots \qquad (6)$$

The nth amplitude $_nH_{\mathbf{k}}(t)$ satisfies the same differential equation as $_1H_{\mathbf{k}}(t)$, except that the equation is no longer homogeneous, the inhomogeneous, exciting term depending on amplitudes of an order lower than n. Assuming these to be already determined in terms of the first-order amplitudes, the resulting equation for $_nH_{\mathbf{k}}(t)$ has the general form

$$_n\ddot{H}_{\mathbf{k}} + \omega_{\mathbf{k}}^2 \,_nH_{\mathbf{k}} = \sum_{\substack{\mathbf{k}_1+\mathbf{k}_2+\ldots+\mathbf{k}_n=\mathbf{k} \\ s_1, s_2, s_3 \ldots s_n}}$$
$$C_{\mathbf{k}_1,\mathbf{k}_2\ldots\mathbf{k}_n}^{s_1,s_2\ldots s_n}(t) \,_1H_{\mathbf{k}_1}^{s_1} \cdot _1H_{\mathbf{k}_2}^{s_2} \cdot \ldots \,_1H_{\mathbf{k}_n}^{s_n}, \qquad (7)$$

where s_j represents a sign-index.

For $n = 2$ the coefficient $C_{\mathbf{k}_1,\mathbf{k}_2}^{s_1,s_2}$ is sinusoidal and the equation becomes

$$_2\ddot{H}_{\mathbf{k}} + \omega_{\mathbf{k}}^2 \, H_{\mathbf{k}} = \sum_{\substack{\mathbf{k}_1+\mathbf{k}_2=\mathbf{k} \\ s_1, s_2}}$$
$$A_{\mathbf{k}_1,\mathbf{k}_2}^{s_1,s_2} \cdot _1H_{\mathbf{k}_1}^{s_1} \cdot _1H_{\mathbf{k}_2}^{s_2} \cdot e^{-i(s_1\omega_{\mathbf{k}_1} + s_2\omega_{\mathbf{k}_2})t} \qquad (8)$$

where the coefficients $A_{\mathbf{k}_1,\mathbf{k}_2}^{s_1,s_2}$ are constant.

The exciting terms on the right-hand side generate steady, harmonic oscillations if

$$(s_1\omega_{\mathbf{k}_1} + s_2\omega_{\mathbf{k}_2})^2 \neq \omega_{\mathbf{k}}^2$$

and nonstationary oscillations with linearly in-

creasing amplitudes if $(s_1\omega_{\mathbf{k}_1} + s_2\omega_{\mathbf{k}_2})^2 = \omega_{\mathbf{k}}^2$. For gravity waves with $\omega_{\mathbf{k}} = \sqrt{gk}$ it follows from the inequalities

$$\sqrt{k_1 + k_2} \leqq \sqrt{k_1} + \sqrt{k_2}$$

and

$$|\mathbf{k}_1 + \mathbf{k}_2| \leqq k_1 + k_2$$

that

$$(\omega_{\mathbf{k}} =)\omega_{\mathbf{k}_1+\mathbf{k}_2} \leqq \omega_{\mathbf{k}_1} + \omega_{\mathbf{k}_2}$$

The substitution $\mathbf{k}' = \mathbf{k}_1 + \mathbf{k}_2$, $\mathbf{k}'' = -\mathbf{k}_2$ yields further

$$\omega_{\mathbf{k}'} - \omega_{\mathbf{k}''} \leqq \omega_{\mathbf{k}'+\mathbf{k}''}$$

so that finally

$$\omega_{\mathbf{k}_1} - \omega_{\mathbf{k}_2} \leqq \omega_{\mathbf{k}_1+\mathbf{k}_2}(= \omega_{\mathbf{k}}) \leqq \omega_{\mathbf{k}_1} + \omega_{\mathbf{k}_2} \qquad (9)$$

The equality sign on the left holds only for $\mathbf{k}_2 = 0$ or $\mathbf{k}_1 + \mathbf{k}_2 = 0$ and the equality sign on the right only for $\mathbf{k}_1 = 0$ or $\mathbf{k}_2 = 0$. It can be shown that the coefficient $A_{\mathbf{k}_1,\mathbf{k}_2}^{s_1,s_2}$ in Equation (8) vanishes for these cases. It thus follows that none of the exciting terms in (8) can satisfy the resonance condition $(s_1\omega_{\mathbf{k}_1} + s_2\omega_{\mathbf{k}_2})^2 = \omega_{\mathbf{k}}^2$, so that the solution $_2H_{\mathbf{k}}(t)$ is composed entirely of steady harmonic oscillations. It follows further that the exciting terms in the differential equation for the next perturbation amplitude $_3H_{\mathbf{k}}$ again consist solely of harmonic components

$$_3\ddot{H}_{\mathbf{k}} + \omega_{\mathbf{k}}^2 \,_3H_{\mathbf{k}} = \sum_{\substack{\mathbf{k}_1+\mathbf{k}_2+\mathbf{k}_3=\mathbf{k} \\ s_1, s_2, s_3}} A_{\mathbf{k}_1,\mathbf{k}_2,\mathbf{k}_3}^{s_1,s_2,s_3}$$
$$\cdot _1H_{\mathbf{k}_1}^{s_1} \cdot _1H_{\mathbf{k}_2}^{s_2} \cdot _1H_{\mathbf{k}_3}^{s_3} \cdot e^{-i(s_1\omega_{\mathbf{k}_1} + s_2\omega_{\mathbf{k}_2} + s_3\omega_{\mathbf{k}_3})t} \qquad (10)$$

where $A_{\mathbf{k}_1,\mathbf{k}_2,\mathbf{k}_3}^{s_1,s_2,s_3}$ is constant.

Equation (10) is the first perturbation equation in which resonance occurs, as it can easily be verified that the resonance condition

$$(s_1\omega_{\mathbf{k}_1} + s_2\omega_{\mathbf{k}_2} + s_3\omega_{\mathbf{k}_3})^2 = \omega_{\mathbf{k}}^2$$

can be satisfied by a suitable choice of $\mathbf{k}_j$ and s_j. The perturbation amplitude $_3H_{\mathbf{k}}(t)$ thus contains unsteady, continuously increasing, resonant components representing a continuous transfer of energy from the wave components $_1H_{\mathbf{k}_1}^{s_1}$, $_1H_{\mathbf{k}_2}^{s_2}$, and $_1H_{\mathbf{k}_3}^{s_3}$ to the resultant component $_3H_{\mathbf{k}}$. Equation (10) was derived independently by Dr. Phillips for the case of two interacting, discrete wave trains for which two of the three wave numbers $\mathbf{k}_1$, $\mathbf{k}_2$, and $\mathbf{k}_3$ coincide.

Although the third order perturbation equation illustrates the main features of the resonance mechanism responsible for the nonlinear energy transfer; we shall find that the perturbation equations have to be developed still further to the fourth and fifth orders in order to actually evaluate the energy flux. The equations for $_4H_\mathbf{k}(t)$ and $_5H_\mathbf{k}(t)$ are not as simple in structure as those for the first three orders as the exciting terms depend partly on the nonstationary perturbations $_3H_\mathbf{k}$ and are thus no longer simply harmonic functions of t. This leads to "higher-order" resonant excitation of the amplitudes $_4H_\mathbf{k}$ and $_5H_\mathbf{k}$, i.e., resonant excitation by terms which are themselves already nonstationary resonant oscillations.

The mechanism of these interactions cannot be discussed in detail here, but the implications for the resulting energy flux will be considered briefly in the next section.

THE ENERGY FLUX

The first step in determining the energy flux resulting from the nonlinear interactions must obviously be to determine the total energy of the sea in terms of the perturbation amplitudes considered in the previous section. The total energy of the sea per unit projection area is

$$E = E_\text{pot} + E_\text{kin} = \rho g \frac{\overline{h^2}}{2}$$
$$+ \rho \int_{-\infty}^{h} \overline{\frac{(\text{grad }\varphi)^2}{2}}\, dz \quad (11)$$

where φ is the velocity potential and the bars denote ensemble means.

We develop E again in a perturbation series:

$$E = {_2E} + {_3E} + {_4E} + {_5E} + \dots \quad (12)$$

In the linear approximation the mean kinetic energy is equal to the mean potential energy, and we obtain, applying Equations (4) and (5),

$${_2E} = \rho g\,\overline{_1h^2} = 2\rho g \sum_\mathbf{k} |_1H_\mathbf{k}^+|^2 \quad (13)$$

In the limiting case of a continuous spectrum Equation (13) takes the form

$${_2E} = \int\int_{-\infty}^{+\infty} {_2F}(\mathbf{k})\,dk_x dk_y, \quad (14)$$

where $_2F(\mathbf{k})dk_x dk_y$ is defined as the energy (in the linear approximation) of all waves travelling in the *positive* $\mathbf{k}$-direction whose wave numbers $\mathbf{k}'$ lie in the rectangular interval

$$\mathbf{k} \leqq \mathbf{k}' \leqq \mathbf{k} + d\mathbf{k}$$

We introduce now the basic hypothesis that the

sea is a Gaussian process in the linear approximation. In this case the linear wave components $_1H_\mathbf{k}^{\pm}$ are statistically independent, and the sea is completely specified statistically by the spectrum $_2F(\mathbf{k})$. Further, it can easily be shown that for this case all odd components in the perturbation series (12) vanish.

In the higher-order expressions for E the mean kinetic energy is no longer equal to the mean potential energy, so that in general we have

$$E = \rho g\overline{h^2} + \Delta E \quad (15)$$

where the perturbation series of ΔE begins with a fourth-order term. ΔE is no longer quadratic in the surface elevation, which, as pointed out by Mr. Tick, precludes expressing E as a spectral integral in the general nonlinear case. However, we shall find that the nonstationary components of E representing the continuous energy flux can nonetheless still be expressed completely in terms of the linear spectrum $_2F(\mathbf{k})$.

The next (non-vanishing) term in the perturbation series (12) is found from Equations (15), (1), and (6) to be

$${_4E} = \rho g \sum_\mathbf{k} \left[\overline{|_2H_\mathbf{k}(t)|^2} + 2\,\text{Re}\overline{_1(H_\mathbf{k}\,_3H_{-\mathbf{k}})}\right] + {_4}(\Delta E) \quad (16)$$

It can be shown that $_4(\Delta E)$ contains only periodic terms and thus does not contribute to the nonlinear energy flux. The first term in the sum is also constant. The remaining term contains the nonstationary component $_3H_{-\mathbf{k}}$, but the mean product $\text{Re}(\overline{_1H_\mathbf{k}\,_3H_{-\mathbf{k}}})$ can also be shown to be constant as the resonant components of $_3H_{-\mathbf{k}}$ are 90 degrees out of phase with the corresponding components of $_1H_\mathbf{k}$. $_4E$ thus contains only stationary components yielding a constant correction term for the total energy of the sea. The term has been analysed in detail by Mr. Tick (with the exception of terms depending on the third-order perturbation amplitude).

The next term in the perturbation series (12) is

$${_6E} = \rho g \sum_\mathbf{k} \left[\overline{|_3H_\mathbf{k}|^2} + 2\,\text{Re}\overline{(_2H_\mathbf{k}\,_4H_{-\mathbf{k}})} + 2\,\text{Re}\overline{(_1H_\mathbf{k}\,_5H_{-\mathbf{k}})}\right] + {_6}(\Delta E) \quad (17)$$

It can again be shown that $_6(\Delta E)$ contains only constant terms. The terms in the sum, however, are now no longer constant, and it is these terms that describe the nonlinear energy flux that we are seeking.

The problem is thus reduced to the determination of the three co-variance products entering in the sum in Equation (17), in which all perturbation amplitudes from the first to the fifth order occur. The perturbations are all solutions of harmonic differential equations in which the exciting terms are random functions of time, and the basic statistical problem is thus to express the covariance products of these solutions in terms of the statistical properties of the corresponding exciting functions. The required relations can be derived from certain asymptotic properties of the solutions. However, it will not be possible to cite or prove these relations here completely, and we shall restrict ourselves to only a few characteristic results.

Let ψ be a solution of the differential equation

$$\ddot{\psi} + \omega_0^2 \psi = p(t) \tag{18}$$

where $p(t)$ is a stationary, random (not necessarily real) function with a continuous spectral density function $f(\omega)$. It can then be shown that for large t

$$\overline{|\psi|^2} = \frac{\pi t}{2\omega_0^2} [f(\omega_0) + f(-\omega_0)] \tag{19}$$

An expression similar to Equation (19), in which the spectral density was expressed in terms of the correlation function of $p(t)$, has been derived by Dr. Phillips. In our specific problem $f(\omega)$ is given implicitly in terms of a multidimensional wave-number spectrum $\tilde{f}(\mathbf{k})$, where $\omega = \omega(\mathbf{k})$, and it is then convenient to express (19) in the more general form

$$\overline{|\psi|^2} = \frac{\pi t}{2\omega_0^2} \int_{-\infty}^{+\infty}\cdots\int \tilde{f}(\mathbf{k})[\delta(\omega(\mathbf{k}) - \omega_0)$$
$$+ \delta(\omega(\mathbf{k}) + \omega_0)]dk_1 dk_2 \ldots dk_n, \tag{20}$$

where δ denotes the Dirac δ-function.

As the exciting term in the differential equation for $_3H_\mathbf{k}(t)$ is a stationary random function, Equation (20) can be applied immediately to obtain the rate of increase of the mean product $\overline{|_3H_\mathbf{k}|^2}$. The linear increase in energy of $_3H_\mathbf{k}$ must be balanced by a corresponding loss in energy of the interacting components representing the exciting term in Equation (10). This energy loss is expressed by the remaining terms in $_6E$, i.e., the mean products of the stationary perturbations $_1H_\mathbf{k}$ and $_2H_\mathbf{k}$ with the nonstationary perturbations $_5H_{-\mathbf{k}}$ and $_4H_{-\mathbf{k}}$ excited by "higher-order" resonant interactions. For large t expressions similar in structure to Equation (20) can also be derived for these products, but as nonstationary exciting forces are involved, the results cannot be formu-

lated as simply as Equation (20) and will not be given here. Once these asymptotic relations have been derived, the determination of the nonlinear energy transfer is then simply a matter of (rather complicated) algebra. The formulation of the final result depends decisively on two properties:

1. As the linear wave components are assumed to be statistically independent, the rate of change of the mean products in $_6E$, representing the energy transfer, can be expressed completely in terms of the linear spectrum $_2F(\mathbf{k})$.

2. The rate of change of the mean products in $_6E$ is determined entirely by resonant interactions in which the perturbation components $_nH_\mathbf{k}(t)$ are excited with their natural frequencies $\omega_\mathbf{k}$. The higher-harmonic, nonlinear components with frequencies unequal to $\omega_\mathbf{k}$ do not participate in the energy transfer. The unsteady components of the perturbations can thus be interpreted directly as perturbations of the linear wave components and, consequently, the mean products in $_6E$ as perturbations of the linear spectrum $_2F(\mathbf{k})$. On account of these two properties the nonlinear energy transfer can be expressed entirely in terms of $_2F(\mathbf{k})$. Dropping the subscript 2, the final result is

$$\frac{\partial F(\mathbf{k})}{\partial t} = \int\int\int\int_{-\infty}^{+\infty} F(\mathbf{k}')F(\mathbf{k}'')F(\mathbf{k}' + \mathbf{k}''$$
$$- \mathbf{k})T_1(\mathbf{k}', \mathbf{k}'', \mathbf{k}' + \mathbf{k}'' - \mathbf{k})dk_x'dk_y'dk_x''dk_y''$$
$$- F(\mathbf{k})\int\int\int\int_{-\infty}^{+\infty} F(\mathbf{k}')F(\mathbf{k}'')T_2(\mathbf{k}, \mathbf{k}', \mathbf{k}'')$$
$$dk_x'dk_y'dk_x''dk_y'', \tag{21}$$

where

$$T_1(\mathbf{k}_1, \mathbf{k}_2, \mathbf{k}_3) = \frac{9\pi}{4\rho^2 g k_1 k_2 k_3} (A_{\mathbf{k}_1,\mathbf{k}_2,-\mathbf{k}_3}^{+,+,-})^2$$
$$\delta(\omega_{\mathbf{k}_1+\mathbf{k}_2-\mathbf{k}_3} - \omega_{\mathbf{k}_1} - \omega_{\mathbf{k}_2} + \omega_{\mathbf{k}_3}) \tag{22}$$

$$T_2(\mathbf{k}, \mathbf{k}_1, \mathbf{k}_2)$$
$$= \frac{9\pi}{4\rho^2 k_1 k_2}\left\{\frac{A_{\mathbf{k},-\mathbf{k}_1,-\mathbf{k}_2}^{+,-,-}\cdot A_{-\mathbf{k}+\mathbf{k}_1+\mathbf{k}_2,-\mathbf{k}_1,-\mathbf{k}_2}^{+,-,-}}{\omega_\mathbf{k}(\omega_\mathbf{k} - \omega_{\mathbf{k}_1} - \omega_{\mathbf{k}_2})}\right.$$
$$\delta(\omega_{\mathbf{k}-\mathbf{k}_1-\mathbf{k}_2} + \omega_\mathbf{k}, - \omega_{\mathbf{k}_1}, - \omega_{\mathbf{k}_2})$$
$$+ \frac{A_{\mathbf{k},\mathbf{k}_1,-\mathbf{k}_2}^{+,+,-}\cdot A_{-\mathbf{k}-\mathbf{k}_1+\mathbf{k}_2,-\mathbf{k}_1,\mathbf{k}_2}^{-,+,-}}{\omega_\mathbf{k}(\omega_\mathbf{k} + \omega_{\mathbf{k}_1} - \omega_{\mathbf{k}_2})}$$
$$\delta(\omega_{\mathbf{k}+\mathbf{k}_1-\mathbf{k}_2} - \omega_\mathbf{k} - \omega_{\mathbf{k}_1} + \omega_{\mathbf{k}_2})$$
$$+ \frac{A_{\mathbf{k},-\mathbf{k}_1,+\mathbf{k}_2}^{+,-,+}\cdot A_{-\mathbf{k}+\mathbf{k}_1-\mathbf{k}_2,-\mathbf{k}_1,\mathbf{k}_2}^{-,-,+}}{\omega_\mathbf{k}(\omega_\mathbf{k} - \omega_{\mathbf{k}_1} + \omega_{\mathbf{k}_2})}$$
$$\left.\delta(\omega_{\mathbf{k}-\mathbf{k}_1+\mathbf{k}_2} - \omega_\mathbf{k} + \omega_{\mathbf{k}_1} - \omega_{\mathbf{k}_2})\right\} \tag{23}$$

and

$$A_{\mathbf{k_1,k_2,k_3}}^{s_1,s_2,s_3} = \frac{1}{3} \{ C_{\mathbf{k_1,k_2,k_3}}^{s_1,s_2,s_3} + C_{\mathbf{k_3 k_1 k_2}}^{s_3,s_1,s_2} + C_{\mathbf{k_2,k_3,k_1}}^{s_2,s_3,s_1} \} \quad (24)$$

with

$$
\begin{aligned}
C_{\mathbf{k_1,k_2,k_3}}^{s_1,s_2,s_3} &= \frac{2[\mathbf{k_2 \cdot k_3} - \ldots - k_2 k_3](\omega_2 + \omega_3)(\omega_1 + \omega_2 + \omega_3)[k_1|k_2 + k_3| - \mathbf{k_1 \cdot (k_2 + k_3)}]}{(\omega_{k_2+k_3})^2 - (\omega_2 + \omega_3)^2} \\
&+ [\mathbf{k_2 \cdot k_3} - \ldots - k_2 k_3] \left[\frac{\omega_1(\omega_2 + \omega_3)}{2g^2}(\omega_2^2 + \omega_3^2 + \omega_2\omega_3) + \frac{\omega_1^2(\omega_2^2 + \omega_3^2)}{2g^2} - \frac{\omega_1^3(\omega_2 + \omega_3)}{2g^2} \right. \\
&\left. - \frac{\omega_1(\omega_2 + \omega_3)|k_2 + k_3|}{g} - \frac{\mathbf{k_1 \cdot (k_2 + k_3)}}{2} \right] \\
&+ \frac{\omega_2\omega_3}{2g}(k_2 + k_3)\mathbf{k_1 \cdot (k_2 + k_3)} - \frac{\omega_1^3}{2g^4}\omega_2\omega_3(\omega_2^2 + \omega_3^2)(\omega_2 + \omega_3) \\
&+ \frac{\omega_1\omega_2^2\omega_3^2}{2g^4}[\omega_2\omega_3(\omega_2 + \omega_3) - \omega_2^3 - \omega_3^3], \qquad (\text{where } \omega_j = s_j\omega_{\mathbf{k}_j}).
\end{aligned} \quad (25)
$$

Equations (21)–(25) can be checked by applying the law of energy conservation, which requires that the total energy of the sea remains constant. This gives the condition

$$\underset{\text{Permut. of } \mathbf{k}_j}{\Sigma} \{ T_1(\mathbf{k_1,k_2,k_3}) - T_2(\mathbf{k_1,k_2,k_3}) \} = 0 \quad (26)$$

INTERPRETATION AND DISCUSSION

Equation (21) can be interpreted in terms of quadruple-interactions in which — under certain resonance conditions — energy is transferred from the three "active" wave components $\mathbf{k_1}$, $\mathbf{k_2}$ and $\mathbf{k_3}$ to a "passive" fourth component $\mathbf{k_4} = \pm \mathbf{k_1} \pm \mathbf{k_2} \pm \mathbf{k_3}$.[1]

The first positive integral in Equation (21) expresses the energy gained by the component $\mathbf{k}$ by all quadruple interactions in which $\mathbf{k}$ represents the "passive" component, whereas the second integral expresses the energy lost by all interactions in which $\mathbf{k}$ represents one of the three "active" components. The gain in energy is independent of, but the loss is proportional to, the value of the spectrum at $\mathbf{k}$. The transfer process can thus be expected to reduce sharp peaks in the spectrum, distributing the energy more evenly over all wave numbers. This can be understood further by examining the quadruple interactions themselves more closely. It can be shown that

interactions between four components $\mathbf{k_1}$, $\mathbf{k_2}$, $\mathbf{k_3}$ and $\mathbf{k_4}$ occur if, and only if, two pairs of wave numbers, say $(\mathbf{k_1}, \mathbf{k_2})$ and $(\mathbf{k_3}, \mathbf{k_4})$, exist such that

$$\mathbf{k_1} + \mathbf{k_2} = \mathbf{k_3} + \mathbf{k_4} \quad (27)$$

and

$$\omega_{\mathbf{k_1}} + \omega_{\mathbf{k_2}} = \omega_{\mathbf{k_3}} + \omega_{\mathbf{k_4}} \quad (28)$$

If these conditions are fulfilled, all four interactions corresponding to the four possibilities of choosing three active components and one passive component occur. It can then be shown that if all four values of the spectrum are equal, the energy transfer is exactly balanced. It thus vanishes generally for an isotropic, white spectrum. The net transfer for four wave numbers also vanishes if both wave number pairs are equal. This is the case, for instance, for all interactions in a uni-directional spectrum, as it can be shown that in this case Equations (27) and (28) have only trivial solutions. However, the unidirectional state is unstable and breaks down for small two-dimensional disturbances and would furthermore probably be found to be nonstationary if the perturbation analysis were extended to higher orders.

In an actual wave spectrum the limiting case of an isotropic, white spectrum is, of course, never attained, as the nonlinear energy flux has to be considered in conjunction with the other processes determining the energy balance of the spectrum. The nonlinear energy flux in a wave spectrum is in many respects very similar to the nonlinear energy flux in a homogeneous turbulence spectrum, which is also generally assumed to favour a more uniform distribution of energy over all

---

[1] In accordance with the definition of $_2F(k)$ the "component $\mathbf{k}$" refers always to the wave component travelling in the positive $\mathbf{k}$-direction.

wave numbers. This suggests an equilibrium structure in a fully developed wave spectrum analogous to the "cascade" structure of a turbulence spectrum. The dissipation of wave energy due to wave breaking and turbulence is probably concentrated in the high wave-number region of the spectrum contributing significantly to the mean-square wave slope. The generation of wave energy by the wind forces, on the other hand, will probably be concentrated more in the region of small wave numbers corresponding to waves with phase velocities nearly equal to the wind velocity. The energy flux from low to high wave numbers required to maintain equilibrium is then supplied by the nonlinear interactions, which transfer energy from the high spectral peak in the energy-generating region to the low-energy region of dissipation at higher wave numbers. For a non-equilibrium spectrum in the development period

the situation will generally be different, as the spectral maximum in this case lies closer to the higher wave numbers. It is possible that in the initial period considerable energy then also flows in the direction of lower wave numbers. It is hoped to investigate these cases further by computation of the right-hand side of Equation (21) for several spectra.

An indication of the order of magnitude of the nonlinear energy flux can be obtained by dimensional analysis of Equation (21). If T is the characteristic time of the energy flux, ϑ the root mean-square wave slope and T_w a suitably defined mean wave period we find

$$T \sim T \cdot \vartheta^{-4} \qquad (29)$$

Assuming the proportionality factor equal to one [a very crude procedure on account of the complicated functions T_1 and T_2 in Equation (21)],

Figure 4-3-1. *Energy flux for a fully-developed spectrum.*

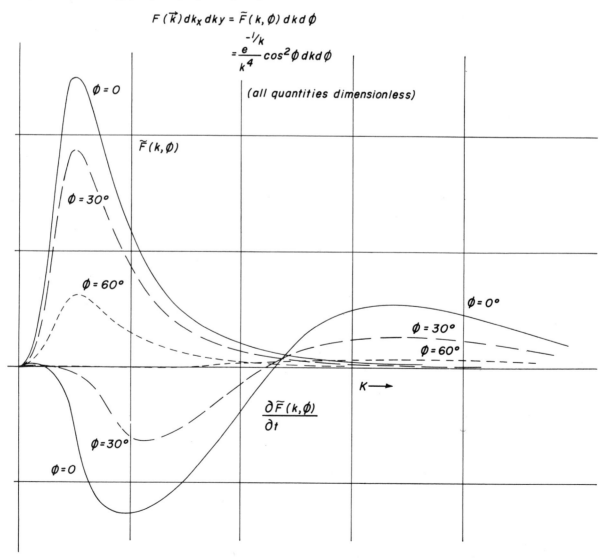

$$F(\vec{k})dk_x dk_y = \widetilde{F}(k,\phi)\,dk\,d\phi$$

$$= \frac{e^{-1/k}}{k^4}\cos^2\phi\,dk\,d\phi$$

(all quantities dimensionless)

we find that for $T_w = 10$ sec. and $\vartheta = \frac{1}{10}$, say, $T = 28h$, which is comparable in magnitude to the development periods of wave spectra.

A more accurate estimate of the order of magnitude of the energy flux was obtained by computing the energy flux for the fully developed spectrum

$$\tilde{F}(k, \phi) = \begin{cases} e^{-1/k} \cdot k^{-4} \cdot \cos^2 \phi, & |\phi| \leqq \dfrac{\pi}{2} \\[2ex] 0 \; |\phi| > \dfrac{\pi}{2} \end{cases}$$

where k and θ are nondimensional cylindrical coordinates, which corresponds to a frequency spectrum

$$e^{-\nu^{-2}} \cdot \nu^{-7} \cdot \cos^2 \phi.$$

The computations were made on an IBM 650,[2] which proved to be rather too small for accurate integration of the integrals in Equation (21). The results should therefore be considered as only qualitative with an inaccuracy factor of the order of two. The resulting energy flux for three values of ϕ is shown in Figure 4-3-1. As expected, the transfer of energy is from longer to shorter waves. As the transfer functions are weighted towards higher wave numbers, the maximal energy loss occurs at higher wave numbers than the maximum

---

[2] The author is indebted to Miss C. Schwarz and Mr. G. Krause for making the computations.

of the spectrum. The tendency to isotropy or wave scattering is small. This may be due partly to the strongly peaked form of the spectrum. A little energy is scattered at angles greater than $90°$ and even at an angle $\phi = -180°$, but the energy flux is of the order of 0.1 per cent and less of the maximum energy flux for $\phi = 0°$. For a wind speed of 10 m/s, the characteristic times of the energy flux in the region $|\phi| < \pi/2$ were found to be a few fractions of an hour for the shorter waves and a few hours for the longer waves, which is comparable with the characteristic times of the generating and dissipating processes in a wind-generated sea.

REFERENCES

Tick, L. J., "A Nonlinear Random Model of Gravity Waves I." Scientific Paper no. 11, N. Y. Univ., Coll. of Engineering, 1958. Also published in J. Math. Mech., Univ. of Indiana.

Phillips, O. M., "On the Dynamics of Unsteady Gravity Waves of Finite Amplitude, Part 1, The Elementary Interactions," *Fluid Mech.*, IX No. 2 (1960), 193–217.

Phillips, O. M., "On the Generation of Waves by Turbulent Wind," *Fluid Mech.*, II (1957), 417–445.

Hasselmann, K., "Grundgleichungen der Seegangs-voraussage," *Schiffstechnik*, VII No. 39 (1960) 191–195.

DISCUSSION

Dr. Longuet-Higgins (prepared comment on the papers concerning nonlinear aspects of the spectrum): Both Mr. Tick and Dr. Pierson have raised the question of whether the third-order interaction terms discovered by Dr. Phillips, which grow with time, represent a real transfer of energy or whether they could be accommodated by slightly perturbing the frequency of the original components.

Now two wave components

$$a_1 \cos(\mathbf{k}_1 \cdot \mathbf{x} - \sigma_1 t) \quad \text{and} \quad a_2 \cos(\mathbf{k}_2 \cdot \mathbf{x} - \sigma_2 t)$$

were shown to give rise to a secular term

$$At \sin[(2\mathbf{k}_1 - \mathbf{k}_2) \cdot \mathbf{x} - (2\sigma_1 - \sigma_2)t], \quad (1)$$

where A is independent of $\mathbf{x}$ and t. Generally the frequency $(2\sigma_1 - \sigma_2)$ of this secular term differs

from either σ_1 or σ_2. But by perturbing the frequency of the first term, for example, we have

$$a_1 \cos[\mathbf{k}_1 \cdot \mathbf{x} - (\sigma_1 + \sigma')t] = a_1 \cos(\mathbf{k}_1 \cdot \mathbf{x} - \sigma_1 t) + a_1 \sigma' t \sin(\mathbf{k}_1 \cdot \mathbf{x} - \sigma_1 t) + 0(a_1 \sigma'^2 t^2), \quad (2)$$

which shows that any secular term derived by this method has itself a frequency σ_1 or σ_2, generally different from $(2\sigma_1 - \sigma_2)$.

Thus I am inclined to think that Dr. Phillips and Dr. Hasselmann are correct in interpreting terms of this type as a genuine transfer of energy from one part of the spectrum to another.

From Dr. Phillips' remarks it would appear that two deep-water waves, travelling in the same direction, and with frequencies σ_0 and $\frac{3}{2}\sigma_0$ (wave numbers k_0 and $\frac{9}{4}k_0$) will generate a third wave travelling in the opposite direction, of frequency $\frac{1}{2}\sigma_0$ and wave number $-\frac{1}{4}k_0$. This suggested the following simple experiment:

In a long wave channel let the wavemaker be given a motion with two harmonic components σ_0 and $\frac{3}{2}\sigma_0$ (for finite depth the ratio must differ slightly from $\frac{3}{2}$), and let the waves be absorbed at the far end of the tank by a "beach" or other wave absorber. Then let the two primary wave trains be cut off, for example by inserting a thin, rigid barrier vertically into the wave channel quite close to the wavemaker. After the primary waves have travelled away from the barrier there will be left a region of almost calm water, in which the tertiary wave, which travels in the opposite direction, may be observed. According to Phillips's analysis, the amplitude of the tertiary wave (in deep water) should be

$$a = C(a_1 k_1)^2 \, (a_2 k_2) L \qquad (3)$$

where L is the distance from beach to barrier and C is a constant of order 1. A somewhat lengthy calculation (unchecked) gave $C = \frac{5}{12}$. The crest-to-trough height of the tertiary waves is $2a$, and this value is further doubled by reflection from the vertical barrier inserted in the tank.

I carried out an experiment on these lines in a wave tank 70 feet long at the Hydraulics Research Station, Wallingford, Connecticut, with the kind permission of Mr. Russell. The parameters were: $a_1 = 0.65$ inch; $a_2 = 0.045$ inch; $a_1 k_1 = 0.045$, $a_2 k_2 = 0.088$; h (mean depth) $= 21.5$ inches. On the basis of the above formula one would expect $a = 0.12$ inches, which would be readily observable.

The experiment showed no trace of such a wave, and the accuracy of the measurements was such that, if a tertiary wave existed, its amplitude a was less than 0.02 inches. This is an apparent contradiction.

[In carrying out the calculation for finite depth it was discovered that in the previous calculation for infinite depth a term had been omitted. Taking this into account, one finds $C = 0$ in Equation (3), although for waves intersecting at any other angle (except 180 degrees), the coupling does not vanish. This explains the null result in the experiment. It also means that in order to establish the interaction experimentally, observations must be made with wave trains that intersect obliquely.

Both theory and experiment suggest that the observations mentioned by Dr. Barber are due to a different cause. *Note added on 12 June 1961.*]

Dr. Eckart: Usually, if one is working with a hydrodynamic problem, it is a good idea to close Lamb and ask oneself what Rayleigh did in this field. I don't know whether Rayleigh did anything with nonlinear gravity waves, but he did do something with a problem that involves nonlinearity, viscosity, and perturbation theory. The problem is an amusing one, and it has been quite thoroughly investigated experimentally. It illustrates the question of the difference between perturbation and numerical order. The experiment is an old-fashioned one.

You have a helmholtz resonator. This is a cross-section. Here you have a lighted candle. If you bring in a vibrating tuning fork to the resonator, the candle flame is blown out. In the more sophisticated experiment that lends itself to a qualitative measurement you have a cylinder closed by cellophane ends containing a fluid. Here you place a crystal oscillator, which can generate ultrasonic waves and a beam of waves to send through the fluid. If the fluid is air, then in a fraction of a second a ring vortex is formed. If it is water, it will take somewhat longer for the vortex to grow to a steady state. The velocity in the vortex turns out to be proportional to the energy in the beam of sound waves.

The formula for this turns out to be independent of the viscosity of the fluid. The time required to reach a steady state, however, is dependent on viscosity, as I have illustrated by air and water. If you make the appropriate perturbation calculation to second order, setting viscosity equal to zero, you get nothing. If you leave the viscosity in, you get the result. You get a driving force on this vortex that is proportional to viscosity. You also get a resistance at the wall which is proportional to viscosity so the steady state is independent of viscosity.

Moreover, the vorticity in this steady state is quite high. You can calculate the motion essentially as an incompressible fluid of constant density but you have to take solutions having no potential. So this case again refers to one of the problems that was brought up today — whether or not it is permissible to neglect vorticity in these higher-order calculations.

The most remarkable thing about this is that the velocity in the vortex is hundreds or even thousands of times greater than the velocity in the sound wave. Yet you can deal with it by perturbation theory. So I think we need not be too afraid if some of the second-order terms turn out to be rather large. The perturbation theory may still apply. The reason is fairly clear in this case. The frequencies are so vastly different that the interaction terms are not of any great importance. There are also many other second-order terms in this problem, some of which are of very small magnitude. At least I hope they are all of a small order of magnitude because this is the one that I calculated at the time these experiments were performed.

Mr. Harris: It seems to me that in any series solutions, such as this perturbation high-order of terms, it is essential to know what the convergence is. Maybe the seventh or ninth order destroys the perturbation theory. I think this should be explained.

Dr. Hasselmann: There is an existence theorem for the convergence of the perturbation series I have used here, but I cannot remember now what the conditions are.

Mr. Harris: There would have to be a function of something. I don't think it could be convergent for all time, for example.

Dr. Hasselmann: I am not quite sure of this point actually. Possibly it does not converge. It is always practically semi-convergent. That is enough. The mathematicians can trouble themselves with this if they want to. Physicists have always assumed that the method works unless the perturbation solutions show some form of irregularity, and I know of no case where this attitude has led them into trouble.

Mr. Tick: I think there are a number of mathematical difficulties here. Since I was one of the originators of this nonlinear attack, I feel justified in cautioning of the danger. In order for perturbation to have any meaning in the continuous spectrum case, there must be some sort of uniformity of correctness of the expansion since the size of the terms depends on wave length. That is to say, the convergence or semi-convergence depends on the wave number being considered.

In discussing the random case of continuous spectra we may have various rates of convergence for different parts of the problem, in which case I think there is chaos, and I think we know very little at this point. Certainly there is no place to turn in the mathematical literature for any discussion of this problem because it has never arisen before.

Second, concerning the proof of existence or nonexistence of certain stationary solutions, I think we want to be careful to de-limit a couple of problems here. The first problem is: is there a stationary solution to the equations? It will certainly be hard to prove. This is the probabalistic version of the LEVI-CIVITA problem.

Second, is there a stationary solution to the third order — whatever that means. I want to stress this point. Here it is best to go back to Rayleigh. In obtaining the solution he had to resort to a certain mathematical technique, namely, to choose a co-ordinate system moving with the phase speed. Such a technique is not available in the two-wave case. It is also not clear to me that the way to remove a secular trend is by frequency perturbation.

If you look through the literature, the secular trend removal techniques were evolved to deal with a particular problem. They provide no guide to other classes of problems. It just works, or it doesn't. First, we don't know whether frequency perturbation is the method. I have never suggested that it is. I suggested that people who have been concerned with the secular method have used this technique.

Second, we don't know if the frequency perturbation is of the form suggested by Dr. Longuet-Higgins. Again I caution you that order is a very tricky notion, which I don't understand.

Mr. Harris: If the perturbation theory gives rise to something that increases with time, it obviously can't apply forever. Whether or not it is physically important can be evaluated when the convergence condition is stated, so we can see whether it becomes divergent very quickly or acts in such a time that it is not important.

There is also the problem that the term of second order may be one not included in the original equation. Or some second-order term not included in the original equation is far more important than the one that arises in the original equation.

Dr. Hasselmann: You get the rate of change of the spectrum at a particular time t, and this rate of change is then valid for all t provided the original assumption that you have a Gaussian process remains valid. This is, in fact, a critical point. The question is: how long does the process, assuming it to be Gaussian originally, retain this property when you begin integrating the integro-differential equation with respect to time? There is no doubt that if you wait long enough, the process will no longer be Gaussian. However, it can be shown that the rate at which the process loses its Gaussian character (apart from the stationary, second-order terms) is at least two orders of magnitude smaller than the rate of energy transfer, so that for the times that enter in integrating the equation the process can be considered to be Gaussian.

Mr. Harris: You may say that theoretically this is not important, but from a practical point of view it is very important. You can't calculate anything unless you have some notion of what length time steps you can use.

Dr. Eckart: I believe that there is one other point of view on this problem that may shed some light on it. If one considers it not in the Eulerian system, but as Pierson proposes, the problem is simplified from a mathematical point of view in that the boundary condition at least is linear.

A number of perturbation techniques become available. But now let us suppose that these do converge. Let us suppose that there are no secular terms. You may still get into trouble because in this case the solution may become multi-valued. The wave profile may take on a double-valued shape. This is clearly a breaker, but the whole question of the nonlinear effects associated with breakers is completely outside the differential equations.

In order to take this into account, one has to introduce techniques that are similar to the shock wave techniques in compressible fluid theory. You won't avoid this difficulty of the breaker and the shock wave technique by staying with the Eulerian method.

Even granting convergence or granting that there is a reasonable interpretation of the secular term, there are still some difficulties that have not been touched upon by any of the speakers today.

Dr. Longuet-Higgins: I feel we can reduce these difficulties of breaking by taking the waves at one-tenth of the amplitude.

Dr. Eckart: Yes. If you restrict yourself in amplitude, which you can on paper, this is fine.

Dr. Longuet-Higgins: Of course you can on paper. But it means that the probabilities of breaking are reduced exponentially. If you have a more or less Gaussian probability of distribution of slopes — which gets more and more Gaussian as you reduce the amplitude — and if you reduce it by half, I imagine you really do greatly reduce the probability of breaking.

Dr. Eckart: Then I will stick my neck out and make this prediction. If you do work on the nonlinear theory and neglect the breakers, the white caps, and the spray, then I think the nonlinear effects will turn out to be negligible.

Dr. Longuet-Higgins: The times taken for the non-linear transfer of energy to become appreciable are inversely proportional to the square of amplitude. On the other hand, the probabilities of breaking are reduced by a very much larger factor.

Dr. Eckart: Let me modify my prediction. You may end up with an explanation of the wind-driven currents or something of this sort. But I don't think you will add very much to the theory of the surface waves themselves. You may add a good deal to the theory of the motions of the sea. Are we in agreement then?

Dr. Longuet-Higgins: There may be a range of wave amplitudes in which the tertiary interactions are appreciable though the wave breaking is not.

RECENT MEASUREMENT AND

ANALYSIS TECHNIQUES

JAMES M. SNODGRASS

CHAIRMAN

D. E. CARTWRIGHT

O N E

THE USE OF DIRECTIONAL SPECTRA IN STUDYING
THE OUTPUT OF A WAVE RECORDER ON A MOVING SHIP

INTRODUCTION

The description of ocean waves as stationary, Gaussian stochastic processes with an "energy" spectrum, expressed as a function of wave number and direction of propagation (or certain other pairs of variables), is now well established as a useful and fairly accurate working model. In its simplest application, to the height of the sea surface above a fixed point as a function of time only, the theory has been well supported by measurements, and standard techniques have been evolved for dealing with the analysis. But if one wants to apply the *directional energy spectrum* in its most general aspect, one finds a good deal of theory relating to it and to its evaluation from hypothetical measurements, but remarkably few practical applications on which one may base technique or know in advance what sort of results to expect.

This situation becomes especially evident when the oceanographer is approached by engineers who require precise answers to wave problems that cannot be properly solved without reference to the directional spectrum. An important example is when the naval architect wants to know how to analyse the oscillatory motions and stresses

of a ship in a complex pattern of ocean waves. Naval architects now realise that the new statistical techniques for dealing with waves, evolved largely by oceanographers in the last fifteen years or so, open up potentially new paths of research on ship behaviour at sea. But it is significant that while there are quite a number of papers in ship research journals which re-expound the principles of analysis of ship motion at sea, first set out by St. Denis and Pierson (1953), and demonstrate the validity of the basic principles of linearity by means of scaled models, there is a notable dearth of published work applying the theory to the concrete case of an actual ship in ocean waves.

A step towards bridging the gap between theory and practice was made by some analytical studies of the various modes of motion of R.R.S. "Discovery II" in the North Atlantic ocean by the author (1957a with L. J. Rydill, and 1957b). In this case the work was simplified considerably by using only data from wave systems in long-crested swells propagating virtually in a unique direction. Application of the same analysis to waves in general weather situations may give poor results. When, as a member of the staff of the National Institute of Oceanography, the author recently became involved in a joint program of research with the National Physical Laboratory and the British Shipbuilding Research Association on the behaviour of ships at sea, he found it essential to evolve a new technique which demanded less restriction of the directional spectrum and could therefore deal adequately with a greater variety of sea states. The essentials of the technique are given in this paper, particularly in relation to the important problem of analysing the performance of a shipborne wave recorder, whose response varies with wave number and frequency, while the ship is underway. Analysis of the ship's motions and stresses, which depend ultimately on this work, is being carried out by members of the staff of N.P.L. and B.S.R.A., and their results will be reported elsewhere.

WAVE RECORDERS

Although limited as a research tool for obtaining information about the directional spectrum, the N.I.O. "shipborne wave recorder" (Tucker, 1956) is probably still the most convenient instrument for obtaining wave records in open sea in any weather conditions. It is particularly useful for the study of ship behaviour because in recording waves as they actually pass the ship it gives a signal strongly coherent with the ship's motions and stresses. This facilitates the evaluation of response functions. However, a disadvantage which has to be overcome for accurate work is the peculiar attenuation function imposed on the spectrum by the recorder. In effect, the amplitude of a wave of length $2\pi/k$ passing the ship with period of encounter $2\pi/\omega$ is attenuated by a factor very nearly of the form

$$C \cdot B(\omega) \cdot A(k) \qquad (1)$$

In this product the factor $B(\omega)$ is due to the characteristics of the electrical circuit internally to the instrument and is fairly accurately expressed by

$$B(\omega) = [1 + (\omega T)^{-2}]^{-3/2} \qquad (2)$$

where T is the time constant of each of three filters, usually 8.8 seconds. This can be corrected for immediately after spectral analysis by dividing spectral densities by B^2.

The factor $A(k)$ represents the relation between the height of water above a fixed point on the ship's hull and the pressure measured there, and is also affected by the ship's heaving response.

If the ship did not interfere with the wave motion, then $A(k)$ would be nearly e^{-kd}, where d is the mean depth of the point concerned. In fact the constant C, incorporated in the recorder system, is chosen to be slightly greater than the reciprocal of the maximum value of $B(\omega)e^{-kd}$ for $k = \omega^2/g$ (ship stationary) and $d = 10$ ft., a typical value, in order that the total product (1) will be fairly near unity for a useful range of frequencies. However, for the accuracy and frequency range required for ship studies this simplification for $A(k)$ is not sufficient, and we cannot ignore the effect of the ship's presence on the pressure signal, particularly for large values of k. Since no exact theoretical form is known for this effect, the only satisfactory procedure is to measure $A(k)$ by direct calibration against another type of wave recorder.

Such a calibration is easily obtained for a stationary ship. One merely puts overboard an accelerometer buoy, of which there are now several varieties available, records simultaneously for a suitably long period of time, and obtains $A(k)$ directly from the ratios of spectral densities since $k = \omega^2/g$. However, the ship researcher is concerned mainly with the output of the recorder when the ship is underway, which may be different. This introduces new difficulties. The obvious difficulty that one cannot conveniently drag a wave-recording buoy through the water at high speed is not serious, since a perfectly good statistical sample of the same wave system can usually be obtained with a stationary buoy within a distance of many miles and a time span of a few hours of the record taken by the ship. The real difficulty lies in interpreting the frequencies ω recorded on the ship in terms of wave number k, or true circular frequency σ of the waves. It is well known that for any long-crested component of the wave system progressing in the direction ψ relative to the ship's head, the relationship between ω and σ is

$$\Phi_\omega(\sigma, \psi) = \omega - \sigma + kv \cos \psi = 0 \qquad (3)$$

where v is the ship's speed, and for deep water $k = \sigma^2/g$. But this relation can be used directly only if the whole wave system is perfectly long-crested in the direction ψ, as considered by Cartwright and Rydill (1957). In a general confused sea all parts of the directional spectrum along the locus $\Phi_\omega(\sigma, \psi) = 0$ contribute to the energy density of the ship's spectrum at frequency ω. Thus, to calibrate the recorder we need some means of estimating or at least approximating the directional spectrum. The problem of deciding which is the best value of k or σ to associate with ω for the purpose of obtaining $A(k)$ is considered below in the section on "Evaluation of $A(k)$."

The instrument used for recording the main dimensions of the directional spectrum was the N.I.O. pitch-roll buoy, which measures wave slope in two perpendicular directions as well as the vertical motion. The theory of this instrument and some results that have been obtained from it are described in another paper at this conference, by Longuet-Higgins, Cartwright, and Smith (1961) [henceforward referred to as L.C.S.], and will not be repeated here. It suffices to say that from cross-spectral analysis of its three components, one obtains for each wave frequency σ the five parameters defined by

$$a_n(\sigma) + ib_n(\sigma) = \frac{1}{\pi} \int_{-\pi}^{\pi} F(\sigma, \phi) e^{in\phi} d\phi,$$

$$n = 0, 1, 2, \quad (4)$$

where $F(\sigma, \phi)$ is the directional wave spectrum. These parameters are by no means sufficient to define $F(\sigma, \phi)$ exactly, but they give certain useful directional properties as functions of frequency, which are difficult to derive in any other way from instruments that can be handled on a ship. Interference between the buoy and waves is negligible for the wave lengths of interest to ship research, and so the buoy's motions can safely be taken to be virtually those of the water surface itself.

The technique used in comparing the two wave recorders was briefly as follows: When waves appeared suitably stable and simple in pattern, the buoy was put overboard and left to record (internally) for about twenty minutes and then brought in; the ship then steamed on the series of courses or "manoeuvre" laid down for its trials, recording the waves on its own instrument and various other motions. The whole manoeuvre comprised a closed polygon of less than twenty miles and was completed in four hours, whereupon a second record was taken with the buoy. From analysis of the buoy records a suitable approximation to the directional wave spectrum was made, and from this was calculated the spectrum which would be derived from a perfect wave recorder moving with the ship, according to each course direction and speed. Finally, the ratios of these calculated spectra to those measured directly were compared on a suitable scale and estimates made for $A(k)$. These processes involve

a number of interesting details, which will now be elaborated in the four following sections.

DIRECTIONAL ANALYSIS

Instead of approximating the surface height by means of doubly-integrating circuits, as in the measurements described in L.C.S., the buoy's vertical acceleration signal was recorded directly. There were several reasons for this. First, the integrating circuits introduce attenuations and phase lags, which are tiresome to correct and may lead to fresh errors; second, the components of slope being virtually components of horizontal acceleration divided by g are more directly comparable with vertical acceleration than with vertical height. In the directional analysis described in L.C.S. some cross-spectra had to be divided by σ^2 and others by σ^4, which can cause errors, as discussed in the next section; using vertical acceleration the whole directional analysis can be done without involving such factors, and only one division by σ^4 is finally necessary (see the following section). A third advantage of dealing with acceleration is that its spectrum is much broader and closer to "whiteness" than that of surface height.

Accelerometers were again allowed to align themselves in the "apparent vertical" direction, that is, normally to the wave surface. In order to avoid the consequent errors at low frequency discussed by Tucker (1959), these readings were corrected to the true vertical by using the slope measurements. If χ_2 and χ_3 are the two components of slope, it is fairly easy to show that the true vertical acceleration χ_1 is given in terms of the apparent vertical acceleration χ_1' to third order approximation by

$$\chi_1 = \chi_1' - \tfrac{1}{2}(g + \chi_1')(\chi_2^2 + \chi_3^2) \quad (5)$$

The correction (5) was achieved by a simple digital process. By reasoning similar to that in L.C.S. the first five angular harmonics of the acceleration spectrum $F''(\sigma, \phi) = \sigma^4 F(\sigma, \phi)$ are given by

$$A_0 = \frac{1}{\pi} C_{11},$$

$$A_1 = \frac{g}{\pi} Q_{12},$$

$$A_2 = \frac{g^2}{\pi} (C_{22} - C_{33}) \quad (6)$$

$$B_1 = \frac{g}{\pi} Q_{13},$$

$$B_2 = \frac{g^2}{\pi} (2C_{23})$$

where $A_n = \sigma^4 a_n(\sigma)$, $B_n = \sigma^4 b_n(\sigma)$, and C_{rs}, Q_{rs} are respectively the co-spectrum and quad-spectrum of the pair χ_r, χ_s. These were computed digitally by the correlation technique.

In L.C.S. are discussed some methods of combining these harmonics to produce weighted estimates of $F''(\sigma, \phi)$ of the form

$$F_N''(\sigma, \phi) = \frac{1}{2\pi} \int_{-\pi}^{\pi} F''(\sigma, \phi') W_N(\phi' - \phi) d\phi'$$

where $W_N(\phi)$ is a weighting function more or less peaked in the direction $\phi = 0$. However, these weighting functions are all much too broad for the present purpose. Quite a narrow band of swell confined to $\pm 10°$, for example, would still give an estimate $F_N''(\sigma, \phi)$ spread over some $\pm 90°$, and this would produce misleading results when applied to the ship. Another approach considered in L.C.S. is to evaluate the two angles ϕ_1, ϕ_2, which minimise the integral

$$\frac{1}{2\pi} \int_{-\pi}^{\pi} F''(\sigma, \phi)$$

$$\cdot 16 \sin^2 \frac{1}{2} (\phi - \phi_1) \sin^2 \frac{1}{2} (\phi - \phi_2) d\phi \quad (7)$$

This is useful for identifying two crossing swells or two predominant directions in wind waves but does not give much information about how $F''(\sigma, \phi)$ is distributed about these directions. For our purpose, where most of the wave energy is in the form of swell confined to a fairly narrow angular band at each frequency, the following approach was found to be more suitable. Suppose for any given value of σ, $F(\sigma, \phi)$ is practically contained within a single zone of angular width $\pm \delta$ about the direction given by $\overline{\phi} = \tan^{-1} B_1/A_1$ (uniquely determined by the signs of A_1 and B_1). Then

$$B_1' = \frac{1}{\pi} \int_{-\pi}^{\pi} \sin (\phi - \overline{\phi}) F''(\sigma, \phi) d\phi \equiv 0$$

$$= \frac{1}{\pi} \int_{-\delta}^{\delta} \phi F(\sigma, \overline{\phi} + \phi) d\phi + 0(\delta^3) \quad (8)$$

showing that $\overline{\phi}$ is in fact very close to the true mean direction. Further, if we write $C_r = \sqrt{(A_r^2 + B_r^2)}$, it can be shown that

$$2 - \frac{2C_1}{A_0} = \overline{(\phi - \overline{\phi})^2} + 0(\delta^4) \quad (9)$$

$$2\overline{\phi} - \tan^{-1} \frac{B_2}{A_2} = \overline{(\phi - \overline{\phi})^3} + 0(\delta^5) \quad (10)$$

$$6 - \frac{8C_1}{A_0} + \frac{2C_2}{A_0} = \overline{(\phi - \overline{\phi})^4} + 0(\delta^6) \quad (11)$$

where

$$\overline{(\phi - \overline{\phi})^n} = \frac{\int_{-\pi}^{\pi} \phi^n F''(\sigma, \overline{\phi} + \phi) d\phi}{\int_{-\pi}^{\pi} F''(\sigma, \phi) d\phi}$$

Thus the expressions (9), (10), and (11) give the mean-square, cube, and fourth deviations of $F(\sigma, \phi)$ from the mean direction $\overline{\phi}$, provided δ is fairly small. Equation (9) is a measure of the "width" of the angular distribution, (10) is a measure of its "skewness," and (11) could be used for a further characteristic of its shape. Another measure of mean-square deviation is the "long-crestedness" parameter

$$\gamma^2(\sigma) = \frac{A_0 - C_2}{A_0 + C_2} \quad (12)$$

discussed in L.C.S., and another type of mean direction is

$$\frac{1}{2} \tan^{-1} \frac{B_2}{A_2} \quad (13)$$

though the latter angle is indeterminate to 180 degrees. Both these last measures have special statistical meanings, but are less suitable for defining mean directions and widths than those defined above. Yet another measure of spread is $\phi_1 - \phi_2$, but this was not used in the present work.

There is no space here for an account of various methods that were tried to fit suitable distributions to these parameters. Some are given in L.C.S. It was found that on the whole, for the spectra considered, the skewness parameter (10) was negligible, being small in magnitude and variable in sign, so a function symmetrical about $\phi = \overline{\phi}$ was suitable. Finally the form

$$F''(\sigma, \phi) = A_0(\sigma) G(s) |\cos \frac{1}{2} (\phi - \overline{\phi})|^{2s} \quad (14)$$

was chosen as a reasonable function with simple properties which has the correct mean direction and total energy density with respect to σ, and an arbitrarily narrow width determined by s (not necessarily an integer). $G(s)$ is a normalising factor to make

$$\int_{-\pi}^{\pi} F''(\sigma, \phi) = \pi A_0(\sigma)$$

so

$$G(s) = 2^{2s-1} \frac{\Gamma^2(s+1)}{\Gamma(2s+1)} \qquad (15)$$

For large s, Equation (14) tends to the form

$$F''(\sigma, \phi) = A_0(\sigma) \left(\frac{\pi s}{4}\right)^{1/2} \exp[-\tfrac{1}{4}s(\phi - \overline{\phi})^2] \quad (16)$$

that is, a Gaussian-type distribution with Standard Deviation $\sqrt{(2/s)}$.

If Equation (14) were a perfect fit to the angular distribution, the parameter s would have to satisfy both the expressions

$$\frac{C_1}{A_0} = \frac{s}{s+1}, \quad \frac{C_2}{A_0} = \left|\frac{s(s-1)}{(s+1)(s+2)}\right| \qquad (17)$$

The values of C_1/A_0 and C_2/A_0 from the analysed records are plotted against each other in Figure 5-1-1, in which is also shown the relationship implied by Equations (17). It is seen that although there is a tendency for C_2 to be relatively too large, on the whole the two ratios increase together in the same sort of way and are rarely very far from the hypothetical curve. The tendency toward larger values of C_2 is perhaps due to the bimodality of wind-wave spectra suggested by some results discussed in L.C.S. However, it was considered too complicated to try to take into account bimodal angular distributions for this work. The calculations were therefore performed on functions of form (14) with s chosen to be the mean of the two solutions to Equations (17). The possible negative solution to the second equation was, of course, ignored.

By means of approximate unimodal angular distributions of type 14 the directional wave spectrum is expressed as the product of a function

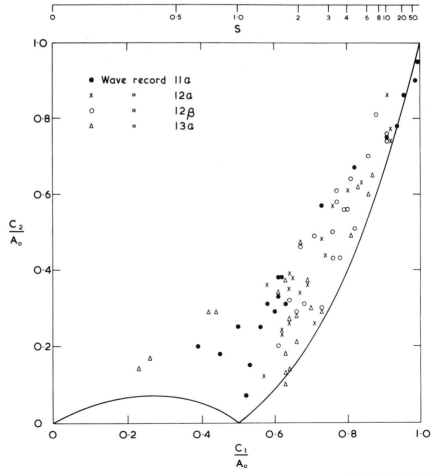

Figure 5-1-1. *Angular harmonic amplitude ratios with theoretical relation according to Equation 17.*

of σ, which is the total spectral density with respect to frequency, and a function of ϕ, which is expressed in terms of two variables $\bar{\phi}$ and s, which will in general themselves vary with frequency. A typical set of values of A_0, $\bar{\phi}$ and s are shown in Figure 5-1-2 for the buoy record 12β taken at about 21.45 on 4-10-1959 from the Ocean Weather Ship "Weather Reporter" at Station K (45°0′N, 16°0′W). The situation as reported at the time was "wave system dominated by long-crested swell from about 295°, with local wind 15–20 knots from about 270°." This is borne out by the weather chart for 00 hrs. 5-10-1959, shown in Figure 5-1-3, where it is seen that the ship was situated near the outer edge of a large depression, and the recorded swell was being generated from the southwest portion.

The swell, around $\sigma = 0.5$, is not very evident from the acceleration spectrum πA_0, but the superimposed diagram of the displacement spectrum (derived from it by the special process described in the next section) shows that the part between 0.4 and 0.6 certainly dominates the rest of the spectrum. Only the frequency range relevant to the ship is shown; beyond this range A_0 tails off to zero well before the "folding frequency"

$\sigma = 6.3$. (The sampling rate was exactly 0.5 sec.) The change from swell to wind waves is seen well in the diagrams of $\bar{\phi}$ and s. $\bar{\phi}$ is around 115 degrees in the swell region, which is correct for the direction towards which the swell is propagating, and the mean angle slowly falls to a steady value at about 90 degrees for the locally generated wind waves. Values of s are high for the swell, indicating a narrow angular spread, and tail off to a roughly constant level of about 3. The smooth curves shown in these two diagrams represent the values assumed for $\bar{\phi}$ and s in the subsequent calculations in order to facilitate integration.

It is clear that we are dealing here with a fairly complex wave system for which there is no sharp dividing line between swell and sea, but a steady transition from one to the other. This is in contrast to the usual assumed models of directional spectra, in which the wind blows in the same direction over vast areas of sea surface, possibly with a small superimposed band of swell totally unrelated to the wind waves. The system described in Figure 5-1-2 is fairly common in the real ocean, and other records used in this exercise, also taken at the edge of depressions, show much the same sort of feature. In one case (13α) the

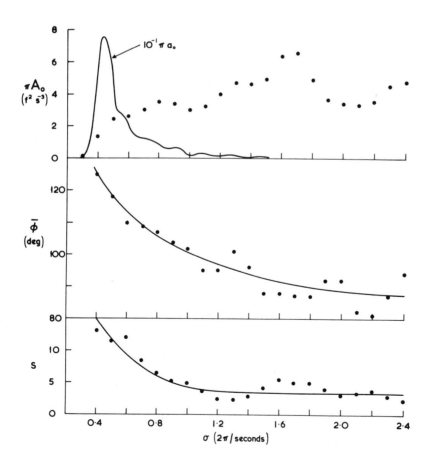

Figure 5-1-2. *Total energy (acceleration and displacement), mean direction, and spread parameter for buoy wave record 12β.*

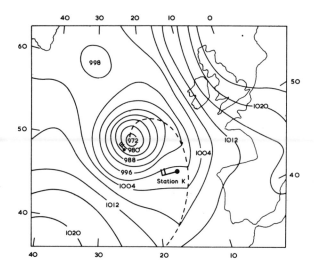

Figure 5-1-3. *Isobaric chart near time of record 12β, taken at Station "Kilo."*

wind wave differed in mean direction from the swell by as much as 88 degrees. A simpler type of analysis assuming all waves unidirectional would give dubious results, so these methods certainly lead to an improvement in accuracy. On the other hand, more complex methods which could take account of bimodal angular distributions would be desirable. One approach would be to attempt to measure a larger number of angular harmonics A_n, B_n, using a more complicated buoy system. This is being investigated.

CONVERSION FROM ACCELERATION TO DISPLACEMENT

In the previous section the directional spectrum of wave acceleration was approximated by means of a product of the form

$$F''(\sigma, \phi) = H''(\sigma)K(\phi) \quad (18)$$

where $H''(\sigma) = \pi A_0(\sigma)$ is simply the frequency spectrum of vertical acceleration, and $K(\phi)$ is the function of direction defined by Equation (14). To obtain the directional spectrum of surface displacement, which is what we require, it is necessary to replace $H''(\sigma)$ in (18) by

$$H(\sigma) = \frac{H''(\sigma)}{\sigma^4} \quad (19)$$

This appears trivial but in fact needs special care, as we shall now see. The usual method of digital spectral analysis, using auto- or cross-correlation (Blackman and Tukey, 1958) produces

statistical estimates of a weighted average of $H''(\sigma)$ etc. over a fairly broad frequency band. That is, we estimate

$$h''(\sigma) = \int_0^\infty H''(\sigma')f(\sigma' - \sigma)d\sigma' \quad (20)$$

where $f(\sigma)$ is large only in the frequency interval or band width $(-w \leqslant \sigma \leqslant w)$ and is of total integral unity. For the analyses shown in Figure 5-1-2, w is about 0.2 in σ, and the successive estimates $h''(\sigma)$ are in steps of 0.1. Generally such a large filter band width is desirable, and in particular for the angular analysis presented in the previous section, ·because the standard error of the estimates is proportional to $w^{1/2}$, in the present case equal to 0.16 of their expected values. But whether $\sigma^{-4}h''(\sigma)$ is a good estimate of

$$\int_0^\infty \sigma'^{-4}H''(\sigma')f(\sigma' - \sigma)d\sigma' \quad (21)$$

is another matter and depends on how both σ^{-4} and $H''(\sigma)$ vary in the intervals $\sigma \pm w$. This is especially important for low frequencies where σ is of the same order of magnitude as w, and $H''(\sigma)$ rises steeply.

As an example of the errors that can arise in converting wide-band estimates of acceleration spectra to displacement spectra, an artificial spectrum with a fairly realistic profile was chosen:

$$H(\sigma) = 10^5\sigma^5 e^{-10\sigma} \quad (22)$$

and a reasonable approximation to a filter function:

$$f(\sigma) = (2\pi s^2)^{-1/2} \exp\left(\frac{-\frac{1}{2}\sigma^2}{s^2}\right) \text{ with } s = 0.05 \quad (23)$$

This filter has the same "equivalent band width" as that produced by a correlation analysis based on about 100 lags at half-second intervals, which is fairly typical. With these functions an exact calculation was made of the desired spectral estimate (21) and of that derived by dividing the estimate (20) by σ^4. Figure 5-1-4 shows the true spectra $H(\sigma)$, $H''(\sigma)$, and the ratio

$$X = \sigma^{-4} \frac{\int_0^\infty H''(\sigma')f(\sigma' - \sigma)d\sigma'}{\int_0^\infty \sigma^{-4}H''(\sigma')f(\sigma' - \sigma)d\sigma'^{-1}}$$

$$= \left(1 - \frac{10s^2}{\sigma}\right)^4 \quad (24)$$

$$\frac{1 + 36q + 378q^2 + 1260q^3 + 945q^4}{1 + 10q + 15q^2},$$

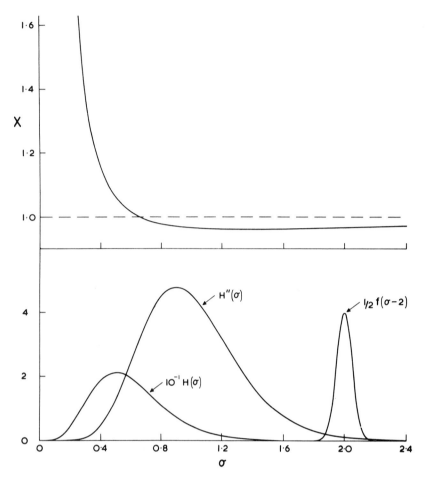

Figure 5-1-4. *Errors in converting from an acceleration spectrum to a displacement spectrum using a wide band filter.*

where

$$q = \frac{s^2}{(\sigma - 10s^2)^2}$$

It is seen that large errors occur on the low-frequency side of the peak where X rises steeply, and although X tends to unity for large σ, it is as low as 0.96 for a considerable part of the range. These errors are important when one is concerned with the ratios of the wave spectrum to the spectra of ship motions or similar quantities, and also affect the conversion of heave acceleration spectra and corrections to wave spectra, such as $B(\omega)$ in Equation 1.

To eliminate this type of error we reduce the filter band width to extreme narrowness. (When s becomes very small, X in Equation (24) becomes practically equal to 1 over the whole working range.) The most effective way of doing this is not to increase the number of lagged correlations, which is wasteful of computer time, but to make a Fourier Series analysis of the original data:

$$P_s + iQ_s = \sum_{r=-(1/2)N}^{(1/2)N} \lambda_r \chi_1^{(r)} \exp \frac{2\pi rsi}{N}$$

$$h_s'' = h'' \left(\frac{2\pi s}{N\Delta t} \right) = \frac{\Delta t}{\pi N} (P_s^2 + Q_s^2) \qquad (25)$$

where $\chi_1^{(r)}$ are the $N + 1$ terms of the acceleration time series (corrected by Equation (5)), Δt is their time separation, and $\lambda_r = \frac{1}{2}$ for $r = \pm \frac{1}{2}N$ and 1 for all other values of r. The spectral estimate h_s'' has a filter band width $2\pi/N\Delta t$, which is about one fiftieth of that normally obtained by the correlation technique. These values may now safely be divided by σ^4 to obtain wave height spectral estimates $h(\sigma)$, but the resulting values have individually high standard error (Coefficient of Variation = 1) and so must be smoothed to reduce the standard error to about the same value as that obtained with the correlation method. A simple smoothing function of suitable form is

$$\overline{h}_s = \frac{1}{p^2} (h_{s-p+1} + 2h_{s-p+2} + \ldots$$
$$+ (p - 1)h_{s-1} + ph_s + (p - 1)h_{s+1}$$
$$+ \ldots + 2h_{s+p-2} + h_{s+p-1}) \qquad (26)$$

This simulates a filter $f(\sigma)$ of triangular form with "effective width" $(3\pi p/N\Delta t)$.

Most of our buoy records consisted of 2,000 read-

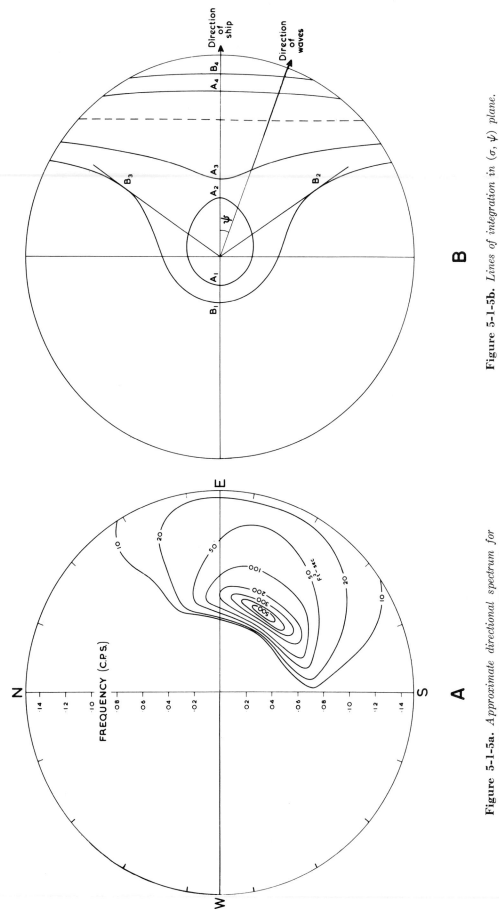

Figure 5-1-5a. *Approximate directional spectrum for wave record 12β based on values shown in Fig. 5-1-2.*

Figure 5-1-5b. *Lines of integration in* (σ, ψ) *plane.*

A

B

FREQUENCY (C.P.S.)

N

W

E

S

·14
·12
·10
·08
·06
·04
·02
·02
·04
·06
·08
·10
·12
·14

10
20
50
100
200
300
500

50 Ft²-sec

20

10

Direction of ship

Direction of waves

ψ

A_1
A_2
A_3
A_4
B_1
B_2
B_3
B_4

ings at half-second intervals. The parameters used for the analysis above were $s \doteq 30(1)330$, $p = 12$, giving a final effective width 0.12 (or 0.018 c.p.s.) for the smoothed filter, which is narrower than that used for the directional analysis and has a correspondingly larger standard error, 0.24 of expectancy. Since our next process is to integrate again over the directional spectrum to obtain $E(\omega)$, which will reduce the standard error further, the figure 0.24 is acceptable and the narrowness desirable. A further advantage of the process just described is that it provides estimates of $\overline{h}_s \doteq H(\sigma)$ which, though smoothed, are spaced at very narrow intervals of frequency (0.001 cycles per second). This facilitates the final integration process to be described in the next section.

The wave-height frequency spectrum $H(\sigma)$ deduced from the above procedure for record 12β is shown at the top of Figure 5-1-2 superimposed on the estimates of the acceleration spectrum from the correlation method. Figure 5-1-5a shows the complete approximate directional spectrum $H(\sigma)K(\phi)$, with $K(\phi)$ deduced from the smooth curves shown in Figure 5-1-2. This spectrum is expressed in units of *feet² per (radian-cycles per second)*, as it was found more convenient to compute in terms of true frequency than in circular frequency σ. For convenience of drawing, only frequencies up to 0.15 c.p.s. are shown, but the skewness of the spectrum towards the higher frequencies is evident. The figures on which subsequent calculations were based extended to 0.32 c.p.s. ($\sigma = 2.01$).

THE SPECTRUM OF ENCOUNTER

Having produced by the methods described in this section and the previous one a tolerable approximation to the directional wave spectrum, it remains to calculate the frequency spectrum experienced by an ideal wave recorder moving on a straight course at uniform speed. The essentials of the theory of this "spectrum of encounter," as it may be called, are given in St. Denis and Pierson (1953), but we shall here emphasize the practical problems that arise in computation.

If the directional angle ϕ of the spectrum $F(\sigma, \phi)$ is measured in the conventional way, clockwise from the north, and the ship keeps a straight course in the direction ϕ', the wave direction relative to the ship's head is $\psi = \phi - \phi'$, again clockwise. We shall write $F(\sigma, \psi)$ for the directional spectrum relative to the ship's head,

assuming ϕ' has been subtracted from the angle in $F(\sigma, \phi)$ in its geo-oriented form.

Starting from any point in the (σ, ψ) plane the basic Equation 3 uniquely determines the circular frequency ω with which the ship encounters the wave components from that region of the spectrum, namely

$$\omega = \sigma - \sigma^2 \tau \cos \psi \quad \text{where } \tau = \frac{v}{g} \quad (27)$$

But any given frequency of encounter ω (which is as a rule indistinguishable from $-\omega$) arises from any wave component along the loci in the (σ, ψ) plane

$$\Phi_\omega(\sigma, \psi) = 0 \qquad \Phi_{-\omega}(\sigma, \psi) = 0 \qquad (28)$$

These loci are fairly complicated geometrically, and fall into two classes according to whether $\omega <$ or $> \frac{1}{4}\tau$, an example of each of which is shown in Figure 5-1-5b. The class $\omega < \frac{1}{4}\tau$ is typified by the three branches passing through the points A_2, A_3, and A_4, the first of which forms a closed loop while the second and third tend asymptotically to the directions $\psi = \pm\frac{1}{2}\pi$. As ω increases, the points A_2 and A_3 approach each other to form a branch point when $\omega = \frac{1}{4}\tau$, after which a single curve appears for all higher values of ω. The latter type of curve, $\omega > \frac{1}{4}\tau$, has a minimum value or $|\psi| = \cos^{-1}(\frac{1}{4}\omega\tau)$ for which $\sigma = 2\omega$, indicated by the tangents at B_2 and B_3. The other branch, through B_4, corresponding to $-\omega$, has much the same properties as in the first case. All branches $\Phi_{-\omega} = 0$ are to the right of the dashed line shown perpendicular to $\psi = 0$ through $(1/\tau, 0)$, and so all frequencies covered by them are greater than $1/\tau$. In the cases analysed, for which τ was always less than 0.8 sec., the wave energy along these branches contributed a negligible proportion of that derived from the main branches Φ_ω, and so they could be ignored.

The energy spectrum with respect to frequency of encounter $E(\omega)$ of the signal sensed by an ideal wave recorder moving with the ship is equivalent to an integral of the directional spectrum along these contours. The integrand can be expressed with either σ or ϕ as independent variable, thus

$$E(\omega) = \int_c F(\sigma, \psi) \left| \frac{\partial \psi}{\partial \omega} \right| d\sigma$$

$$= \int_{c^1} \frac{H(\sigma)[K(\psi) + K(-\psi)] d\sigma}{\sigma^2 \tau |\sin \psi|} ,$$

$$\cos \psi = \frac{\sigma - \omega}{\sigma^2 \tau} \quad (29)$$

or

$$E(\omega) = \int_c F(\sigma, \psi) \left| \frac{\partial \sigma}{\partial \omega} \right| d\psi$$

$$= \int_{c^1} \frac{H(\sigma)[K(\psi) + K(-\psi)]d\sigma}{\sqrt{1 - 4\omega\tau \cos \psi}} ,$$

$$\sigma = \frac{[1 \pm \sqrt{(1 - 4\omega\tau \cos \psi)}]}{2\tau \cos \psi} , \quad (30)$$

where the contours c^1 are restricted for convenience to the lower half plane $(0 \leqslant \psi \leqslant \pi)$. Of the above two forms, (29) is preferable for the main computation, since $H(\sigma)$ is already given in small steps of σ, and it avoids the repeated solutions of quadratics necessary to (30). However, the integrand in (29) has singularities like $(\sigma - \sigma_0)^{-1/2}$ at the points A_1, B_1, A_2, A_3 where the contours approach $\psi = 0$ or π. To cope with these, we carry out the numerical quadrature of (29) over the main range of σ (Simpson's rule is sufficient) as far as the last or the last but one value of σ for which $|\cos \psi| < 1$. With σ in steps of $2\pi \times .001$ sec^{-1} this value will usually be such that $\sin \psi \geqslant 0.2$ near $\psi = \pi$, or $\sin \psi \geqslant 0.1$ near $\psi = 0$. The remaining part of the integral is then simply evaluated by use of the integral from (30), whose integrand is quite well behaved in these regions. Moreover, $H(\sigma)$ varies but slightly over the latter ranges of ψ and can with sufficient accuracy be taken to be constant, while $\cos \psi$ scarcely varies either. Thus the integral (30), over the small range $\psi = 0$ to ψ' say, can be adequately expressed in the simple form

$$H(\sigma')(1 - 4\omega\tau)^{-1/2} \int_0^{\psi'} [K(\psi) + K(-\psi)]d\psi \quad (31)$$

where σ' is the given value of σ for which ψ is nearest to 0. The integral near $\psi = \pi$ is treated similarly. It is worth noting that while the integrand of Equation (30) is tractable at $\psi = 0$ and π, it has singularities at B_2 and B_3 where $\cos \psi = \frac{1}{4}\omega\tau$, while the integral (29) is carried quite normally past these points.

Expressed as a continuous function of ω, $E(\omega)$ can be shown to have always a logarithmic singularity at $\omega = \frac{1}{4}\tau$, due to the behaviour of the integral (30) near $\psi = 0$ when ω approaches this value. This occurs on all courses theoretically but is most prominent in following seas. It is of no consequence practically, however, since all spectral estimates of $E(\omega)$ are inevitably smoothed over a sufficiently wide band for the very sharp

peak at $\frac{1}{4}\tau$ to appear in the analysis of measurements. (Otherwise it could conceivably be used as an accurate measure of ship speed.) It merely means that in evaluating the integrals (29) and (30), values of ω excessively close to the critical value have to be avoided.

The above method of evaluating $E(\omega)$ is obviously more accurate than any simplified method based on a unidirectional spectrum as used in Cartwright and Rydill (1957). In head seas it appears, however, that the results of the two methods do not differ very much, but quite large differences can occur on other courses. In particular it is interesting to contrast the results of the two methods in a following sea, depicted in Figure 5-1-6. In this figure the true frequency $f = \omega/2\pi$ and the spectra $E(f) = 2\pi E(\omega)$ are used for convenience. The unidirectional method [assuming $F(\sigma, \psi)$ exists only for $\psi = 0$], calculated for $\tau = 0.600$ sec, the value applicable to the "following sea" course on Manoeuvre 12, gives the continuous curve, which rises to a singularity like $(f - f_0)^{-1/2}$ at the critical frequency, shown by the dotted line, and then ceases to exist. No energy lies beyond the critical frequency because the Φ_ω locus is then of the type B in Figure 5-1-5b, which does not cross the line $\sigma = 0$, and the wave energy in the region of $\Phi_{-\omega}(\sigma > 1.8$ sec$^{-1})$ is negligible. The circles represent the few points calculated by the full integral method, giving values below the smooth curve and then continuing well beyond the critical frequency on account of the extension of $F(\sigma, \psi)$ on either side of the direction $\psi = 0$. No indication is given of the logarithmic

Figure 5-1-6. *Following-sea spectrum: full line*
unidirectional: circles
Using directional spectrum: crosses
measured, manoeuvre No. 12, course E.

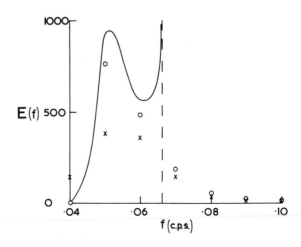

singularity at the critical frequency, which is much weaker than that shown by the full·curve.

The crosses in Figure 5-1-6 represent the spectra derived from the shipborne wave recorder on this course. Those at $f = 0.06$ and 0.07 c.p.s. are lower than the calculated values because waves in the direction $\psi = 0$ are reduced by the hydraulic breakwater effect of the propellor race, but beyond the critical frequency where the waves come from other directions, they are seen to be in quite reasonable agreement and only slightly lower than the calculated values on account of the attenuation function $A(k)$ (Equation 1).

EVALUATION OF A(k)

As previously stated, before or after each set of wave records made with the pitch-roll buoy, the ship (O.W.S. " *Weather Reporter* ") steamed on a series of courses, taking continuous records of its behaviour and of the output from the shipborne wave recorder. These manoeuvres were organised and instrumented (except for wave recorders) by the British Shipbuilding Research Association. The author is concerned only with the wave records, which were digitised directly at one-second intervals on punched tape and later subjected to spectral analysis under the supervision of Dr. Hogben of N.P.L. This analysis, based on 1,000 sec records with 50 lagged correlations, produced spectral densities $E_s(f) = 2\pi E_s(\omega)$ at frequencies $f = \omega/2\pi = 0.01(0.01)0.30$ c.p.s., which were immediately corrected for the electrical attenuation $B(\omega)$ [Equation (1)]. The spectra were then ready for evaluation of $A(k)$ by comparison with spectral densities at these frequencies derived from the buoy for each speed and course heading, using the processes described in the three preceding sections. The processing of the buoy data, apart from the initial semi-automatic digitisation stage, involved for each manoeuvre about six hours' working time of a fast electronic computer (*Deuce*), followed by about a month's work on desk machines, taken up mainly with the quadrature of some 200 integrals [Equation (29)].[1]

A typical set of values of $E(\omega)$ derived from the buoy and the corresponding values from the ship's records corrected for the electrical attenuation, $E_s(\omega)/B^2(\omega)$, are shown in Figure 5-1-7, where

---

[1] For this work the author is indebted to his colleagues Miss D. Catton and Miss W. Haynes.

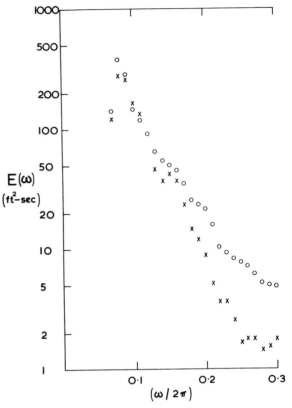

Figure 5-1-7. *Spectra of encounter: circles Deduced from directional spectrum for perfect wave recorder: crosses measured, manoeuvre No. 12, course J.*

it is seen that they correspond fairly well at low frequencies but the latter values fall off with increasing frequency on account of the attenuation $A(k)$. The ratios

$$\mu = \frac{E(\omega)B^2(\omega)}{E_s(\omega)} \quad (32)$$

are in fact statistical estimates of relatively smooth functions which approximate to $1/A^2(k)$ if we assume a suitable relation between wave number k and frequency of encounter ω. There is, of course, considerable scatter in the values of μ since the two records, although samples of the same statistical process, are quite "incoherent." The coefficient of variation of μ, or (standard error ÷ expectancy)^2 is about 0.1. On the other hand, the ship's wave record and the components of its motion are rather strongly coherent, so that the response functions derived from ratios of their spectra are remarkably smooth and accurate. To obtain a similarly smooth estimate of the correcting function $1/A^2(k)$, some fairing of the scattered values μ is therefore necessary. Merely to correct the response functions of the ship's motions, one could draw or compute a suitable smooth curve for each course as a function of ω approximating to the values μ. But such functions would not in themselves give any insight into the fundamental behaviour of the instrument's wave attenuation as a function of k and could not be used to derive the attenuation on any other courses or at other speeds. It is preferable to relate values of μ from all courses to a common base of $k = \sigma^2/g$ and then estimate a single smooth function through the ensemble of values. The function for each separate course can then be derived from the one function by a backwards transformation.

The difficulty here is suitably to define k or σ as a function of ω on any course. As was seen in the preceding section, the spectrum for any given frequency of encounter ω is derived from an integral over the directional spectrum along a path that covers a wide range of frequencies and directions. In practice the bulk of this integral will come from a fairly narrow range of frequencies (or ranges if more than one branch is involved), and there is a definite lower limit to σ, its value at $\psi = \pi$. Somewhere around the center of the range is the value of σ most appropriate to the function $A(k)$. For simplicity this value of σ was defined by

$$\bar{\sigma}_n = \frac{\int_{c_n^1} \sigma F(\sigma, \psi) \left| \frac{\partial \psi}{\partial \omega} \right| d\sigma}{\int_{c_n^1} F(\sigma, \psi) \left| \frac{\partial \psi}{\partial \omega} \right| d\sigma} \tag{33}$$

where the suffix n applies to each separate branch c_n^1 of the complete path $\Phi_\omega(\sigma, \psi) = 0$. In general when $\omega < \frac{1}{4}\tau$, we should thus define at most three values $\bar{\sigma}_1$, $\bar{\sigma}_2$, and $\bar{\sigma}_3$, corresponding to the distinct branches through A_1, A_3, and A_4 in Figure 5-1-5b. But in the majority of cases $\omega > \frac{1}{4}\tau$, and the branch through B_4 is negligible. Hence, only one value $\bar{\sigma}_n$ is relevant, which we shall call $\bar{\sigma}$. In referring the measurement μ to the variable $\bar{\sigma}$, we are in effect using an approximation

$$A^2 \frac{\bar{\sigma}^2}{g} = \frac{\int_{c^1} A^2 \frac{\sigma^2}{g} F(\sigma, \psi) \left| \frac{\partial \psi}{\partial \omega} \right| d\sigma}{\int_{c^1} F(\sigma, \psi) \left| \frac{\partial \psi}{\partial \omega} \right| d\sigma} \tag{34}$$

which is exact only in the limit when $F(\sigma, \psi)$ is a delta function at $\sigma = \bar{\sigma}$. However, it should make

a reasonable compromise for the unimodal swell spectra considered in this paper.

Values of $\bar{\sigma}$ obtained from the buoy record number 12β (whose directional spectrum is shown in Figure 5a) for a head sea course (A), a beam sea course (C) and a following sea course (E), are shown in Figure 5-1-8, together with the curve of $\sigma(\omega)$ calculated for the same ship speeds on the assumption of a unidirectional spectrum (Equation 3). For values of $\omega < \frac{1}{4}\tau$, the value $\bar{\sigma}_1$ was used, since most of the integral usually came from branch 1. It is seen that they agree fairly well at low frequencies, where the swell is almost unidirectional anyway, but where at high frequencies the angular spread increases and the mean direction changes, the two methods give rather different results. This is particularly so for the following-sea, E, where for reasons discussed in the preceding section, the unidirectional assumption fails for $\omega > \frac{1}{4}\tau$, whereas the full integral continues to give meaningful values. Also shown in Figure 5-1-8 are values of

$$\bar{\psi} = \cos^{-1} \frac{\bar{\sigma} - \omega}{\bar{\sigma}^2 \tau} \tag{35}$$

which always exist and may be regarded as the mean directions in which the wave components with encounter frequency ω approach the ship. Owing to the equivalence of $+\psi$ and $-\psi$, we have conventionally taken $\bar{\psi}$ always in the interval $0 < \bar{\psi} < \pi$. The horizontal broken lines are the unidirectional values 180 degrees, 90 degrees, and 0, respectively. It is interesting to note that from this definition $\bar{\psi}$ (or $\bar{\psi}_n$ defined by $\bar{\sigma}_n$) can never be exactly equal to 0 or π, that is, the effective wave direction can never be a perfect head sea or following sea, since the values of σ at $\psi = 0$ or π are always maxima or minima on any particular branch. This is an unavoidable but quite reasonable aspect of ship motions in confused seas.

In order to determine $A(k)$ the values of μ were plotted on a logarithmic scale against $\bar{\sigma}^2$ for the "head sea" courses A and J, "bow sea" B and H, and "beam sea" C and G, and the results are shown in Figure 5-1-9 for three separate manoeuvers, at different ship speeds, and for the stationary ship. The pairs B, H and C, G were nominally for waves on the starboard and port bow and beam respectively, but the wave conditions were not quite identical, because of the variation of ϕ in the directional spectra. Similar calculations were made for the "following sea" and "quartering sea" courses, but these are not in-

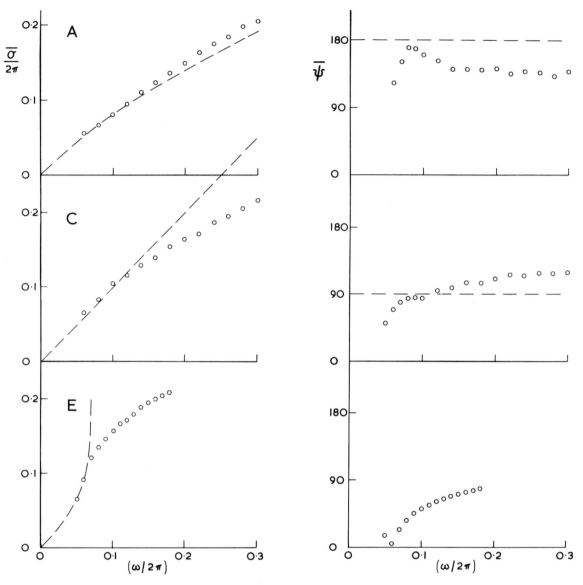

Figure 5-1-8. *Mean frequency and direction related to frequency of encounter.*
Circles: from directional analysis
Broken lines: for unidirectional waves
A: head sea   C: beam sea   E: following sea

cluded, partly because they are of little interest to the ship researcher, and partly because these courses involve waves near the direction $\psi = 0$, which are seriously disturbed by the propellor race, as was pointed out in connection with Figure 5-1-6.

In manoeuvre *SK* 12, for which the wave system had the nearest approach to long-crestedness, the values of μ clearly approximate to a single function, which is fairly represented by the straight line shown. The use of such a function implies that within about ± 90 degrees of head seas the

response $A(k)$ of the wave recorder is virtually independent of direction, ψ, for which there is no clear contrary evidence. The line was calculated to be the best fit to cut the vertical axis at 0.69, which is the known value of $1/C^2$ [in Equation (1), C is fixed instrumentally at 1.2], and ignoring the few points for largest $\bar{\sigma}$ for which μ tends to fall off. These last values are ratios of very small spectral densities quite near the level of random noise and so are not worth including in the calculation. The effect of noise is also clear in the last few values of $E_s(\omega)$ in Figure

5-1-7, which appear to be reaching a low constant level. The waviness apparent at small values of $\bar{\sigma}$ are due probably to bad resolution of the spectrum near its peak by two different processes. The straight line implies the simple relation

$$A(k) = e^{-kD}, \quad k = \frac{\bar{\sigma}^2}{g} \qquad (36)$$

where in this case $D = 17.3$ feet.

Similar remarks apply to the other manoeuvres SK 11 and 13, though there is considerably more scatter, probably on account of the greater skewness and spread in the directional spectrum. For SK 13 there was a difference of 88 degrees in $\bar{\phi}$ from low frequency to high frequency. Straight lines through $(0, 0.69)$ were estimated as for SK 12, except that the values of μ for course G in SK 11 were ignored as being dubious. The

Figure 5-1-9. *The ratios μ for head, bow and beam seas, on three manoeuvres, and for the stationary ship.*

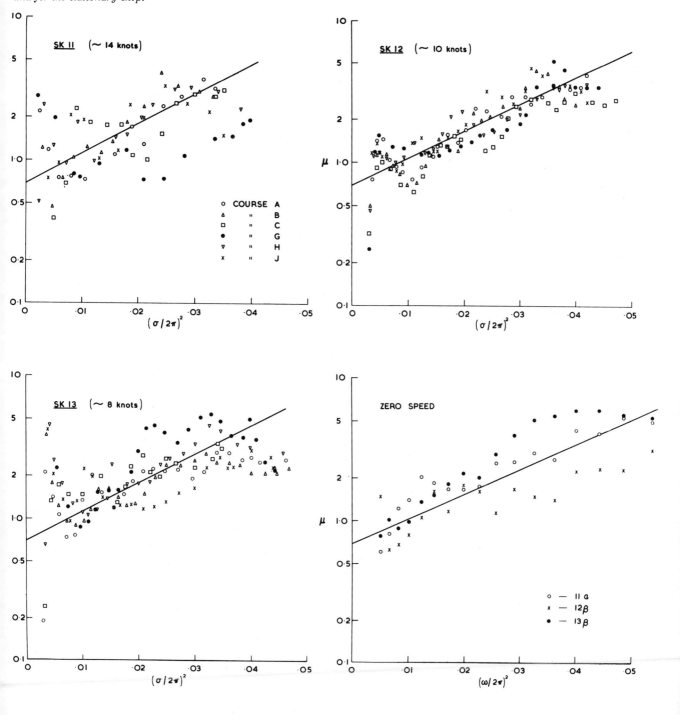

fourth diagram included in Figure 5-1-9 shows values of μ derived by direct comparison of frequency spectra ($\omega = \sigma$) when the ship was nominally stationary at the same time as the buoy recording. The amount of scatter in the three comparisons shown is surprising, and two others giving absurdly high values at high frequency were discarded. The reason for this scatter is probably that the ship had a slight unrecorded forward motion, as is commonly the case in the hove-to condition. The slight motion renders the assumption $\sigma = \omega$ invalid and distorts $E(\omega)$ at high frequencies of varying degree according to the wave direction. The best line through these points however has a slope similar to those in the other three diagrams for the ship underway, and this confirms the appropriateness of the mean frequency $\bar{\sigma}$ used in the latter. It should be noted, however, that the calibration of the instrument for comparison with ship motions on any particular course does not depend on the choice of the parameter $\bar{\sigma}$, since in using it one reverses the relation between $\bar{\sigma}$ and ω. The actual values of D corresponding to the four diagrams are:

Manoeuvre	Average speed	D
SK 11	14 knots	18.9 feet
SK 12	10	17.3
SK 13	7	18.6
—	zero	16.2

Except that the "stationary" case has a rather lower value of D than do the others, there is no obvious trend with speed. In view of the scatter in all cases we may regard the four results as consistent with D equal to about $17\frac{1}{2}$ feet. Now the actual depth of the pressure-sensing heads of the wave recorder at the time was 7.15 feet, so it behaves for large wave numbers like a pressure meter at about $2\frac{1}{2}$ times its actual depth, or $D = 2.5d$. This is not unreasonable, on account of the interference of the ship's hull, and in fact it has been shown by Korvin-Kroukovsky and Jacobs (1958) that to a first approximation the effect of a (circular) hull on waves is to square the exponential decay of pressure variations with depth, and there are other factors depending on the ship's speed. The full interference theory is of course much more complicated and is outside the scope of this paper. The exponential law implied by the straight lines in Figure 5-1-9 is only a compromise for obtaining a practical answer from somewhat scattered data. A more precise assessment would require essentially a method of obtaining a still more precise formulation of the directional spectrum. However, such methods are either far too elaborate to be within the bounds of possibility for practical, full-scale ship research or can be said to exist at present only in theory.

ACKNOWLEDGMENTS

The work described in this paper was a contribution to a joint effort for research into the seagoing qualities of ships by the National Physical Laboratory, the British Shipbuilding Research Association, and the National Institute of Oceanography. The N.I.O. buoy was instrumented by Mr. N. D. Smith and the records taken by Mr. B. J. Barrow with the help of other members of the trials party and the officers and men of O.W.S. "Weather Reporter." Miss D. B. Catton devised special programs for some of the calculations done by electronic computer, and Miss W. Haynes digitised the buoy records and did a great deal of the arduous non-automatic computations.

* * *

REFERENCES

Blackman, R. B. and J. W. Tukey, *The Measurement of Power Spectra*, New York, Dover Pubs., 1958.

Cartwright, D. E. and L. J. Rydill, "The Rolling and Pitching of a Ship at Sea," *Trans. Inst. Nav. Archit.*, IC (Boston, 1957a), 100–135.

Cartwright, D. E., "On the Vertical Motions of a Ship in Sea Waves," *Symposium on the Behaviour of Ships in a Seaway, Wagenigen* (1957b), Chapter 1.

Korvin-Kroukovsky, B. V. and W. R. Jacobs, "Pitching and Heaving Motion of a Ship in Regular Waves," *Trans. S.N.A.M.E.* (New York, 1958).

Longuet-Higgins, M. S., D. E. Cartwright and N. D. Smith, "Observations of the Directional Spectrum of Sea Waves and of Air Pressure Fluctuations at the Sea Surface," in this publication, 1961.

St. Denis, M. and W. J. Pierson, "On the Motions of Ships in Confused Seas," *Trans. S.N.A.M.E.*, LXI (New York, 1953), 332–357.

Tucker, M. J., "A Shipborne Wave Recorder," *Trans. Inst. Nav. Archit.*, XCVIII (London, 1956), 236–250.

Tucker, M. J., "The Accuracy of Wave Measurements made with Vertical Accelerometers," *Deep Sea Research*, V (London, 1959), 185–192.

M. J. TUCKER

T W O

RECENT MEASUREMENT AND ANALYSIS TECHNIQUES
DEVELOPED AT THE NATIONAL INSTITUTE OF OCEANOGRAPHY

INTRODUCTION

N.I.O. and its predecessor, the Oceanographic Group of the Admiralty Research Laboratory, have devoted considerable effort over a period of sixteen years to wave research. In the field of technique, our efforts to record and analyse waves for research purposes have on the whole been successful, though "he who never made a mistake never made anything." We have found, however, that recording waves for civil engineering purposes is much more difficult, and in fact, even taking a world-wide view, no more than two or three really successful wave recorders have been developed for this application. Every civil engineering installation presents different problems, and one may devote a lot of effort to overcoming these in one case, only to find a new and equally difficult set facing one in the next. A further difficulty is that the staff on the site, particularly when this is overseas and one cannot speak to them personally, are often unsympathetic to the equipment, and they get annoyed and lose interest at the first difficulty. Probably most installations use bottom-pressure-meter type wave recorders, and in moderate winds producing short

waves, these give apparently false recordings owing to the attenuation of the shorter waves with depth. Correction using the apparent period and attenuation factors from tables is of little help: the apparent period of the waves on the surface may be four seconds, and on the recording six seconds. Use of the factor corresponding to either of these periods will give the wrong answer. The reaction of the engineer on the site, who doesn't believe in instruments anyway, is to say, "It's no good," and lose interest.

Over the years we have built up a number of ideas on how to set about measuring and analysing waves, and these will be set out below. They owe a lot, of course, to other people's ideas and experience.

PRINCIPLES GOVERNING THE DEVELOPMENT OF WAVE-MEASURING INSTRUMENTS

In the design of instruments two factors of fundamental importance are sometimes overlooked. These are that the *user* must have confidence in the accuracy of the measurements and that the easier the analysis of the results, the more likely they are to be used. In the case of wave recording, both of these factors point to the measurement of absolute height (or pressure) because recording of a tidal cycle will then give a convincing check on the calibration of the equipment, and there is no necessity for any correction of the results for the variation of the response of the instrument itself with frequency, though hydrodynamic response factors will usually still need correction. Such an instrument also has the advantage that if it is sufficiently accurate, the long waves (of several minutes' period) may be filtered from its output and recorded separately. It is not, of course, practicable to record absolute height on the deep sea where no fixed platform is available as a reference.

Fixed sensitivity is desirable, since then the records are not wasted if someone forgets to note the setting of the sensitivity control, and the records do not go off scale by mistake. This may necessitate high resolution recording to obtain adequate precision over the possible range of wave heights to be measured, but this range is not usually very great.

In a shore-based installation the biggest single item of expenditure is often the cost of the cable, and if it has to be specially manufactured, the time required for this can postpone the date of installation. It is therefore an advantage if the instrument requires only a simple coaxial or 2-core cable. Such cables are relatively cheap and can often be obtained "off the shelf."

These last two considerations indicate a measuring head which gives a frequency dependent on the wave height, that is, an f.m. system. Frequency can be measured and recorded with extremely high precision; two cores suffice to carry both the power supply to the measuring head and the output signal back to the shore; in addition, the characteristics of the cable do not affect the calibration, and the output can be telemetered by radio if necessary.

For routine wave recording, self-contained wave recorders, that is, instruments laid on the sea bed for several weeks, or possibly months, at a time, and recording within themselves, have been found to be unsatisfactory. Only too often it is found on recovery that something has gone wrong with the device, and the records are lost. Such a loss may spoil a year's set of records. For some research purposes where the wave recorder is in operation for only a short time before it is recovered and the records examined, this is not so important, but it is still a significant factor.

For fixed installations, instruments that measure the variations in pressure as the waves pass overhead are still the most practical in most circumstances in spite of the severe disadvantage of their inability to measure short waves satisfactorily. This is partly because of the great expense of installing structures capable of supporting an instrument passing through the water surface, and partly because of the lack of any really satisfactory surface-height recorder capable of handling the range of levels required, which may be seventy feet in an exposed situation (waves plus tides). For some civil engineering applications, the insensitivity to short waves may be an advantage, since it is sometimes only the longer waves that are important.

For near-shore recording, then, it seems that an absolute pressure gauge, mounted as close to the surface as practicable, with an f.m. output and connected by cable to a recorder ashore, is likely to be the most satisfactory instrument for general use. As far as the author is aware, Snodgrass, Munk, and Tucker (1958) at the Scripps Institution of Oceanography were the first to develop such a system.

For recording waves on deep water, many people have tried using the still water below the action of the waves as a reference. Such systems typically either have a surface-height measuring device held steady by a drogue in deep water, or arrange for a buoy on the surface to raise and lower a pressure meter or integrating current-meter suspended in the deep water. In order to obtain reasonable response to the longer waves, such a system requires a suspension at least 100 m long. We have found such systems to be unsatisfactory. The equipment is usually clumsy and difficult to handle in stormy weather, the suspension may be subject to appreciable stretch; differential currents, wind drag, or drag through the cable connecting the instrument to the ship can cause the wire to tilt from the vertical, introducing drift into the record and unknown factors into the response.

The most satisfactory deep-sea wave recorders so far developed are those that measure the motions of a buoy. In their simplest form these contain a vertical accelerometer measuring the component of acceleration perpendicular to the water surface, or in the direction of the resultant acceleration, which is, in principle, the same thing. Better accuracy can be obtained if the accelerometer is mounted on a gyroscope so that it measures the component of acceleration in the true vertical. Either the signals can be integrated twice before

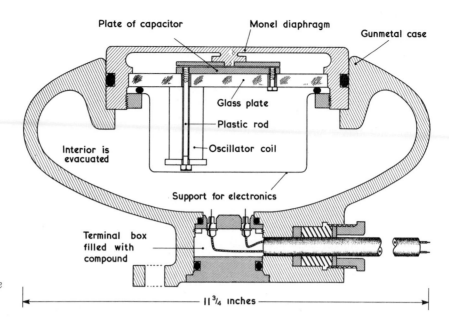

Figure 5-2-1. *Diagram of the measuring head.*

recording to give wave elevation, or if the power spectrum is being obtained, the acceleration spectrum can be determined and converted to the elevation spectrum by multiplying by $1/\omega^4$. By also measuring pitch and roll, a useful amount of information can be obtained about the directional spectrum of the waves (see the paper presented to this conference by Longuet-Higgins, Cartwright, and Smith). Such systems are eminently practicable and can be considered as fully established.

To obtain more information about the directional spectrum is difficult, and N.I.O. has not yet succeeded in producing any equipment that will do this. The problem is, of course, receiving a great deal of attention by workers in several countries.

THE F.M. PRESSURE RECORDER

This is a pressure-meter type wave recorder connected to the shore by a cable.

A diagram of the measuring head is shown in Figure 5-2-1. The pressure acts on a diaphragm carrying one plate of a parallel plate capacitor. The separation of the capacitor plates at zero pressure is 0.015 inch and is reduced to 0.0015 inch at a pressure corresponding to 200 ft. of water. This capacitor is the tuning capacitor of an L.C. oscillator, whose frequency is thus a measure of pressure.

The measuring-head circuit is shown in Figure 5-2-2. The power supplies are fed down a twin-core or coaxial cable. The oscillator is not de-

Figure 5-2-2. *The measuring head circuit.*

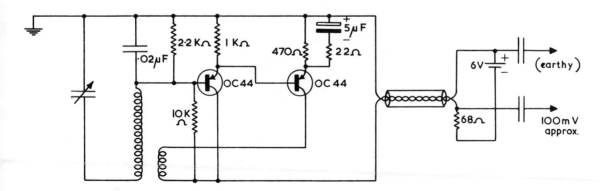

coupled, so the supply current fluctuates, and approximately 100 mV of signal is developed across the 68Ω load resistance at the shore end (if the cable is short enough to produce little attenuation).

The measuring head and oscillator have been designed to give maximum stability against changes in temperature and supply voltage. The overall temperature coefficient at atmospheric pressure is approximately 1 pt. in 10^4 of full scale (corresponding to approximately 0.25 inch of water) per degree Centigrade. It has not been possible to measure it at other pressures, since we have not so far been able to maintain these sufficiently constant. Supply voltage changes produce a negligible effect. The calibration curve of frequency against pressure is not linear, but over a normal working range it may be regarded as linear for most practical purposes.

The frequency-measuring arrangement used for routine wave recording is shown in Figure 5-2-3 and is self-explanatory. At the present time it uses thermionic valves since the use of transistors presents some problems. (For example, the impedances in the wave/tide filter are too high for transistor circuits.)

One advantage of this instrument is its flexibility. An R.C. oscillator using thermistors in the frequency-determining network has been connected in parallel with the pressure oscillator. Thus, a frequency dependent on temperature also appears across the 68Ω load resistor and is arranged to be a low frequency so that it may be filtered out and measured. Long waves may be measured by connecting a suitable filter and output stage to the output of the diode-pump frequency meter; such a system is at present in use and appears to be satisfactory. For research purposes, the output may be recorded digitally using a counter-type frequency meter feeding a tape punch.

One minor disadvantage of the present design is that it is rather too heavy for ease of handling during calibration.

PNEUMATIC WAVE RECORDER

In this instrument an air-filled rubber bag is fixed to the sea bed, suspended a fixed distance above it by a float, or mounted on a pile. The air in the bag takes up the pressure of the water around it,

Figure 5-2-3. *The frequency-measuring arrangement.*

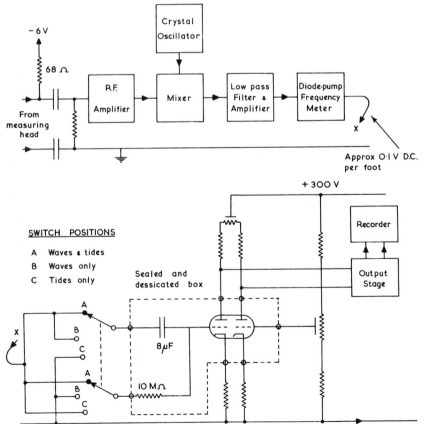

which varies as the waves pass overhead. The bag is connected by a hosepipe to a pressure recorder ashore.

The principle is simple and attractive, not least because no power supplies are necessary. However, a number of unexpected snags arise in practice, mainly in connection with the design of the sea unit and with the arrangements for filling it with the correct amount of air. One might cite the operators in the Persian Gulf, who, when the temperature is 120 degrees F in the shade, find that the effort required to pump up the sea unit using a hand pump is more than they can manage. N.I.O. is slowly overcoming the problems but can't claim that the instrument is 100 per cent satisfactory yet.

For unattended intermittent operation in remote places, a synchronous-motor chart drive is used, driven from a transistor oscillator, and switched by a spring-driven programming clock.

WAVE-MEASURING BUOYS

A description of the principle and practice of wave measurement using the N.I.O. buoys is given by Longuet-Higgins, Cartwright, and Smith, and an example of their use in a practical problem is given by Cartwright in papers presented to this conference. Only a very brief description will be given here, therefore.

The self-contained buoy is cast in aluminium and is circular, about six feet in diameter, and one foot deep. It contains batteries, a vertical accelerometer, pitch and roll gyros, electronics, a multi-channel photographic recorder and a programming clock. It is lined up in the wind direction by means of a small drogue attached to it by a rope bridle. It has been used satisfactorily in winds up to Force 7.

Though this buoy is a fully practical device and has been used a great deal, it is rather large and heavy to handle, and in common with all self-contained devices, suffers from the disadvantage, already discussed, that occasionally it is found on recovery that something has not operated correctly and no records have been obtained. A smaller and lighter buoy has been made, therefore, which is connected by a cable to the ship where the outputs are recorded. In this buoy a single gyroscope with a vertical axis carries a light vertical accelerometer and has pitch and roll pick-ups on its gimbal bearings. This and its associated electronics are contained in a water-tight can fixed in the middle of a circular wooden disc four feet in diameter and four inches thick. The light multicore cable that connects it to the ship is kept slack, but the tension is sufficient to control the alignment of the buoy.

These buoys allow the zero order, first, and second angular harmonics of the wave spectrum to be determined.

PRINCIPLES OF RECORDING AND ANALYSIS

The analysis of wave records falls into three categories:

1. For most routine recordings, only a height and period are required from each record, and these are then subject to statistical analysis.

2. For research purposes and for the development of prediction formulae, the energy-spectrum of a non-directional recording may be required.

3. For other research purposes, such as the measurement of directional spectra and the study of ship motion, cross-power spectra between records may be required.

For the simple analysis, it is possible to devise systems that record mean wave height and period directly; for example, the system described by Snodgrass and Putz (1958) for attaching to the output of an electrical wave meter or that developed by Wemelsfelder (described in Ferguson, Wemelsfelder, and Santema, 1957) for a purely mechanical system. Such instruments are usually arranged to take an occasional ordinary wave record. We have not, however, felt the need for such systems so far. We believe that full wave records should in any case be taken at frequent intervals, partly because they usually reveal any fault that has developed in the system, and partly because we often subsequently select a series of these records and compute their frequency spectra for research purposes. Having got the records, a manual analysis based on sound statistical principles has been devised which is quick and simple (see below).

For obtaining the power spectrum of a non-directional recording, the photoelectric analogue analyser (Tucker, 1956) is still generally used. This has the advantage that almost any form of record can be converted into a form suitable for analysis on it by one of a number of simple, if sometimes rather laborious, techniques, and it gives a more detailed analysis than the usual digital procedure. It has two major limitations. First, the records must not contain more than about 200 waves of the highest frequency of interest, which limits the statistical accuracy. Second, it is limited in accuracy of calibration to about ± 10 per cent and in relative accuracy within a spectrum to about ± 5 per cent. These record lengths and accuracies suffice for many purposes, but when better accuracy is required, digital methods are used. For this, the records can be recorded either directly on 5-hole tape, or recorded in graphic form and digitised on the equipment described below.

For obtaining directional spectra and for some special purposes, such as the study of ship motion, the cross-power spectra between pairs of records are required. When this problem first seriously arose, N.I.O. had no analogue equipment capable of performing such analysis. The photo-electric correlator (Tucker, 1952) would go part of the way, but its accuracy is poor, it will not handle long records, and its output correlograms require Fourier analysis to give the cross-spectra. Development of a special analogue machine would be expensive, and the resulting instrument would not be very flexible. Suitable digital computer programs were, however, already available, and are comparatively easy to modify as required. Thus, everything pointed to the use of digital techniques for this purpose, and these have, in fact, been adopted.

Having started on the use of high-speed digital computers, N.I.O. has been steadily extending its range of programs and of ancillary equipment. Many of these techniques are not, of course, N.I.O.'s original conception, but we hope that before long we shall have an unusual range of facilities available.

SIMPLE MEASUREMENT OF WAVE RECORDS

Though this system is not yet fully standardised even at N.I.O., it is thought to be worth presenting here in the hope that it may be discussed at the meeting. The instructions, which are illustrated in Figure 5-2-4, are as follows:

1. Measure off a 10-minute length of the record, and consider only waves in this interval.

2. Draw in a mean water-level line by eye.

3. Count the number of crests N_c.

4. A crest is defined as a point where the water level is momentarily constant, falling to either side. Some crests may be below mean water level.

5. Count the number of times N_z that the record crosses the zero line moving in an upward direction.

6. Measure the height A of the highest crest and the height B of the second highest crest, measuring from the zero line.

7. Measure the depth C of the lowest trough and the depth D of the second lowest trough, measuring from the zero line and taking both quantities as positive.

8. Record

$$H_1 = A + C$$
$$H_2 = B + D$$
$$T_c = \frac{600}{N_c} = \text{period of crests}$$
$$T_z = \frac{600}{N_z} = \text{period of zero crossings}$$

The theoretical basis for this system of measurement is given by Cartwright and Longuet-Higgins

Figure 5-2-4. *Simple measurement of wave records.*

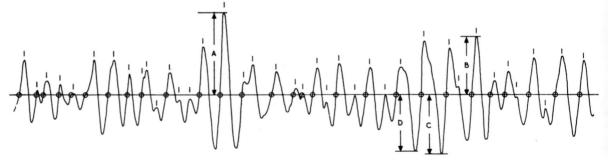

(1956) and by Cartwright (1958) and is briefly as follows (see also Putz, 1954):

The statistical distribution of wave heights is governed by the r.m.s. wave height $H_{\text{r.m.s.}}$ and by a spectral-width parameter ϵ.

From the measurements the best estimate of ϵ is

$$\epsilon^2 = 1 - \left(\frac{T_c}{T_z}\right)^2 \qquad (1)$$

$H_{\text{r.m.s.}}$ is the r.m.s. deviation of the surface from mean water level and is estimated as follows.

From $H_1 : H_{\text{r.m.s.}}$
$$= \tfrac{1}{2} H_1 (2\theta)^{-1/2} (1 + 0.289\theta^{-1} - 0.247\theta^{-2})^{-1} \quad (2)$$

From $H_2 : H_{\text{r.m.s.}}$
$$= \tfrac{1}{2} H_2 (2\theta)^{-1/2} (1 - 0.211\theta^{-1} - 0.103\theta^{-2})^{-1},$$
$$\text{where } \theta = \log_e N_z \quad (3)$$

These are the best estimates to a good degree of approximation.

The statistical errors in these estimates are less than might be expected, and are not much worse than that of the mean of the highest one-third of the waves in the records. The formulae for them are complicated, but in a typical case where $N_c = 100$, $\epsilon = 0.8$, the proportional standard error in the estimate of $H_{\text{r.m.s.}}$ from H_1 is approximately 13 per cent and from H_2 about 10 per cent.

In practice, for many civil engineering purposes, the relevant wave height is H_1 and the relevant period T_z. If $H_{\text{r.m.s.}}$ is required, it would be a simple matter to prepare tables of $H_1/H_{\text{r.m.s.}}$ and $H_2/H_{\text{r.m.s.}}$ against T_z.

DIGITAL RECORDING, AND DIGITISATION OF ANALOGUE RECORDS

N.I.O. now has a digital recorder that will record an input voltage as a pattern of holes on 5-hole teleprinter tape. The equipment can record one, two, or four channels at a maximum rate of five readings per second with a resolution of 0.1 per cent of full scale.

Each channel has a recording potentiometer fitted with a coded disc on the pen drive shaft. The pattern on the disc corresponding to the angular position of the shaft is read photo-electrically, stored in relays, and then punched onto the tape using three successive rows of holes. The code used is Watts Reflected Decimal with a parity digit added. This code is a form of cyclic progressive binary-coded decimal and is used for instrumental reasons. After every four readings, an identification "comma" is punched. The instrument was manufactured by Hilger and Watts, Limited.

Either this digitizer can be used to record the output of a wave meter directly, or it can be fitted to the output of a photo-electric curve-follower. This curve-follower is an improved version of that described by Tucker and Collins (1947) and will follow line records and convert them into a varying electric voltage. It must have records in the form of lines on plain paper or on transparent film. Records in other forms can often be traced onto charts suitable for feeding into the machine.

Some records, notably those from the self-contained N.I.O. buoy, are more easily digitised on semi-manual digitisers (made by Southern Instruments or Benson-Lehner) to which we have access at the Royal Aircraft Establishment. These records, on 70 mm. film, have several traces which may cross and which subsequently have to be cross-correlated, so that matching of time-scales is important. In the R.A.E. instruments a cross-wire is moved onto the record, and depressing a pedal then causes the reading to be punched onto a computer card. The readings from all the traces at a particular time are punched in turn onto the same card; the record is moved forward, the card replaced by a new one, and the process repeated.

A system for recording digitally the output of an F.M. measuring head is in process of being developed. In principle it is similar to that used by Munk and Snodgrass at the Scripps Institution of Oceanography. The number of cycles in the signal is counted for, say, 1 second on an electronic counter, and the state of the decades is then punched onto 5-hole tape. Such a system is capable of very high resolution, and using the F.M. pressure recorder described above and digital filtering techniques, it should allow long waves to be filtered out of the ordinary wave record.

PROCESSING OF DIGITAL RECORDS

The digitiser recording on 5-hole tape is unfortunately not too reliable and makes on the average one error in about 200 readings. The code is also not one of the usual digital computer codes. The first stage in handling a tape from this instrument is therefore to feed it through a computer programmed to change the code and look for errors.

It first makes sure that the pattern of holes forms a legitimate code, then decodes them and then takes first differences. If these exceed a certain value (fed in with the programme), it regards the reading as an error. It also makes sure that the correct number of rows of holes occurs between "commas." The record is then punched out in standard code with zeros where the errors occurred. The serial number of the errors is also given, so that the operator can go through the tape and punch in corrected or interpolated readings by hand.

The programmes for correlation and Fourier transformation are based on the well-known principles first set out by Tukey and will not be described here.

* * *

ACKNOWLEDGMENTS

The techniques described above have been developed by a quite numerous team at N.I.O. These include (in alphabetical order) L. A. Baxter, R. Bowers, Miss D. Catton, D. E. Cartwright, L. A. Draper, M. J. Harris, M. S. Longuet-Higgins, F. E. Pierce, and N. D. Smith.

REFERENCES

Cartwright, D. E. and M. S. Longuet-Higgins, "The Statistical Distribution of the Maxima of a Random Function," Proc. Roy. Soc. A, CCXXXVII (1956), 212–232.

Cartwright, D. E., "On Estimating the Mean Energy of Sea Waves from the Highest Waves in a Record," Proc. Roy. Soc. A, CCXLVII (1958), 22–48.

Ferguson, H. A., P. Wemelsfelder and P. Santema, 19th International Navigation Congress, 207–231. London, 1957.

Putz, R. R., "Statistical Analysis of Wave Records," Proc. 4th Conf. on Coastal Engg. (1954), 13–24.

Snodgrass, F., W. Munk and M. J. Tucker, "Off-shore Recording of Low-frequency Ocean Waves," Trans. Am. Geophys. Union, XXXIX (1958), 114–120.

Snodgrass, F. E. and R. R. Putz, "A Wave Height and Frequency Meter," Proc. 6th Conf. on Coastal Engg. (1958), 209–224.

Tucker, M. J., "A Photoelectric Correlation Meter," J. Sci. Instrum., XXIX (1952), 326–330.

Tucker, M. J., "The N.I.O. Wave Analyser," Proc. 1st Conf. on Coastal Engg. Instruments (1956), 129–133.

Tucker, M. J. and G. Collins, "A Photo-electric Curve-Follower," Electronic Engg. XIX (1947), 398–400, 403.

A DATA ACQUISITION AND REDUCTION SYSTEM

FOR WAVE MEASUREMENTS

ABSTRACT

A brief description is given of an instrumentation system particularly advantageous in those problems requiring the simultaneous recording of a large number of variables upon which extensive calculations are to be made using an electronic digital computer. The system has been used for the acquiring, recording, and reduction of sea surface wave elevations detected by stainless steel resistance wires. Good resolution and reliable operation is obtained.

INTRODUCTION

An efficient and practical means for the acquisition, recording, and reduction of data is needed in experimental programs in which several variables are measured and on which it is expected to make extensive calculations. Such programs arise in the study of ocean waves. Examples are the determination of the directional spectrum using an array of detectors and in investigations relating more generally to air-sea boundary processes.

An instrumentation system suitable for these purposes can be assembled using, for the most part, commercially-available equipment which (a) is easily capable of recording twelve data channels and more if necessary, (b) permits recording the data at a station remote from the detectors, (c) records and stores the data by efficient and reliable means, and (d) converts the data from analogue to digital form for entry into a digital computer. The system is adaptable to a variety of investigations in the field of oceanography.

The telemetering techniques that are used are not at all new. They have been in use now for some years in the fields of aircraft and missile development, and telemetering standards have been established.

The method of detecting the sea surface elevation uses a stainless steel wire that is supported vertically and is partially immersed in the sea water. By supporting the wire from a fixed platform, an accurate measurement of the sea surface elevation as a function of time can be made. Details such as sharp-pointed crests and breaking crests have been clearly observed on graphic recordings. The breaking waves were identified by short but distinct vertical steps in the record at, or near, the crest of the wave. Use of 0.015-inch diameter wire in wind seas with significant heights of from less than one foot to as high as about twenty feet has been satisfactory.

This method of wave measurement and the

instrumentation system has been described in detail by Farmer and Ketchum (1960). The instrumentation system, with some of its more general applications in oceanography, has also been described in the *Proceedings of the Conference on Automatic Data Handling for Oceanographic Observations* (1960).

THE SYSTEM REQUIREMENTS

Before setting forth various requirements of the system, there are two specific assumptions that will be made:

(a) The raw data will be assumed to be sensed as a continuous function of time and recorded in analogue form.

[*Note:* The data here are referred to as "raw" primarily in that they should experience a minimum of distortion, filtering, or other modification which would reduce their value prior to the initial recording. The method of recording should permit data frequencies to extend from zero cycles per second to an adequately high value. For most ocean wave work, an upper limit of two cps is sufficient, but an upper frequency limit of from 20 cps to over 100 cps may be needed for small wind waves, ripples, or capillary waves.]

(b) The main analysis of the data will be carried out on electronic digital computers because these computers can carry out a wide variety of calculations and they are generally available to the research laboratory.

These two assumptions basically specify the instrumentation system. The objective in recording the data in analogue form is to preserve as much of the data as the transducer is capable of detecting. In the reduction and analysis, the original data may be operated on in a variety of ways, without altering or destroying it.

Various requirements that ought to be considered are:

(a) The ability to record data at a station remote from the detectors. The means of transmission can be either by radio or electrical cable.

(b) The capability of transmitting and recording a number of variables simultaneously.

(c) The analogue to digital converter, the need for which is clearly implied in the initial assumptions, should be electronic.

(d) The analogue to digital conversion time should be sufficiently short to permit the conversion of at least three, if not all, of the data channels within the individual sample time interval.

(e) The digital output should be either in a suitable or in a readily adaptable form for direct entry into a computer.

(f) A means for visual inspection or monitoring of the data should be provided for use during the initial recording and during the data reduction.

(g) The raw data should be recorded in permanent form for ready reference.

(h) The equipment should be portable, particularly those components used to record and monitor.

(i) Developments necessary to set up the system should be at a minimum.

(j) Costs should be kept at a minimum.

(k) The instrumentation system should be adaptable to a broad range of problems.

TELEMETERING STANDARDS

The telemetering techniques used in the instrumentation system to be discussed follow standards that were established by the Inter-Range Instrumentation Group (IRIG) to insure compatibility among the various transmitting, receiving, and data-handling equipment. A vast amount of experience has gone into the establishment of these standards and into the development of the various pieces of commercially available telemetering equipment. Techniques are being continually developed to improve the efficiency, reliability, and speed of all phases of data handling, particularly within the framework of the IRIG standards. These established telemetering techniques and the IRIG standards are compatible with the two assumptions specifying the instrumentation system, and are well suited to fulfill most of the requirements mentioned above.

Telemetering is discussed in detail in texts such as Nichols and Rausch (1958) and Borden and Mayo-Wells (1959) and in the *Proceedings of the National Symposium on Space Electronics and Telemetry* (1959).

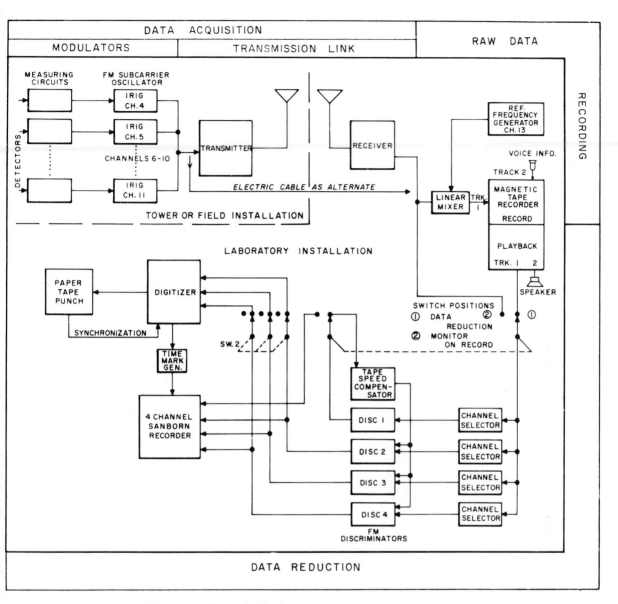

Figure 5-3-1. *A data acquisition, recording and reduction system.*

AN INSTRUMENTATION SYSTEM

Figure 5-3-1 illustrates in diagrammatic form a system which fulfills the stated requirements. The diagram has been patterned after a system which is in operation at the Woods Hole Oceanographic Institution. The basic functions within the system are listed around the border of the figure. These are:

1. *Data acquisition*
   (a) modulators — including the transducers, measuring circuits, and subcarrier oscillators.
   (b) transmission link — radio or cable

2. *Raw data recording*
   (a) magnetic tape recorder

3. *Data reduction*
   (a) magnetic tape playback
   (b) data channel selectors and discriminators
   (c) tape speed compensation
   (d) graphic recorder for monitoring
   (e) digitizer and digital storage

The type telemetry used is a simple example of frequency division multiplex and is referred to as FM-FM telemetry. The radio frequency carrier is frequency modulated with a group of subcarriers, each of which has a different center frequency in the audio frequency spectrum. Each subcarrier is frequency modulated by a data signal. Details of this are left to the references, but it will be noted that:

IRIG Channel	Center Frequency	Maximum Intelligence Frequency
No. 1	.4 kc/s	6 cps
6	1.7	25
13	14.5	220

The maximum intelligence frequency is a function of the IRIG channel center frequency. Sufficient frequency response is available for most oceanographic applications.

The radio link would be applicable when data is to be transmitted from a buoy to a ship or shore receiving station. In other applications an electrical cable may be substituted, eliminating the need for the radio frequency carrier.

The detectors and measuring circuits are special equipment which depend on the type of measurement to be made and may not be commercially available.

The provision for monitoring the data visually is provided by the graphic recorder and requires the channel selectors and the discriminators. It is shown in the circuit as available for use during the initial recording and the data reduction. To monitor the data visually while it is being recorded, it is convenient to use a commercially-available switchable, multichannel, quick-look discriminator. For economy, however, the precision discriminators of the data reduction equipment could be used.

Portability of the equipment is achieved mainly through modular assembly of the components according to function. Attention is devoted also to size and weight. The magnetic tape recorder is essential for the recording of the raw data. It is the only practical and efficient way to record directly the modulated subcarriers and then at a later time to play back the data for reduction and analysis. For many applications a relatively inexpensive "hi-fidelity" type magnetic tape recorder, both portable and economical, is adequate for recording the raw data. Most such recorders have an upper frequency response in excess of 15 kc, and it is possible to record on one track the IRIG data channels Nos. 1 through 13. On a two-track or stereo recorder the number of channels can be doubled, or the second track can be used for supplemental voice information.

In selecting an electronic digitizer, attention must be given to its speed of operation and the format of the output digital data. A programmer, which will have the function of switching in the various data channels and providing for the necessary timing of the operation, will be associated with the digitizer. Since all the data channels cannot be digitized simultaneously, they must be switched in sequentially. The speed of operation of the digitizer will be dictated by the total number of data channels to be digitized in one operation and the maximum rate at which any one data channel is to be sampled. The numeric output can be recorded on punched paper tape, digital magnetic tape, or punched cards. In any case the selection of the type digital storage will depend on the maximum rate of output of the digitizer in data words per second and the number of significant digits per word.

The final analysis is presumed to be carried out at the laboratory. The data reduction equipment may be permanently installed there, thus requiring separate field equipment. The total amount of equipment, however, may not be so extensive that it would be impractical to take to sea, so the data could be reduced between periods of observation. With large amounts of data appreciable time could be saved.

When information is in the form of frequency deviations, as is the case with the FM IRIG data channels, it is necessary, at least without special consideration, to maintain a one-to-one ratio of the record and playback speeds of the magnetic tape. The data reduction must then be done in real time. The time required for this operation is kept at a minimum by providing a sufficiently fast digitizer and compatible digital storage so that most or all of the data channels can be handled in one operation.

The experimental needs and available budget will dictate the extensiveness of the system. One advantage of the system is its modular form. Starting with an adequate analogue to digital converter, the remainder of the system can be added to as the need arises. Since use of the IRIG standards permits interchangeability of a large selection of commercially available equipment, the foregoing description has been kept general. The modest system which was assembled at the Woods Hole Oceanographic Institution at a cost of approximately $15,000, has adequately performed its function in several wave research projects.

WAVE ELEVATION MEASUREMENT

Stainless steel resistance wire can be used to provide a simple and accurate means for the measurement of wave elevation. The method to be outlined is restricted to sea water measurements. The wire is vertically supported and partially immersed in the sea water. As is illustrated in Figure 5-3-2, the wire is driven from a constant current source at audio frequency. If the resistance of the ground return conductor is small compared to that of the resistance wire and if the electrical resistance of the sea water path is constant, then observed voltage changes between the top of the resistance wire and ground plane conductor will result from changes in length (resistance) of the unimmersed portion of the wire. A direct and

Figure 5-3-2. *Schematic diagram of resistance wire detector and measuring circuit.*

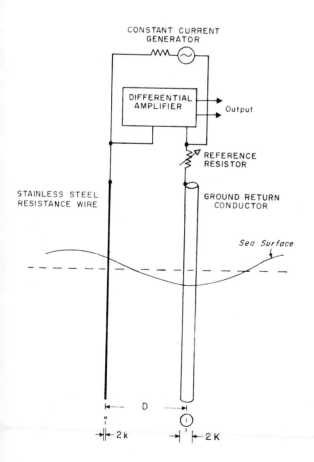

linear measurement of the sea surface elevation results. Accurate measurements can be made only if the wires are supported from a fixed platform, restricting the use of this type of instrument.

It is necessary to determine the minimum length of wire which must be immersed at all times. Also of concern is the constancy of the electrical resistance of the water path between the wire and the ground plane, the effect of wetting the wire, and the expected resolution of the measurements. These problems will be discussed in this order.

Assume the wire to be supported parallel to a larger cylindrical conductor, which will serve as the ground return in the electrical circuit. Both conductors are partially immersed in sea water. If the length of the conductors and the depth of water are great, it is possible to consider the immersed portion of the system as a transmission line with series resistance per unit length determined by the type of wire and shunt conductance per unit length determined by the geometry, the conductivity of the water, and the polarization impedance of the wire water interface.

The polarization impedance is complex, as it has a capacitive susceptance and conductance. The capacitive effect may be kept negligible by using frequencies above about 1 kc/s. The conductance is in series with that of the water path. This total resistance must be constant, or fluctuations in its value must be small compared to the expected resistance change due to changes in length of the unimmersed portion of the wire. From static calibration tests small variations about the mean expected output voltage are observed and are attributed to this polarization effect.

From the assumed geometry of two parallel cylindrical conductors, the shunt conductance per unit length of the line is determined to be (Farmer and Ketchum, 1960):

$$g = \frac{2\pi\sigma}{\ln\left[\frac{K}{k}\left(\frac{D^2}{K^2} - 1\right)\right]} \qquad (1)$$

where σ = conductivity of the water, mhos/in.

k = radius of the wire

K = radius of the ground plane

D = center to center distance between the wire and ground plane

To obtain this expression it is assumed that the

wire radius is small compared to the distance D. Tucker and Charnock (1955) obtain a slightly different expression, but the conductance determined by either equation does not differ greatly.

If the current in the wire above the water surface is assumed as a constant value, I, and the submerged length of wire is great, then, using the transmission line analogy, the current i and the voltage e along the wire are found to be simple exponential functions of the depth y below the sea surface.

$$i = I \exp \left(- \sqrt{\rho g}\, y \right) \qquad (2)$$

$$e = I \sqrt{\frac{\rho}{g}} \exp \left(- \sqrt{\rho g}\, y \right) \qquad (3)$$

where I = current in wire above sea surface, a constant

ρ = resistance per unit length of the wire

y = distance along submerged length of wire measured from sea surface

At some depth below the surface the current in the wire will be very small compared to the initial value I. Assuming this minimum length of wire or critical depth, Y_c, to be that depth at which the current i is 1 per cent of I, then

$$Y_c = \frac{4.60}{\sqrt{\rho g}} \qquad (4)$$

If the wire is always immersed to at least this depth, it may be assumed to be essentially of infinite extent, and the voltage drop from the wire to the ground plane, through the water path, will be constant. It is under these conditions that any change in the voltage drop across the full length of the resistance wire will result only from a change in length of the unimmersed portion of the wire, the desired operating condition.

Sea water of 32 $^0/_{00}$ salinity and temperature 15 degrees C has a conductivity of 0.102 mho/in. As an example, assume $k = 0.075$ inches, $K = 4$ inches, $D = 6$ feet. Then $g = 0.0657$ mhos/in. For stainless steel wire of 0.015 inches diameter, $\rho = 2$ ohms/ft. and the critical depth is 44 inches. From this example, and it will be found to be so for other reasonable geometric conditions, it is evident that the required critical depth is a length of wire which may be easily accommodated in practice. It should be stated again that this length of wire must be maintained below the lowest expected wave trough. Excessively long lengths of wire would be awkward to handle and undesirable, but would be required with fresh water

which has a salinity in the order of 0.01 $^0/_{00}$. The conductivity for this salinity is 0.00076 mhos/in., and the critical depth is increased by over an order of magnitude.

In the transmission line analogue, it is assumed that the free surface remains level even though it may rise and fall. This will not be the case when actual waves are being measured. Numerous small waves may be present between the wire and ground plane, or the free surface may have an appreciable slope due to the presence of a large wave. It is difficult to assess accurately the increase in resistance of the water path due to these waves. However, an estimate of the effect can be made. For accurate measurements any resistance change must be small compared to that due to changes in length of the unimmersed wire. From Equation (3) the total electrical resistance below the water surface is equal to $\sqrt{\rho/g}$ and is called the characteristic impedance. Assume that the surface has a 10 degree slope. With the conditions of the previous example the characteristic impedance is 5.52 ohms and the 10-degree slope increases this value by 0.01 ohms. This is equivalent to about $\frac{1}{16}$ inch on the 0.015 inch diameter stainless steel wire. Thus an error of about $\frac{1}{2}$ of 1 per cent would be indicated for a 1-foot difference in elevation between the wire and the ground plane. This effect will probably be small in most measurements; however, depending on the required precision, it may require further investigation. Using a value of conductivity for fresh water, the above error would increase about an order of magnitude.

When the water level is receding down the wire, as will occur when a wave is passing by, some water will cling to and run down the wire, lagging behind the main water surface. This water run-off problem has been considered by Tucker and Charnock (1955) when insulated wires are used and operated as cylindrical capacitors. Kinsman (1960) has also shown how this can affect the measurements. With resistance wires, the error due to run off can be shown to be negligible. The water film on the wire will have an electrical resistance and will form a continuous shunt resistance between the wire and the water surface. Consider the wire diameter to be 0.015 inch, as before, and a water film thickness of 0.030 inch, a thickness considerably greater than that which can be observed. As the resistance per unit length of a wire is inversely proportional to its area and conductivity, the resistance of the water film can be computed to be 2,200 ohms/in. This is more than four orders of magnitude greater than the resistance of the wire. Thus, the water film is effectively short circuited by the resistance wire, and its effect is negligible. Dynamic testing similar to that done by Kinsman for a capacitance probe has not been carried out for the resistance wire, but a qualitative test was performed in which the voltage output from the wire was read directly on a vacuum tube voltmeter as the wire was given a sudden vertical displacement of one foot. Following this displacement the voltmeter showed no recognizable lag as might be caused by the water film running down the wire. Such an effect can be readily observed using a $\frac{3}{8}$-inch diameter teflon insulated rod operated as a capacitor.

Static calibrations, in which the wire was raised and lowered in discrete steps, indicated the predicted linear relation between voltage output and length of unimmersed wire. These tests were carried out over a wire 10 feet in length. Other tests were carried out over shorter lengths of wire primarily to determine the effect of wire length below the water surface. In the latter tests, even with incremental steps of one inch, smooth resultant curves with only minor irregularities which could be attributed to the reading of the meter could be drawn. By another test, a measure of the mean minimum resolution of wire length was obtained in an experiment in which a measurement was made of the difference in elevation between two wires that were raised and lowered simultaneously. The indicated difference in elevation slowly varied about a mean value. As considerable care had been taken in the design and testing of the differential amplifier, this varying signal was attributed to a surface effect on the wire. After cleaning with degreasing agents the observed difference in elevation changed with length but did not disappear. The rms deviation of these fluctuations from the mean was 0.17 inches for a 10-foot length of wire. This deviation was greater than that observed previously. A possible explanation lies in the fact that the observed "wave-like" variations in elevation difference occurred with variable "wave lengths" of one, two, or three feet along the wire. From the appearance of these variations the mean resolution would be a function of length of wire used. It is concluded that if full scale is allowed to range from two feet to ten feet, a mean measurement precision of at least 1 per cent of full scale may be easily attained and the same precision should be expected for shorter lengths of wire.

It is desirable to use a differential amplifier for the resistance wire measuring circuit, one side being connected to the wire detector and the other side through a reference resistor to ground. The reference resistor is adjusted to the approximate resistance of the mean unimmersed length of stainless steel wire. Full scale of the amplifier output can then be set to correspond to the maximum expected range of wave heights. This permits the maximum wave height range to equal approximately the full range of the IRIG data channels.

REFERENCES

Borden, P. A. and W. J. Mayo-Wells, *Telemetering System*, New York, Reinhold Publishing Co., 1959.

Farmer, H. G. and D. D. Ketchum, "An Instrumentation System for Wave Measurements, Recording and Analysis," *Proc. 7th Conference on Coastal Engineering*, 1961. Berkeley, Calif., Council on Wave Research, Univ. of California.

Kinsman, B., *Surface Waves at Short Fetches and Low Wind Speeds — a Field Study*, Tech. Report XIX (1960), Ref. 60-61, Chesapeake Bay Institute, The Johns Hopkins University.

Nichols, M. H. and L. I. Rausch, *Radio Telemetry*, New York, John Wiley and Sons, Inc., 1958.

Proceedings of the Conference on Automatic Data Handling for Oceanographic Observations. Ref. No. 60-10. An unpublished manuscript, Woods Hole Oceanographic Institution, Woods Hole, Mass., 1959.

Proceedings IRE, National Symposium on Space Electronics and Telemetry (Sept. 28-30, 1959).

Tucker, M. J. and H. Charnock, "A Capacitance Wire Recorder for Small Waves," *Proc. 5th Conference on Coastal Engineering*, 1955. Berkeley, Calif., Council on Wave Research, Univ. of California.

COMMENTS

Dr. Cox: Did you compare the spectra of slopes with the spectra of the elevation? I suggest this as a way of checking the operations, because if you had together the slopes cross wind and up and down wind, you should get a spectrum which is just (wave number)^2 times the spectrum of the elevations.

Mr. Farmer: I have not done this as yet. The spectrum arrived only a few weeks ago. I agree that it should be done.

Dr. Hicks: We measured the dynamic result with the capacitance probe.

M. S. MACOVSKY

G. F. MECHLIN

F O U R

A PROPOSED TECHNIQUE FOR OBTAINING DIRECTIONAL

WAVE SPECTRA BY AN ARRAY OF INVERTED FATHOMETERS

ABSTRACT

A new technique for measuring directional spectra of ocean waves is described briefly. It calls for a linear array of inverted acoustic fathometers mounted on the deck of a submarine for sampling surface conditions. The array is pointed as an antenna both by changing submarine heading (true steering) and by electronic sequencing of the transducers ("electronic" steering). A combination of these two steering concepts is developed for removing directional ambiguities. It is shown finally that eight different submarine courses would be required per test to define spectrum directionality adequately.

INTRODUCTION

A paper recently prepared by Dr. Walter Munk on "The ULCER Equipment as a Directional Wave Recorder"[1] will be reviewed. The original, which was given limited distribution to others in the field for commentary, will be reproduced verbatim in most sections. In brief, the paper deals with the use of recordings of surface wave profiles obtained by a linear array of inverted fathometers mounted on the upper side of a submarine to determine directional wave spectra.

In the recent development of the Polaris Fleet Ballistic Missile System analytical studies and test programs were obviously concerned with evaluation of ship and missile responses to the variety of sea conditions likely to be encountered. Dr. Munk worked with the Westinghouse Electric Corporation on this program and assisted immeasurably in identifying the oceanographic variables that might affect significantly the underwater launch concepts. During the course of this work it became evident that the submarine platform offers an unusual opportunity for obtaining directional wave spectra. A linear array of inverted fathometers had already demonstrated the capability of evaluating qualitatively both sea severity and directionality. Dr. Munk's paper examines the type of maneuvers and the characteristics of the recording system that would be required to obtain meaningful quantitative directional wave spectra using the array. Such a system is motivated by two objectives: (1) to provide a suitable measuring technique for improved quantitative characterization of the oceans, and (2) to provide the submarine, perhaps in a tactical

---

[1] (Oct. 17, 1960). Distributed by Advanced Systems Engineering, Westinghouse Electric Corporation, Sunnyvale, California.

RECORDINGS MADE IN 27' OF WATER
SCRIPPS PIER   LA JOLLA, CALIF   2 FEB. 1961

PAPER SPEED = 3.72 MM/SEC

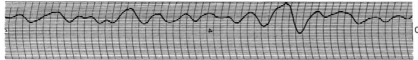

INSHORE (EASTERNMOST) SURFACE SCANNER #3   CAL = 4.728 MM = 1 FT.

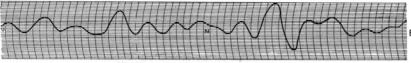

MK X   CAL = 10 MM = 1 FT. OF H₂O

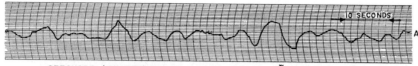

OFFSHORE (WESTERNMOST) SURFACE SCANNER #4   CAL = 4.728 MM = 1 FT.

Figure 5-4-1. *Sample records of inverted fathometers compared with simultaneous pressure measurements.*

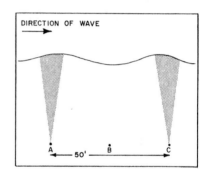

version, with information of its environment in order to optimize the success of its mission.

A brief description of the requirements on the measuring system will be presented, followed by the theoretical aspects of the proposed scheme. Samples of surface profile data already taken will be given.

CONCEPT IN BRIEF

Acoustic Sensor Array: The scheme suggested by Dr. Munk consists of an array of upward-pointing fathometers distributed along the deck of a submarine. Each sensor transmits and receives the echoed ultrasonic pulse. The time elapsed between the outgoing pulse and the first reflected signal is, of course, some measure of the instantaneous depth to the point of measurement. Sample records taken by two such fathometers in a test off Scripps' pier are shown on Figure 5-4-1. Note the record of a pressure transducer installed on the sea floor half way between the two fathometers, all three being in a line normal to the expected crest lines.

With the submarine proceeding at low speed along several judiciously selected headings relative to the sea, the records obtained from an array of these fathometers can be stored digitally on a common tape. Cross-spectral analyses (numerical "electronic steering") of the records can be conducted for each course in order to remove ambiguities otherwise inherent in the analyzing of array records only on true ship headings.

This will be amplified later. Obviously, all records would require correction for ship motions, attitudes, and depth.

The frequency band of the spectra observed by a submarine installation of this type would, of course, be limited by the length of the submarine, and by the maximum operating depth. Assuming that end transducers can be pointed outward from the vertical to a limited extent, an effective length greater than the submarine dimension is attainable. This is illustrated schematically in Figure 5-4-2.

The most serious problem with this scheme arises in the "aliasing" ambiguities that are likely to occur. Any waves shorter than twice the spacing of the transducers will contribute to the computed spectrum unless a suitable method of spacial and/or temporal prefiltering can be applied. Each of these prefiltering schemes poses problems.

Spacial Prefiltering: Assume that each transducer transmits a narrow conical beam subtending

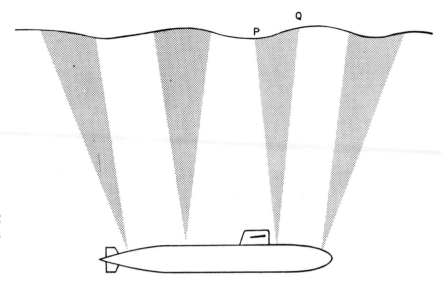

Figure 5-4-2. *Inverted fathometer array with outward-pointing end transducers.*

a total angle of 3 degrees. Hence, at a mean transducer depth of 100 feet the surface is illuminated over a circular patch having a diameter of approximately 5 feet. By broadening the beam (by reducing the carrier frequency or changing the transducer design) averaging over larger patches of the sea surface is possible. While achieving spacial prefiltering, this approach calls for the following design criteria:

(a) Avoidance of mutual interference or crosstalk.
(b) Weighting of echoes to account for large virtual distance to peripheral points (such as Q in Figure 5-4-2) of the illuminated patch. It would be preferable to illuminate the surface with a sound intensity diminishing smoothly and monotonically from the center outward; e.g., varying in a Gaussian fashion.

Temporal Prefiltering: Additional filtering of records can be achieved by taking time averages of wave height. Phase lag is introduced by this procedure when smoothing is done in real time, but is of no concern when recorded data are symmetrically filtered by using both future and past values.

Temporal filtering is effective provided (1) that averages are taken over a time interval greater than the period of the shortest significant waves; (2) that the averages are formed from a number of discrete looks at the surface by each transducer. The time interval between looks is determined by the beam dimensions and transducer depth. For example, for a total beam angle of 3 degrees, and transducer depth of 100 feet, a surface circular patch of 5 feet is illuminated. (Shorter waves are eliminated by spacial smoothing.) Sampling at $\frac{1}{4}$-second intervals requires

only that there be no wave periods shorter than $\frac{1}{2}$ second.

With judicious selection of transducer spacing, operating depth, and combined spacial and temporal filtering, it appears feasible to examine wave spectra up to frequencies of 0.2 cps. The low-frequency side is limited by the inability to resolve directionality for wave lengths comparable to the length of the array. Assuming that the end transducers can be pointed outward (axially) at sufficient depth, it may be possible to obtain useful information down to 0.05 cycles per second. Although this is definitely restrictive in spectral scope, it offers an opportunity to examine the high energy band of ocean wave spectra.

THEORETICAL CONSIDERATIONS

Adopted Conventions: The primary objective of this wave measuring technique is to determine the directional spectrum $E(f, \theta)$. In wave number space notation, $k = (4\pi^2 f^2)/g$, where f is the frequency parameter and g the gravitational acceleration, the energy spectrum (mean-square surface elevation) is given by

$$\int_{-\infty}^{\infty} \int_{-\infty}^{\infty} E(l, m) dl \, dm$$

Here l and m are the component wave numbers $l = k \sin \theta$, and $m = k \cos \theta$, and $E(l, m)$ is the energy contributed from wave numbers in the range $l \pm \frac{1}{2}\delta l, m \pm \frac{1}{2}\delta m$. Letting $E^+(l, m)$ and $E^-(l, -m)$ designate the half space spectra for positive and negative m respectively, then

$$E'(l, m) = E^+(l, m) + E^-(l, -m) \qquad (1)$$

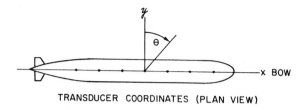

TRANSDUCER COORDINATES (PLAN VIEW)

WAVE-NUMBER COORDINATES

Figure 5-4-3. *Coordinate systems of directional wave sonar array.*

is by definition the two-dimensional spectrum and represents the directional spectrum folded along the m-axis.

Any linear, scalar array of the type proposed cannot distinguish fore from aft. It can provide information concerning the two-dimensional spectrum, but not the true directional spectrum. The interpretation of such an array by methods of "true" and "electronic" steering will follow.

True Steering: Consider the hypothetical array of $(2N + 1)$ transducers along the upper side of the submarine, extending from $X = -\frac{1}{2}D$ to $X = +\frac{1}{2}D$ giving a total of N intervals. Assume that an elementary wave train of frequency f approaches from direction θ, as illustrated in Figure 5-4-3. Then the equation expressing the instantaneous wave height at each measuring point is $h = A \cos(lx + my + \omega t)$, where again l and m are the component wave numbers $l = k \sin \theta$ and $m = k \cos \theta$, and A is the wave amplitude. If the "aliasing" problem is reduced to insignificance by proper selection and placement of the trans-

ducers, then a meaningful integrated sum of the transducer outputs can be given by

$$\bar{h} = \frac{1}{D} \int_{-D/2}^{D/2} h(x, 0) dx$$

$$= \frac{A \sin \frac{1}{2} lD}{\frac{1}{2} lD} \cos \omega t. \qquad (2)$$

This is the expression for the typical diffraction pattern from a finite slit. Examination of this equation shows that for waves of length $l \gg D$, the recorded integrated wave height is simply $\bar{h} = A \cos \omega t$ and hence has the same amplitude as the simple train. For shorter waves, reduction in $\bar{h}$ as compared to h occurs. For example, for $\lambda = D$, $\bar{h}$ vanishes.

Suppose a given record of $\bar{h}$ has been frequency analyzed, and an analysis of one narrow frequency band ω is performed in the ω, θ-plane. Letting $G^2(\omega, \theta) = \left[\dfrac{\sin \frac{1}{2} lD}{\frac{1}{2} lD} \right]^2$, typical plots of functional relationship between G^2 and θ are given in Figure 5-4-4 for three different wave periods. [Note that $\frac{1}{2} lD = \frac{1}{2}D(\omega^2/g) \sin \theta$.] The function G^2 is the quadratic gain factor. The following special cases will amplify the significance of G^2:

(1) Suppose the wave system consists of a single "pencil beam" from θ. With the submarine array axis normal to the direction of the wave travel, the mean-square value of $\bar{h}(\omega)$ is $A^2(\omega)$. At other angles to the wave direction, the recorded mean-square value is reduced in the ratio G^2.

(2) For waves longer than D, the gain factor reaches a minimum at $\theta = 90°$ (waves head-on). For shorter waves, the gain factor has two or more zeros, with intervening side lobes. Thus, there are two or more array orientations for which the pencil beam at a given frequency may result in $\bar{h} = 0$.

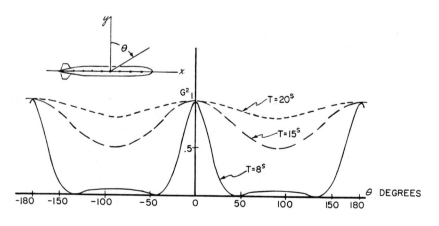

Figure 5-4-4. *Gain factor dependence on wave direction for different wave periods.*

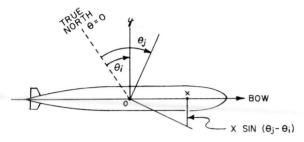

Figure 5-4-5. *Phase lag in "electronic steering."*

(3) For $\theta = \pi$, $G^2 = 1$ for all frequencies. This implies that a submarine array cannot distinguish port from starboard.

(4) Assuming equal radiation from all directions [$E(\omega, \theta) = E(\omega)$] rather than a "pencil beam," then regardless of submarine orientation, the mean-square signal is

$$E(\omega) \int_{-\pi}^{\pi} G^2(\omega, \theta)d\theta \qquad (3)$$

(5) The above can be generalized for any wave spectrum. Let θ be the direction relative to true north, and let θ_i be the orientation of the submarine normal to port as illustrated in Figure 5-4-5. Then the mean-square output is given by

$$F(\omega, \theta_i) = \int_{-\pi}^{\pi} E(\omega, \theta)G^2(\omega, \theta - \theta_i)d\theta \qquad (4)$$

Hence, the estimated energy is a convolution of the true energy. For an ideal antenna the wave energy is sampled from an infinitely narrow source, i.e., $G^2(\omega, \theta - \theta_i) = \delta(\theta - \theta_i)$. For this case $F(\omega, \theta_i) = E(\omega, \theta_i)$. Here the gain factor will have limited width and side bands, but the sampling is not too poor provided that the main lobe is narrow compared to the angular width of the true wave spectrum and provided that the side lobes contain small energy as compared to the main lobe. In a rising sea the angular spread is said to be of the order of 45 degrees to either side of the wind. It would be desirable, then, to have the main lobe narrower than ± 30 degrees. From the functional expression for G^2 (assuming $G^2 = 0$ at $\theta = \pm 30°$), we get

$$0 = \sin \pi = \sin (\tfrac{1}{2} Dl) = \sin \left(\frac{D\omega^2}{2g} \sin \theta \right)$$

so

$$\pi = \frac{D\omega^2}{2g} \sin 30° \qquad (5)$$

and

$$T = \sqrt{\frac{\pi D}{g}}$$

With end transducers pointing outward at an angle of 15 degrees from the vertical, an effective array length $D = 500$ feet may be possible. This would permit measurement of directional spectra for waves of period $T = 7$ sec. and smaller. Some estimates of directionality could be obtained with the main lobe greater than ± 30 degrees, as would be the case with waves of longer period.

Electronic Steering: By lagging transducer signals in the summing and averaging processes, true steering can be augmented by proper electronic circuitry. For example, suppose it is desired to estimate the wave energy from any direction θ_j; for some particular frequency ω. As indicated in the sketch, Figure 5-4-5, let θ_i designate as before the direction of the port normal from true north. For any arbitrary direction $\theta_j \neq \theta_i$, the output of the transducer at x is lagged by some amount so that the lagged signal is in phase with the transducer at $x = 0$. At the instant a wave crest appears at $x = 0$, it leads the signal at a distance x by $x \sin (\theta_j - \theta_i)$. The phase lead is then $(2\pi x/L) \sin (\theta_j - \theta_i)$ radians or $\tau = (2\pi x/c) \sin (\theta_j - \theta_i)$ seconds.

The lagged mean is then

$$\overline{h} = \frac{1}{D} \int_{-D/2}^{D/2} h(x, 0, t - \tau)dx$$

$$\overline{h} = \frac{A}{D} \int_{-D/2}^{D/2} \cos [(l - l_j)x - \omega t]dx, \qquad (6)$$

where

$$l_j = k \sin (\theta_j - \theta_i)$$

is the projected wave number along the x-axis for waves from θ_j.

It is desirable to estimate the extent to which the lagged mean favors θ_j over any other direction θ, whose wave number component is $l = k \sin (\theta - \theta_i)$. Replacing l in the previous expression for $\overline{h}$,

$$\overline{h} = \frac{A \sin \tfrac{1}{2}(l - l_j)D}{\tfrac{1}{2}(l - l_j)D} \cos \omega t. \qquad (7)$$

This is obviously maximized for $l = l_j$, i.e., for $\theta = \theta_j$. The gain factor is now

$$G^2(\omega, \theta) = \left\{ \frac{\sin[\kappa(\sin \alpha - \sin \alpha_j)]}{\kappa(\sin \alpha - \sin \alpha_j)} \right\}^2, \qquad (8)$$

where

$$\kappa = \tfrac{1}{2}kD$$

$$\alpha = \theta - \theta_i \qquad \alpha_j = \theta_j - \theta_i$$

The previous case of *true steering* corresponds to $\theta_i = \theta_j$, and hence

$$G^2(\omega, \theta) = \left\{ \frac{\sin\,(\kappa\,\sin\,\alpha)}{\kappa\,\sin\,\alpha} \right\}^2$$

$$G^2(\omega, \theta) = 1 - \tfrac{1}{6}\kappa^2\alpha^2 + \ldots \quad \text{for small } \alpha$$

$$= \frac{\sin^2\,\kappa}{\kappa^2} \quad \text{for } \alpha = 90° \tag{9}$$

This can be envisioned as a reduction in mean-square amplitude with the variation in the angle α between the submarine normal and the wave direction. The variation is obtained by physical orientation of the submarine ($\alpha = 0°$: port beam sea, $\alpha = 90°$: following sea).

As before, consider a narrow directional wave. By selecting, for example, a fixed submarine orientation so that waves come from the port beam ($\alpha = 0$), the gain function generated by steering electronically (varying α_j)

$$G^2(\omega, \theta) = \left\{ \frac{\sin\,(\kappa\,\sin\,\alpha_j)}{\kappa\,\sin\,\alpha_j} \right\}^2 \tag{10}$$

is the same as if the submarine had turned. On the other hand, for the submarine headed constantly into the waves, $\alpha = 90°$ and

$$G^2(\omega, \theta) = \left\{ \frac{\sin\,[\kappa(1 - \sin\,\alpha_j)]}{\kappa(1 - \sin\,\alpha_j)} \right\}^2 \tag{11}$$

Obviously, G^2 is maximized for both α_j and $\alpha = 90°$. For $\alpha_j = 90° + \epsilon$

$$G^2(\omega, \theta) = 1 - \tfrac{1}{24}\kappa^2\epsilon^4 \quad \text{for small } \epsilon, \tag{12}$$

whereas for the case where $\alpha = 0°$ (port beam sea)

$$G^2(\omega, \theta) = 1 - \tfrac{1}{6}\kappa^2\alpha^2 \quad \text{for small } \alpha. \tag{13}$$

Figure 5-4-7. *Quadratic gain plot illustrating directional ambiguity between 80° and 100°.*

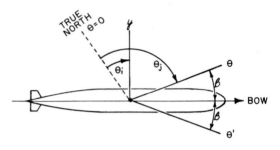

Figure 5-4-6. *Directional ambiguity.*

Hence the quadratic gain factor is less sensitive in the head sea ($\alpha = 90°$) orientation.

Derivation of the Directional Matrix from a Combination of "Steering" Techniques: It will now be demonstrated how a combination of "true" and "electronic" steering may be used to determine the directional spectra.

Consider a wave train from direction θ lying $\beta°$ to the port bow, as in Figure 5-4-6. With "electronic" steering only, i.e., for a fixed submarine heading θ_i, the direction of the wave train θ cannot be distinguished from θ'.

To prove this, note that

$$\theta_i + 90° = \theta + \beta \tag{14}$$

so that

$$\theta' = \theta + 2\beta = 180° + 2\theta_i - \theta \tag{15}$$

By definition,

$$\sin\,\alpha = \sin\,(\theta - \theta_i)$$

$$\sin\,\alpha' = \sin\,(\theta' - \theta_i)$$

$$= -\sin\,(\theta_i - \theta) = \sin\,\alpha \tag{16}$$

From the quadratic gain formula

$$G^2(\omega, \theta) = \left\{ \frac{\sin\,[\kappa(\sin\,\alpha - \sin\,\alpha_j)]}{\kappa(\sin\,\alpha - \sin\,\alpha_j)} \right\}^2 \tag{8}$$

it is obvious that $G^2(\omega, \theta) = G^2(\omega, \theta')$.

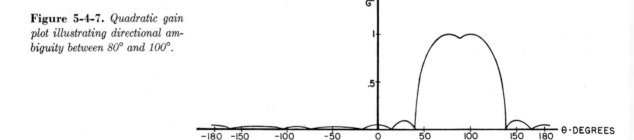

To illustrate this ambiguity, consider the submarine to be heading east; then $\theta_i = 0$. Let $\theta_j = 80°$, i.e., "antenna" pointed just north of east. A plot of $G^2(\omega, \theta)$ is sketched in Figure 5-4-7. Note the ambiguity for $\theta = 80°$ and $\theta = \theta' = 100°$, which for simplicity,[2] may be considered to be two delta functions in the directions 80° and 100°

$$G^2(\omega, \theta) = \delta(\theta - 80°) + \delta(\theta - 100°) \quad (17)$$

The directionality of the energy spectra can be determined crudely by letting the submarine cruise on two headings: first due east, then due south. For each of these headings, the recorded data are analyzed by "electronic steering" for three directions: ahead, astern, and abeam (port beam). For each frequency band, this results in a total of six estimates of energy:

θ_i	θ_j	α_j	θ'_j	E_{ij}	$= E_j + E'_j$
0°	270°	270°	270°	$E_{0,270}$	$= E_0 + E_{270}$
0°	0°	0°	180°	$E_{0,0}$	$= E_0 + E_{180}$
0°	90°	90°	90°	$E_{0,90}$	$= E_{90} + E_{90}$
90°	0°	270°	0°	$E_{90,0}$	$= E_0 + E_0$
90°	90°	0°	270°	$E_{90,90}$	$= E_{90} + E_{270}$
90°	180°	90°	180°	$E_{90,180}$	$= E_{180} + E_{180}$

Here E_{ij} is the mean-square energy for submarine orientation θ_i and antenna direction θ_j; E_j is the energy from the 90° sector centered on θ_j; and E'_j the energy from the 90° sector centered on θ'_j. The above six equations in four unknowns can be solved for the four directional energy spectra.

Determination of energy from additional azimuths by "electronic steering" in the laboratory after the data has been collected is not fruitful. For example, "pointing" the antenna toward the port bow and port quarter leads to the four additional entries of the above table, namely

θ_i	θ_j	α'_j	θ'_j	E_{ij}	$= E_j + E'_j$
0°	315°	315°	225°	$E_{0,315}$	$= E_{315} + E_{225}$
0°	45°	45°	135°	$E_{0,45}$	$= E_{45} + E_{135}$
90°	45°	315°	315°	$E_{90,45}$	$= E_{45} + E_{315}$
90°	135°	45°	225°	$E_{90,135}$	$= E_{135} + E_{225}$

---

[2] The general matrix for the true antenna pattern has been derived by Dr. Munk but will not be reproduced. Copies of the original are available upon request.

These four additional equations are not independent, since the Wronskian determinant is zero.

Obtaining spectral information, therefore, from additional sectors requires additional submarine headings. To generalize, the following table illustrates number of submarine headings.

β	Unknowns u	Legs $\frac{u}{2}$	Looks $\frac{u}{2}+1$	Equations $\frac{u}{2}\left(\frac{u}{2}+1\right)$	Degrees of Freedom $\frac{u}{2}\left(\frac{u}{2}-1\right)$
180°	2	1	2	2	0
90°	4	2	3	6	2
45°	8	4	5	20	12
22.5°	16	8	9	72	56
11.25°	32	16	17	272	240

The first column gives the angle between submarine orientations; the second column, the number of unknowns; the third, the number of required ship headings; the fourth, the number of "looks" for each heading; the fifth, the total number of equations thus obtained; and finally the sixth shows the number of degrees of freedom thus achieved. Certainly the degree of accuracy desired would depend upon the number of degrees of freedom. A procedure that yielded 100 degrees of freedom implies a standard deviation of approximately 10 per cent in all of the observed values. Hence, in terms of the above tabulation, this would require between 8 and 16 legs. In terms of duration this requires a test time of about 1800 seconds per leg (allowing for a leg duration 100 times the longest period of consequence). For a test sequence, therefore, of 16 legs, each one-half hour in duration, a complete test would require a total of eight hours.

CONCLUDING REMARKS

The preceding sections have described only briefly a new concept for determining directional wave spectra. Considerable development of sensing, recording, and analyzing techniques would be required to bring the system to fruition. Once accomplished, however, data thus obtained by submarines on station would provide the background information so vitally needed in designing and optimizing systems affected by the sea.

P. S. DE LEONIBUS

FIVE

POWER SPECTRA OF SURFACE WAVE HEIGHTS ESTIMATED FROM RECORDINGS MADE FROM A SUBMERGED HOVERING SUBMARINE

ABSTRACT

The technique of obtaining surface wave records with an inverted echo sounder from a submerged hovering submarine, and some of the errors associated with such a wave measuring system, are discussed. Examples of digital power spectral estimates obtained from recordings are presented. Significant wave heights obtained by these wave spectra are compared to hindcast values using the Pierson-Neumann spectra. The agreement is fair.

INTRODUCTION

The general problem of measuring and recording waves in the open ocean has been approached from several points of view (References 3, 4, 6, and 8). One of the more recent methods used by the Hydrographic Office uses an array of inverted echo sounders mounted on the deck of a submarine. The Hydrographic Office has obtained and analyzed wave height data recorded at keel depths of 80 to 100 feet (Reference 2). A submerged submarine used as a wave measuring platform has several advantages. One of the principal advantages is maneuverability — the submarine's capability of penetrating into high wave generat-

ing areas without being affected appreciably by the wave motion to the extent of not being able to operate the wave measuring equipment. It has the disadvantage of platform instability — the response of a submarine to the wave motion being measured. This disadvantage can be overcome to some extent by operating at greater depths, for example 300 feet. At such depths a submarine will respond appreciably only to lower wave frequency components. However, present instrumentation will require some modification if it is to operate at keel depths greater than 120 feet.

INSTRUMENTATION AND RECORDING PROCEDURES

The instrumentation used at present by the Hydrographic Office is the array of nine Sonic Surface Scanners mounted on the deck of the USS *Redfin*. In addition, the EDO (a standard fathometer) was used on the global circumnavigational cruise of the USS *Triton* to obtain surface wave records in several oceans.

The Sonic Surface Scanner consists of nine transducers mounted on the deck of a submarine. These are spaced 33 feet apart (Figure 5-5-1). The transducers are mounted face upward and are

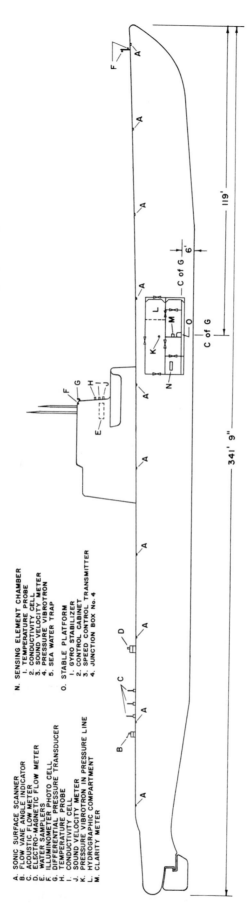

Figure 5-5-1. *Oceanographic instrumentation locations — USS Redfin (SS-272).*

A. SONIC SURFACE SCANNER
B. FLOW VANE ANGLE INDICATOR
C. ACOUSTIC FLOW METER
D. ELECTRO-MAGNETIC FLOW METER
E. WATER SAMPLERS
F. ILLUMINOMETER PHOTO CELL
G. DIFFERENTIAL PRESSURE TRANSDUCER
H. TEMPERATURE PROBE
I. CONDUCTIVITY CELL
J. SOUND VELOCITY METER
K. PRESSURE VIBROTRON IN PRESSURE LINE
L. HYDROGRAPHIC COMPARTMENT
M. CLARITY METER

N. SENSING ELEMENT CHAMBER
  1. TEMPERATURE PROBE
  2. CONDUCTIVITY CELL
  3. SOUND VELOCITY METER
  4. PRESSURE VIBROTRON
  5. SEA WATER TRAP

O. STABLE PLATFORM
  1. GYRO STABILIZER
  2. CONTROL CABINET
  3. SPEED CONTROL TRANSMITTER
  4. JUNCTION BOX No. 4

essentially inverted echo sounders. Each transducer in turn measures distance between itself and the sea surface directly above in a 3 degree cone. By sequencing from one transducer to the next aft along the deck of the submarine, a wave profile comparable to the length of the submarine can be obtained. The complete sequence takes approximately 0.54 seconds. The Sonic Surface Scanner was designed to provide data accurate to the nearest foot.

The output of all nine transducers is available, but the primary interest at this stage is in the power spectra of the output of one transducer. A recording from one transducer is, therefore, the instantaneous height of the sea surface above the submarine as a function of time. This is given in terms of the two-way travel time required for a sound wave front to travel from the transducer to the sea surface and return.

Assume the velocity of sound in ocean waters to be 5000 ft/sec. (The resulting error in this assumption is very small.) Travel time for the sound wave can be expressed

$$t = \tfrac{1}{5000} \text{ sec./ft.} = 0.2 \text{ millisec./ft.} \qquad (1)$$

Since we are concerned with a two-way travel time (the time required for the sound beam to go from the submarine transducer to the sea surface and return), the effect is the same as if the travel time were doubled. Thus, the effective travel time per foot is

$$t = 0.4 \text{ millisec./ft.} \qquad (2)$$

In this way, changes in sea surface height above the submarine are measured in terms of the two-way travel time. These changing values of sea surface height above the submarine are recorded as pulse packets on an AM channel of a tape recorder. The oscillator signal which forms the pulse packet is a 2500 cycle per second sine wave. The number of feet to the sea surface above the transducer is given in terms of the number of oscillations according to

$$d(\text{feet}) = N \times \binom{\text{oscillator}}{\text{frequency}} \times \binom{\text{travel time of}}{\text{sound per foot}}$$

$$= N \times (2.5 \text{ kc}) \times (0.4 \text{ millisec/ft}) = N \qquad (3)$$

where N is the number of oscillations that occur during the time the sound wave travels to the sea surface and returns, and is numerically equal to the number of feet. Each transducer has 60 milliseconds in which to "fire" and accept a return

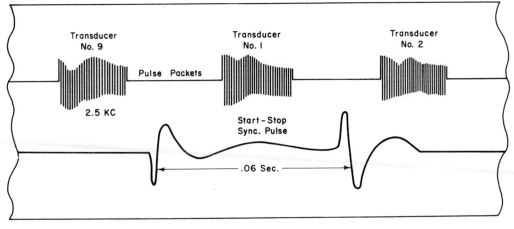

VISICORDER CHART PAPER

Figure 5-5-2. *Example of pulse packets and start-stop synchronizing pulse used in sonic surface scanner wave height measuring system, U. S. Navy Hydrographic Office.*

signal; therefore, a depth limitation is imposed on this system. For example, if sound velocity were equal to 5000 ft/sec., a sound beam could travel a total distance of 300 feet in 60 milliseconds. Therefore, the maximum operating depth is somewhat less than one-half this distance. The instrumentation problem of increasing the operating depth of the system is complicated and may involve changing the basic system frequency from one megacycle to some smaller value.

To identify Transducer No. 1, a synchronizing signal is recorded on a separate channel, which provides a negative pulse and a subsequent positive pulse 60 milliseconds later. A typical sequence of pulse packets (including the synchronizing signal provided only for Transducer No. 1) is shown in Figure 5-5-2. All the other transducers (including No. 1) fire at a time interval of 60 milliseconds for each transducer. The entire sequence of 9 transducers requires 540 milliseconds.

Assume that the oscillation count of the pulse packet recorded for Transducer No. 1 is desired (Figure 5-5-3). The scanner pulse packet signals recorded on one channel of a magnetic tape re-

Figure 5-5-3. *Block diagram of the playback system for sonic surface scanner wave height measuring system, U. S. Navy Hydrographic Office.*

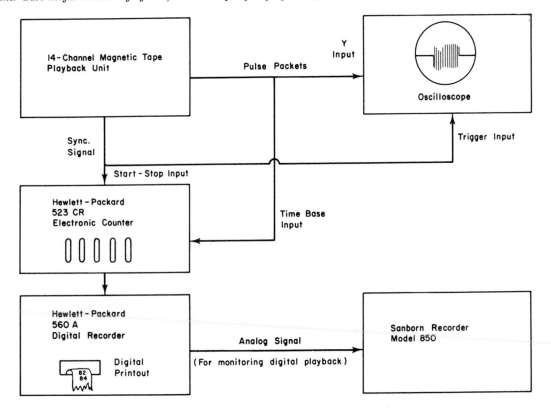

corder are fed into the external time base input of the time interval counter and monitored on an oscilloscope. The synchronizing signal from another channel is fed into the start-stop input in order to identify Transducer No. 1.

Numerical values printed out on a digital recorder give changing heights of the sea surface above the transducer. As a check on the quality of the digital printout, a Sanborn Recorder, Model 850, is used to record the analog output from the digital recorder. Since the printer output is given directly in feet, these values are coded subsequently on punched cards for high speed computations of spectra on a digital computer.

EFFECT OF SUBMARINE MOTION ON SURFACE WAVE MEASUREMENTS

Sonic Surface Scanner wave measurements at a keel depth of 100 feet and during lower sea state

conditions will not be affected seriously by the submarine moving in response to the subsurface wave motion. However, as the sea surface wave height grows under wind action or if low frequency swell propagates over the hovering submarine, the low frequency components will increase the amplitudes of the submarine's motion. In effect, wave measurements will be made with respect to a moving reference system. For example, if water depth is great, a single low-frequency swell of 0.05 cycles per second (20-second period), will have only 20 per cent of the surface wave height attenuated at 75 feet, and only 26 per cent will be attenuated at 100. feet. Now if the submarine behaves as a particle, the heave amplitude of the neutrally buoyant, hovering submarine should be nearly in phase with the wave motion at the surface (neglecting for the moment all other components of the submarine motion). This will tend to make the height of the sea surface above the moving transducer appear shorter than it actually would be with respect to a stationary platform. In

Figure 5-5-4. *Power spectra of surface wave heights.   Cruise 8, Run 3.*

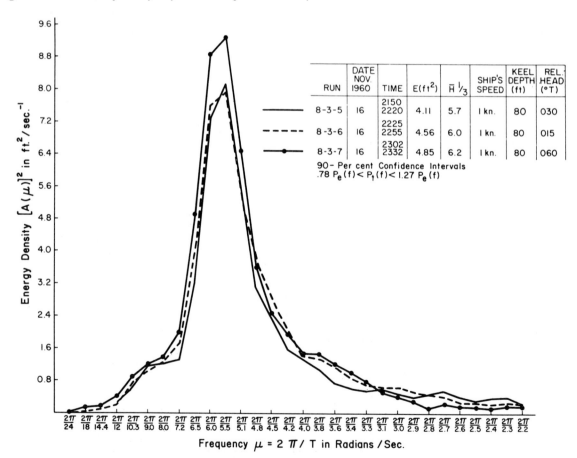

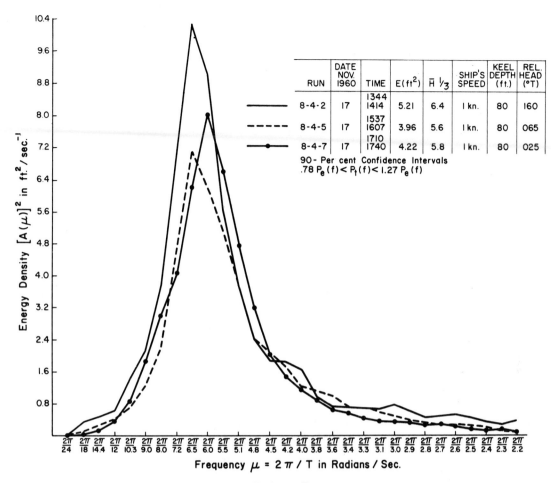

RUN	DATE NOV. 1960	TIME	E(ft²)	H̄ ⅓	SHIP'S SPEED	KEEL DEPTH (ft.)	REL. HEAD (°T)
——— 8-4-2	17	1344 1414	5.21	6.4	1 kn.	80	160
- - - 8-4-5	17	1537 1607	3.96	5.6	1 kn.	80	065
—•— 8-4-7	17	1710 1740	4.22	5.8	1 kn.	80	025

90- Per cent Confidence Intervals
.78 P_e (f) < P_t (f) < 1.27 P_e (f)

Figure 5-5-5. *Power spectra of surface wave heights, Cruise 8, Run 4.*

general, the submarine will execute motion in all six degrees of freedom. Effects of pitching and rolling will tend to increase the length of the path over which the sound beam has to travel; this tends to make the recorded wave motion appear higher than actual wave motion. In any event, a correction must be applied to the original data or possibly to the spectrum.

EXAMPLES OF POWER SPECTRA OF SURFACE WAVE HEIGHTS

Figures 5-5-4 and 5-5-5 illustrate power spectra of wave heights recorded in deep water about 200 miles east of Cape Hatteras, North Carolina. These spectra were computed by the digital estimation formulae of Tukey (References 1 and 7). The 90-per cent confidence intervals are determined by computing the number of degrees of freedom according to the formula

$$\text{Number of degrees of freedom} = \frac{2Tn}{m\Delta t} \quad (4)$$

Tn is the duration of the record in seconds, m is the number of lags, and Δt is the sampling interval in seconds. For example, with $Tn = 1440$ seconds, $m = 60$, and $\Delta t = 0.6$ seconds, spectral estimates in Figures 4 and 5 are distributed with a *chi*-square distribution with 80 degrees of freedom. The 90-percent confidence intervals can be determined from a table of the *chi*-square distribution. For 80 degrees of freedom, the true spectral density $P_t(f)$ is bounded by the estimated spectral density $P_e(f)$ according to

$$0.78P_e(f) < P_t(f) < 1.27P_e(f) \quad (5)$$

These two sets of spectra are fairly narrow with periods of maximum spectral energy between 5.5 and 6.5 seconds. Significant wave heights, $\bar{H}\frac{1}{3} = 2.83 \sqrt{E}$, where E is the area under the spectra graphs, were found to be about 6 feet for these particular examples.

TABLE I

SUMMARY OF RESULTS DERIVED FROM SURFACE WAVE SPECTRA AND COMPARISON TO HINDCAST WAVE DATA

Run	Date 1960	Time (Z)	Relative Heading (°T)	Values from Measured Wave Spectra		Values from Hindcast Wave Data	
				$H\frac{1}{3}$ (FT)	T-Band (Sec)	$H\frac{1}{3}$ (FT)	T-Band (Sec)
8-3-5	16 Nov.	2150–2220	030	5.7	2.5–14.4	6	1.0–7.0
8-3-6	16 Nov.	2225–2255	015	6.0	2.5–14.4	7	2.0–8.0
8-3-7	16 Nov.	2302–2332	060	6.2	2.5–14.4	8	2.0–8.0
8-4-2	17 Nov.	1344–1414	160	6.4	2.5–14.4	4	2.0–8.0
8-4-5	17 Nov.	1537–1607	065	5.6	2.5–14.4	4	2.0–8.0
8-4-7	17 Nov.	1710–1740	025	5.8	2.5–14.4	4	2.0–8.0
	1959						
4-2	29 Oct.	0520–0550	165	5.5	2.5–14.4	3	1.5–7.8
4-3	29 Oct.	0600–0640	158	5.4	2.5–14.4	3	1.5–7.8
4-4	29 Oct.	0650–0730	157	5.6	2.5–14.4	3	1.5–7.8
4-5	29 Oct.	0745–0815	100	5.1	2.5–14.4	4	2.0–8.3
6-1	1 Nov.	1235–1320	102	6.3	2.4–12.0	5	2.0–8.8
6-2	1 Nov.	1327–1403	156	5.6	2.4–12.0	5	2.0–8.8
6-3	1 Nov.	0407–1433	160	6.0	2.4–12.0	5	2.0–8.8
6-4	1 Nov.	1513–1551	152	6.7	2.4–12.0	5	2.0–8.8

COMPARISON OF RESULTS DERIVED FROM SPECTRA TO HINDCASTING

Table 1 presents a summary of results derived from wave spectra and a comparison to hindcast wave data using the methods of Pierson-Neumann (Reference 5). The first six entries (November 1960) refer to the spectra of Figures 5-5-4 and 5-5-5; the last eight entries (October, November 1959) were derived from spectra computed from data of an earlier cruise of the *Redfin* (Reference 2). Significant height values compare reasonably well; however, hindcast significant height values are smaller except in the first three cases. The highest periods from hindcasting are 7.0 to 8.8 seconds, while the highest periods from the measured spectra are 12.0 to 14.4 seconds.

SUMMARY AND CONCLUSIONS

The Sonic Surface Scanner method appears to be a reliable means of obtaining wave records in the open ocean and should be particularly useful in regions of high wave generation. The problem of correcting for the effect of submarine motion has to be solved from a practical point of view. In the examples presented here, the effect of submarine motion does not appear to be too serious. For example, spectra shown in Figures 5-5-4 and 5-5-5 do not vary greatly at several different rela-

tive headings under wave conditions shown in Table 1. This will not be the case, however, when much of the wave energy is located at lower frequencies.

An instrumentation problem involves converting the pulse signals to an equivalent analog signal so that electronic analyzers may be used to estimate power spectra. The possibility of using the array of nine transducers to estimate some of the properties of directional spectra presents an interesting challenge to oceanographers in this field.

REFERENCES

1. Blackman, R. B. and J. W. Tukey, *The Measurement of Power Spectra from the Point of View of Communications Engineering.* New York: Dover Publications Inc., 1959.

2. DeLeonibus, P. S., *Power Spectrum Analysis of Wave Motion, Submarine Roll Angle, and Relative Cross-flow Velocities*, Cruise II, USS *Redfin*, Technical Report No. 100, U. S. Navy Hydrographic Office. 1961, 61 pp.

3. Marks, W. and R. G. Tuckerman, "A Telemetering Accelerometer Wave Buoy," 1960. Pages 283 to 286 of this report.

4. New York University, Department of Meteorology and Oceanography, *The Directional Spectrum of a Wind-Generated Sea as Determined From Data Ob-*

tained By the Stereo Wave Observation Project by J. L. Chase *et al.*, 1957, 267 pp.   Contract NONR 285 (03).

5. Pierson, W. J., Gerhard Neumann and R. W. James, *Practical Methods for Observing and Forecasting Ocean Waves by Means of Wave Spectra and Statistics*, No. 603 (1955), 284 p.   Based on New York University, Department of Meteorology and Oceanography, Technical Report No. 1, 1953, 322 pp.   Contract No. N189S-86743.

6. Tucker, M. J., "A Ship-borne Wave Recorder," *Proceedings of the First Conference on Coastal Engineer-ing Instruments*, Berkeley, California, October 31–November 2, 1955, 112–118.   Printed in 1956.

7. Tukey, J. W., "The Sampling Theory of Spectrum Estimates," *Symposium on Applications of Autocorrelation Analysis to Physical Problems*.   Woods Hole, Massachusetts, 13–14 June, 1949, pp. 47–67. Washington, D. C.: Office of Naval Research, U. S. Navy Department, 1950, 79 pp.   Navexos-P-735.

8. U. S. Navy, Hydrographic Office, *Electric Wave Staff* (Hydrographic Office Model Mark I), Hydrographic Office Technical Report 9, 1955, 15 pp.

A STEP-TYPE RECORDING WAVE GAGE

INTRODUCTION

For several years California Research Corporation, a subsidiary of Standard Oil Company of California, has been engaged in studies of the forces exerted by ocean waves on offshore structures. These studies were undertaken to obtain design information for the large number of offshore drilling platforms constructed and operated by the company. In the course of this investigation it was necessary to determine the elevation of the sea surface as a function of time, as surface waves travel past a particular point. Initially, wave profile measurements were made using a type of step-resistance wave gage developed by the Beach Erosion Board.[1]

After extensive use of the Beach Erosion Board's wave gage, several of its operating characteristics pointed to certain modifications that would improve the system. The most undesirable characteristic of the wave gage was that in actual use the calibration constant was not linear and was influenced by changes in local environment, such as marine growth and water properties.

As a result of our experience with the BEB wave gage, a modified gage was developed. The wave gage consists of three major components: (1) A wave staff, which is the sensing element

of the system, (2) a recording unit that is easily adapted to record either analog or digital information, and (3) a program unit, which provides for the completely automatic operation of the gage at unmanned stations. This paper describes briefly the three components of the modified wave gage.

MAJOR COMPONENTS OF THE WAVE GAGE

Wave Staff: The wave staff is assembled from a series of ten-foot sections of steel pipe. Stainless steel electrodes are placed at equal intervals along the length of each pipe section. A portion of a typical staff is shown in Figure 5-6-1. Each electrode is electrically connected to the recording system by wires carried internally in each pipe section. The electrodes are insulated from the pipe sections by nylon bushings. A stainless steel ground bar runs the length of each staff section opposite the row of electrodes. This bar is electrically grounded to each staff section, which is in turn grounded to the recording system. Thus, as in the BEB staff, an electrical circuit is completed by the presence of salt water between the submerged electrodes and the ground bar. The ten-foot staff sections are filled with wax after all internal wiring is completed. The wax filler protects the interior of the staff from damage by sea water in the event of a leak at the couplings

---

[1] Caldwell, J. M., "The Step Resistance Wave Gage", *Proceedings of the First Conference on Coastal Engineering Instruments*, Council of Wave Research, (1956), Chap. 5, 44.

Figure 5-6-1. *Wave staff sections.*

wave staff of any desired length as long as a sufficient number of wires are provided to accommodate the wiring from lower sections. A waterproof plug is attached to the top section of the staff, and the wiring between this plug and the recording instrumentation is protected by rubber hoses. A typical installation of a sixty-foot wave staff is shown in Figure 5-6-2.

Wave staffs up to sixty feet in length have been mounted successfully on a great variety of offshore structures, and on several occasions a shorter staff has been installed on an anchored buoy. Typical installations are illustrated in Figures 5-6-3 and 5-6-4.

The structure-supported wave staff can be fabricated from relatively small diameter pipe and

Figure 5-6-2. *Wave staff installation.*

between sections or due to a damaged electrode housing.

Individual sections of the wave staff are assembled by means of water tight unions attached to the end of each section. The union not only serves as a mechanical coupling, but houses the electrical plugs which connect the wires from adjacent wave staff sections. The mating surfaces of each union are sealed by a rubber *o*-ring.

Pipe sections can be protected from corrosion by any number of suitable coatings. Our experience has shown that commercially-available products containing epoxy resins or similar plastic materials are satisfactory coatings for this purpose.

The ten-foot sections may be assembled into a

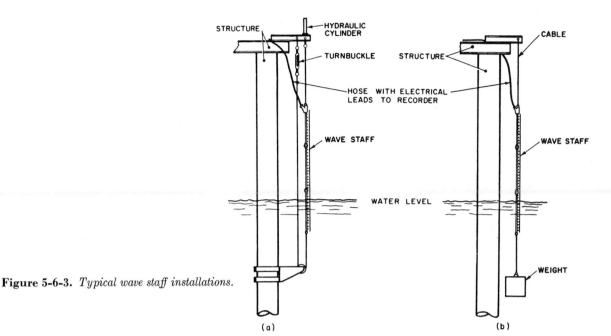

Figure 5-6-3. *Typical wave staff installations.*

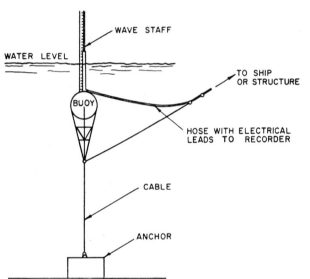

Figure 5-6-4. *Buoy mounted wave staff.*

secured in place under a large axial tension to resist lateral motion and bending deflections that would result from wave forces. The staff can be secured at top and bottom to brackets on the supporting structure, and an axial force applied by an appropriate hydraulic system (Figure 5-6-3a). An alternate method involves supporting the wave staff at its top and applying an axial force by means of a large weight attached to the unsupported bottom section (Figure 5-6-3b).

With a buoy-mounted wave staff (Figure 5-6-4), the roll stability of the unit is maintained by using a totally submerged float that is sufficiently buoyant to produce a large force in the anchoring cable. As the wave staff and buoy assembly are subjected to wave forces, rotation of the unit is resisted by the anchor line tension. The twenty-foot floating wave staff shown in Figure 5-6-5 has been used successfully at several locations along the California coast. This particular staff was used to measure wave heights at the anchoring site of floating drilling barges.

Figure 5-6-5. *Buoy mounted wave staff.*

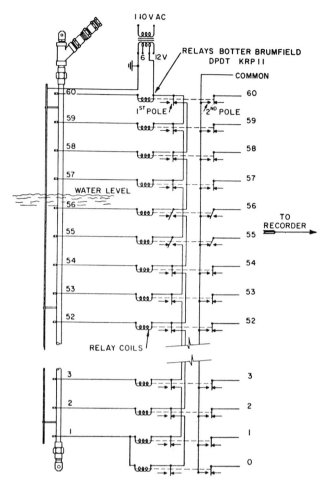

Figure 5-6-6. *Wave gage relay circuit.*

Recording System: The wave gage recording system consists of an array of electrical relays energized through the wave staff electrodes, a modulated signal source, and a recording or display unit. This system was designed to provide an output signal that is proportional to changes in water level and is independent of the power source employed to energize the wave staff proper.

As shown in Figure 5-6-6, each wave staff electrode is connected to an individual relay that in turn modulates a signal source. These relays are activated in sequence as the circuit associated with each relay coil is completed by water covering the electrode. The complete relay system is designed in such a way that only the relays associated with the two highest submerged electrodes are energized at any one time. Relays 56 and 55 are shown energized in Figure 5-6-6. One set of relay contacts modulates the recorded signal, while the second set disconnects power from the lower electrodes. As the water level moves up, relay 57 (in Figure 5-6-6) is energized thereby closing the

contacts shown at the left of the figure and at the same time removing power from relay 55. Conversely, if the water level decreases, relay 56 will drop out thereby allowing relay 54 to be energized. Thus, referring to the left of Figure 5-6-6, the contacts of the two relays immediately below the water surface are closed while all others are open. The relay array can therefore easily be incorporated into the proper circuitry to modulate an appropriate signal source as a function of water level.

A similar circuit can be designed with only one relay activated at a time. However, the successive opening and closing of individual relays will produce severe transient fluctuations in the modulated signal during the small time interval between the opening of one set of relay contacts and the closing of the next. Because at least one relay is always energized at any time in the system shown in Figure 5-6-6, transient fluctuations of the signal during the opening and closing of successive relays are minimized.

The modulated signal from the relay unit can

Figure 5-6-7. *Wave gage voltage divider.*

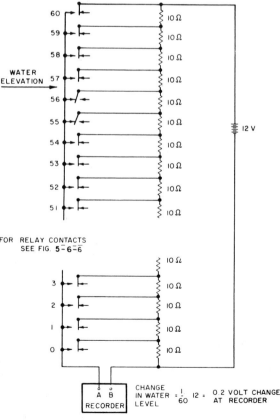

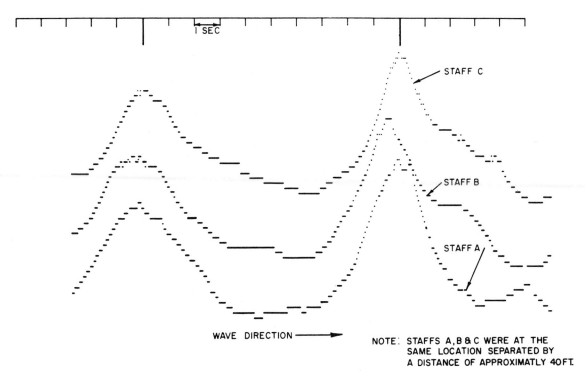

Figure 5-6-8. *Sample analog wave gage record.*

be recorded by either analog or digital methods. If an analog recording system is desired, the wave staff relays are connected to a variable voltage divider, as shown in Figure 5-6-7. Referring to Figure 5-6-7, the output of the voltage divider measured between points A and B is a voltage linearly related to the water elevation. The output voltage is equal to 0 when the wave staff is out of water and to 12 volts when it is completely submerged. Recording the output voltage of the divider as a function of time results in a step-type record, where each step represents a change in water elevation equal to the distance between electrodes. An enlarged sample of a typical record is shown in Figure 5-6-8. Each step in this record is equal to a 6-inch change in water elevation.

To obtain a digitized signal, the wave staff relays are connected to a matrix of diodes of the type shown in Figure 5-6-9. The output from this diode matrix is a coded digitized signal that is equal to the number of electrodes under water at any time. The six-channel matrix shown in Figure 5-6-9 is designed to produce a Gray code for a signal ranging between 0 and 64. An important advantage of the Gray code, a reflected binary code, is that at the instant the signal changes from one value to another, the coded signal has no ambiguous values. The output signal from a matrix of this type is compatible with most recording units using punched paper tape or with multiple head magnetic tape systems.

Figure 5-6-9. *Wave gage coding matrix.*

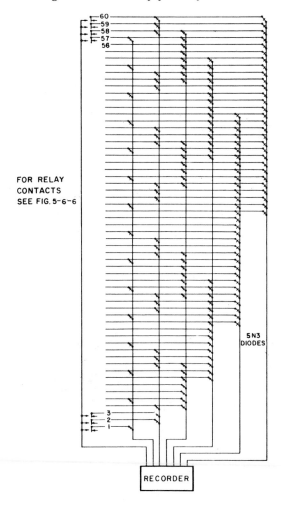

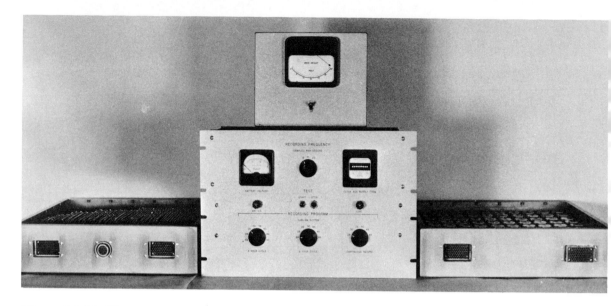

Figure 5-6-10. *Wave gage relay unit, programmer and coding matrix.*

Program Unit: An important advantage of the wave staff system described here is that it is easily adapted to fully automatic installations where recording times and intervals are controlled by a preset programmer. A simple addition to the relay array shown in Figure 5-6-6 will allow a programmer to be activated by any of the relays associated with each wave staff electrode. A number of electrical circuits can be devised to time and control the recording period according to the information required. For example, a system can be designed to sample wave heights periodically, and if during that period a preselected electrode is wetted, to start the recording system. Thus the system will record only when activated by preselected wave amplitudes.

A digital paper tape recording system is shown in Figures 5-6-10 and 5-6-11. In Figure 5-6-10 the wave gage relay unit is on the right, the coding matrix is on the left, and the programmer for controlling the desired recording sequence is in the center. In this particular application the programmer can be set to record water elevation every $\frac{1}{5}$, $\frac{1}{10}$, or $\frac{1}{20}$ of a second. The programmer can be set to record every four hours if a predetermined wave staff electrode is wetted; to record every two hours, if a second higher electrode is wetted; and to record continuously as long as a third electrode is wetted at any time during the recording cycle. The length of the recording period is twenty minutes; however, if desired, the period may be varied over a wide range. Figure 5-6-11 shows the recording unit used in this system. It consists of a Friden paper tape punch

Figure 5-6-11. *Wave gage punched paper tape recorder.*

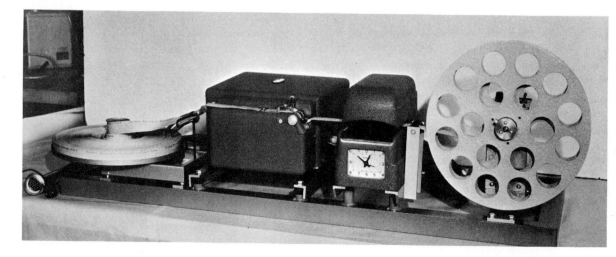

along with tape reels and a time stamp that automatically prints time and date on the tape at the start of every recording period.

COMMENTS

The wave gage described here has evolved from experience acquired in eleven installations. Individual installations were tailored to the needs of the particular location and the information desired. At the present time three systems are in operation, and a fourth is under construction. All are completely automatic, and recording programs are energized when wave heights reach certain preselected levels. One installation uses a 30-foot staff in 30 feet of water and a Friden paper tape punch to record digitized data. A second identical unit is mounted on a structure in 17 feet of water. The third consists of a 60-foot wave staff in 100 feet of water and uses an oscillograph to record photographically an analog signal. All of these units are mounted on structures in the Bay Marchand area of the Gulf of Mexico off the Louisiana shore. The fourth unit will have a punched paper tape recorder and will be installed off the California coast.

The advantages of the type of wave gage described here include the following·

(1) The wave gage is self-calibrating. With the analog system each step is equal to the distance between electrodes, and in the digital system the coded output is exactly equal to the number of electrodes under water.

(2) The signal produced by the analog system is linear for all water levels.

(3) In both cases, the information obtained is a direct measure of the surface elevation and can easily be recorded continuously as a function of time.

(4) The use of relays to modulate an independent signal decreases the system's sensitivity to sea growth and salinity changes. (Calibration of the system is insensitive to wave staff environment.)

(5) The system allows the water surface elevation to be digitized directly, thus keeping to a minimum the number of data reduction processes.

The major disadvantages are:

(1) The wave staff must be mounted either on or in close proximity to a structure.

(2) The resolution of the system is dependent on the distance between electrodes.

The handling of the vast amount of data accumulated by instrumentation of the type described here presents a major problem. To process and analyze this amount of data is expensive and time-consuming; consequently, we have limited data reduction to those records of most interest for our problems. At the present time, a portion of our records are on punched paper tape, and can be analyzed by automatic reading equipment and digital computers. The remainder of the records are in analog form and can be digitized using semiautomatic equipment before being analyzed by means of a digital computer.

Some of our most interesting wave height data were recorded in the Gulf of Mexico between 1955 and 1959. Data for waves ranging up to about 20 feet in height were recorded during a number of storms and hurricanes. The water depth at the recording location, Bay Marchand, Louisiana, was 30 feet, and the recording period was approximately 20 minutes every two hours throughout a storm.

Although in the past we have been interested primarily in wave profile measurements as they pertain to measured wave forces, we are now proceeding with a statistical analysis of the wave height records. At present a study of the correlation functions and power spectra computed from wave height records obtained during hurricanes and lesser storms is in progress. A statistical analysis of recorded wave amplitudes is also under way. We hope to publish the results of these studies in the near future.

* * *

ACKNOWLEDGMENTS

Over the years many people have contributed to the development of the instrumentation described here. These include; Messrs. V. Schoettle, D. O. Seevers, V. E. Sjogren, L. Skjelbreia, E. L. Thomas, and V. B. Waithman.

JOSEPH M. CALDWELL

LEO C. WILLIAMS

SEVEN

THE BEACH EROSION BOARD'S WAVE SPECTRUM ANALYZER

AND ITS PURPOSE

The wave measurement program of the Beach Erosion Board is devoted for the most part to long-term records to develop the statistical wave picture or "wave climate" at a selected location. This program has been under way for some 12 years. No less than 30 stations have been occupied for periods of 6 months or longer during this 12-year period. One of these, at Huntington Beach Pier in the Los Angeles area, has operated for almost the entire 12 years.

The Board has frequently as many as 5 stations in operation at a given time with prospects of as many as 10 or 12 in the near future. With this number of stations in operation the problem of the sampling interval and the length of a given sample become important.

The sampling interval for most of our ocean gages has been selected as 4 hours, giving us 6 records a day from each station. With 5 stations in operation this entails an analysis of 30 records a day, or 11,000 a year. With 10 stations, a daily analysis of 60 records is involved. Those acquainted with the analysis problem recognize that 60 records a day represents a sizeable load even for the simpler methods of analysis.

The length of the individual record is also of importance. Until recently, our analysis was made by eye, i.e., manually, from a pen-and-ink

chart record. A 7-minute record was used for several years, due principally to the difficulty of studying a longer record visually. With improved understanding of wave variability, we are now shifting to a 20-minute record as the standard length. Concurrently we are moving away from visual analysis to an electronic analysis of the record.

In considering the type of analyses to be made we recognized that magnetic tape and punched tape were available as the recording medium holding the record to feed into the analyzer. We chose the magnetic tape as giving a more compact record and presenting fewer recording difficulties at the wave gaging sites. Our gages are frequently attended by relatively unskilled personnel, and the magnetic tape recorder appeared to be the more practical for our needs.

As finally developed, our recorder uses standard $\frac{1}{4}$-inch magnetic tape at a recording speed of $\frac{1}{2}$ inch per minute (0.008 inches per second). This is about $\frac{1}{900}$ the speed found on standard voice recorders at $7\frac{1}{2}$ inches per second. We found that no commercial recorders were available for this low speed and therefore fabricated our own recorders. The tape speed was selected after tests to determine the minimum speed at which a reliable recording could be made. This minimum speed is that which will advance the tape sufficiently between crest and trough to prevent the recording head from erasing the crest trace as the head is recording the following trough. At the $\frac{1}{2}$ inch-per-minute speed, a 2-second wave can be recorded without the recording head partially erasing the preceding wave. Under these conditions of a 2-second wave period and a $\frac{1}{2}$ inch-per-minute tape speed the wave crest signals are only 0.0166 inches apart on the tape. Attempts to operate at a lower tape speed resulted in a loss of accuracy due to the erasing action described above.

Concurrently with the selection of the recording speed, a selection was being made of the analyzer. The remainder of this paper will be devoted to a description of this analyzer and the meaning of the various types of analyses which can be made by it.

The general requirement for the analyzer was that it reduce the wave record to a spectrum plot; this plot was expected to show the average wave heights associated with the various wave periods represented in the spectrum. The limited funds available to the Board precluded the complete development of this analyzer in our own shop. Therefore, we attempted to find as many as possible of the components on the commercial market and if necessary, to modify them to fit our needs. The rest of the items we made in our electronic shop.

As selected, modified, or developed, the analyzer consists of the following pieces of equipment:

(a) A "reading" device for scanning the 20-minute magnetic tape record. This device is a rotating drum 20 inches in circumference with two pick-up heads 180 degrees apart. These two heads scan the 10-inch sector of magnetic tape (representing a selected 20-minute record) in succession until the analysis of the sector has been completed. The peripheral speed of the drum is 62.5 inches per second, a speed increase of 7,500 times over the recording speed. Thus, a 2-second period signal on the tape appears as a 3,750 cps signal from the scanner, a 3-second period appears at 2,500 cps, and a 30-second period signal appears as a 250 cps signal from the scanner.

(b) A frequency mixing device which has the effect of converting the 2,500 cps signal to a 99,500 cps signal and the 250 cps signal to a 97,250 cps signal. In effect, this adds 97,000 cps to the basic frequency of the signal.

(c) A set of filters and detectors for continuous automatic sweeping of signal frequencies between 97,000 cps and 122,000 cps and indicating the relative magnitude of the signals being accepted by the filter. These frequencies encompass those of item (b) above.

(d) An electronic converter for converting the filtered signal to a linear average, a square average, a peak value, or a cumulative signal.

(e) An amplifier for converting the converted signal to a d.c. signal suitable for driving the y-axis pen of a rectangular pen-and-ink recorder.

(f) A synchronizing device between the automatic scanning filters of (c) and the x-axis drive of the pen-and-ink recorder. This enables the pen-and-ink recorder to plot automatically the strength of the filtered signal against the wave period.

(g) A cathode-ray oscillograph, which delineates the trace of the signal being picked up from the magnetic tape. This delineation assists the operator in positioning the tape on the scanning drum and in detecting any gross irregularity in the tape record.

It is evident that the heart of the equipment is the electronic scanning and filtering equipment described in (b), (c), and (d) of the preceding paragraph. This equipment is capable of scanning automatically in continuous increments all signal components between 97,000 cps and 122,000 cps. This scanning is done as part of a filtering arrangement which admits only a selected frequency hand-width as the device searches, or scans, the signal from 97,250 cps to 100,750 cps. In other words, the filters act as an opening of a certain width, 5 cps, 50 cps, 200 cps, depending on the filter selected. This opening is then moved progressively through the signal as it searches for components that will pass through the filter. Thus, at the beginning of the search a 200-cycle filter would be accepting all signals in the record with a frequency of between 97,150 cps and 97,350 cps. Half way through the search it would be accepting all signals in the record between 98,650 cps and 98,850 cps. At the end of the search it would be accepting all signals between 100,650 cps, and 100,850 cps. These relationships are shown on Figure 5-7-1.

If we arrange our sweeping of the magnetic tape record so that a 3-second ocean wave appears as a 99,500 cps signal in front of the filters and a 30-second wave appears as a 97,250 cps signal, then we can tabulate the relationships shown on Table I.

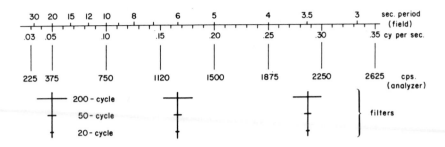

Figure 5-7-1. *Basic Relations.*

TABLE I

BAND-PASS PERIODS OF FILTERS

Basic Wave Period	Limiting Periods Admitted by Filter Widths of		
(sec.)	5 cycles	50 cycles	200 cycles
3	2.99 3.01	2.93 3.07	2.80 3.20
6	5.98 6.02	5.74 6.25	5.12 7.18
10	9.97 10.03	9.30 10.70	7.8 13.8
15	14.8 15.1	13.5 16.6	10.5 25.6
20	19.7 20.3	17.5 23.2	12.8 45.5
30	29.4 30.7	25.0 41.5	16.4 66.7

It is important to recognize that the filter width is the index to the compass of wave periods that will be accepted by the analyzer at a given time and read out to the spectrum recording device. Thus, if we use a 5 cps. filter (0.0007 cps for wave frequency) and we are searching the record for the 10-second period waves, the analyzer would sense and read out to the recorder only those waves lying between about a 9.97-second period and 10.03-second period. If only one wave appeared in a 20-minute record that fell within the above period limits, the "average height" read out by the analyzer at the 10-second point would be very low. In effect, the analyzer assumes that the 10-second wave is occurring at 10-second intervals (thus a total of 120 times in 20 minutes). It then, in effect, divides the impulse from the single 10-second wave height by 120 and reports an average height of $\frac{1}{120}$ the actual height of the single 10-second wave.

From the above, it can be seen that it is somewhat misleading to narrow the filter opening too much. What we can do is to decide what scope of wave periods are essentially 10-second waves as far as our immediate needs are concerned and then open up the filter to accept all waves whose periods are within that range. Thus, if we decide that all waves of from 9.3-second to 10.7-second periods can be handled as 10-second waves, then we can open up the filter to accept waves within these limits. For our analyzer this would entail a filter band-width of about 50 cy.

A study of Table I shows that a 5-cy filter is probably too narrow in that the range of wave periods admitted is probably too small. The use of this filter could be expected to result in a highly irregular spectrum. This is demonstrated by Figure 5-7-2, which shows the spectrum analysis of a single 20-minute record or "skid" from Atlantic City. It is seen that the use of the 5-cy filter results in a very broken record, which would be difficult to interpret.

On Figure 5-7-2 are also shown analyses of the same wave record using 20-cy, 50-cy, and 200-cy filters. A study of the four curves of this figure indicates that the 50-cy and 200-cy filters give a spectrum analysis which appears to have more practical meaning for statistical purposes than do the analyses given by the narrower 20-cy and 5-cy filters. A decision as to filter width should of course be made with the ultimate use of the data in mind.

The equipment has capabilities in addition to that of plotting the linear average spectrum. The following are instantly available by manually setting the control dials on the filtering and amplifying components:

(a) Linear average
(b) Square average (energy)
(c) Linear peak
(d) Square peak
(e) Cumulative linear average
(f) Cumulative square average

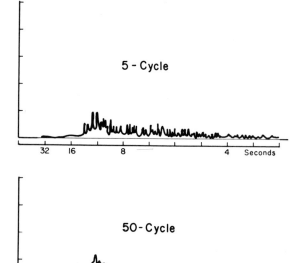

5 - Cycle

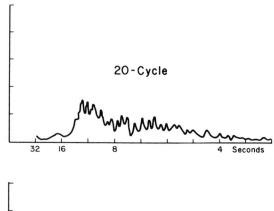

20 - Cycle

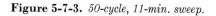

50 - Cycle

200 - Cycle

Figure 5-7-2. *Linear Ave., 11-min. sweep.*

Samples of a number of these are shown on Figure 5-7-3.

The length of time required to obtain the analyses is also of interest. Assuming an analysis load of 60 records per 8-hour work day, the average time available per record is 8 minutes. Thus the length of analysis is of some economic importance. This length of analysis, or sweep time, is variable on the equipment, with manual settings for 2.2, 4.4, 11.0, and 22.0 minutes available. The electrical inertia in the filters and amplifiers prevents an immediate response of the equipment to

Figure 5-7-3. *50-cycle, 11-min. sweep.*

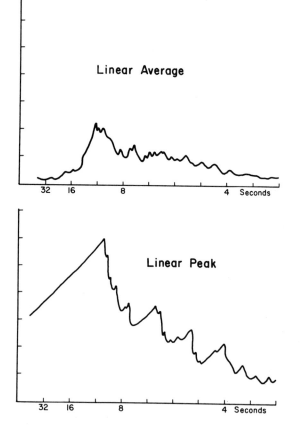

Linear Average

Linear Peak

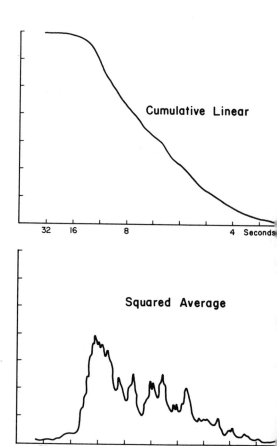

Cumulative Linear

Squared Average

TABLE II

Analyzer Response Characteristics
(Per Cent)

Filter	200 cycles				50 cycles				20 cycles				5 cycles				2 cycles			
Sweep (min)	2.2	4.4	11.0	22.0	2.2	4.4	11.0	22.0	2.2	4.4	11.0	22.0	2.2	4.4	11.0	22.0	2.2	4.4	11.0	22.0
Wave Period (sec)																				
1	64	80	95	98	47	66	89	95	41	67	81	90	47	40	82	92	44	66	100	90
2	65	83	96	100	40	59	83	95	44	57	57	67	27	29	82	95	56	56	31	58

(sweeping range = 0–25,000 cps)

Filter	200 cycles				50 cycles				20 cycles				5 cycles				2 cycles			
4	100	100	100	100	93	99	100	100	65	78	96	100	59	77	74	85	75	80	79	82
8	100	100	100	100	94	100	100	100	80	93	99	100	67	81	74	98	50	60	80	87
16	100	100	100	100	92	98	100	100	75	91	99	100	40	55	78	96	24	47	60	70
32	100	100	100	100	92	98	100	100	75	91	99	100	28	49	76	90	28	40	62	77

(sweeping range = 0–2,500 cps)

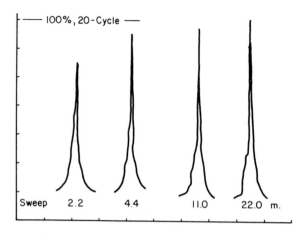

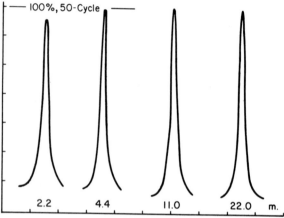

Figure 5-7-4. *Sine Wave, 4-sec. period.*

the signals sent forward from the tape scanning head. The relation between amplitude response and sweep time is shown on Table II. The responses were obtained by analysing a set of sine wave signals at periods of 4, 8, 16, and 32 seconds with various sweep times. The actual spectrum plots of a number of selected sine waves with varying sweep intervals are shown in Figure 5-7-4.

A study of Table II indicates that the relative response is between 90 per cent and 100 per cent for all sweep intervals when 200-cy and 50-cy filters are used. The combinations of shorter sweep intervals and narrower filters (20-, 5-, and 2-cy), however, cause a rapid falling off of relative response, the response being only 28 per cent with a 2-cy filter when using a sweep interval of 2.2 minutes.

The ability of the analyzer to detect and separate the components in a complex wave train was demonstrated by preparing a set of special tapes on which was transcribed a complex wave pattern.

The periods and amplitudes of the recorded components (usually four in number) were known with exactitude. The spectrum analysis made by the equipment was then checked back against the original components. As one example, a combination of 4-, 5-, 6-, and 7-second sine waves of uniform amplitude were imposed simultaneously on the magnetic tape. The spectrum analyses in Figure 5-7-5 show how the analyzer was able to identify the original component waves. The sharpness of identity varied with the filter open-

Figure 5-7-5. *Sine waves, 2.2-min. sweep.*

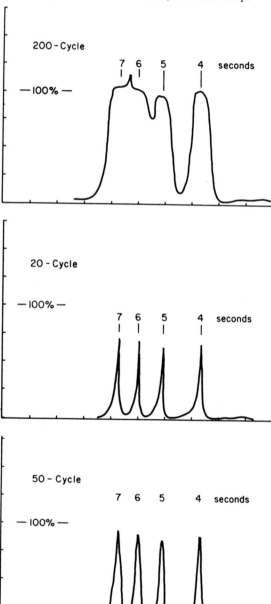

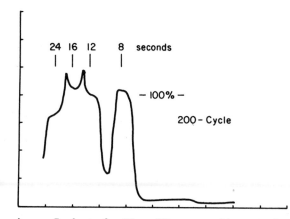

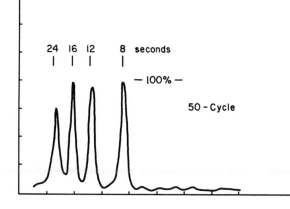

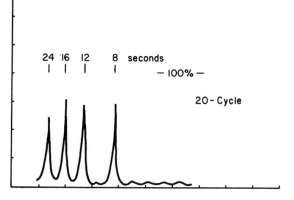

Figure 5-7-6. *Sine waves, 2.2-min. sweep.*

ings. In fact, the 50-cy filter was wide enough to give an overlap between the 6-second and 7-second waves and produce an excessive peak at about the $6\frac{1}{2}$-second period position on the spectrum. This excessive peak is necessarily present on this record as both the 6-second and the 7-second waves occurred their maximum number of times in the test tape record; therefore, any significant degree of filter overlap of necessity may produce such a peak. In an ocean wave train with its normal distribution of wave periods use of the wider filters tends to erase valleys rather than to generate such peaks. This coalescence of energy to give an excessive peak is found also in Figure 5-7-6, which shows the analyses of a test tape containing 8-, 12-, 16-, and 24-second waves.

As a final exhibit, Figure 5-7-7 shows the result of analyzing a tape record of a 3.5-ft, 7.9-second wave, as reproduced in the large wave tank at the Beach Erosion Board. The pen-and-ink record shows a very uniform wave in the tank; the spectrum analysis also shows a very uniform wave to be present with a 10 per cent second harmonic.

An appendix to this paper presents a spectrum study of the waves from Hurricane Donna as it passed off Atlantic City, N. J., on September 11-12, 1959. This appendix was prepared by C. L. Bretschneider of the staff of the Beach Erosion Board. It is of interest as the spectra at successive times show clearly the change in wave train characteristics as the hurricane approached from the south and then moved on north to the New England area.

In conclusion, it may be said that the Beach Erosion Board electronic wave analyzer is now a working tool. Additional work is yet to be done on the complete physical meaning of the spectra delineated by the analyzer, although much of the basic work on this interpretation has been done and has been reported at this conference.

Figure 5-7-7. *Test waves, 200-cycle filter.*

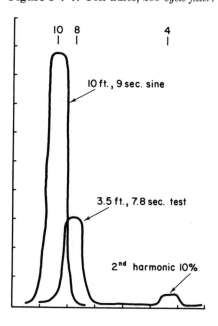

3.5 ft., 7.8 sec. test wave in wave test tank

COMMENTS

Dr. Deacon: What sort of wave recorder was used in the test tank when you got the second harmonic?

Mr. Caldwell: The same type staff as we use in the field except that it has ten contacts per foot of length instead of five per foot.

WAVE SPECTRA FROM HURRICANE DONNA, 1959

Of immediate interest to the coastal engineer are waves of hurricane origin. The Beach Erosion Board wave station at Atlantic City, New Jersey, was in operation during Hurricane Donna, September 11-12, 1959. The Beach Erosion Board step-resistance wave gage is located in about 17 feet mean low water. Waves were recorded simultaneously on paper tape of the conventional type Brush recorder and also on the magnetic tape of the magnetic tape recorder. The Brush recorder operates for 20 minutes during each 4-hour period, and the magnetic tape recorder operates continuously, except for two 20-minute periods each day for calibration.

The results of the paper chart analysis are given in the paper "A One-Dimensional Wave Spectrum" by Bretschneider on pages 41–56 of this book.

Figure 5-A-1 is a typical example of the wave spectra obtained from the wave spectrum analyser with the oscillator set at 0-2,500 cps. The horizontal scale in frequency is from 0 to 0.333 cycles per second. As can be seen, the spectrum is not complete, since there are waves of higher frequency than 0.333. When the setting of the oscillator is 0-25,000 cps, the scale in frequency is from 0 to 3.33 cycles per second, and all the waves would be included. Figure 5-A-1 shows the presence of a 10-second low swell with small wind waves of about 4 to 5 seconds predominating.

Figure 5-A-2 shows the corresponding integrals

of the linear average and square average of the typical example, Figure 5-A-1. Near the far left of the graph, the difference between the curves of the integrated square average and integrated linear average noise level is related to the mean wave height. Similarly, the difference between the integrated square average and the integrated square average noise level is related directly to the mean-square wave height.

Figures 5-A-3 and 5-A-4 represent the only hourly wave spectra (20 minutes each) for linear wave average, and Figures 5-A-5 and 5-A-6 are the corresponding wave spectra for square average. The noise levels in each case have been subtracted, and it should also be noted that the gain setting for Figures 5-A-3 and 5-A-5 is twice that for Figures 5-A-4 and 5-A-6. It is interesting to note as the hurricane approached Atlantic City, that the 10-second swell was little changed, but the wind waves increased and grew toward lower frequencies until they engulfed the swell completely at the peak of the hurricane. Shortly after the peak of the hurricane (12:00 to 12:20) the wave staff suffered damage by the hurricane and became inoperative.

Figure 5-A-7 shows the complete wave spectra (oscillator setting 0-25,000 cps), linear average, for four of the records. From Figure 5-A-7 it can be seen that there is considerable wave activity for frequencies greater than 0.333 seconds.

Figure 5-A-8 shows the integrated linear aver-

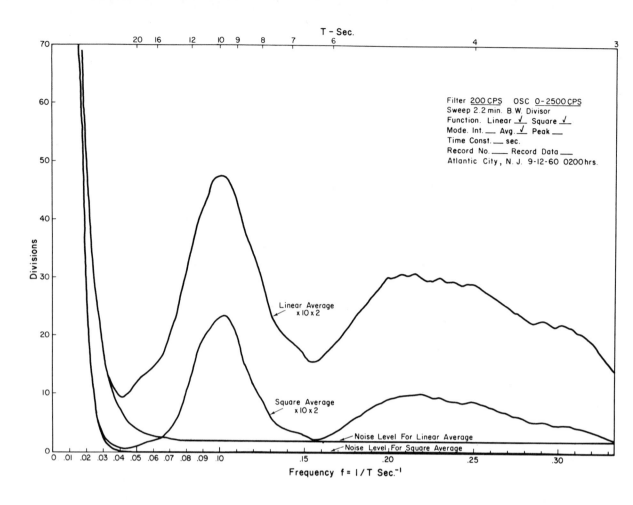

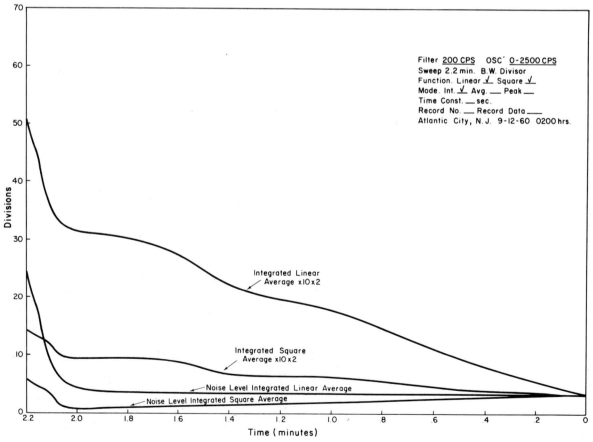

Figure 5-A-1, 5-A-2. *Sample spectrum record.*

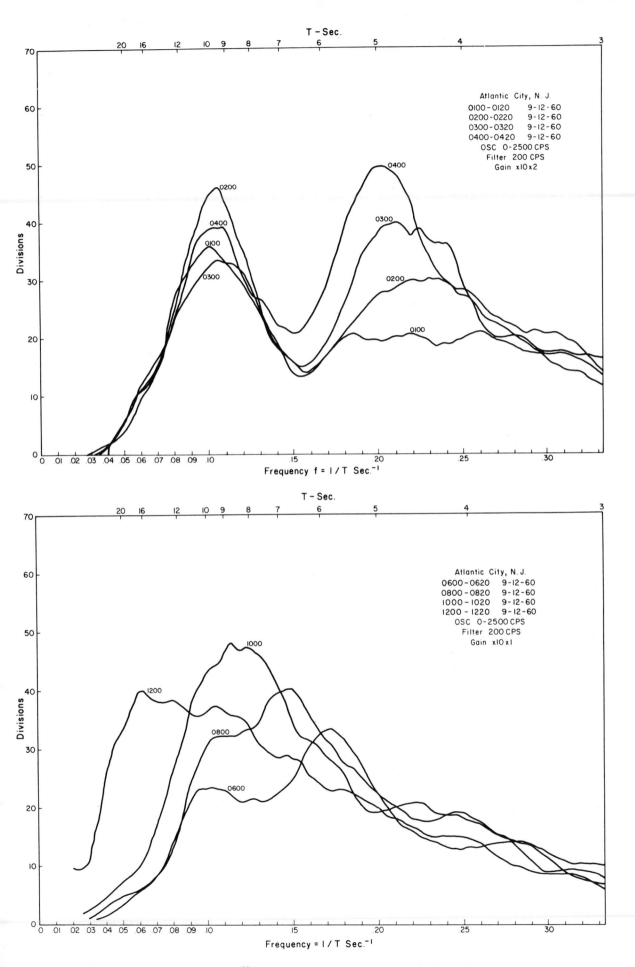

Figure 5-A-3, 5-A-4. *Composite spectra linear average.*

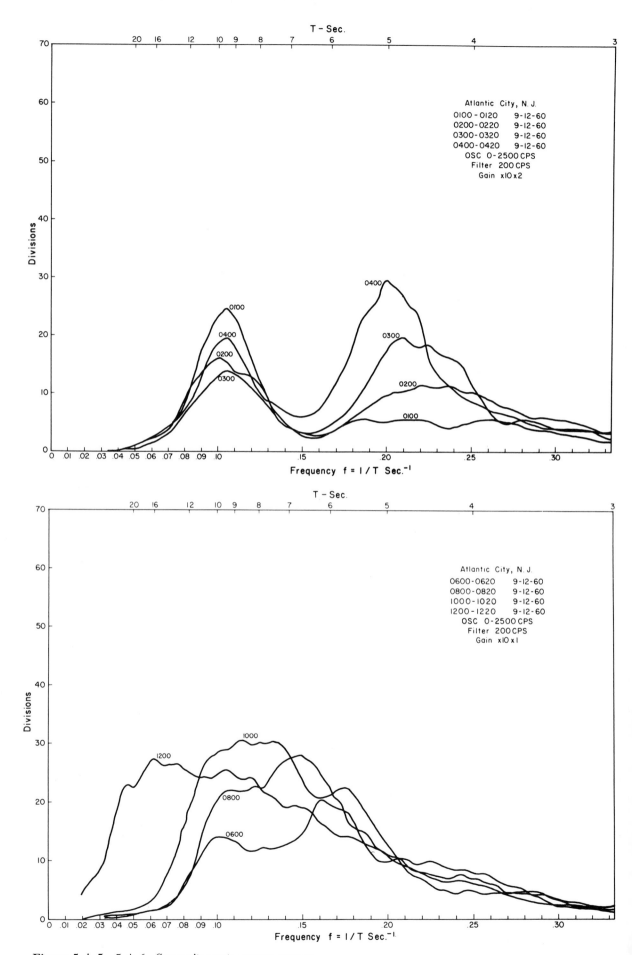

Figure 5-A-5, 5-A-6. *Composite spectra square average.*

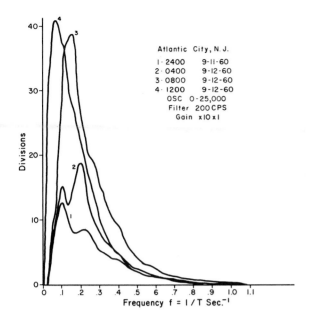

age of the wave spectra given in Figures 5-A-3 and 5-A-4. The noise level was subtracted, and the gain setting was the same in all cases. The divisions on the right are linearly related to the mean wave height, and this relationship is normally obtained by calibration. The details of a direct calibration have not been worked out satisfactorily because of possible nonlinear effects of the recorded waves. However, a field calibration can be used to advantage to obtain at least limited information. For example, the mean wave heights are available from the analysis of some of the paper tapes for Hurricane Donna and are tabulated in the paper by Bretschneider (1961). Figure 5-A-9 shows a plot of the mean wave height from paper tape versus divisions from the integrated linear average from the spectrum analyser for an oscillator setting of 0-2,500 cps; Figure 5-A-10 shows the same results except for the oscillator setting of 0-25,000 cps. The intercept at about $H = -0.5$ feet for zero division could be due in part to noise not accounted for or to nonlinear calibration for low wave heights.

When analysing other wave records by using the spectrum analyzer, it may be necessary to check the field calibration curves.

Figure 5-A-7. *Composite spectra linear average.*

Figure 5-A-8. *Composite integrated linear average.*

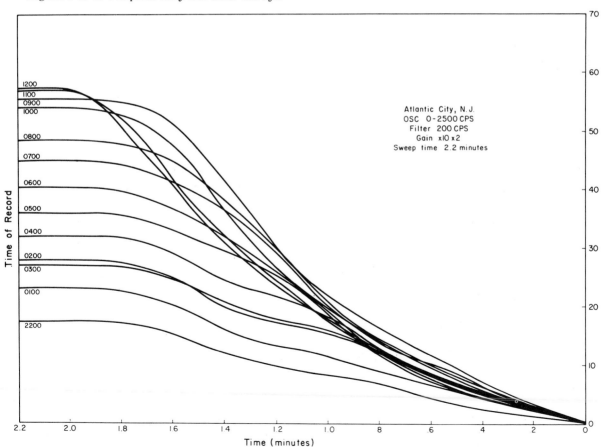

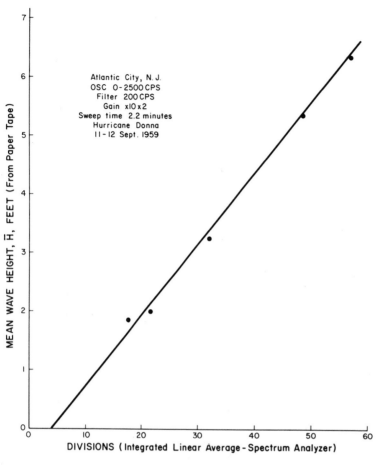

Figure 5-A-9. *Field calibration.*

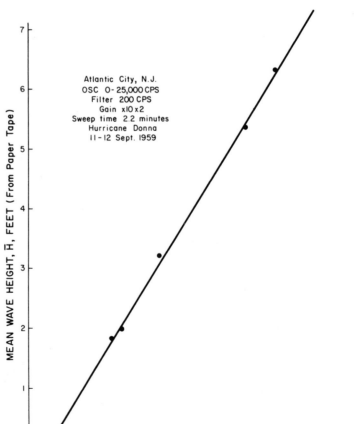

Figure 5-A-10. *Field calibration.*

WILBUR MARKS

PAUL STRAUSSER

E I G H T

A LOW FREQUENCY SPECTRUM

AND CROSS-SPECTRUM ANALYZER[1]

ABSTRACT

The David Taylor Model Basin spectrum analyzer is described. The extension to cross-spectrum analysis by use of matched filters is discussed. Some preliminary experiments to check the method provide a general verification but show the need for further experimentation on the matched filters and phase-shifting components of the system.

INTRODUCTION

The motions of a ship in a seaway, waves in a storm, and many geophysical phenomena are classified as random processes. Time histories of such processes can be converted to energy spectra. This permits statistical inferences to be made regarding the physical behavior of the system under investigation for all time (and space) where stationary conditions apply. If a particular event is being studied without regard to cause or effect, its auto-spectrum will describe that event through a frequency decomposition of the time history that represents it. If, however, it is desirable to relate one event to another, say the pitch and the heave of a ship, then it is necessary to calculate the phase relationship between the same frequency components in the two records. This is accomplished by obtaining the cross-spectrum of the two records. The cross-spectrum is composed of two parts: the co-spectrum, which defines the in-phase energy of the two systems, and the quad-spectrum, which defines the 90-degree out-of-phase energy in the two systems. Resolution of these two components will yield the desired phase relationships. In the case of the directional spectrum of ocean waves one method of measurement requires calculation of the phase differences between the wave components in the records simultaneously obtained by pairs of wave probes suitably spaced.

This report describes the Taylor Model Basin cross-spectrum analyzer, which is presently capable of producing, from an input of two simultaneous signals, the spectrum of each signal as well as the co- and quad-spectra of the pair of signals, each realization displayed on an x-y recorder at one and the same time. This report will also describe some initial analysis experiments aimed at verifying the usefulness of the system as a reliable cross-spectrum analyzer.

---

[1] The work reported here was carried out at the David Taylor Model Basin, Washington, D. C.

MATCHED-FILTERS METHOD OF CROSS-SPECTRUM ANALYSIS

Consider two random functions, $f(t)$ and $g(t)$, measured simultaneously for a period T. The cross-spectral density is defined as

$$c_{f,g}(\omega) + iq_{f,g}(\omega) = \frac{1}{2\pi}\int_{-\infty}^{\infty} R_{f,g}(\tau)e^{i\omega\tau}d\tau \quad (1)$$

where $c_{f,g}$ is the cosine component (co-spectral density) and $q_{f,g}$ is the sine component (quad-spectral density) of the cross-spectral density, and the cross-covariance function is defined by

$$R_{f,g}(\tau) = \lim_{T\to\infty}\frac{1}{2T}\int_{-T}^{T} f(t)g(t+\tau)dt \quad (2)$$

If the signals $f(t)$ and $g(t)$ are passed through linear filters, the respective outputs, $f^*(t)$ and $g^*(t)$ are given by

$$\left.\begin{aligned} f^*(t) &= \int_{-\infty}^{\infty} f(x)K_1(t-x)dx \\ g^*(t) &= \int_{-\infty}^{\infty} g(x)K_2(t-x)dx \end{aligned}\right\} \quad (3)$$

where K_1 and K_2 are the impulse responses of the filters. The average product of the outputs of the filters is

$$\overline{f^*(t)g^*(t)} = \int_{-\infty}^{\infty} R_{f,g}(\eta)\psi(\eta)d\eta \quad (4)$$

where

$$\psi(\eta) = \int_{-\infty}^{\infty} K_1(\zeta)K_2(\zeta+\eta)d\zeta \quad (5)$$

as proven in Reference 1, and $\zeta = t - x$, and $\eta = x_1 - x_2$.

If the impulse responses of the filters (K_1 and K_2) are properly selected, $\psi(\eta)$ can be made proportional to either $\sin\eta$ or $\cos\eta$ with the result that the average products of the outputs of the filters $[\overline{f^*(t)g^*(t)}]$ yield $c_{f,g}$ or $q_{f,g}$. For the second-order linear filters used in the Taylor Model Basin system, it is shown (Reference 1) that

$$\left.\begin{aligned} K_1 &= A_1 e^{-\alpha t}\cos\,(\omega t + \phi_1) \\ K_2 &= A_2 e^{-\alpha t}\cos\,(\omega t + \phi_2) \end{aligned}\right\} \quad (6)$$

Substitution of Equations (5) and (6) in Equation (4) yields

$$\overline{f^*(t)g^*(t)} =$$
$$\frac{A_1 A_2}{4\alpha}\left[\cos\psi\int_{-\infty}^{\infty} R_{f,g}(\eta)e^{-\alpha|\eta|}\cos\omega\eta d\eta\right.$$

$$\left. - \sin\psi\int_{-\infty}^{\infty} R_{f,g}(\eta)e^{-\alpha|\eta|}\sin\omega\eta d\eta\right] \quad (7)$$

If α is taken sufficiently small, the damping factor $e^{-\alpha|\eta|}$ has little effect on $\overline{f^*(t)g^*(t)}$; the result is

$$\left.\begin{aligned} \int_{-\infty}^{\infty} R_{f,g}(\eta)e^{-\alpha|\eta|}\cos\omega\eta d\eta &\simeq c_{f,g}(\omega) \\ \int_{-\infty}^{\infty} R_{f,g}(\eta)e^{-\alpha|\eta|}\sin\omega\eta d\eta &\simeq q_{f,g}(\omega) \end{aligned}\right\} \quad (8)$$

and

$$\overline{f^*(t)g^*(t)} \simeq$$
$$\frac{A_1 A_2}{4\alpha}\left[\cos\phi c_{f,g}(\omega) - \sin\phi q_{f,g}(\omega)\right] \quad (9)$$

If the phase angle (ϕ) is zero, the resulting average product of the outputs of the filters is the co-spectrum ($c_{f,g}$). If the phase angle is 90 degrees, the result is the quad-spectrum ($q_{f,g}$). Consequently, matched filters combined with a multiplier and 90-degree phase-shifter can produce the desired cross-spectral densities of two simultaneous random signals.

The phase angle between the same components is then given by

$$\epsilon(\omega) = \tan^{-1}\frac{-q_{f,g}(\omega)}{c_{f,g}(\omega)} \quad (10)$$

The same ends can be accomplished by a single filter, but computation of the quad-spectrum requires differentiation of one of the signals before multiplication, and it is usually difficult to obtain accurate differentiation over the entire frequency range of interest. The matched filters method has convenience of operation, involves minimum design and construction of special components, and is highly accurate in principle.

GENERAL DESCRIPTION OF CROSS-SPECTRUM ANALYZER

The Taylor Model Basin analog spectrum analyzer was first assembled in 1959, at which time its purpose was to convert time histories of ship motions and waves into energy spectra. While cross-spectrum analysis was not considered at that time, it was realized that such computations would eventually be required (References 2 and 3). Accordingly, the assembled system comprised two analyzers driven by a common oscillator as well as two square-law integrators and two x-y

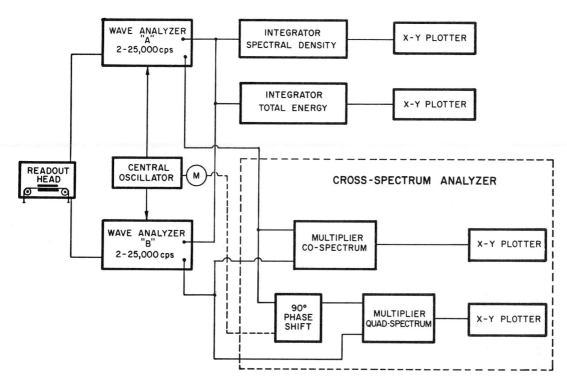

Figure 5-8-1. *Block diagram of TMB cross-spectrum analyzer.*

plotters. The net result was the simultaneous generation of two spectra, one for each of two input signals. The unique feature of the original system was the installation of specially matched filters such that the same output resulted from passing the same signal through both filters. This is critical to cross-spectrum analysis, because the product of the outputs of the matched filters is the co-spectrum or in-phase component of the two signals while the product of the output of one filter and the output of the other filter, phase-shifted 90 degrees, is the quad-spectrum or 90-degree out-of-phase component of the two signals, as has been shown.

To complete the cross-spectrum analysis system, a multiplier was added, 90-degree phase-shifting circuitry was installed, and two additional *x-y* recorders were included.

Figure 5-8-1 is a block diagram showing the basic operation of the analyzer system and its options. Each of two FM signals, representing the random signals to be analyzed, are fed simultaneously to analyzers *A* and *B*, respectively. The analyzers contain the filters which separate the frequency components in the random signals. The central oscillator selects the center frequency to be analyzed, and the filters determine the frequency

band to be passed. There is a choice of four filters, 2, 5, 10, and 20 cps. Reference 3 explains in detail the operation of the oscillator, amplitude modulation, behavior of filters, and analysis technique; these matters will not be discussed here. Suffice it to say, the selected filter should be narrow enough to give adequate resolution of the spectral density being measured. For cross-spectral analysis, even greater resolution is required (Reference 4).

The outputs of the analyzers are voltages proportional to the amplitudes of the frequency being examined. These outputs are fed either to the spectral density integrator or total energy integrator and then to the associated *x-y* plotters. These same outputs are also fed to the co-spectrum multiplier, and the resulting outputs are displayed on the third *x-y* recorder. Last, the output of analyzer *A* is fed to the 90-degree phase-shifter and thence to the quad-spectrum multiplier, where it is combined with the output of analyzer *B*; the resulting output is displayed on the remaining *x-y* plotter. The end product of analyzing a pair of random signals is four displays on *x-y* plotters comprising:

1. Spectral density (or cumulative density) of signal 1,

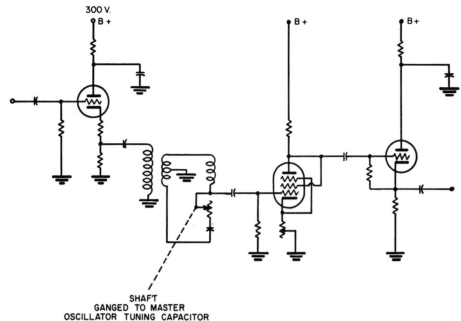

300 V.

SHAFT
GANGED TO MASTER
OSCILLATOR TUNING CAPACITOR

Figure 5-8-2. *Circuit diagram of constant voltage 90° phase-shifter.*

2. Spectral density (or cumulative density) of signal 2,
3. Co-spectrum of signal 1 and signal 2, and
4. Quad-spectrum of signal 1 and signal 2.

The components comprising the cross-spectrum analyzer are all commercially available (References 5-7), with the exception of the constant voltage phase shifter which was developed at the Taylor Model Basin. A schematic drawing of the 90-degree phase-shifter is shown in Figure 5-8-2. The important feature of this component is the application of a variable resistor ganged to the tuning condenser of the oscillator that permits accurate 90-degree phase shifting for all frequency components.

INITIAL ANALYSIS EXPERIMENTS

It now remains to be established that supplementing the original system with a multiplier and phase-shifter, in conjunction with the matched filters, will yield reliable estimates of the co- and quad-spectra. To this end, several experiments were devised using existing FM tape records of a full-scale seakeeping trial.

Figure 5-8-3 shows the output of the cross-spectrum analyzer for simultaneous inputs of wave height and roll angle. The upper figure shows a composite of the wave height and roll auto-spectra while the lower figure shows a composite of the co- and quad-spectra of the random signals.

To verify the computed co-spectrum, a simple summing circuit was installed in the system between the readout head and wave analyzer A. Therefore, the records $f(t)$ and $g(t)$ are added together and fed through one analyzer system. The result graphed on the x-y plotter is the spectrum of the signal $f(t) + g(t)$. The components of this combined spectrum S_{f+g} can be evaluated by considering the autocorrelation function of the two records

$$\overline{[f(t) + g(t)][f(t + \tau) + g(t + \tau)]}$$
$$= \overline{f(t)f(t + \tau)} + \overline{g(t)g(t + \tau)}$$
$$+ \overline{f(t)g(t + \tau)} + \overline{g(t)f(t + \tau)} \quad (11)$$

If the Fourier cosine transform of Equation (11) is taken termwise, the result is

$$S_{f+g} = S_f + S_g + 2c_{f,g} \quad (12)$$

where the co-spectrum is defined in Equations (1) and (2). The spectrum of the sum of the wave and roll records appears in the top part of Figure 5-8-4. If the spectra of roll (S_f) and of wave (S_g) are subtracted from S_{f+g} and the remainder halved, the result is an estimate of the co-spectrum using a single filter. The co-spectra obtained by matched filters and by a single filter are plotted in Figure 5-8-4(b), where it is seen that the two curves are in fair agreement. The single-filter method is by no means a standard of comparison, and the fair agreement is quite satisfactory for a first attempt at verification.

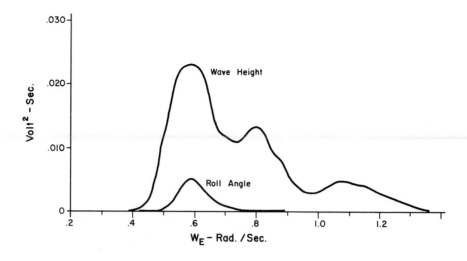

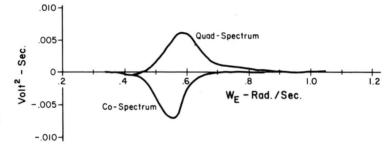

Figure 5-8-3. *Spectra and co- and quad-spectra of wave height and roll angle.*

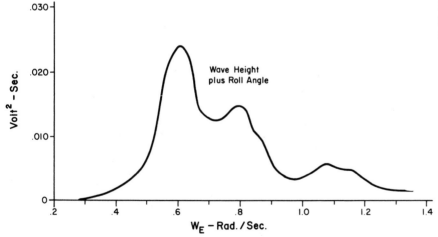

Figure 5-8-4a. *Spectrum of the sum of the wave height record and roll angle record.*

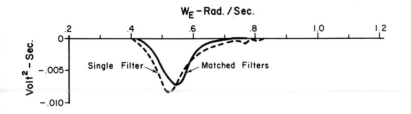

Figure 5-8-4b. *Comparison of co-spectra of wave height and roll angle computed by matched-filters and by single-filter method.*

Please note that the single-filter method used here is not the same as the usual single-filter method, which requires consecutively passing the sum and difference of the two signals through the filter and then taking the difference between the mean-squared outputs. The result is $4c_{f,g}$ directly. A little computational labor is added by the method applied here, but additional temporary electronic circuitry is bypassed. The single-filter method is not used for evaluating the quad-spectrum estimate because of the differentiation problem mentioned earlier. Instead two signals with a known quad-spectrum are treated.

Figures 5-8-5(a), and 5-8-5(b) show the roll amplitude and roll velocity spectra corresponding to the simultaneous recording of roll amplitude and roll velocity. Figure 5-8-5(c) shows the co- and quad-spectra of the two signals. It was expected that the co-spectrum would contain none of the spectral energy and the quad-spectrum would contain all of it, but there is some energy in the co-spectrum, which suggests that there may be some phase-shifting differences in the matched filters. If all the spectral density were concen-

trated in the quad-spectrum, the phase relationship between the two signals should be 90 degrees for all frequencies. Instead the phase angles computed by Equation (10) and shown in Figure 5-8-5(d) indicate a phase difference between 0 and 5 degrees. This is not too serious, but it implies that further experiment with the matched filters is desirable.

Another test involved the treatment of the simultaneous recording of wave height and heave (acceleration). The spectra of the two inputs appear in Figure 5-8-6(a) and the co- and quad-spectra of the two signals appear in Figure 5-8-6(b). Comparison of the co-spectrum obtained by the single-filter and matched-filters methods is shown in Figure 5-8-6(c), and again fair agreement is found. A quad-spectrum is generated by treating only the wave height record. The output of analyzer A is phase-shifted 90 degrees and multiplied by the output of analyzer A. The result should be zero but is actually very small, as seen in Figure 5-8-6(d). The quad-spectrum of wave-and-wave is plotted against the wave spectrum (which is also the co-spectrum of

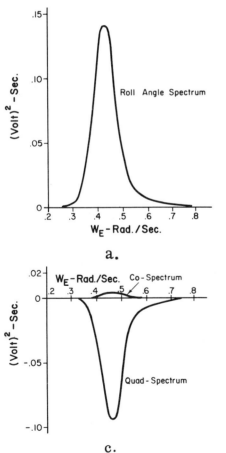

a.

c.

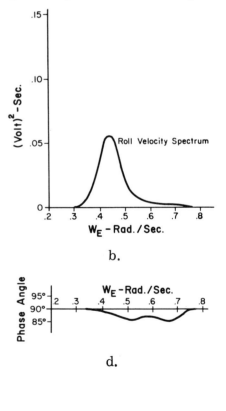

b.

d.

Figure 5-8-5. *Spectra, co- and quad-spectra, and phase angles of roll angle and roll velocity.*

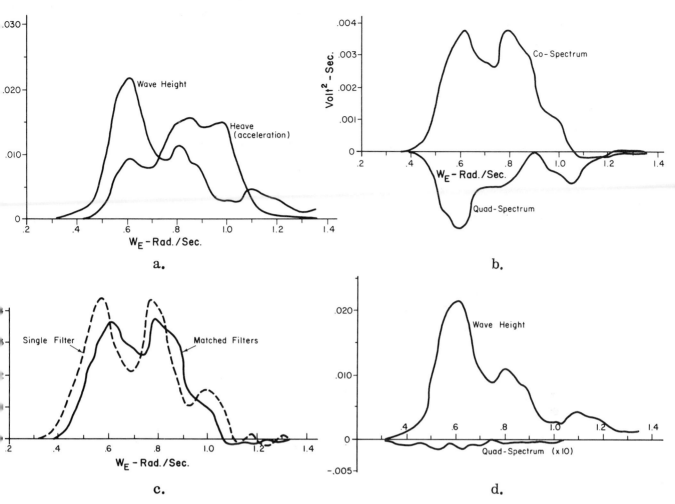

Figure 5-8-6. (a) *Spectra of wave height and heave (acceleration); (b) Co- and quad-spectra of wave height and heave; (c) Comparison of co-spectra of wave height and heave computed by two different methods; (d) Quad-spectrum of wave height and wave height.*

wave-and-wave) but is ten times larger than it really is; otherwise it would not be seen.

SUMMARY

The preliminary experiments described in this report indicate that the Taylor Model Basin cross-spectrum analyzer is capable of producing co- and quad-spectra with some measure of accuracy. There is some evidence that the filters are not perfectly matched [Figure 5-8-5(c)]. Although the 90-degree phase-shifter was not isolated for testing, its use with the filters did not show a greater error than that of the filters above [Figure 5-8-6(d)].

The system as it presently exists is probably adequate for estimating cross-spectra. However, additional tests should be made for further verification. In particular it is recommended that

simple experiments with known signals, such as square waves, should be undertaken. Further, comparisons of the type made previously for auto-spectra (References 2 and 3) should be made between the cross-spectra computed for this paper and cross-spectra of the same inputs obtained on digital computers. The warning in Reference 4 regarding the high resolution required for cross-spectral analysis should be heeded. The narrowest pair of matched filters in the system is 5 cps, and this may not be narrow enough. Speeding up the magnetic tape by a factor of 2 will effectively double the resolution, which should be adequate for most recorded random signals.

REFERENCES

1. Uberoi, M. S. and E. G. Gilbert, "Technique for Measurement of Cross-Spectral Density of Two Random Functions," *Review of Scientific Instruments,* XXX, No. 3 (1959), 176–180.

2. Marks, Wilbur and P. E. Strausser, "Data Reduction Methods at the Taylor Model Basin," TMB Report 1361, *Transactions Twelfth American Towing Tank Conference*, 1959.

3. Marks, Wilbur and P. E. Strausser, "SEADAC—The *Taylor Model Basin Seakeeping Data Analysis Center*," TMB Report 1353, July, 1960.

4. Pierson, W. J., Jr. and J. F. Dalzell, *The Apparent Loss of Coherency in Vector Gaussian Processes Due to Computational Procedures With Applications to Ship Motions and Random Seas*, College of Engineering, New York University, 1960.

5. *Instruction Booklet for TP-625 Wave Analyzer System*, Technical Products Corp., Los Angeles, California.

6. *Model MU/DV Duplex Multiplier/Divider and MU/DV-3M-659*. G. A. Philbrick Researchers, Inc., Boston, Massachusetts.

7. *Instruction and Operating Manual for Model 3 Autograf x-y Recorder*, F. L. Moseley Co., Pasadena, California.

WILBUR MARKS

ROBERT G. TUCKERMAN

N I N E

A TELEMETERING ACCELEROMETER WAVE BUOY[1]

INTRODUCTION

The primary basis of successful scientific endeavor has always been the inseparable companionship of theory and experiment. That one is more prominent than the other, at any given time, is a natural consequence of the variable rate of progress toward the goal — a general theory describing a physical process and experimental verification of the theory. Research effort dedicated to describing the state of the sea typifies the dual importance of theory and experiment.

It is apparent from the many different sea state definitions that are available today that experimentation is lagging behind theory. The need for observations is not only to verify theory but to provide direction for theoretical work which has outraced the safe bounds of experimental verification. And what is needed is many observations, under different conditions, in different places.

Probably the most useful type of observation is the time history of the waves passing a fixed point or a spatial equivalent. Such an observation should be about 30 minutes long, and should be made in stationary wave conditions. An accurate description of the winds at the observation

point would increase greatly the value of that observation.

An accelerometer wave-buoy (*Splashnik*), developed at the Taylor Model Basin for research on ship behavior, meets these specifications. In particular, it is well suited for use with weather ships where wind observation is routine. The operation of the *Splashnik* will be described briefly, as will some initial experiments which demonstrated its value for wave measurement.[2]

THE WAVE MEASUREMENT SYSTEM

The *Splashnik* consists of a buoy assembly containing an accelerometer and transmitter (battery powered) mounted in a wooden box (1' × 1' × 18'') in the center of a raft (3' × 3' × 4''). A transmitting antenna sits atop a six-foot pole mounted in the center of the wooden box. Figure 5-9-1 shows a sketch of the *Splashnik*. Figure 5-9-3 shows the accelerometer-transmitter unit inside the *Splashnik*.

The output of the vertical accelerometer is converted to a signal that varies in frequency with

---

[1] The wave measuring system described in this paper was conceived and developed at the David Taylor Model Basin, Washington, D. C.

[2] A more complete description of the *Splashnik*, detailing its mechanical and electrical operation, can be found in Marks, W. and R. G. Tuckerman, "*Splashnik* — A Disposable Wave Buoy." Seventh Conference on Coastal Engineering.

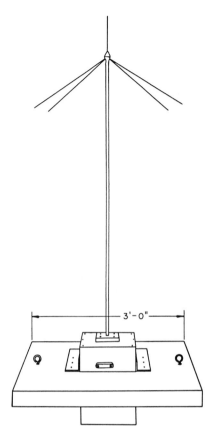

Figure 5-9-1. *The Splashnik.*

acceleration and is transmitted (FM) to the receiving station, which may be a weather ship close by. The signal is received by a receiving antenna on the ship, which in turn relays the signal to the receiver, where the variable frequency is converted to a variable d-c voltage, still proportional to acceleration. This d-c voltage is passed through a low-pass filter, which conveniently eliminates the high-frequency clutter that contributes little energy to the wave spectrum. The filter output is recorded (Figure 5-9-2).

Figure 5-9-2. *Wave buoy sensing and recording system.*

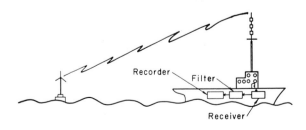

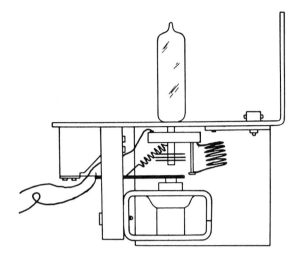

Figure 5-9-3. *Electronic system of Splashnik. Transmitter unit appears in upper portion, accelerometer and damper in lower portion.*

Three features of the *Splashnik* may be troublesome:

1. double integration of acceleration to wave elevation,
2. tilt of accelerometer, which is recorded as acceleration, and
3. drift of the system with net water particle motion.

To make the *Splashnik* available on a large-scale basis, it was developed on the principle of cheap construction. At a cost of about $150 it is not necessary to always recover it. This may also make the *Splashnik* useful for measuring directional spectra where many measurements may be required simultaneously. However, a penalty is usually incurred when low quality components are used, and in this case the very simple electronics (accelerometer and transmitter) make double integration of the acceleration record virtually impossible by standard techniques. However, the acceleration spectrum $A(\omega_e)$ can be easily computed, and its "double integration" to a vertical displacement spectrum $Z(\omega_e)$ is obtained algebraically by the operation

$$Z(\omega_e) = \frac{1}{\omega_e^4} A(\omega_e) \qquad (1)$$

When the *Splashnik* is on the side of a wave it measures a resultant acceleration made up of wave acceleration and gravity. The wave acceleration

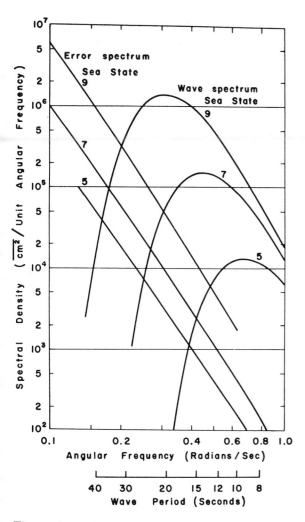

Figure 5-9-4. *Wave spectra computed from Neumann's formula for an equilibrium wave system, and the spectra of the errors introduced by measuring the waves using a buoy containing an unstabilized accelerometer. . . . (from Tucker, 1959)*

has a horizontal component. Acceleration is therefore measured in the "apparent" vertical, that is, perpendicular to the orientation of the *Splashnik* float. The induced error is related to the cosine of the angle between the "apparent" vertical and true vertical. This error has been investigated theoretically (Tucker, 1959),[3] and it is found, for example, that in a sea state 6, the r.m.s. wave height is in error by less than four per cent. In general, tilt of the accelerometer will introduce little error in the general description of the seaway (Figure 5-9-4).

[3] Tucker, M. J., "The Accuracy of Wave Measurements Made with Vertical Accelerometers," *Deep Sea Research*, Vol. 5 (1959), 185-192.

The *Splashnik* will drift with the net forward motion of the water particles. This is not considered to be serious, since the total energy in the spectrum will be nearly conservative, and for relatively slow drift, the spectral density distortion with frequency is not great.

INITIAL EXPERIMENTS

Once the wave measurement system is built, it is necessary to establish confidence in its performance, and this is best accomplished by comparing the results obtained from the *Splashnik* with those of a reliable wave measurement device, under identical test conditions.

Initial tests were made at the David Taylor Model Basin, where irregular long-crested waves were generated with spectral peaks appropriate to wave lengths of 15 and 20 feet respectively. The waves were measured directly by a fixed capacitance probe and by the *Splashnik*. The *Splashnik* acceleration spectra were transformed according to Equation (1) and superimposed on the wave spectra measured by the capacitance probe. The agreement in shape was good; the agreement in total energy (from which wave height statistics are calculated) was even better.

The model tank tests were quite successful, but they were made in long-crested waves of relatively high frequency. It was necessary to test under actual sea conditions in order to establish any real confidence in the system.

Preliminary tests in Chesapeake Bay indicated that the *Splashnik* had a life in excess of 8 hours and a range of about 11 miles over flat water. Since transmission of the signal is on a line-of-sight basis, one expects trouble in high seas as separation of *Splashnik* and ship increases.

In a recent full-scale trial the *Splashnik* system was tested, in conjunction with the National Institute of Oceanography shipborne wave recorder, in moderate states of sea (4–5). Several buoys were used in this experiment with varying degrees of success. One *Splashnik* turned over, which was quite unexpected. Three or four *Splashniks* transmitted only for short periods (5–10 minutes) before their signals were lost. One or two failed to transmit at all, because their batteries were shaken loose. (Batteries are now firmly secured.) Several, however, transmitted successfully for periods ranging from half an hour to more than three hours.   It is believed that lengthening the transmitting antenna by one foot and the *Splashnik* float by one foot on each side will increase chances of successful transmission and reception of the signal.

Several simultaneous wave recordings were made with the *Splashnik* and the shipborne wave recorder. The energy spectrum analysis of one such 20-minute event appears in Figure 5-9-5. The shipborne wave recorder was advancing into the waves at about 2.5 knots (necessary for the ship to maintain headway) while the *Splashnik* drifted in the opposite direction at about 1 knot. In order to compare the ouputs of the two systems, it was necessary first to convert the acceleration spectrum to a wave height spectrum by Equation (1).   Next, the converted wave height spectrum was advanced in the direction of the shipborne wave recorder at 3.5 knots by the frequency transformation

$$\omega_e = \omega - \omega^2 \frac{v}{g} \cos \chi \qquad (2)$$

where the Jacobian

$$J = \frac{\partial \omega}{\partial \omega_e} \qquad (3)$$

is introduced to conserve total energy in the transformed spectrum.   The result of this transformation is the computed wave spectrum in Figure 5-9-5.

Figure 5-9-5. *Comparison of wave height spectra computed from records obtained by the Splashnik and by a shipborne wave recorder — Case II.*

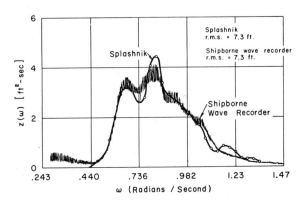

In all, four experiments were made to validate the use of the *Splashnik*, two in the model tank and two at sea.

The capacitance probe used in the tank tests is a well established piece of equipment and considered to be reliable.   The shipborne wave recorder is considered reasonably reliable, but the transformation given by Equations (2) and (3) presupposes that all of the waves are long-crested and unidirectional.   This was not the case, and the magnitude of the error involved in the transformation is not known.   Furthermore, no hydrodynamic corrections were made for the shipborne wave recorder.   However, all four cases were successful in locating the upper and lower frequency limits as well as the frequency of maximum energy.   The total energy in the spectrum, which determines the distribution of wave heights, is a good statistic for comparison and is independent of any frequency transformation.   Table I shows the measurement of total energy in the four cases studied thus far.

TABLE I

COMPARISON OF TOTAL ENERGY IN WAVE SPECTRA OBTAINED BY *Splashnik* AND OTHER MEANS

Case	Capacitance Probe	Splashnik	Shipborne Wave Recorder
1	14.82	14.99	
2	31.95	35.88	
3		6.12	5.76
4		7.30	7.30

SUMMARY

There is good indication that the *Splashnik* can be usefully employed in collecting large amounts of wave data.   However, before it is heavily relied upon, more comparative tests of the type just described should be carried out.   It should be mentioned that accelerometer buoys, like the *Splashnik*, have been developed and are presently in use, notably in the Netherlands and in the United Kingdom.

TEN

WAVE MEASUREMENTS MADE BY THE

NATIONAL INSTITUTE OF OCEANOGRAPHY

INTRODUCTION

The National Institute of Oceanography has been making instrumental measurements of sea waves since 1945. An account is given here of wave measurements made in the North Atlantic Ocean and around the coasts of Britain since that time, indicating what records are available and summarising the information that has been extracted from these records.

TERMINOLOGY

The "wave height" is the vertical distance from crest to trough and the "wave period" is the interval of time between the passage of two consecutive crests past a fixed point.

The symbols used are as follows:

H_{max} – maximum wave height on a record (measured in feet).

T – mean crest period (measured in seconds).

T_f – period of maximum height on the spectrum (measured in seconds).

METHODS OF WAVE MEASURING

The first wave recordings were made with a pressure type recorder placed on the sea bottom. This measured the difference in pressure as the wave crests and troughs passed over it. It could of course be used only near the coast as the wave height is attenuated with depth and it is possible to measure the pressure differences at the bottom only in fairly shallow water. Another limiting factor is the length of cable necessary to connect the instrument with the recording unit on shore. With the development of the shipborne wave recorder it became possible to measure waves in the deep ocean, and most of the wave records mentioned here have been made with this instrument. Various types of wave recorders have been described by Tucker (1953), and he has given a detailed account of the shipborne wave recorder (1956).

PERRANPORTH

A series of wave recordings was made near Perranporth on the north coast of Cornwall from August 1945 to January 1947. The recorder was a "Cam-

TABLE I (a)

DISTRIBUTION IN $^0/_{00}$ OF WAVE HEIGHTS AND PERIODS AT
PERRANPORTH FOR THE SUMMER MONTHS (APRIL-SEPTEMBER), 1946

Number of Observations: 970

Wave Period (seconds)

Max. Wave Ht. (ft.)	6	7	8	9	10	11	12	13	14	15	16	17	18	19	Total
1			1	3	15	12	4	3	3	3					44
2		5	7	15	16	17	10	7	4	3				2	86
3	1	12	29	38	19	20	6	1	2	3	1				132
4	2	11	25	37	25	23	15	6				1			145
5	1	13	26	35	31	29	18	8			1				162
6	2	7	10	15	21	25	9	6		3	2				100
7	1	5	17	15	22	11	4	3	1						79
8		2	9	9	20	18	7	5	1	2					73
9	1	1	5	10	5	6	5	2		2		1			38
10	3	2	7	6	3	9	5	3	2	3					43
11			4	9	6	3	3	4		1					30
12	1	1		3	5	7	2								19
13		2	1	1	2	9		2	1						18
14			1		1			1		1					4
15			1	6		3	1	1							10
16			1			2	1								4
17						1									1
18			1				1								2
19							1	1							2
20															
21			1		1										2
22							1	1							2
23					1										1
24															
25															
26							1								1
Total	12	61	145	203	192	197	94	53	14	21	4	2		2	1000

bridge" Pressure Recorder placed on the sea bottom about a mile from the coast. The depth was 35 feet at low water springs. Recordings were made six times a day, and each record was Fourier analysed. Values of H_{max} and T_f were obtained, the heights being corrected to allow for the attenuation with depth at the appropriate period. The results for the entire year 1946 are summarised in Tables I(a) and (b), Table I(a) referring to the summer months April to September and Table I(b) to the winter months January to March and October to December. The distribution of wave heights and periods is shown in parts per thousand. The highest wave measured during the year was 33 feet.

WAVE MEASUREMENTS ON LIGHTSHIPS

Since November 1956 wave measurements have been made on board certain of the lightships near the coast of Britain with the co-operation of the Corporation of Trinity House. One shipborne wave recorder has been in use throughout. From November 1956 to January 1959 it was installed on the Morecambe Bay Lightship in the Irish Sea, and some very interesting results were obtained from there. In order to extend the work to cover longer fetches, the recorder was then moved to the Smiths Knoll Lightship in the North Sea off the coast of East Anglia. Records from here are available for the period March 1959

TABLE I (b)

DISTRIBUTION IN $^0/_{00}$ OF WAVE HEIGHTS AND PERIODS AT
PERRANPORTH FOR THE WINTER MONTHS (OCTOBER-MARCH), 1946

Number of Observations: 1015

Wave Period (seconds)

Max. Wave Ht. (ft.)	7	8	9	10	11	12	13	14	15	16	17	18	19	20	Total
1		2	5	19	8	17	5	2		1					58
2	1	2	8	12	24	33	11	7	6	1					105
3		5	3	18	30	19	13	9	5	4	2		2		110
4	4	5	9	20	22	25	19	11	2	3	3				123
5	2	3	8	8	27	27	15	7	7	4	1			1	109
6	2	6		2	7	21	14	6	2	2	3			1	66
7	3	4		5	7	14	10	9	5	6	3		1		66
8	1	1	1	2	8	8	10	3	3	1	1	1			40
9	1		1	1	4	1	11	4	11	4	3	3			45
10	1	1		3	3	11	13	9	8	5	3	1			57
11			2	5	1	8	3	9	4	5		2		1	40
12		1	1	3	4	6	5	3	5	2	1				31
13		2	2		3	2	1	1	3	6	2	3			25
14		1	1		2	7	3	1		3	3				21
15					2	7	4	2	7		1		1		24
16			2	2	1	5	3	5	3	1	4	1			27
17					1	9	8		1	2					21
18				2	1	1	1								5
19						3			2	1	1	2			9
20				1	1				1		2	1			6
21						2		1			1				4
22										1					1
23									1		2				3
24												1			1
25															
26										1					1
27															
28															
29															
30															
31													1		1
32															
33						1									1
Total	15	33	43	103	156	226	149	88	76	53	36	15	5	2	1000

to May 1960. The recorder was then moved again to the Helwick Lightship in the Bristol Channel, southwest of the Gower Peninsula, and we have records from there for the period from August 1960 up to the present time. Next winter it is hoped to install the recorder on the Seven Stones Lightship, a very exposed position, from which we should obtain very interesting records during times of Atlantic storms.

MORECAMBE BAY LIGHTSHIP

This lightship is 15 miles from the coast in a depth of 12 fathoms. The recorder was fixed on the hull of the ship 6 feet below the waterline. Records were taken for about 11 minutes every hour from 0900 to 1800. The maximum wave height and mean wave period were found for every record. The distribution of heights and periods for the

TABLE II (a)

DISTRIBUTION IN ⁰/₀₀ OF WAVE HEIGHTS AND PERIODS AT MORECAMBE BAY LIGHTSHIP FOR DECEMBER 1956 AND JANUARY AND FEBRUARY 1957

Number of Observations: 895

Wave Period (seconds)

Max. Wave Ht. (ft.)	2	3	4	5	6	7	8	9	10	Total
0										57
1		22	31	58	32	8	3			154
2	17	32	32	45	66	17	5			214
3		8	11	29	48	9				105
4	1	3	8	23	71	23	4	1		134
5				8	30	6	3			47
6				2	22	11	3			38
7					34	32	4			70
8		1		1	8	17	4			31
9					6	20	13			39
10				1		10	12	2		25
11					2	9	4	2		17
12				1	3	8	4			16
13					6	7	3	1		17
14					2	3	1	·		6
15					1	1	5	1		8
16					1	6	3	1		11
17						1				1
18					1	3	2			6
19							1	1		2
20						1				1
21										
22							1			1
Total	18	66	82	167	320	176	85	25	4	1000

TABLE II (b)

DISTRIBUTION IN ⁰/₀₀ OF WAVE HEIGHTS AND PERIODS AT MORECAMBE BAY LIGHTSHIP FOR MARCH, APRIL, AND MAY 1957

Number of Observations: 605

Wave Period (seconds)

Max. Wave Ht. (ft.)	2	3	4	5	6	7	8	Total
0								352
1		40	25	23	35	12	1	136
2	26	58	35	18	30	5	3	175
3		28	28	56	·17			129
4	5	12	17	38	24			96
5	1			3	17	2		23
6			20		15			35
7			11		15			26
8			2		10			12
9			5		7			12
10								
11								
12								
13								
14					2			2
15					1			1
16					1			1
Total	32	138	105	176	174	19	4	1000

TABLE II (c)

DISTRIBUTION IN ⁰/₀₀ OF WAVE HEIGHTS AND PERIODS AT MORECAMBE BAY LIGHTSHIP FOR JUNE, JULY, AND AUGUST 1957

Number of Observations: 918

Wave Period (seconds)

Max. Wave Ht. (ft.)	2	3	4	5	6	7	8	9	Total
0									344
1		81	36	15	8	7			147
2	29	45	38	28	5	2			147
3		22	25	57	3	1			108
4		9	17	34	4				64
5		2	1	3	14	2			22
6				29	16				45
7			1	12	20				33
8				13	21				34
9				2	6				8
10				6	1				7
11					2	3			5
12					4				4
13					7	1			8
14					1	3			4
15					3	1			4
16					1	1	2		4
17						2			2
18					2			1	3
19					1	1	2		4
20						1	1		2
21						1			1
Total	29	159	118	199	105	37	7	2	1000

TABLE II (d)

DISTRIBUTION IN ⁰/₀₀ OF WAVE HEIGHTS AND PERIODS AT MORECAMBE BAY LIGHTSHIP FOR SEPTEMBER, OCTOBER, AND NOVEMBER 1957

Number of Observations: 900

Wave Period (seconds)

Max. Wave Ht. (ft.)	2	3	4	5	6	7	Total
0							136
1		76	33	18	10	2	139
2	41	46	28	12	4		131
3		29	26	39			94
4	2	39	39	67	6		153
5		2	10	10	18		40
6		4	16	42	18	1	81
7			7	22	27		56
8	1	2	6	14	18		41
9			3	10	20		33
10				6	19	5	30
11				1	13		14
12					13	6	19
13					2		2
14					6	2	8
15				1	6	2	9
16					6	2	8
17					2	1	3
18						1	1
19							
20					1		1
21							
22							
23							
24							
25							
26							
27							
28						1	1
Total	44	198	168	242	187	25	1000

four seasons, using data from December 1956 to November 1957, is shown in Tables II(a), (b), (c), and (d). The highest wave recorded during this time was 28 feet. The period range covered from 2 to 10 seconds, 5 seconds being the most common.

SMITHS KNOLL LIGHTSHIP

This lightship is in 27 fathoms of water and about 30 miles from the coast. Records were taken every 2 hours, and the distribution of heights and periods is given in Tables III(a), (b), (c), and (d). The highest wave recorded here was 24 feet, but the modal value of height is 2.5 feet, as compared with 0.5 feet for Morecambe Bay. The values of period are very similar in both cases.

TABLE III (a)

DISTRIBUTIONS IN $^0/_{00}$ OF WAVE HEIGHTS AND PERIODS AT SMITHS KNOLL LIGHTSHIP FOR DECEMBER 1959 AND JANUARY AND FEBRUARY 1960

Number of Observations: 916

Wave Period (seconds)

Max. Wave Ht. (ft.)	3	4	5	6	7	8	9	Total
0			1					1
1	8	21	7					36
2	7	26	18					51
3	5	29	39	26	5			104
4		13	82	31	11	1	1	139
5		13	54	45	2			114
6		4	51	43	11			109
7		8	31	56	7	1		103
8		1	25	45	11			82
9			15	27	19			61
10		1	12	35	10			58
11			8	16	9			33
12			5	17	4	5		31
13			2	7	10	3		22
14			2	10	6	1		19
15				3	5	2		10
16			2	3				5
17				1	1	2		4
18			1	3		1		5
19						1		1
20				1				1
21				1		2		3
22					3			3
23				3		1		4
24						1		1
Total	20	116	355	373	114	21	1	1000

TABLE III (b)

DISTRIBUTION IN $^0/_{00}$ OF WAVE HEIGHTS AND PERIODS AT SMITHS KNOLL LIGHTSHIP FOR MARCH, APRIL, AND MAY 1959

Number of Observations: 1069

Wave Period (seconds)

Max. Wave Ht. (ft.)	3	4	5	6	7	8	Total
0	10	7	10	6	3		36
1	22	34	32	21	10	6	125
2	18	54	60	28	8	2	170
3	3	32	65	22	10	1	133
4	3	19	53	36	15	1	127
5		10	39	45	10		104
6		3	39	40	7	3	92
7			22	20	3		45
8			19	27	4	1	51
9		1	11	15	4		31
10			12	5	2	1	20
11			6	9	7	1	23
12			1	8	3		12
13				5	4		9
14				4	3	1	8
15			1	4	3		8
16				2	1		3
17				3			3
Total	56	160	370	300	97	17	1000

TABLE III (c)

DISTRIBUTION IN $^0/_{00}$ OF WAVE HEIGHTS AND PERIODS AT SMITHS KNOLL LIGHTSHIP FOR JUNE, JULY AND AUGUST 1959

Number of Observations: 1026

Wave Period (seconds)

Max. Wave Ht. (ft.)	3	4	5	6	7	8	Total
0	11	36	22	8	1	1	79
1	50	94	66	34	4		248
2	19	39	88	43	9	1	199
3	6	22	74	52	9	1	164
4		2	61	46	3		112
5		5	26	29	4	1	65
6		2	22	24	5	1	54
7			15	11	4		30
8			4	11	1		16
9			7	10	1		18
10			1	6			7
11			1	3			4
12			1	1			2
13				1			1
14				1			1
Total	86	200	388	280	41	5	1000

TABLE III (d)

DISTRIBUTION IN ⁰/₀₀ OF WAVE HEIGHTS AND PERIODS AT
SMITHS KNOLL LIGHTSHIP FOR SEPTEMBER,
OCTOBER, AND NOVEMBER 1959

Number of Observations: 1085

Wave Period (seconds)

Max. Wave Ht. (ft.)	3	4	5	6	7	8	Total
0	25	23	5	4			57
1	59	59	11	5	2		136
2	14	65	55	14			148
3	8	51	57	14	1		131
4	1	28	69	16			114
5	17	59	21	1			98
6	3	44	17	3			67
7		7	28	15	2		52
8		1	17	21	3		42
9		1	19	12	6		38
10			10	14	3		27
11			6	5	4	1	16
12			5	10	5	3	23
13			4	2	5		11
14			2	5	5		12
15				3	2	1	6
16				3	3	1	7
17			1	4	2		7
18					2	1	3
19							
20					3	1	4
21					1		1
Total	127	338	327	151	49	8	1000

HELWICK LIGHTSHIP

The Helwick lightship is in a more exposed position than the other two we have considered. It is in 22 fathoms of water near the Helwick Bank. Records have been taken every 3 hours since the end of August 1960. Quite a lot of swell from Atlantic storms reaches there, and the waves are high for coastal waters. The maximum recorded so far is 34 feet, and the most frequent height is about 10 feet during the winter months. The periods are still quite short, averaging about 5 to 6 seconds. The distribution for the months of September, October, and November is shown in Table IV(a) and for December, January, and February in Table IV(b).

WEATHER SHIP RECORDS

Wave measurements have been made in the open ocean since February 1953. A wave recorder is fitted on one of the ocean weather ships, initially the *Weather Explorer* and later the *Weather Reporter*. The ship occupied various weather stations in the eastern North Atlantic, but the majority of our records come from stations *India* (58°N, 19°W) and *Juliett* (52°N, 20°W). Records are taken 8 times a day while the ship is at sea, and these are now available covering a period of 8 years. Much of the work on wave generation and wave spectra done at N.I.O. has been based on these records.

TABLE IV (a)

DISTRIBUTION IN ⁰/₀₀ OF WAVE HEIGHTS AND PERIODS AT
HELWICK LIGHTSHIP FOR SEPTEMBER,
OCTOBER AND NOVEMBER 1960

Number of Observations: 726

Wave Period (seconds)

Max. Wave Ht. (ft.)	3	4	5	6	7	8	9	10	11	Total
1		1	2	8	3					
2		3	18	25	8	1	3			
3	1	11	41	8	15	7				
4		19	37	19	8	8		3		
5	3	10	44	18	11	4	3	1		
6	3	23	54	23	6	1				
7	7	30	43	14	5					
8	3	19	41	15	3					
9	5	10	25	28	9					
10	3	11	14	18	6	2				
11	3	6	17	10	12					
12	1		15	25	5	2				
13	1	1	6	11	9				1	
14			4	8	6	3				
15		1	3	3	3					
16			3	3	1	1				
17			1	10	6	1				
18			1	4	5	1				
19			1	3	3					
20			3	3	4					
21			3	4	1					
22		1		1	4					
23										
24										
25			1		3					
26			1							
27			1							
28				2		1				
29										
30										
31					1					
32										
33					1					
34								1		
Total	30	145	373	259	136	44	7	5	1	100

TABLE IV (b)

DISTRIBUTION IN ⁰/₀₀ OF WAVE HEIGHTS AND PERIODS AT HELWICK LIGHTSHIP FOR DECEMBER 1960 AND JANUARY AND FEBRUARY 1961

Number of Observations: 720

Wave Period (seconds)

Max. Wave Ht. (ft.)	3	4	5	6	7	8	9	10	11	Total
1										
2			1	2						3
3		1	6	3	3			1		14
4	3	13	11	10	8	2		1		47
5	3	7	14	8	6	3		3		44
6		7	26	17	14	14	2	1		81
7	4	17	14	26	13	18	4	1		97
8	1	7	22	29	13	11		5		88
9	7	7	17	24	22	12	1			90
10		4	21	25	11	8		2	1	72
11	1	4	8	25	14	11	3		2	68
12	1	1	22	35	14	6	4			83
13		1	13	22	15	6	2		1	60
14			11	12	13	8	3	6		53
15		1	1	14	14	10	4	2	1	47
16			4	8	12	4		3		31
17			1	4	6	3	1	3		18
18			1	4	10	7	2			24
19	1			5	6	7				19
20			1	7	3	2	1	1		15
21			1	4	6					11
22				6	3				1	10
23				2			1			3
24				3	3					6
25			1				2	1		4
26						4				4
27						1				1
28				2		1				3
29				3						3
30										
31						1				1
Total	21	70	195	281	216	151	30	30	6	1000

shown in a separate column in the table. The highest wave recorded during these 8 years was 60 feet.

TABLE V

DISTRIBUTION IN ⁰/₀₀ OF WAVE HEIGHTS AND PERIODS FOR HEIGHTS OVER 30 FEET MEASURED BY O.W.S. "WEATHER EXPLORER" IN 1953 AND 1954

Number of Observations of Waves of All Heights: 2352

Wave Period (seconds)

Max. Wave Ht. (ft.)	7	8	9	10	11	12	13	14	15	16	Ship Moving	Total
30		2	2	1	1	1					1	8
31		1	3	3	2							9
32		1	3	1	1	1					1	8
33	1	2	4	2	1						2	12
34		1	1	1	1						1	5
35		1	1	1	1						2	6
36		2	2	1	2						3	10
37		1	3	1	1	1					1	8
38		1	2	1	1							5
39		1	3								1	5
40		1	2					1				4
41			1									1
42			2	1							1	4
43			1	1								2
44			1	1								2
45			1		1						1	3
46			1				1				1	3
47				1		1	1					3
48				1								1
49		1										1
50		1		1								2
51											1	1
52												
53							1					1
Total	1	14	30	17	16	5	2	2	1		16	104

In Table V a distribution is given of maximum wave heights and mean periods for wave heights of over 30 feet for the years 1953 and 1954. When the ship is moving, as is often the case in order to keep on station in heavy seas, it is impossible to measure the period, and these observations are

REFERENCES

Tucker, M. J., *Dock and Harbour Authority*, November, 1953, p. 207.

Tucker, M. J., *Trans. Instn. Nav. Archit.*, xcviii (1956), 236. London.

PROBLEMS AND

APPLICATIONS

WILBUR MARKS

CHAIRMAN

WILBUR MARKS

GENERAL SURVEY OF PROBLEMS AND APPLICATIONS OF THE WAVE SPECTRUM*

In every engineering problem where an effect due to waves is being studied, some description of the state of the sea is required to make interpretation of that effect meaningful. The spectral description of the sea surface has been generally adopted because it permits a wide range of interpretation of wave conditions. To illustrate the ways in which the wave spectrum is applied to engineering problems, some of its features will be mentioned, and the way in which they relate to specific engineering problems will be discussed. Thus certain aspects of the spectrum that require further treatment will be emphasized.

There are two methods of obtaining a wave spectrum: (1) association of the observed wind field (from weather maps) with a particular theoretical-empirical spectral formulation and (2) measurement of the waves and calculation of the spectrum according to mathematical definitions. The method used will depend upon the nature of the problem and the resources of the investigator. There is need of further research in the development of both these techniques.

The wave spectrum defines the distribution of energy with frequency, and further distributes the energy in each elemental frequency band according to direction of travel (directional spectrum).

This is the most general form of the spectrum. The importance of the directional spectrum in virtually all applied problems, and the present scarcity of knowledge (theoretical or experimental) is well realized and need not be underscored here.

However, many uses can be derived from the energy-frequency relations alone (scalar spectrum). An operation, such as oil drilling, requires knowledge only of the scalar spectrum and, in particular, the significant wave height derived from it. A reasonably reliable spectral formulation is required. Equally important is the reliability of wind-fetch-duration parameters and the methods for extracting such information from weather charts.

Different engineering problems require concentration in different parts of the wave spectrum. Ships, of course, are interested in virtually all frequencies present because of the variation in ship length and the variation in speed, which converts wave frequencies into frequencies of encounter. Harbors and fixed structures may be sensitive to long period swell, while a radar scanning the sea surface is interested primarily in the higher frequencies that provide reflecting surfaces for incident signals. The problem itself assigns importance to specific frequencies, not the relative energy content. Consequently, accuracy in defining the entire structure of the spectrum is a prime goal of wave research.

In many instances, the wave spectrum, as such, is not as valuable as some other directly related descriptive form. Transport of sediment, forces on structures, and flow around bodies are often more easily treated by considering the velocity or acceleration spectrum of the waves. These may be obtained either from direct measurement with suitable transducers or by algebraic operation on the wave-height spectrum. Other useful functions of the wave-height spectrum are the pressure spectrum as related to underwater bodies and the spectrum of the slopes of surface waves in connection with the radar return problem. Some statistical properties of the waves depend on higher-order moments of the wave spectrum, which means multiplication of spectral ordinates by powers of the frequency. This further emphasizes the importance of accurate spectral definition at all frequencies regardless of relative energy content.

The wave spectrum, as so far discussed, provides a reference for evaluation of the behavior of a system responding to the waves. However, in cross-spectrum analysis, the cause and effect hypothesis is more intimately examined. A particular wave spectrum is combined with the basic response properties of the system to predict its behavior in that seaway or, inversely, the wave spectrum is combined with the response spectrum of the system to predict its basic response characteristics. When the wave spectrum is used for prediction purposes, serious questions arise as to its nonlinear properties. Here the bi-spectrum is believed to play an important role. The concept of the bi-spectrum is new to oceanography, and a great deal of attention is required in this area.

In order to apply the wave spectrum to engineering problems, a number of operational techniques must be developed, and these must be of the same order of reliability as that required of the spectrum itself. Following is a list of some of the "second-order" knowledge needed to make the wave spectrum most useful:

1. Partial development of the spectrum; fetch and duration limitations, variability of the wind field.
2. Moving fetches.
3. Dispersion.
4. Attenuation with distance and depth.
5. Refraction due to bottom contours.
6. Diffraction and reflection by obstacles.
7. Release of energy in breaker zone.
8. Stability; air-sea temperature differences.
9. Currents.
10. Viscosity and friction.

From the user's point of view, the wave spectrum is a powerful tool. However, there is still much to be done, and a reliance is placed on the theoretician and experimenter to continue development of spectral concepts for further useful application.

---

* This article is a summary of a lecture given by Mr. Marks.

RICHARD W. JAMES

T W O

WAVE FORECASTING

INTRODUCTION

All operations that the Navy conducts at sea are affected by surface wave conditions. Thus, predictions of the seaway one to three days into the future form an important part of the environmental information required for efficient operational planning. With the increasingly complex technology of the modern navy, however, the oceanographer must be prepared to provide more than the single wave height and period forecasts of the past. Now he must compute period bands, maximum and average periods, the distribution of wave heights against periods, and other parameters, in exact detail. It is apparent then that it is very important to the wave forecaster to know just what the correct form of the wave spectrum is and how the seaway grows and decays.

WAVE FORECASTING OPERATIONS

As an example of the nature of wave forecasts prepared by the Hydrographic Office's Oceanographic Prediction Division past and present in support of naval operations, consider the following:

Towing and Marine Installations: A number of wave forecasts have been prepared for sea-sensitive tows of heavy equipment and for the installation of structures at sea. A prime example of these operations were the forecasts provided the three Texas Tower radar stations located off the coast of northeastern United States. In each case, predicted wave conditions and recommended routes for the tow were given the Officer-in-Charge. Items of special importance were the minimum fetch lengths required to generate a given wave height and period, since the routes were coastal and the Towers could be adversely affected by long, high waves. At present we are providing a similar service for the transport of a *Saturn* rocket booster from New Orleans to Cape Canaveral.

WAVE CHARTS

An invaluable aid to the forecaster, wave charts represent a graphic picture of areas of high waves over the ocean at a given time. Both synoptic and prognostic wave charts were first prepared at the Hydrographic Office in 1953 and have been disseminated via radio facsimile since 1955. Although prognostic wave charts are presently prepared manually, there are several independent programs for using high speed electronic computers in their preparation. To date wave charts have not been drawn to portray more than the significant wave height.

SHIP ROUTING

Long-range prognostic wave charts are used in ship routing. Using these charts and a knowledge of how the routed ship behaves in various seaways, one can compute an optimum time track, or a track of maximum comfort or safety, as desired. The Hydrographic Office commenced the Navy's ship routing program in 1956 with a total of 34 experimental routes. At present some 1,600 optimum tracks are provided the Navy each year. Since a basic concept of ship routing is to circumvent areas of high waves, it is important that the decay of ocean spectra, dispersion, angular spreading and similar effects be better defined.

SEA-KEEPING TRIALS

There are two facets to this operation; first, the use of long-range wave forecasts (and climatology) to select a general area with a high probability of exhibiting the desired unidirectional energy spectra; and second, the preparation of short-term forecasts giving the exact location and track ships should follow to best observe the specified seaway. All possible information concerning the wave spectra is desired for correlation with the motions of the ships—both surface and subsurface ships.

AMPHIBIOUS OPERATIONS

The value of deep-water wave and surf forecasts to amphibious forces is self-evident. What is not evident is that although period band and other characteristics of the deep-sea spectra are very important in predicting the nature of the surf, little has been done to extend these wave spectra models to shallow water.

CONCLUSION

There are many more applications that could be mentioned, including the use of spectral information in mine warfare, antisubmarine warfare, air-sea rescue, and submarine operations. Since the Navy operates around the world, there is almost always some ship experiencing heavy seas or applying one of the types of forecasts described above. Although there is a great deal of disagreement as to the exact form of the ocean wave spectrum, the forecaster has attained a fair degree of accuracy with the present models. It is hoped that the discussions of this conference will stimulate further improvements in the forecasting procedures upon which he depends.

MANLEY ST. DENIS

THREE

SEAS, SHIPS, STATISTICS

In recent years a considerable advance has been made in the theory of the strains and motions to which a ship is subject in a seaway. The work developed so far gives encouragement to the hope of achieving eventually a fair degree of realism in the analytical approach to a group of problems that have been treated up to the present in an entirely empirical fashion.

There is, perhaps, sufficient reason for the slow progress in this field. The problems are all of a highly complex nature, and before they could be solved in a manner that made for a reasonable degree of realism, it was necessary to develop a sufficient body of knowledge in stochastic processes. This was by no means the only prerequisite, but until a decade ago it was the most pressing one, and even today it remains the aspect of the problem that requires the most attention.

Almost ten years have passed since the introduction of a statistical formulation of the seaway, and it is perhaps opportune to reflect at this time, not so much on the progress made, but rather on what developments should be undertaken as next steps. I will try to make this assessment from the point of view of the ship designer and operator and bring out what they still need from their co-workers in oceanography and statistics in order to develop an integrated theory of ship responses to the sea from which predictions can be made with a fair degree of confidence.

There is, to be sure, hardly a design or operational problem related to the ship in which sea conditions do not enter as an important element. Waves are responsible for a large fraction of the strains suffered by vessels and consequently enter into the proportioning of the ships' structure and into the design of the form of those hull regions (bow and stern) subject to heavy wave impact; sea conditions are responsible for the vibrations induced by slamming and by emerging propellers; they account for all the oscillations and enter, therefore, into the determinations of stability, freeboard, safety at sea, and stabilization. To close an incomplete list, sea conditions also determine the loss of speed in heavy weather and, consequently, enter into the determination of powering and the planning of commercial schedules and naval operations.

In all these problems the solutions are functions of a wave-induced excitation. If this be given, solutions to the problems are to be sought within the bounds of analytical mechanics. Indeed, such solutions may not be necessarily forthcoming in certain cases when, for example, the coefficients of the equations escape determination, as occurs at present with the equations of the oscillatory response of a ship advancing in waves or when slamming. But this aspect of the problem is not the immediate concern of the oceanographer and, consequently, will be passed over here.

The wave excitation is obtained by integration of the dynamic pressure over the submerged surface of the hull. It may be noted in passing that this integration runs into serious difficulty when the underwater surface changes as the result of the vessel's oscillations. One could overcome this difficulty by assuming a (sinusoidal) motion and regarding it as a parameter, and then, having derived the excitation on this basis, by evaluating the resulting motion and comparing it with the assumed one. Upon coincidence through an iterative procedure, one would have the correct solution. It is fairly obvious that this is a lengthy procedure, even if the excitation is regular; for irregular seas the task might well become monumental.

The dynamic pressure is related to the seaway through the Bernoulli equation, which is expressible in terms of the slope and time rate of the velocity potential. With some lack of rigor, but considerable analytical convenience, the velocity potential is resolved into three velocity components: the first accounting for the wave system alone, the second for the diffraction of the wave system by the vessel, the third for the flow surrounding the oscillating body in calm water resistance of the ship. The seaway enters only into the first two components. Of these, the second can be related to the first for a particular hull geometry. Thus, in this context, the interest is placed on the first component, i.e., on the velocity potential of the wave system. There being a direct relation between this component and the wave elevation, one is led finally to deal with the latter, or rather with the plurality of wave elevations, which in its most general form represents the confused seaway.

According to present concepts the seaway is described as an ergodic-stationary (or quasi-ergodic-stationary) stochastic process having a spectral distribution. Randomness is introduced into the description of the seaway in either of two ways: in the relative phase lags of component wave trains (Pierson, 1952) or in their amplitudes (Cote, 1954).

The two descriptions are equivalent, but the first appears to be perhaps more readily grasped by those who observe the sea, while the second is probably more appealing to the statistician.

The wave systems comprising the statistical ensemble known as the seaway are governed by nonlinear differential equations subject to a nonlinear kinematic condition at the free surface. This is very pleasant to the mathematician for,

the equations not having been solved, he sees a lifetime of work ahead. But this is also somewhat discomforting to the ship designer and operator, who can consequently look forward only to partial solutions and empirical rules sometimes rather gross.

Since the nonlinearities in the equations of wave motion are progressive and not essential, it is feasible to introduce linearizations. Whether these linearizations are meaningful or not depends upon the particular application.

The simplest solution to the seaway is given by assuming the fluid to be inviscid, with consequent validity of the potential theory; by linearizing the underlying energy (Bernoulli equation); by satisfying the kinematic condition at the free surface at its mean value and not on the wave profile; by postulating that the pressure at the surface is constant; and by introducing a stationary Gaussian probability distribution of wave ordinates.

Such a restrictive set of conditions leads to the first-order linear-Gaussian model by Pierson or the equivalent one by Cote.

Such descriptions have worked well and have provided the oceanographic and nautical fraternities with an understanding of the seaway not attainable through the extremely idealized models of classical theory; in particular, they have made possible the interpretation of observed wave data and the development of forecasting (and hindcasting) techniques.

The assumption of a Gaussian probability distribution of wave ordinates, though made for mathematical convenience, was verified reasonably well in nature for low and moderate sea states and yielded some helpful derivations (Kato, Motora, Ishikawa, 1957).

A Gaussian distribution of wave ordinates converges into a Rayleighan distribution of amplitudes if the spectrum is narrow, but if the spectrum is very broad (white-noise), the distribution of amplitudes tends toward the Gaussian (Rice, 1944, 1945; Cartwright and Longuet-Higgins, 1956).

The second derivation, which also received good confirmation, was that if the frequency of occurrence of sea conditions follows a Gaussian distribution, then the frequency of occurrence of amplitudes follows a Galton (log-normal) distribution (Jasper, 1956).

The linear, ergodic-stationary Gaussian model of the seaway has some inherent limitations:

(1) It is not valid for high and extreme sea conditions in that it does not yield realistic profiles of high waves or reasonable frequencies of occurrence.

(2) It does not describe the waves within or close to a storm-generating area particularly when winds change rapidly in direction and intensity, as occurs in a hurricane.

For the nautical man these limitations are quite serious for it is in the most severe sea states, when his ship is in the greatest danger, that he is particularly interested.

The linear Gaussian model gives too orderly a distribution of wave elevations for high sea states. It is valid only if, to misquote a well-known phrase, "Nature in the raw is seldom wild."

In ship design and operation one is interested in the solution to two problems of ship behavior in a seaway: the first is the establishment of the condition of survival; the second is the determination of the performance (or loss in performance) of the vessel in waves. Since a ship must be able to survive in any sea, it follows that for the condition of survival only extreme cases are of any significance. The argument that extreme conditions are rare events is not one that can reasonably be made when discussing survivability.

It is interesting to note that when the naval architect has approached the problem of the extreme sea state, he has done so indirectly and without any recognition of its statistical nature. When dealing with the problem of the maximum longitudinal bending stress, simple relations have been introduced between wave height (h) and wave length (λ), either the traditional

$$h = 0.05\lambda$$

or the more recent

$$h = 1.1 \sqrt{\lambda}$$

both valid for all values of λ. Since for constant wave height the maximum bending moment occurs in head or following seas when the wave length is approximately equal to the ship length (L), λ is made equal to L in the above expressions thus relating the ship to the seaway. As the length of the ship is increased, such waves give unrealistic values of bending moment, and, therefore, of stress. The solution is not to modify the seaway but to introduce an allowable stress that increases with ship length. Though this procedure is workable, it is hardly rational.

When it comes to the condition of survival, hardly more rationality is evident. A ship is assumed to be safe in a seaway if her restoration is positive when she is heeled over to 60 degrees in calm water. This corresponds to reducing the whole system of differential equations of motion in six coupled degrees of freedom to the single one for uncoupled roll and then eliminating from this one the inertial and damping reactions and the excitation.

It is not difficult to realize from these two examples that the naval architect could abandon to advantage such gross empiricism. Whether he will do so depends in part upon whether alternate solutions to these problems are, first, more realistic, and second, easily interpretable, and hence, simple.

In seeking to improve the linear, ergodic-stationary Gaussian model, one proceeds by removing in turn each restrictive assumption. It might be brought out in this connection that the assumptions of linearity and of a Gaussian distribution of ordinates are, to some extent, mutually bound.

So long as the model is linear, it admits a unique spectral representation and departures from ergodicity and stationarity can be conveniently related to changes in the energy spectrum of the sea as a function of time. Nonstationarity is related to the generating meteorological conditions and to the oceanic environment so that non-stationarity enters into a model of the seaway in an essentially empirical fashion. This aspect will be discussed below in connection with empirical spectra of the seaway.

Nonergodicity, on the other hand, can be dealt with to some extent analytically at least as far as the propagation of waves in the absence of generative forces is concerned. Reference is made in this connection to the nonergodic model by Rosenblatt (1957), in which the amplitudes of the wave trains do not remain constant with direction but vary as Hankel functions of the first kind. According to this model, the waves progress almost radially outwards from the center of the storm, decreasing in height roughly with the square root of their distance from the center. At a large radial distance this description approaches the Pierson model first cited.

This model seems to explain to some extent the changing length and height characteristics of waves as they depart from the storm area where they were generated.

It does not appear that this model has been

put to any use in problems of wave forecasting or considered in the statements of energy transfer between frequencies.

Since the linearized wave theory rests not on one but on two important linearizations, each of these needs to be discussed separately.

The first linearization is that of the Bernoulli equation, the consequence of which is that the theory is restricted in validity to waves of small amplitude. Since these are sinusoidal, the validity of a Gaussian distribution of wave elevations follows as a statistical corollary. Removal of the linearization of the Bernoulli equation leads to the (nonlinear) theory of waves of finite amplitude, a better representation for which is given by the trochoid (Lamb, 1932). However, a statistical ensemble of trochoids no longer has a Gaussian, but instead a skewed, distribution of ordinates. This skewness increases with wave steepness and with the degree of confusion of the sea (short crestedness), particularly with the attainment of conditions of instability (breaking waves). However, a methodology to deal with non-Gaussian distributions is largely wanting and does not promise to be, when developed, as simple as that for a Gaussian distribution.*

The Galton distribution of wave amplitudes with frequency of occurrence is of considerable help in obtaining an idea of the extreme sea behavior of ships, but it does not lead to definitions of the most probable maximum value of ship responses during the lifetime of the ship and to confidence limits. There are two conditions that must be recognized to this end: the first is that wind-generated seas are bounded as to their dimensions, simply because the natural causes of generation and the boundary conditions (wind strength, duration, and fetch) are in themselves limited. There must consequently be a cut-off at some high sea state. The other condition to be recognized is that the ship is in essence a filter whose nonlinearity increases with amplitude of motion. Since the latter is related directly to sea state, it follows that the ship's behavior in extreme seas cannot be predicted simply on the basis of her performance in low and moderate seas — nor can the inverse be assumed.

The models of the seaway discussed above are purely descriptive: they are expressible in terms of a sea spectrum but do not describe it, neither

do they relate it to the generating meteorological and oceanographic conditions. Some empirical descriptions of the spectrum have been proposed, but there appears to be some controversy over their validity.

I will not attempt to resolve the controversy in this note but will confine myself to some comments on the usefulness to the ship designer of the present form of the spectral descriptions.

A description of the spectrum of the sea may be given in one of three forms: a) through its cause, b) through an effect, or c) independently of either.

For the purpose of ocean wave forecasting, the first appears to be advantageous because of the relative ease with which the generating causes can be measured and because the direct relation between wind and sea results in a unique solution. The sea spectra of Neumann (1954), of Roll and Fischer (1956), of Darbyshire (1955), and of Bretschneider, fall into this classification. In all these the energy spectrum is related to wind velocity or wind gradient velocity.

A description of the sea spectrum in terms of an observable effect, such as glitter, has not as yet been proposed.

Purely descriptive representations of the sea spectrum appear to be advantageous for observations in the scientific laboratory, where it may not be possible to reproduce the natural causes of a sea condition.

A description of the sea spectrum independent of cause and effect is that of Voznessensky and Firsoff (1957), which strangely exhibits an energy content at frequencies below the observable.

These spectra are scalar spectra, i.e., functions purely of wave frequency. Since the response of a ship depends on her orientation with respect to the sea, such scalar spectra are inadequate. It is necessary for application to ship problems to know the vector or directional spectrum. The only such spectrum proposed as yet is an interpretation of the SWOP data (Chase *et al.*, 1957) for one sea condition. There is a saying that one swallow does not make spring, and, by analogy, data on one sea condition are not synoptic. For want of such synoptic data on the sea, it is somewhat unfeasible to compare ship patterns of response confidently.

To overcome such a deficiency, it has been proposed to refer the responses of ships to a small number of actual sea conditions (only one at the present) for which the directional spectrum has

---

* The paper by Pierson on "Models of Random Seas Based on the Lagrangian Equations of Motion" is of considerable interest in this connection.

been determined and to regard these sea conditions as standards of a sort. The idea seems to have merit as an interim measure but is bound eventually to be superseded by a synoptic statement that yields the directional spectrum for all sea conditions along with the probable frequency of occurrence of each.

One last comment on the sea spectrum: What is needed to predict ship behavior is the directional spectrum not only of the fully developed sea, but of partially developed seas as well, since for the extreme sea conditions in which the nautical fraternity is interested, fully developed seas are rarely, if ever, generated. In any event, the interpretation of sea trial data requires a knowledge of how the directional spectrum changes with the development of sea states and what modification it undergoes with the ever-transient conditions found in nature.

REFERENCES

Cartwright, D. E. and M. S. Longuet-Higgins, "The Statistical Distribution of the Maxima of a Random Function," *Proc. Roy. Soc.*, A, ccxxxvii (1956).

Chase, J., L. J. Cote, W. Marks, E. Mehr, W. J. Pierson, F. C. Ronne, G. Stephenson, R. C. Vetter and R. G. Walden, *The Directional Spectrum of a Wind-Generated Sea as Determined from Data Obtained from the Stereo Wave Observation Project*. Technical Report, New York University, College of Engineering, 1957.

Cote, L. J., *Certain Problems Connected with the Short Range Prediction of Sea Surface Height*. Technical Report No. 4, New York University, College of Engineering, 1954.

Darbyshire, J., "An Investigation of Storm Waves in the North Atlantic Ocean," *Proc. Royal Soc.*, A, ccxxx (1955).

Jasper, N. H., "Statistical Distribution Patterns of Ocean Waves and Wave-Induced Ship Stresses and Motions, with Engineering Applications," *Trans. Amer. Soc. Nav. Arch. and Mar. Engineers*, LXIV (1956).

Kato, M., S. Motora and E. K. Ishikawa, "On the Rolling of a Ship in Irregular Wind and Wave." *Proc. Symposium on the Behavior of Ships in a Seaway*, Netherlands Ship Model Basin, 1957.

Lamb, H., *Hydronamics*, New York: Dover Publ., 1932.

Neumann, G., "Zur Charakteristik des Seeganges," *Arch. Meteorol., Geophys., Biokl.*, A7.

Pierson, W. J., *A Unified Mathematical Theory for the Analysis, Propagation, Refraction of Storm-Generated Ocean Surface Waves*. Technical Report, New York University, College of Engineering, 1952.

Rice, S. O., "Mathematical Analysis of Random Noise," *Bell System Technical Journal*, XIII (1944), XIV (1945).

Roll, H. U. and G. Fischer, "Eine Kritische Bemerkung zum Neumann-Spektrum des Seeganges," *Deut. Hydrogr. Zeitsch.*, Band 9, Heft 1, 1956.

Rosenblatt, M., "A Random Model of the Sea Surface Generated by a Hurricane," *Jour. Math. and Mech.*, VI, No. 2 (1957).

St. Denis, M. and W. J. Pierson, "On the Motion of Ships in Confused Seas," *Trans., Soc. Nav. Arch. and Mar. Engrs.*, LXI (1953).

Voznessensky, A. I. and G. A. Firsoff, "Statistical Analysis of Data Concerning Rolling of Ships." *Proc. Symposium on the Behavior of Ships in a Seaway*, Netherlands Ship Model Basin, 1957.

JOSEPH M. CALDWELL

F O U R

SHORE PROCESSES AND COASTAL ENGINEERING

The most significant changes in shoreline formations from an engineering standpoint result from the action of the ocean waves on the shore face. This wave action has two basic results: one is the creation of a littoral current along the shore face; the second is the stirring up of the sand on the beach face by the oscillatory current within the waves themselves. The sand in turn may undergo motion in two directions: it may move alongshore under the influence of the littoral current, or it may move onshore or offshore depending upon the type of wave action. In fact, its travel may be in a combination of these two basic directions.

ALONGSHORE MOVEMENT

The alongshore movement is referred to as the littoral drift of the sand. The alongshore littoral current and the littoral drift are, in fact, the result of the angularity of approach of the waves to the beaches. In the rare case of a wave train exactly onshore there would theoretically be no littoral current and no littoral drift; this seldom, if ever, happens in nature.

The direction of the littoral current and littoral drift varies from day to day depending upon the location and direction of the storm winds which generate the waves. Most areas have a dominant direction of the littoral drift and an average rate of littoral drift. For instance, the average net rate of drift along the south shore of Long Island is in the order of 400,000 to 500,000 cubic yards per year to the west. In the Palm Beach area the net drift is some 350,000 cubic yards per year to the south. This, of course, is not the total sand movement, but is the net difference between the movement up-coast and the movement down-coast at the locations named. The total sand in transit (up-drift plus down-drift) may greatly exceed the net littoral drift.

ONSHORE-OFFSHORE MOVEMENT

Waves accompanying a local storm are generally referred to as short waves because the wave length is short in relation to the wave height. These waves tend to pull sand off the shore face and move it into deep water. Thus, these local storm waves generally result in a deterioration of the beach. On the other hand, waves from a distant storm (commonly referred to as swells) are generally long waves in that their length is very great compared to the wave height. These long waves tend to push material from deep water onto the shore face, resulting in an accreting beach.

This onshore-offshore movement is sometimes seasonal in that local storms may be most dominant in certain months, say, during winter and spring, while distant swells may be most dominant in the summer months. With this arrangement we

Figure 6-4-1. *View of Port Hueneme, California, taken in 1938 before installations of harbor and jetties. White lines delineate the harbors and jetties as constructed in 1940, the seawall constructed in 1942, and the subsequent accretion updrift (northwest) and erosion downdrift (southeast) of the jetties. The net littoral drift is approximately 1,000,000 cubic yards per year from northwest to southeast.*

would find a wide beach in the summer and a narrow beach in the winter. For this reason it is desirable to have enough sand on the shore face in summer so that during the stormy winter months there is still enough sand beach to protect the back-shore from storm wave action.

ENGINEERING CONSIDERATIONS

The alongshore littoral drift as described above is a very important factor in coastal engineering. If any natural or man-made obstacle serves to interrupt the movement of this littoral drift along the shore face, the usual result is severe erosion of the beach down-drift from the obstacle. The obstacle may be a natural obstacle, such as a newly created inlet, or a man-made obstacle, such as a breakwater. The effect of an inlet is to trap the littoral drift in either the inner or outer bars, thereby denying the normal sand supply to the down-drift beach. The tendency of a breakwater is to impound the littoral drift on the up-drift side and thereby to deny the sand to the down-drift beaches. This action may result in disastrous erosion to the downdrift area. An example of such erosion is shown in Figure 6-4-1.

A continual supply of littoral drift into an inlet will finally either close the inlet, cause the inlet to migrate, or finally stabilize the inlet in such a way that the drift is passed across the inlet in an intermittent fashion.

Most of our shore erosion problems have been created by the presence of inlets or by the installation of man-made works, such as breakwaters or jetties which interrupt the littoral drift. The solution to these problems generally involves determining the rate of the littoral drift and then taking necessary steps to see that the sand which is being denied the down-drift beaches is once again furnished to these beaches. This may be done by pumping the impounded sand past the obstacle or by adding sand from a new source. Another alternative, of course, is to install a sea-wall or bulkhead to protect the eroding down-drift shore; however, this is generally a very expensive and not too satisfactory solution to the problem.

From the above it can be seen that the coastal engineer is interested in the type of wave action reaching the shore face in the problem area. He needs to know the frequency of waves or swells from the various directions and the characteristics (wave height and wave period) of the wave trains approaching from these directions. These factors are basic to a complete understanding of the engineering problem and to a working out of the best solution.

It should be recognized that the relationships among wave energy, wave direction, and littoral drift are not yet completely defined. Considerable work needs yet to be done in both the prediction and the understanding of wave action and in the measurements of the littoral drift rates in order to improve the solutions to coastal engineering problems.

ROBERT L. WIEGEL

FIVE

SOME ENGINEERING ASPECTS OF WAVE SPECTRA

ABSTRACT

Two aspects of waves and the effects of waves on coastal works are considered. One aspect is the relationship between wave spectra and the mixing of surface waters, which is of prime importance in the functional design and operation of an ocean outfall sewer. The other is the lack of reliability of wave data and forecasting techniques and the effect this has on design and operations when considered in conjunction with other equally unreliable data and/or concepts.

WAVE SPECTRA AND THE MIXING OF SURFACE WATERS

In nearly every engineering application concerned with ocean waves it is the information on the water motions associated with the waves that is necessary for functional and structural design. An example of this is the discharge of sewage and industrial wastes into the ocean.

The mixing of the effluent with the receiving waters may be considered in two parts: first, mixing in the immediate vicinity of the discharge point, and second, the movement and further dilution of the sewage-sea water mixture. A general discussion of these phenomena has been given by Pearson (1956), while specific studies of the mixing in the immediate vicinity of the discharge

point or line have been made by Rawn and Palmer (1930), Rawn, Bowerman, and Brooks (1960), Abraham (1960), and Hart (1961); a specific study of the dilution of sewerage by currents has been made by Brooks (1961), and a specific study of the mixing by wind waves has been made by Johnson (1961). In this paper consideration will be given only to the mixing due to waves, either directly or indirectly through the effect of waves on thermoclines.

Wave theory has been developed almost entirely for irrotational fluid motion. That waves are not irrotational in the generating area is readily apparent to an observer. Figure 6-5-1 is an example of the type of motion that does occur, which shows that a surface current (shear flow) and wind waves are generated simultaneously. Furthermore, it is a highly turbulent shear flow, as can be made evident by introducing dye into the water. This has been done in the laboratory by Johnson (1961). In these studies it was found that the dye concentration observed downwind from the injection line was the result of (1) jet mixing at the manifold (see Albertson, Dai, and Rouse, 1948); (2) mixing near the surface due to the wind generated waves; and (3) the backflow in the lower water layers in the channel.

The proper functioning of an ocean outfall sewer is complicated by many factors. One factor is the difference in density between the effluent and the receiving waters; another factor is the presence

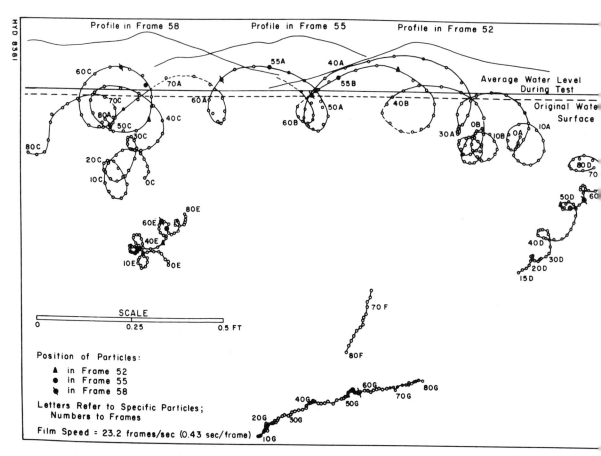

Figure 6-5-1. *Particle paths in wind waves. Note that particles near the water surface tend to follow an orbital path; however, when a particle is at the crest of a wave the motion due to surface drag of the wind is several times the orbital diameter.* (*From Johnson and Rice, 1952*)

or absence of a thermocline layer (and its associated density gradient) topped by a mixed surface layer.

The relationship between temperature (hence, density in water near the ocean surface) and depth is of interest for several reasons, one being its importance in the operational characteristics of an ocean outfall sewer. Sewage effluent has a density approximately equal to that of fresh water. It is discharged on or near the bottom and tends to rise to the surface largely because it is less dense than the surrounding sea water. (It may also have a vertical component of momentum upon leaving some types of diffusers.) As it rises, it mixes with the surrounding sea water, and the mixture becomes denser than the issuing effluent (Rawn and Palmer, 1930; Rawn, Bowerman, and Brooks, 1960; and Abraham, 1960). Often the mixture reaches the surface and spreads out, resulting in a large patch of discolored water. If a thermocline and a mixed surface layer exist in the sea above the sewer outfall, the mixture of effluent and sea water may never reach the surface because the mixture may be more dense than the

mixed surface layer (Rawn, Bowerman, and Brooks, 1960; Hart, 1961).

The third case is intermediate in that the mixture is more dense than the mixed surface water but the momentum of the mixture carries it to the surface; it then plunges below to about the top of the thermocline, where it spreads as a submerged field. Examples of these possibilities are shown in Figure 6-5-2. The thickness of the sewage-seawater field is greater in the intermediate cases than where the mixture spreads out at the surface. In Figure 6-5-2 the Froude number is the velocity of the effluent jet leaving the orifice divided by $\sqrt{gD(\rho_n - \rho_0)/\rho_0}$, where g is the acceleration of gravity, D is the orifice diameter, ρ_n is the mean density of the receiving fluid at the orifice before mixing, and ρ_0 is the density of the effluent before mixing. The other parameter that is useful in predicting the type of sewage field that will occur is $(\rho_h - \rho_w)/\rho_0$, where ρ_h is an average mass density of the mixed effluent-seawater jet in the middle of the thermocline, and ρ_w is the mass density of the mixed surface water prior to the sewage being discharged.

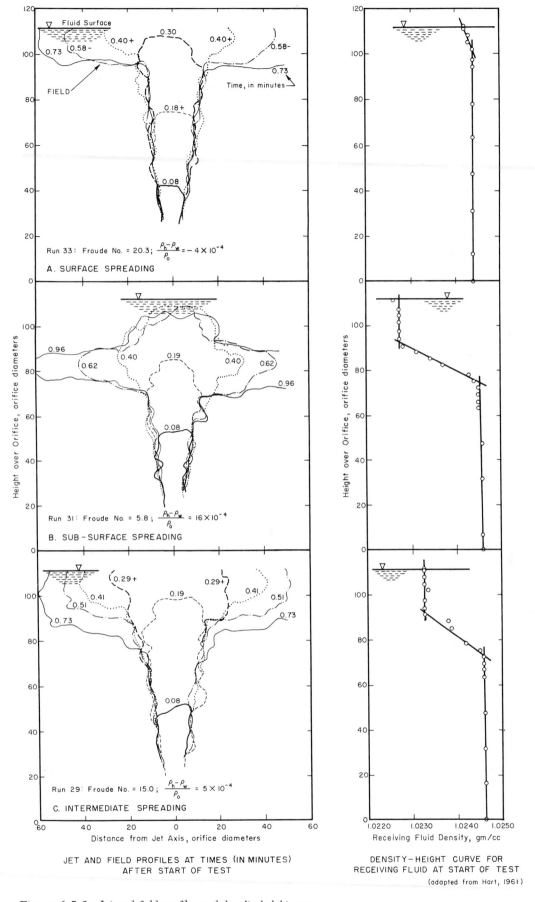

Figure 6-5-2. *Jet and field profiles and density-height curve.*

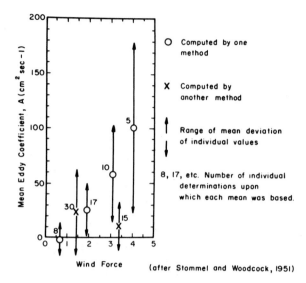

Figure 6-5-3. *Mean eddy coefficients as functions of wind force computed by two different methods.*

In some regions where ocean outfall sewers are in operation, or are proposed, thermoclines exist during certain seasons of the year, and do not exist during other seasons; furthermore, thermoclines and the mixed surface layer change with varying conditions of cloud cover, currents, winds, and waves. One of the main criteria in studying the changes in a thermocline and the surface mixed layer, and the effects of these changes upon the sewage mixture, as well as the direct effect on the mixing of the sewage, is the "eddy coefficient." The eddy coefficient in the surface regions of the ocean has been considered to be a function of the wind strength, and computed values indicate considerable scatter (Stommel and Woodcock, 1951), as shown in Figure 6-5-3. It is proposed at this time that one of the reasons for the scatter is that eddy diffusivity is related more closely to the wave spectrum generated by the winds than to the wind itself. Thus not only are the wind strength and variability important, but also the fetch and duration. Some data relating the mixing of sea water to the state of the sea have been obtained by Ichiye (1953), but only averages have been published so that the relative amount of scatter of the data is unknown to the author.

There is some indication that swell is not important to the mixing process (Munk, 1947) as apparently it is essentially irrotational. Seas are important, as Munk's experiment showed. Waves were generated in a tank by an oscillating plunger. Two layers of water of slightly different density were distinguished by mixing dye with the lower layer. The "swell" did not cause mixing of the two layers. When light winds were blown over the surface (13 ft./sec.) no mixing occurred, but when the winds were increased to about 23 ft./sec., breaking (white caps) occurred, and mixing took place. Wiegel (1954) caused destruction of a thermocline in the laboratory by generating breaking waves by wind, and the mixing was rapid.

Phillips (1958a) has developed a theory for a steady state energy spectrum for wind-generated waves, this condition coming into existence when the energy transfer from the wind to the water in the form of waves is balanced by the dissipation of mechanical energy by the turbulence generated by breaking waves. Some measurements (Burling, 1955; Phillips, 1958b) have shown that a portion of the energy spectrum of waves is predicted by Phillips' theory (Figure 6-5-4). If one accepts this, then the portion of the energy spectrum of waves that matches the curve due to Phillips should be useful in predicting the amount

Figure 6-5-4. *The frequency spectrum $\phi(\omega)$ from the SWOP wave-pole data. The solid curve represents the equilibrium range spectrum $\phi(\omega) \sim 7.4 \times 10^{-3} g^2 \omega^{-5}$. (After Phillips, 1958b)*

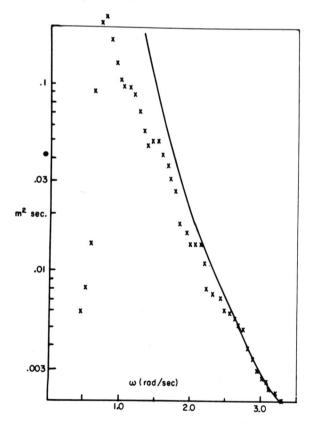

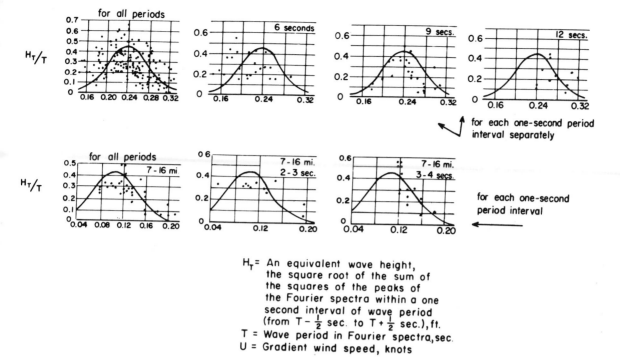

H_T = An equivalent wave height, the square root of the sum of the squares of the peaks of the Fourier spectra within a one second interval of wave period (from $T - \frac{1}{2}$ sec. to $T + \frac{1}{2}$ sec.), ft.

T = Wave period in Fourier spectra, sec.

U = Gradient wind speed, knots

T/U, Ratio of wave period (seconds) to $\frac{3}{2}$ x surface wind speed (knots)

Figure 6-5-5. *Examples of the relationships between H/T and T/U. (after Darbyshire, 1952)*

of mixing that will take place, and the depth of this mixing. Then perhaps we can relate the winds, fetches, and duration through an eddy coefficient to the mixing.

Figure 6-5-6. *Ratio of the wave heights to the square of the apparent wave periods plotted against the square of the ratio of the apparent wave period to the wind velocity. (after Neumann, 1953)*

RELIABILITY

Let us consider the data upon which several of the existing wave forecasting techniques are based. Some of the original data of Darbyshire (1952) are shown in Figure 6-5-5; although additional data have been obtained, the scatter is still of the same order. The original data of Neumann (1953) are plotted in Figure 6-5-6. The original data of Sverdrup and Munk (1947) are shown in Figure 6-5-7 for the "fetch limited" case and in Figure 6-5-8 for the "duration limited" case, together with additional data. There are many reasons for the scatter: poor observations; nonstandard wind observations with respect to height of the anemometer; effects due to unsteady winds, varying fetches, and moving fetches; difficulty introduced by the simplified concepts of "fetch limited," "duration limited," and "fully arisen sea" cases; and variation of atmospheric stability. More information is needed on the unsteady case, as shown in Figure 6-5-9 for waves in the laboratory, and the effect of air stability (represented approxi-

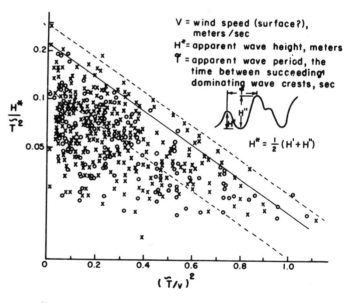

V = wind speed (surface?), meters/sec

H^* = apparent wave height, meters

T = apparent wave period, the time between succeeding dominating wave crests, sec

$H^* = \frac{1}{2}(H' + H'')$

Observations, Long Branch wave records:

o $\begin{cases} \text{May 3, 1948} \\ \text{May 5, 1948} \end{cases}$

x $\begin{cases} \text{October 6, 1948} \\ \text{October 7, 1948} \end{cases}$

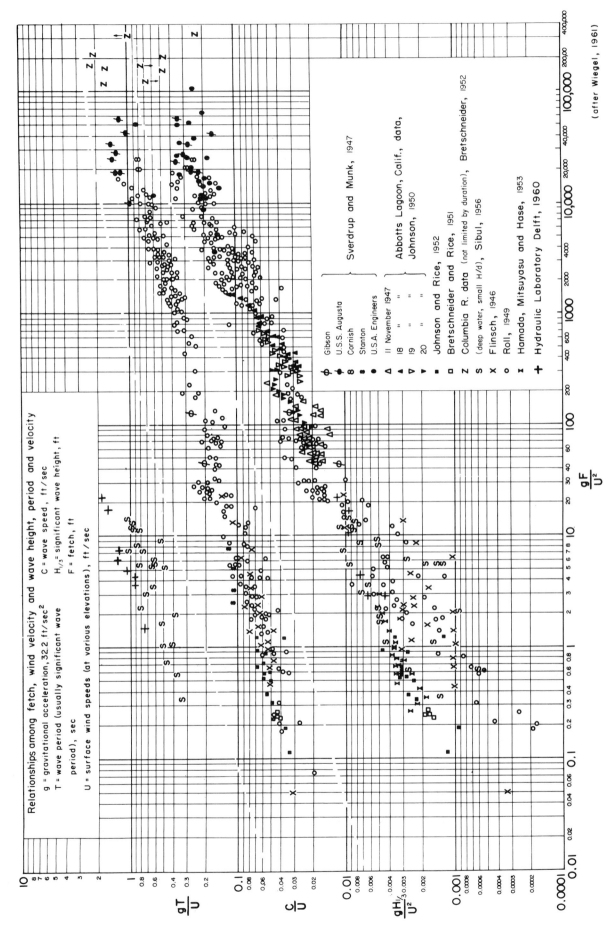

Relationships among fetch, wind velocity and wave height, period and velocity

g = gravitational acceleration, 32.2 ft/sec²   C = wave speed, ft/sec

T = wave period (usually significant wave $H_{1/3}$ = significant wave height, ft
       period), sec   F = fetch, ft

U = surface wind speeds (at various elevations), ft/sec

Gibson   } Sverdrup and Munk, 1947
U.S.S. Augusta
Cornish
Stanton
U.S.A. Engineers

11 November 1947   } Abbotts Lagoon, Calif., data,
18   "   "   "   Johnson, 1950
19   "   "   "
20   "   "   "

■   Johnson and Rice, 1952
□   Bretschneider and Rice, 1951
Z   Columbia R. data (not limited by duration), Bretschneider, 1952
S   (deep water, small H/d), Sibul, 1956
X   Flinsch, 1946
O   Roll, 1949
⋈   Hamada, Mitsuyasu and Hase, 1953
+   Hydraulic Laboratory Delft, 1960

$\dfrac{gF}{U^2}$

$\dfrac{gT}{U}$ $\dfrac{C}{U}$ $\dfrac{gH_{1/3}}{U^2}$

(after Wiegel, 1961)

Figure 6-5-7. *Relationships among fetch, wind velocity and wave height, period and velocity.*

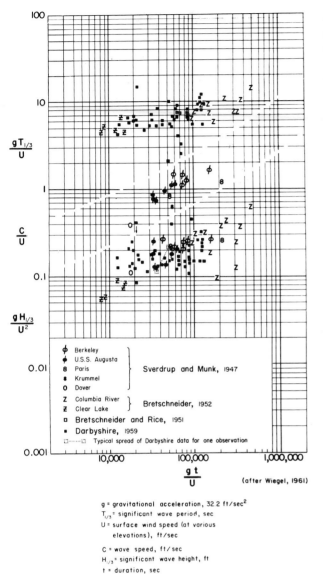

g = gravitational acceleration, 32.2 ft/sec²
$T_{1/3}$ = significant wave period, sec
U = surface wind speed (at various
      elevations), ft/sec

C = wave speed, ft/sec
$H_{1/3}$ = significant wave height, ft

t = duration, sec

Figure 6-5-8. *Relationships among duration, wind velocity and wave height, period and velocity.*

mately by the difference in temperature between the surface water and the air), as shown in Figure 6-5-10 (Brown, 1953) and also found by Roll (1952).

Regardless of the reasons, the one thing the three sets of data have in common is the spread of data. How does this affect engineering designs? Let us consider an example. The presentation given in Figures 6-5-7 and 6-5-8 will be used for this example, but either of the other two sets of data could have been used to illustrate the problem. Assume a storm that is nearly station-

ary with a duration of about 15 hours, a fetch of about 200 nautical miles, and a surface wind speed of 30 knots. These data, together with Figures 6-5-7 and 6-5-8, show that the waves are "duration-limited," that the significant wave height $H_{1/3}$ would be between 10.4 ft. and 22.4 ft., and that the significant wave period $T_{1/3}$ would be between 7.9 and 12.6 sec. Now suppose that the waves had to travel 1,000 nautical miles from the storm to the area in which an offshore platform is being constructed. Use of the curves given by Bretschneider (1952) indicates that $H_{1/3}$ would be between 2.6 and 6.7 ft., and $T_{1/3}$ would be between 10.8 and 17.0 sec. Use of the other forecasting procedures would have led to similar results.

Let us apply this information to the calculation of wave-induced horizontal forces on a circular pile 2 ft. in diameter in 51 ft. of water. Rather than go through a calculation leading to the result-ant force and bending moment on a pile, let us consider the force on a 1-ft. section of such a pile 12 ft. below the still-water surface. The measured relationship between force and wave height for an average wave period of 13 sec. is shown in Figure 6-5-11. For a wave 2.6 ft. high the force would be between a maximum of 10 lbs. and a minimum of 5 lbs. For a wave 6.7 ft. high the maximum force would be about 50 lbs. and the minimum about 20 lbs. The total possible spread then would be from 5 to 50 lbs., a factor of ten. If the variation due to possible wave periods between 10.8 and 17.0 sec. were considered, the force spread would be even greater.

The spread of forces indicated above is less than would be the actual case because in the area con-sidered wave refraction is important. Not much is known about the refraction of irregular short-crested waves, except that the refraction is more complicated than in the case of long-crested peri-odic waves (Longuet-Higgins, 1956). Considering the latter case, only laboratory tests by Wiegel and Arnold (1957) show considerable variation in the bending of the waves and hence in the wave heights.

A simple case has been considered. In reality the engineer must design either for a fatigue failure associated with the total number of waves in the desired life of the structure or for the maximum expected force. This may be related either to the highest probable wave or to a group of very high waves leading to a quasi-resonant, dynamic con-dition related to pile array geometry and eddy formation kinematics. In addition, because the

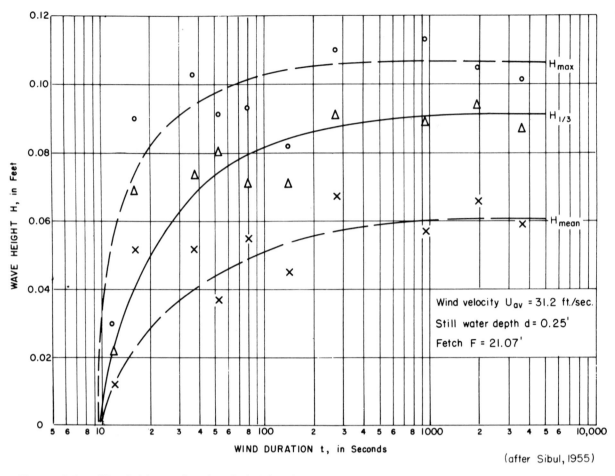

Figure 6-5-9. *Wave height as a function of wind duration.*

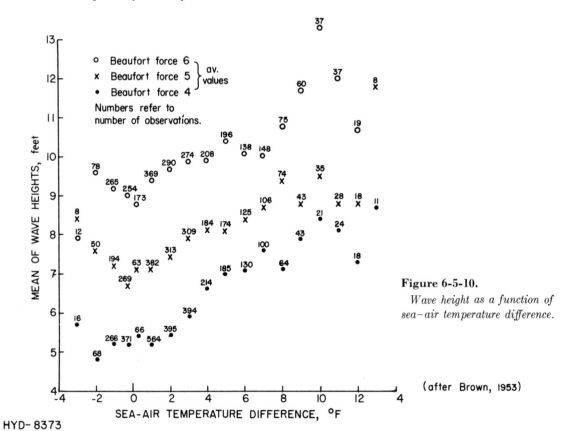

Figure 6-5-10.

Wave height as a function of sea–air temperature difference.

(after Brown, 1953)

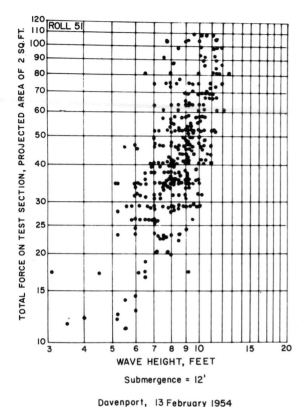

Figure 6-5-11. *Measured force on a section of a pile versus wave height.*

number of times a pile is flexed affects its fatigue breaking strength, the longer the pile has been installed, the lower will be the force needed to break it. Thus, as time goes on, the maximum wave-induced force the pile can resist will decrease.

Meteorological charts issued by separate agencies differ, and the conclusion drawn from them by different meteorologists varies. A study has been made to determine the effect of "hindcasted" wave conditions on different weather maps analyzed by one person, and of three meteorologists experienced in wave forecasting analyzing the same set of weather maps, all using the same wave forecasting procedure (Bretschneider, Todd, and Kimberley, 1950). The terms "hindcasting" and "forecasting" as used herein refer to the reduction of weather maps to wave characteristics, and do not include the forecasting of weather first, followed by the reduction of the forecast weather conditions to wave characteristics. The three sets of weather maps were U. S. Navy (12 hour surface

maps and 3 millibar isobars), U. S. Air Force (6 hourly surface maps and 3 millibar isobars), and U. S. Weather Bureau (12 hourly surface maps and 5 millibar isobars). Comparisons were made for an interval of several months and included the problem of wave decay. Some of the values calculated by Bretschneider, Todd, and Kimberley (1950), but not included in their report, are presented in Figures 6-5-12 and 6-5-13.

It is difficult to determine the reliability of a design based upon the type of data described above. It depends upon the type of scatter, that is, whether they are systematic deviations, Gaussian distributions, or something in between. One of the difficulties is that part of the spread of the data in Figures 6-5-5 to 6-5-8 is due to different forecasters estimating values of F, U, and t from one or more sets of weather maps, so that the spread of data in Figures 6-5-5 to 6-5-8 is not independent of the spread of data in Figures 6-5-12 and 6-5-13. It certainly indicates that there should be several forecasters, as well as several sets of weather maps to get a more reliable set of mean wave conditions from which to work.

For given wind conditions the prediction of the most probable maximum is even more uncertain than the prediction of the significant wave height (Wiegel, 1949; Putz, 1952; Longuet-Higgins, 1952). The prediction of the most probable maximum must be based upon a mean wave height and the number of waves in a given storm, which in turn must be based upon a study of weather maps over many years. Care must be taken in choosing the number of years, and the particular years, for which the information on the weather maps will be reduced to wave characteristics. Danielson, Burt, and Rattray (1957) examined weather maps for the years 1900 to 1952 in order to determine what percentage of the storms occurring in the Gulf of Alaska were extremely severe (high wind, great fetch, and long duration — at least 24 hours). This study showed that most of the severe storms occurred in groups of a few years, with relatively less stormy groups of years in between. A simplified visual description of this can be seen in Figure 6-5-14, where the percentages of times extremely high winds accosted ships in the Gulf of Alaska during the month of January are given for the years 1900 to 1952.

Suppose an operation is to be undertaken on an offshore structure, such as placing riprap around the base of the piles to prevent scouring. One type of information needed is whether or not a

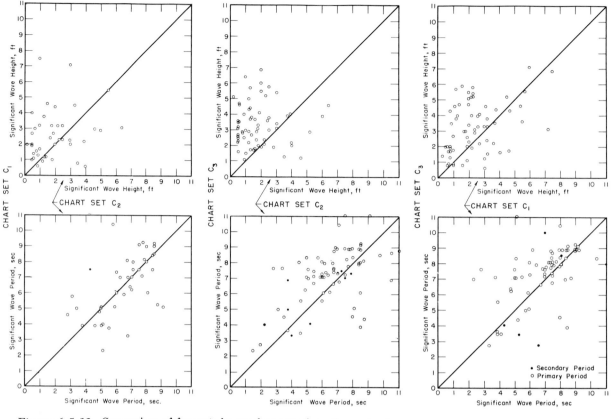

Figure 6-5-12. *Comparison of forecasts by one forecaster from three sets of weather charts, C_1, C_2, and C_3.*

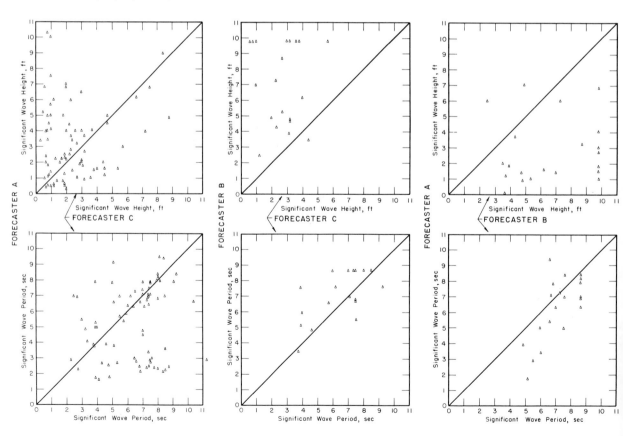

Figure 6-5-13. *Comparison of forecasts by three forecasters, A, B, and C, from one set of weather charts.*

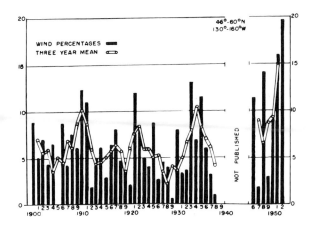

Figure 6-5-14. *Percentage of winds of force 8 or greater which were reported by ships in the Gulf of Alaska during January 1900-1952. (After Danielsen, Burt and Rattray, Jr., 1952)*

barge can be used on a particular day to place the riprap. This depends upon how far the tug must tow the barge and the maximum seas in which this particular operation can be performed. Little information is available on operational limits with respect to sea conditions; these data indicate that for a dump barge and tug a wave 3 ft. high would be about the limit, with no indication as to associated wave period (Glenn, 1950; Santema, 1955). The problem is to forecast in advance whether the waves (significant wave height) would be less than or greater than 3 ft. during the time necessary to tow the barge to the site, dump the rock, and return to the base. If it is forecast that the sea conditions will be operationally safe and the waves are higher than forecast, then there is the possibility of damage to, or loss of, the equipment. If the waves are forecast to be higher than the operational limit, but they are actually lower, then the cost of the equipment and crew are lost for that day.

Instead of a comparison of the accuracy of forecasts made with different forecasting procedures, weather maps, etc., one point will be emphasized. Isaacs and Saville (1949) made a study based upon the original data of Sverdrup and Munk (1947) in which they made 271 forecasts for one region (a nine-month interval) and 201 forecasts for another region (an eight-month interval). While their findings are no longer completely applicable in detail, one observation is still valid. It was found that 97 per cent of the recorded significant increases in wave heights were forecast, but 23 per cent of the forecast wave trains

failed to arrive. According to the authors, the rather large proportion of nonarrivals apparently came from the erroneous selection of fetches, frequently the result of difficulty in determining the limits of the effective angles of the winds with respect to the point at which the waves were recorded. This would cause a needless cancellation of operations on a number of days.

ACKNOWLEDGMENT

A part of the work presented in this paper was supported by National Science Foundation Grant G-14557.

REFERENCES

Abraham, G., "Jet Diffusion in Liquid of Greater Density, " *Jour. Hyd. Div., Proc. ASCE,* LXXXVI, No. HY6, Paper 2500 (1960) 1–13.

Albertson, M. L., Y. B. Dai, R. A. Jensen and Hunter Rouse, "Diffusion of Submerged Jets," *Proc. ASCE,* LXXIV, No. 10 (1948) 1571–1596.

Bretschneider, C. L., "The Generation and Decay of Wind Waves in Deep Water," *Trans. Amer. Geophys. Union,* XXXIII, No. 3 (1952) 381–389.

Bretschneider, C. L., and E. K. Rice, "The Generation and Decay of Wind Waves in a Sixty-Foot Channel." Univ. of Calif. Inst. of Eng. Res., Berkeley, Calif., 16 pp. , Technical Report 3-327, 1951. (Unpublished)

Bretschneider, C. L., D. K. Todd and H. L. Kimberley, "Comparisons of Wave Forecasts," Univ. of Calif., Inst. of Eng. Res., Berkeley, Calif., Tech. Rept. 29–39, 32 pp. (unpublished).

Brooks, Norman H., "Diffusion of Sewage Effluent in an Ocean Current," *Proceedings of First International Conference of Waste Disposal in a Marine Environment.* New York: Pergamon Press, 1961.

Brown, P. R., "Wave Data for the Eastern North Atlantic." *The Marine Observer,* XXIII No. 160 (1953) 94–98.

Burling, R. W., "Wind Generation of Waves on Water." Ph.D. thesis, Imperial College, University of London, 1955.

Danielson, E. F., W. V. Burt and M. Rattray, Jr., "Intensity and Frequency of Severe Storms in the Gulf of Alaska," *Trans. Amer. Geophys. Union,* XXXVIII, No. 1 (1957) 44–49.

Darbyshire, J., "The Generation of Waves by Wind," *Proc. Roy. Soc.,* Ser. A, CCXV (1952) 299–329.

Darbyshire, J., "A Further Investigation of Wind-Generated Waves," *Deutsche Hydrographische Zeitschrift*, XII, No. 1 (1959) 1–13.

Flinsch, H. V. N., "An Experimental Investigation of Wind-Generated Surface Waves." Unpublished Ph.D. thesis, Univ. of Minn. (1946)

Glenn, A. H., "Progress Report on Solution of Wave, Tide, Current, and Hurricane Problems in Coastal Operations," *The Oil and Gas Journal*, IL (1950) 174–177.

Hamada, T., H. Mitsuyasu and M. Hase, *An experimental study of wind effect upon water surface*. Report of Transportation, Technical Research Institute, Tokyo, 1953, 22 pp.

Hart, William Eldredge, "Jet Discharge into a Fluid with a Density Gradient." *J. Hyd. Div., Proc. ASCE*, Vol. 87, No. HY 6 (1961), 171–200.

Hydraulic Laboratory, Delft, *Golfaanval haringuliet-sluizen*. Deel II, "Systematisch Onderzoek Golfanngroei en Dynamische Golfbelasting." Code 32.79, M 399-II (1960) 61 pp.

Ichiye, T., "On the Effect of Waves upon the Vertical Distribution of Water Temperatures," *Records of Oceanographic Works in Japan*, New Series, I, No. 1 (1953) 63–70.

Isaacs, J. D. and Thorndike Saville, Jr., "A Comparison between Recorded and Forecast Waves on the Pacific Coast," *Annals of the New York Academy of Sciences*, LI, Art. 3 (1949) 502–510.

Johnson, J. W., "Relationship between Wind and Waves, Abbots Lagoon, California," *Trans. Amer. Geophys. Union*, XXIX, No. 3 (1950) 671–681.

Johnson, J. W., *Mixing and Dispersion by Wind Waves*. Univ. of Calif., Inst. of Eng. Res., Tech. Rept. 138–5.

Johnson, J. W., and E. K. Rice, "A Laboratory Investigation of Wind-Generated Waves," *Trans. Amer. Geophys. Union*, XXXIII, No. 6 (1952) 845–854.

Longuet-Higgins, M. S., "On the Statistical Distribution of the Heights of Sea Waves," *J. Mar. Res.*, XI, No. 13 (1952) 245–266.

Longuet-Higgins, M. S., "The Refraction of Sea Waves in Shallow Water," *Jour. Fluid Mechanics*, I (1956) Part 2, 163–176.

Munk, Walter H., "A Critical Wind Speed for Air-Sea Boundary Processes," *Jour. Mar. Res.*, VI, No. 3 (1947) 203–218.

Neumann, Gerhard, *On Ocean Wave Spectra and a New Method of Forecasting Wind-Generated Sea*. U. S. Army, Corps of Engineers, Beach Erosion Board, Tech. Memo. No. 43, 1953, 42 pp.

Pearson, Erman A., *An Investigation of the Efficacy of Submarine Outfall Sewage and Sludge*. State of California, State Water Pollution Control Board, Pub. No. 14, 1956, 154 pp.

Phillips, O. M., "The Equilibrium Range in the Spectrum of Wind-Generated Waves," *Jour. Fluid Mechanics* IV (1958a) Part 4, 426–434.

Phillips, O. M., "On Some Properties of the Spectrum of Wind-Generated Ocean Waves," *Jour. Mar. Res.*, XVI, No. 3 (1958b) 231–240.

Putz, R. R., "Statistical Distributions for Ocean Waves," *Trans. Amer. Geophys. Union*, XXXIII, No. 5 (1952) 685–692.

Rawn, A. M., F. R. Bowerman and Norman H. Brooks, "Diffusers for Disposal of Sewage in Sea Water," *Jour. Sanitary Engineering Div., ASCE*, LXXXVI, No. SA2 (1960), Part 1, 65–105.

Rawn, A. M., and H. K. Palmer, "Predetermining the Extent of a Sewage Field in Sea Water," *Trans., ASCE*, XCIV (1930) 1036–1086.

Roll, H. U., "Über die Ausbreitung der Meereswellen unter der Wirkung des Windes (auf Grund von Messungen im Wattenmer)," *Deutsche Hydrographische Zeitschrift*, II, No. 6.

Roll, H. U., "Über Gröszenunterschiede der Meereswellen bei Warm- und Kaltluft," *Deutsche Hydrographische Zeitschrift*, V, No. 2/3 (1952) 111–113.

Santema, P., "About the Estimation of the Number of Days with Favorable Meteorological and Oceanographical Conditions for Engineering Operations on the Sea Coast and in Estuaries," *Proc. Fifth Conf. on Coastal Engineering*, Council on Wave Research, The Engineering Foundation, 1955, 405–410.

Sibul, Oswald, *Laboratory Study of the Generation of Wind Waves in Shallow Water*. U. S. Army, Corps of Engineers, Beach Erosion Board, Tech. Memo. No. 72, 1955, 35 pp.

Stommel, Henry and Alfred H. Woodcock, "Diurnal Heating of the Surface of the Gulf of Mexico in the Spring of 1942," *Trans. Amer. Geophys. Union*, XXXII, No. 4 (1951) 565–571.

Sverdrup, H. U., and W. Munk, *Wind, Sea and Swell, Theory of Relations for Forecasting*. U. S. Navy Hydrographic Office, Pub. No. 601, 1947, 43 pp.

Wiegel, R. L., "Analysis of Data from Wave Recorders on the Pacific Coast of the United States." *Trans. Amer. Geophys. Union*, XXX (1949), 700–704.

Wiegel, R. L., "Final Report: Wave Instrumentation." Unpublished 19 page Tech. Rept. 3-372 for Univ. of Calif., Inst. of Eng. Res., 1954.

Wiegel, R. L., "Wind Waves and Swell," *Proc. Seventh*

Conf. on Coastal Engineering, Council on Wave Research, The Engineering Foundation (1961) 1–40

Wiegel, R. L., and A. L. Arnold, *Model Study of Wave Refraction.* U. S. Army, Corps of Engineers, Beach Erosion Board, Tech. Memo. 103, 1957, 31 pp.

Wiegel, Robert L., Kenneth E. Beebe and James Moon, "Ocean Wave Forces on Circular Cylindrical Piles," *Trans. ASCE*, CXXIV, Paper No. 2967 (1959) 89–116.

COMMENTS

Dr. Russell: I would like to emphasize Professor Wiegel's observations on the importance to the operator of offshore facilities of accurate forecasting of sea conditions. Many oil companies and other concerns rely on commercial forecasting services for daily prediction of weather and sea conditions at the site of offshore activity. These activities, to mention only a few, include the building of structures, drilling or coring from floating barges, and routine transportation of men and materials in the daily operation of offshore facilities. As is pointed out in this paper, an unpredicted worsening of sea conditions can be both dangerous and expensive. In addition a "false alarm" that predicts adverse seas which do not materialize can be very expensive if it causes an unnecessary decrease in activity.

Not only is it important to be able to forecast the effect of large storms on offshore operations, but in many cases an increase in wave height of only a few feet will considerably influence the methods used in performing certain operations. Therefore, I would like to reiterate that research activity aimed at a greater understanding of the many facets of wave height spectra, forecasting of sea conditions, and related areas of physical oceanography not only are of great interest but can be of considerable practical importance to those conducting offshore operations.

We have had several opportunities to observe the ability of forecasters to predict weather and wave conditions on a day-by-day basis. At times programs have been established to attempt a formal analysis of the performance of various forecasters. As a result of our observations and analyses we have arrived at some general conclusions as to the reliability of forecasting services presently available. At this time I am able to describe our general conclusions without referring to a particular series of observations, geographical locations, or individual forecasting concerns.

In order to describe the reliability of a forecasting service, I will define the following terms. A "successful" forecast is defined as the prediction of a significant increase in wave height within a particular time period. An unsuccessful forecast is either (1) the prediction of an increase in wave height that does not occur or that occurs at a significantly later time; or (2) an increase in wave height that was not predicted or was predicted to occur at a later time. Based on these definitions, our general experience is that roughly 60 to 70 per cent of the forecasts received on a routine daily basis are successful. The remaining 30 to 40 per cent are about evenly divided between the two categories listed above, namely, false alarms and the unpredicted worsening of wave conditions. Of the unsuccessful forecasts, the arrival time was in error more frequently than the approximate magnitude of the predicted wave height change.

The accuracy of most forecasting services in general tends to improve as the forecasters gain experience in handling the different problems associated with particular geographic locations. An important advance in obtaining better forecasting services would undoubtedly result from more reliable and correct basic weather data. Of course, some of the most important improvements in weather forecasting will result from good basic research programs, such as those being discussed at this conference.

SIX

RADAR SEA RETURN AND OCEAN WAVE SPECTRA

This paper reviews the characteristics of radar energy back-scattered from the sea. The bibliography is by no means complete, but enough references are given to aid further study of the subject. A basic reference text is Kerr (1951).

The discussion is confined to radars in which the transmitter and receiver are located at the same point in space. Figure 6-6-1 illustrates some of the terms used. Angles are measured from the horizontal, so that when a radar ray is normally incident on a patch of water, the grazing angle and water slope are complementary. It will also be necessary to use the angle between the radar ray and the water surface, which will be called the true grazing angle. The illuminated patch illustrated in Figure 6-6-1 is an area of the sea from which the energy is returned to produce the instantaneous radar echo. It is of width $R\phi$ and radial length $CT/2$ (C = velocity of light, T = pulse duration; $\frac{1}{2}$ because of the round trip). The radar echo is the sum of the returns from the individual scatters in the patch.

Another term used in the following discussion is that of "forward scattering." Figure 6-6-2 illustrates two paths by which energy may reach a given point. The resultant of the two depends upon grazing angle, sea state, and polarization. For a plane reflector and a horizontally polarized wave the forward reflected wave is of unity amplitude and reversed in phase. For a vertically polarized wave the amplitude has a minimum (about

0.1) at Brewsters angle (about 10 degrees for $\lambda = 3$ cm). Below this angle the phase of the reflected wave is about 180 degrees (the same as horizontal), but above the angle it is approximately 0 degrees. Therefore, near the surface the two waves more nearly cancel on horizontal polarization than they do on vertical polarization.

One last term is needed, namely, the critical angle (θ_c in Figure 6-6-3). It is the angle below which the radar echo per unit area of sea, called σ_0, decreases rapidly with angle as grazing is approached. It is a function of sea state, polarization, and wave length. For orders of magnitude, $\theta_c \approx 3°$ at $\lambda = 10$ cm and is roughly proportional to λ. For angles less than θ_c, σ_0 has been observed to vary roughly as θ to the fourth power (θ^4), and this can be given some theoretical justification (Ament, 1960).

INDIVIDUAL SCATTERER VELOCITY

Beginning with the longer radar wave length ($\lambda = 30$ meters), Crombie (1955) and Stutt et al. (1956) measured the doppler shift of radar return from the sea and found that the velocity of the radar scatterers was almost identically that of the gravity waves of length L, such that $L = \lambda/2$. From the narrow velocity spectrum observed very little else does any echoing.

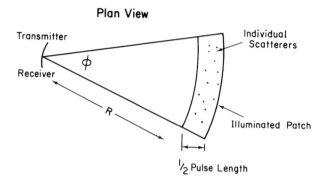

Figure 6-6-1.

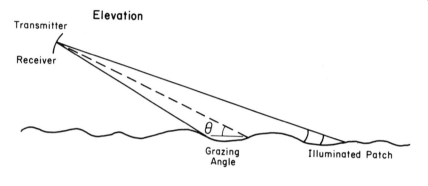

Figure 6-6-2.

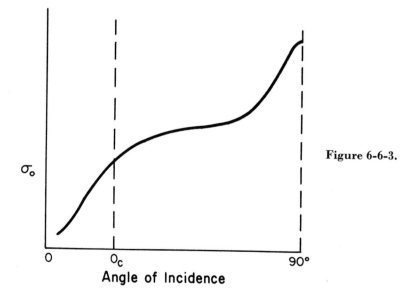

Figure 6-6-3.

Radar Freq. (Mcs)*	*Calc Doppler Freq. (cps)*	*Measured Doppler Freq. (cps)*
13.56	0.376	0.38** (Crombie)
18.39	0.437	0.425 (Lincoln Lab)
24.70	0.507	0.50 (" ")

* I. Ranzi has extended this list to 4 Mcs and 28 Mcs.
** Ocean wave velocity ≈ 8 knots.

Though day-to-day variations as large as 10 per cent are recorded, the general conclusion seems obvious that the radar scatterers are the gravity waves of wave length near to the resonant length ($\lambda/2$). Further support for this interpretation is found in the observation (Crombie) of a second line in the velocity spectrum at the velocity corresponding to $L = \lambda$. Though not given explicitly, the observed line widths in the spectrum appear to be much less than $\pm.03$ cps $= \pm.25$ knots (Crombie).

In this same wave length region, Hoffman (1955) has calculated approximately the return from a sea represented by two sine waves and found rough agreement in magnitude with observation when he used wave length L near λ. Here his comparison is with observations in which the radar energy was first bounced off the ionosphere, then off the sea, at an angle of 12 degrees, and returned by the same path.

To emphasize the differences, consider next the shortest radar wave lengths. For example Hicks et al. (1958) examined the doppler spectrum at $\lambda = 3.2$ cm and found a more or less continuous Gaussian spectrum often centered at zero velocity with a half-power width not greater than ± 2.5 kts. The big difference between this result and the long wave lengths is that essentially the same velocities are observed from $\lambda = 1.25$ cm to $\lambda = 55$ cm (cf. Goldstein, page 581). These velocities suggest that the radar scatterers are moving with particle velocities (orbital motion of water in gravity waves) and perhaps also ocean current velocities. Foam, breaking waves, and spray are not necessarily excluded by these velocities. Considering the radar scatterers to be waves small enough to be carried along at the particle velocity of the dominant gravity waves limits the possible scattering wave lengths to ones much smaller than those producing the particle velocities. Stated in this way, it constitutes a very weak limitation, restricting scattering wave lengths to, say, less than 10 meters. The observation that oil slicks are distinguishable as areas of diminished sea re-

turn with ($\lambda = 3$ cm) radars (General Electric Co., 1960) suggests that much shorter ocean wave lengths are involved in radar backscattering, and this approach via the ocean wave lengths that are damped by an oil slick would appear to be fruitful.

The boundary between long and short radar wave lengths, that is, those that scatter only from resonant ocean waves and those with a continuous velocity spectrum below about 5 knots is not well defined. Ament et al. (1958) reported what might have been resonance effects and further occasional radar scatterers moving with dominant wave speed (12–18 knots, $L = 25$–50 meters) with a ($\lambda =$)1.5 m radar. This again could be taken as an indication that rarely is the ratio of ocean to radar wave length, L/λ, as great as 15.

These and other arguments could be advanced for the size of the radar scatterers, but it follows from almost any model of the sea that only scatterers of dimensions approximately equal to λ could scatter the observed amount of energy near grazing incidence (cf. Goldstein, page 521).

A THEORY OF SOME RECENT MEASUREMENTS

It would be well for the terminology involved to inject at this point a theory of sea clutter. Katzin (1957) proposed that the sea surface be considered as a collection of flats or facets with slopes given by the Cox and Munk (1954) statistics. If these facets are electrically isolated, the reflection from one such is known, and the radar echo can be approximated as the sum of the randomly phased individual scatterers in the illuminated patch. This theory has the advantage of making the dependence of backscatter on water slope and smoothness explicit rather than just derivable from wave spectra.

From Katzin's model the important scatterers in the case where none of the water surface is viewed normally are of dimensions comparable to λ (diameter approximately $\lambda/2\pi$) because larger facets scatter mostly in the forward direction, and the echo from smaller ones decreases rapidly with scatterer size. At larger angles of incidence only those facets viewed normally are important, and all facets that are large compared to λ are about equally important.

Katzin invokes coherent forward scattering to explain the angular dependence of σ_0 below the critical angle, an explanation to which we will return later. Also for lack of data on the subject, he assumed that facet size and facet slope are independent.

Schooley (1961) has recently published facet size data from a small water-wind tunnel. Wave lengths from the capillary range at least up to 20 cm are generated in it. The wave slopes generated are slightly larger than those found by Cox and Munk (1954) at all wind speeds from about 10 to 25 knots. Schooley used flatness tolerances of 1, 3, 5, and 10 mm and found a distinct dependence of facet size on wave slope. For example, if the flatness tolerance is considered to be $\lambda/10$, then the average facet length (at a 15-knot wind speed) varied from about 2λ near zero slope to less than $\lambda/2$ at 30 degrees slope. The curves are actually unsymmetric, the largest facet lengths occur on the back (seen when looking down-wind) of a wave with a slope of a few degrees; but on the back of the wave the facet length decreases more rapidly with increasing slope than on the front of a wave. Schooley (to be published) has calculated via Katzin's model, using measured facet sizes, a reasonable dependence of back-scatter ratio up-wind and down-wind upon grazing angle. This gives further support to calculations made from the facet model of the sea.

WAVE LENGTHS $L \gg \lambda$

An obvious effect of the large ocean waves is the shadowing of the troughs by the crests, and of course the smaller the angle of incidence, the greater the shadowing effect. Figure 6-6-4 is a good example. Though it illustrates regular waves approaching a beach, with proper instrumentation it could be used in the open sea for measurement of wave crest velocity and direction. The range resolution of Figure 6-6-4 is 5 feet, and 1 foot resolution is presently available in laboratory radars.

Another effect of the large waves is to make available for forward scatter large (relative to λ) areas whose average slope is not zero. This forward reflection from tilted areas has very little effect on the usual measurement of reflection coefficient because the transmitter and receiver must be placed well above the water surface, and the net received signal is the random-phase addition of many such surfaces. The forward reflected illumination of individual wave tops is greatly affected, however, because under the proper geo-

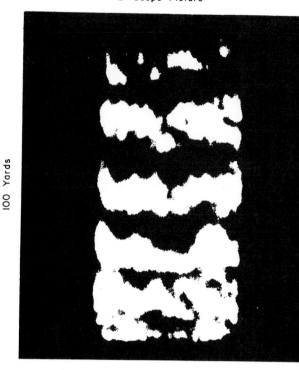

B - Scope Picture

100 Yards

10 Degrees

$\frac{1}{5}$ Sec. Sweep Time

Figure 6-6-4. *Sea Echo on Radar B-scope (vertical scale is range, horizontal scale is azimuth.)*

metric conditions this secondary illumination falling on them is not randomly phased.

The discussion of forward scatter is ultimately tied to the variations of sea echo with polarization, so these two subjects are discussed together below.

POLARIZATION AND FORWARD SCATTER

The general features of the polarization dependence (V/H) of backscatter are given in Figures 6-6-5 and 6-6-6 for $\lambda = 25$ cm and $\lambda = 3$ cm, which are essentially simultaneous data. These are reproduced from Macdonald (1956). Vertical polarization (electric vector in the plane of the water normal) giving the larger echo is the usual rule although the reverse can be observed near grazing (0 degrees) under rough sea conditions (cf. Goldstein, 1951, page 498). Several features should be noted in Figures 6-6-5 and 6-6-6.

(1) Increasing ratio with wave length

(2) Increasing ratio with decreasing sea roughness

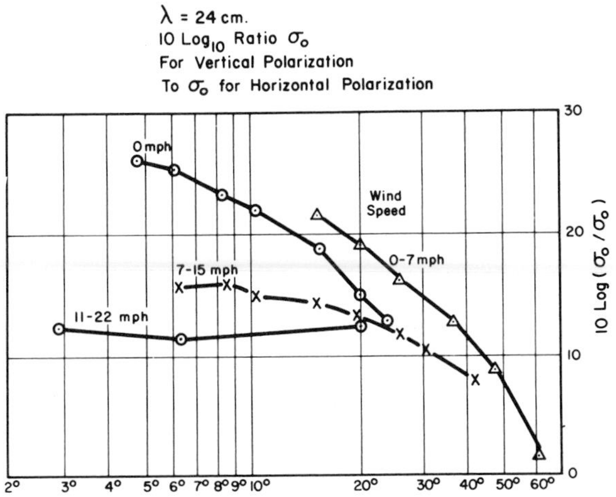

λ = 24 cm.
10 Log₁₀ Ratio σ₀
For Vertical Polarization
To σ₀ for Horizontal Polarization

Figure 6-6-5. *Ratio of sea echo on vertical polarization to that on horizontal polarization* ($\lambda = 24\ cm$)

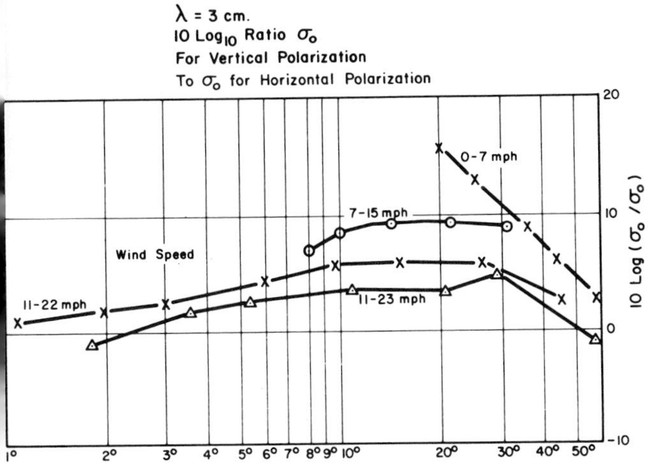

λ = 3 cm.
10 Log₁₀ Ratio σ₀
For Vertical Polarization
To σ₀ for Horizontal Polarization

Figure 6-6-6. *Ratio of sea echo on vertical polarization to that on horizontal polarization* ($\lambda = 3\ cm$)

(3) The maximum ratio can occur at angles as large as 30 degrees and return to unity ratio at grazing.

(4) The angle of maximum ratio decreases with decreasing sea state.

The first two observations have the correct trend to be explained by the forward scatter mechanism. Ament (1960) has given a heuristic explanation of the unity ratio at grazing, but the value 30 degrees is an order of magnitude too large for the usual forward scatter computation:

$$\frac{2\pi L(1 - \cos\theta)}{\lambda} = \frac{\pi}{2} \qquad (1)$$

where L is an ocean wave length associated with the characteristic wave height, θ is the grazing angle, and λ' the radar wave length. The equa-

tion says merely that the lengths of the two paths in Figure 6-6-7 by which energy reaches P are very nearly equal and, assuming the reflection coefficients of smooth water, more of the direct illumination is cancelled in the case of horizontal polarization than vertical polarization. Even for L as small as 25 m, $\lambda = 10$ cm, θ must be less than 2.5 degrees.

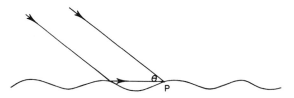

Figure 6-6-7. *Ray paths from transmitter to point P*

It is at this point in the discussion that we will try to extend the explanation of sea clutter phenomena beyond what the author has found in the literature by extending the use of Katzin's facet assumption. Rearranging the previous equation,

$$\cos\theta = 1 - \frac{\lambda}{4L} \qquad (2)$$

Obviously θ could be as large as 40 degrees if $L = \lambda$. Second, if the whole surface in Figure 6-6-7 were tilted at angle $-\phi$ so as to decrease the effective grazing angle, then

$$\cos(\theta - \phi) = 1 - \frac{\lambda}{4L} \qquad (3)$$

and the maximum grazing angle satisfying this condition is increased by ϕ. The above two simple considerations suggest the assumption that the sea is "piece-wise" smooth, and it follows that if the pieces have a polarization dependence, their "random phase" sum will have the same dependence. This is no more than the extension to smaller segments of the sea of the interference phenomenon well known for larger segments.

Katzin's model of the sea assumed small facets as the reflectors. Though he did not apply it to explain the polarization ratio, this can obviously be done qualitatively. Picking a facet size to do this will call for adjusting a parameter to fit the observations; however, it will be shown not only that there is a natural way to pick facet sizes from Rayleigh's roughness criterion (cf. Kerr, page 411), but that doing so explains some observations of the sea's reflection coefficient as well as the polarization ratio (V/H) of backscatter.

It will be assumed that at all grazing angles to a rough sea, the largest facet diameters are given by L, where $H/L = \frac{1}{7}$ and $(H/\lambda) \sin \theta = \frac{1}{8}$. Therefore, $L/\lambda = 0.88/\sin \theta$. The second assumption implies that the sea is rough when viewed at an angle θ and that the roughness can be attributed to waves of height H which by the first assumption ($L = 7H$) are fully developed. Qualitative justification for assuming only one facet size is that longer waves would only tilt this facet to a different viewing angle and shorter waves could not make it appear rough being limited by $H \leqslant L/7$. These will be the facets effective for forward scatter and "near normal" backscatter. Substituting $0.88/\sin \theta$ for L/λ in

$$2\pi L \frac{1 - \cos \theta}{\lambda} \leq \frac{\pi}{2}$$

shows that the relationship is satisfied for all actual grazing angles less than 30 degrees. Other numerical indications of the reasonableness of this assumption are given in the paragraphs below.

From the equation for radar area per unit area of a flat plate,

$$\sigma_0 = \frac{4\pi A}{\lambda^2} = \left(\frac{\pi L}{\lambda}\right)^2$$

at vertical incidence $\sigma_0 = (\pi.88)^2 = 7.6$, which is in reasonable agreement with observation (see Goldstein, page 505).

The reflection coefficient of the sea is measured, as in Figure 6-6-8, either by varying the receiver height to change the relative phase of the two paths or with a narrow beam to separate the two paths. Using the scattering equation

$$P_R = \frac{P_T G a \sigma_0 A \sin \theta}{(4\pi R^2)^2} \tag{4}$$

for the indirect path and

$$P_0 = \frac{P_T G a}{4\pi (2R)^2} \tag{5}$$

for the direct path, where "a" is the absorbing area of the antenna, "A" is the effective illumi-

Figure 6-6-8. *Geometry of Reflection Coefficient Measurements*

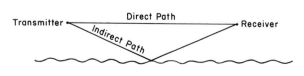

nated horizontal area of the sea, "G" is antenna gain, etc., the reflection coefficient (power) is

$$\rho^2 = \frac{\sigma_0 A \sin \theta}{\pi R^2} \tag{6}$$

For forward scatter $\sigma_0 = 4\pi A/\lambda^2 = (\pi L/\lambda)^2$, and the voltage reflection coefficient is

$$\rho = \left(\frac{\pi L}{\lambda}\right)\left(\frac{A \sin \theta}{\pi R^2}\right)^{1/2}$$

For small values of θ the effective area A is limited in the azimuthal direction by the narrow scattering pattern of the large facets. The angle is approximately $\lambda/2L = \theta/1.75$ radians. In the θ direction the effective area is limited by the variation of σ_0 with θ. Since $\sigma_0^{1/2} \propto L/\lambda \propto 1/\sin \theta$ the effective area is measured by $\theta/2$. Therefore, the effective horizontal illuminated area is

$$A = \left(\frac{\pi}{4}\right)\left(\frac{\theta}{1.75}\right)\left(\frac{\theta}{2}\right)\frac{R^2}{\sin \theta} \tag{7}$$

and

$$\rho = 0.74$$

This is much too large for the reflection coefficient of a surface that is rough as assumed in the derivation; however, for large values of θ, the effective area A is ordinarily limited by the antenna beamwidth to

$$A = \frac{\pi}{4} \frac{\psi a \psi e \, R^2}{\sin \theta}$$

and

$$\rho = \frac{0.88\pi}{2 \sin \theta} (\psi a \, \psi e)^{1/2} \tag{8}$$

where ψa and ψe are the antenna beamwidths. Ford and Oliver (1945) measured reflection coefficients at large angles using 1.2 meter parabolas at $\lambda = 9$ cm. Hence for $\theta = 30°$,

$$\psi a = \psi e \approx \frac{1}{27}$$
$$\rho = 0.10 \tag{9}$$

This is about in the middle of the range of values that Ford and Oliver (1945) observed when they tried to simulate the sea with "wet wavy" ground or wire netting.

Beard did a beam swinging experiment with a 0.3° beam at $\theta = 0.8°$ and found that ρ decreased rapidly a beamwidth away from the specular point. We calculate the facet beamwidth as

$$\frac{\theta}{1.75} \approx 0.45° \tag{10}$$

This is a satisfactory explanation of an isolated measurement, but the model should be checked by beam swinging experiments at other values of θ. This much agreement does seem to warrant more precise calculations using measured water slope (Cox and Munk), facet sizes versus slope (Schooley), and slope versus water height (Farmer, 1956).

A NEW INSTRUMENT

Morrow (1960) reports the successful flight test of an airborne radar designed to measure wave heights by measuring the variations of aircraft altitude. The system is an X band (3 cm) FM/CW, vertically-looking radar. The antenna beamwidth is about 3° and illuminates a 6-ft. patch of water when the aircraft is at 125 ft., the operational altitude. With its 200 Mc bandwidth, the wave height accuracy obtained is at least 1 ft. At present simultaneous measurements of wave height by this airborne radar and a wave staff on a Texas Tower are being processed for the wave spectrum.

CONCLUSIONS

In the wave length region $\lambda = 10$ m observations indicate that radar scattering is dependent only on the ocean waves of length $L = \lambda/2$ and λ. In the wave length region $\lambda \leq 1$m a model is presented which indicates that in a rough sea the secondary illumination of backscatters is dependent upon ocean wave lengths $L \leq 0.88\lambda/\sin\theta$, where θ is the grazing angle. The contributing values of L increase as the sea becomes smoother.

REFERENCES

Ament, W. S., "Reciprocity and Scattering by Certain Rough Surfaces," *IRE Transactions on Antennas and Propagation*, AP-VIII, No. 2 (1960).

Ament, W. S., J. Burkett, F. C. Macdonald and D. L. Ringwalt, "Characteristics of Radar Sea Clutter; Observations at 220 Mc," U. S. Naval Research Laboratory Report 5218, November 19, 1958.

Beard, C. I., *Coherent and Incoherent Scattering of Microwaves from the Ocean*. Electronic Defense Labs, Mountain View, Calif., Report No. EDL-E53, 1960.

Cox, C. and W. Munk, "Statistics of the Sea Surface Derived from Sun Glitter," *J. Marine Research*, XIII (1954) 198–227.

Crombie, D., "Doppler Spectrum of Sea Echo at 13.56 Mc/s," *Nature*, CLXXV (1955) 681–682.

Farmer, H. G., "Some Recent Observations of Sea Surface Elevation and Slope." Unpublished manuscript, No. 56–37, Woods Hole Oceanographic Institute, 1956.

Ford, L. H. and R. Oliver, "An Experimental Investigation of Reflection and Absorption of Radiation of 9-Cm Wavelength." *Phys. Soc.*, LVIII (1945) 265–280. London.

General Electric Co., *Monthly Status Report*, No. 1, Nonr-2628-(00), 1960.

Goldstein, H., *See below* Kerr, *Propagation of Short Radio Waves*.

Hicks, B. L., N. Knoble, J. J. Kovaly, G. S. Newell and J. P. Ruina, *Sea Clutter Spectrum Studies Using Airborne Coherent Radar III*. Univ. of Ill. Control Systems Lab, Report R105, 1958.

Hoffman, W. C., "A Theoretical Model for High-Frequency Backscatter from the Sea Surface via the Ionosphere," *J. Atmosphere and Terrestrial Physics*, VII (1955) 278–284.

Katzin, M., "On the Mechanism of Radar Sea Clutter," *Proc. IRE*, XLV (1957) No. 1.

Kerr, D. E., *Propagation of Short Radio Waves*. New York: McGraw-Hill Book Co., Inc., 1951.

Macdonald, F. C., "Sea Clutter at X and L Bands." Unclassified report in *Classified Symposium Record*, Univ. of Michigan, Feb. 7–9, 1956.

Morrow, C. M., *Ocean-Wave-Profiling Radar System*. Report of NRL Progress, 1960, 32 pp.

Schooley, A. H., "Relationship Between Surface Slope, Average Facet Size, and Facet Flatness Tolerance of a Wind Disturbed Water Surface," *J. Geophysical Res.*, LXVI (1961) No. 1.

Stutt, C. A., S. J. Fricker, R. P. Ingalls and M. L. Stone, *Preliminary Report on Ground-Wave Radar Sea Clutter*. MIT Lincoln Lab Tech Report No. 134, 1956.

Ranzi, I., "Experiments on Backscatter of H. F. Radiowaves from Open and Coastal Seas," Centro Radioellectrico Sperimentale, G. Marconi-Roma, March 1, 1961, AFCRC Contract AF(61(052))–139.

GENERAL DISCUSSION

This section includes: (1) an informal panel discussion, held in the evening of the fourth day of the conference, ranging across many topics presented during the conference sessions, and moderated by Dr. Walter Munk and (2) a paper submitted following the conference by John W. Tukey commenting on several of the principal papers presented.

O N E

PANEL DISCUSSION

Dr. Munk: Gentlemen, this is by far the greatest concentration of talent on our subject at a single time in a single room that has ever taken place and (I would presume) that ever will take place. All of us are most impressed with the progress that has been achieved during the last few years. It is demonstrably true that in no other branch of physical oceanography has there been such expansion. During the last ten years the subject of waves has gone from an art to a science.

One way of indicating the enormity of this change is to point out that in these past three days I have yet to see a slide showing a wiggly wave record plotted against time! It used to be that when we attended wave meetings, people would show thousands of slides plotting sea level against time. The display that comes closest at this conference is Dr. Tick's theoretical realization in the time domain of a certain type of power spectrum.

I am still troubled by one apparently unsolvable problem. When I obtained the program from Dick Vetter showing that we would meet here for four long days, I was horrified. One wants to go home and do some work. At the same time, most of us object to going to meetings where everybody is rushed through so that he hardly has a chance to give the substance of his talk. Yet here we have sat for three days and sometimes have even felt the pinch of time! Hence, in our expanding subject this may have been our last oppor-

tunity to look at the entire subject at one time in one room. In the future we will be in the unfortunate situation of having to resort to brief discussions of some particular branch of the subject. I bemoan the passing of the old days!

This gives me a chance to thank Dick Vetter, on behalf of everyone here, for an incredible job of organizing the meeting. As far as I can see, he lost a bet by working for an outfit like the National Academy of Sciences. He ought to be employed by some profitable organization like the Statler Hotels! He has gone — although this was never stated explicitly in the invitations — to great lengths to stop us from getting out of his reach and from being distracted by outside influences. I had no idea Easton, Maryland, was so far away from anything! In fact, please notice that in the state which has the largest coastline of any in the Union, he managed to find a place where we were out of sight of waves so we could not be distracted by seeing the real thing!

At least we had the chance, due to Norman Barber's artistry, to keep ourselves somewhat close to reality by looking at his charming drawing (see Figure pp. 188).

I propose that we discuss three central questions:

1. What measurements should be taken for a systematic study of the problems of wave generation? Surely some good things have been done, but compared to the very large effort in the general field there has been relatively little effort, relatively few people who have really worked on *systematic* measurements dealing specifically with the study of wave generation.

2. Could one make laboratory studies of wave decay? Here we may think of finding out what happens to a swell as it travels very long distances. The problem of wave motion from deep into shallow water requires systematic measurements. So does the problem of waves going from still water into currents.

3. What synoptic wave measurements should now be taken in the light of our much more sophisticated view of the subject? Should directional buoys be placed in weatherships? Should directional recordings replace non-directional recordings? The problems of digital recording analysis are part of this question.

The first speakers dealing particularly with instrumentation will be Tucker and Snodgrass. I would like them to consider these three questions and also the much more severe requirements that are now imposed on instrumentation by the interest in nonlinear problems. This problem has not been faced explicitly and is quite serious. For example, our work at Scripps, depending entirely on the Snodgrass bottom pressure recorder, has to be re-examined because to some extent every bottom pressure recorder does contain a nonlinear contribution from the dynamic pressure. This has not been severe in the past but might be severe in future work. Associated meteorological measurements deserve attention. Finally, does anyone have any modern ideas on how to record breakers, white cap density, and things of this sort systematically?

First, Mr. Tucker:

Dr. Tucker: On the subject of wave generation, one of the critical measurements at the moment seems to be that of the air pressure distribution over the sea surface. From this, if one knew it precisely in relation to the surface profile, one could in principle calculate the amount of energy being fed into the waves. I think this is independent of any theory of generation; one can calculate the work done by the pressure on the moving water surface.

However, as we saw from Dr. Longuet-Higgins' measurements, this is a very difficult thing to do with the necessary precision. The difficulty is this. Suppose we consider the simplest case of a long-crested wave train passing through still air with a buoy on the surface measuring the air pressure, then one measures very large pressure variations which do not affect wave generation. One gets not only the static head due to the variation in elevation of the water surface, but also dynamic pressures induced by the motion of the air particles which are equal to and in the same sense as the static pressures. This is perhaps a little subtle. In the water the static pressures are cancelled by the dynamic pressures at the surface; from the water's point of view the wave surface is a constant pressure surface. But in the air above the water the same sorts of motions occur upside down; so the static pressures add to the dynamic pressures.

The pressure changes one is looking for make up a very small percentage of these (1 or 2 per cent), so one has to have very precise instrumentation if one hopes to sort them out.

A favorable factor is that these static and dynamic pressure changes which feed no energy into the waves are in phase with the wave profile, whereas the ones you are *looking for* are out of phase. One is therefore looking for a small phase difference between the pressure and wave profiles. It is conceivable that one could get these measurements with sufficient accuracy to get a useful result. In fact, the measurements that Dr. Longuet-Higgins reported do show slight phase shifts, but they are so small that they are not significant within the accuracy of his measurements.

Another approach is being followed by Charnock. This is to record the pressure fluctuations on a stationary platform. (In his case he used the beach.) He argued that if you get an on-shore wind flowing from the sea and measure the pressure fluctuations on the beach, they will be reasonably characteristic of the pressure fluctuations at sea because the regime would not have had time to change very much. He did this, and the pressure fluctuations were very much smaller than expected, at least an order of magnitude smaller than was assumed in Phillips' original theory.

Dr. Deacon: There was one striking result that was not mentioned. He found something that went with the velocity of sound.

Dr. Tucker: That is right. He had an array of pressure detectors on the beach so that he could get the wave length as well as the frequency. He found long pressure waves going with the velocity of sound. I think they were double the frequency of the sea waves. He thought he was finding the second-order pressure variations in the air and that these were propagating with the velocity of sound. However, this is still speculation.

When Professor Pierson was talking a couple of days ago, he said that there were no wave recorders that were effective over a wide range of frequencies. Actually deep sea wave buoys *do* cover a remarkably wide range of frequencies. In principle they will measure waves with wave lengths of from a foot or two right up to the longest waves. This does give one a chance to measure the second-order terms in the wave profile.

One last comment. Walter Munk mentioned that pressures of the $\frac{1}{2}\rho V^2$ type acting on a pressure recorder on the sea bed can introduce spurious second-order terms. Bob Wiegel pointed this out to me first, and it can be a very important effect. Waves have quite large particle velocities associated with them in shallow water; and if the pressure recorder is not well streamlined, one can get important dynamic pressures developed. In fact, it doesn't take much imagination to work out a case where they are 20 per cent of the wave height. In designing pressure recorders one has to have this effect in mind for accurate results. In one case we had to put the pressure recorder on the sea bed with a wide flat fairing around it.

Mr. Frank Snodgrass: As an electrical engineer, I feel that the question put to me at this time should be reversed. The question that I usually ask is: What measurements do you want to make? I then try to do a good job of getting this data. As an instrumentation engineer, I should not presume to tell you what measurements should be made.

However, one experiment we have in mind regarding ocean waves (made possible by new techniques of measuring and analyzing directional spectra data) is the direct measurement of the attenuation of swell over great distances.

We want to establish a directional recording system at San Clemente Island, as was done for our directional wave study. From there, along the path of waves being propagated from the Southern hemisphere, we find a very convenient island, Tahiti, where we would like to establish a second station. By measuring the energy of the waves passing Tahiti and the energy of the waves

arriving at San Clemente, we should be able to determine the attenuation. If the installation does not look too difficult, a second directional station will be installed at Tahiti, but a simple nondirectional station can be used if more elaborate directional installation proves impractical. Whether or not a two-point measurement will be sufficient to determine the attenuation is questionable. More stations along the path of the waves may be required if we are to examine effects due to the ocean currents, cross swell, winds, or other factors, that may affect the attenuation of the waves.

As to the future requirements of instruments to measure ocean wave spectra, the influence of computers has been very great and certainly will impose new requirements on instruments. The use of graphical data describing the time history of the sea surface will become less useful. The data should be in a form that can be applied directly to the input of the computer. At least the data should be easily transferred for computer input.

At Scripps we plan to record digitally since we have a digital computer. We do not intend to handle the data between the original recording and final analysis. In addition to the more formal analysis programs such things as editing of the data, error testing, and corrections will be done by the computer. A special method of running correlations to predict the next value will be used to detect errors. If the predicted value should not agree with the recorded value within a prescribed limit, the data point will be considered to be in error and will be discarded. A best-fit value as calculated by the prediction will be inserted in its place. Automatic error correction requires that we do not have too many data points in error. Greater emphasis must be placed on reliability of the measurements. In order to get greater reliability we have made certain changes in our instruments. We use solid-state circuits to eliminate electronic tubes wherever possible. We have tried to eliminate all mechanical relays. If they must be used, we use the very best hermetically-sealed, mercury-wetted types. Elimination of high-voltage electrolytic condensers is desirable since these components have always been troublesome. Packaging the equipment in moisture-tight compartments, dehydrating the air, and providing a cooling system helps to reduce failures caused by dust, humidity, salt air, and temperature.

Certainly we will need far more data in future studies. I was rather surprised to hear that 43 million-odd holes punched in digital tape last year in our directional wave study were completely inadequate. Dr. Barber indicated that instead of three instruments we should have twenty. Dr. Tukey very casually suggested that we should have ten times the length of the records. With very simple arithmetic it looks as if in the next experiment we should punch something like three billion holes in our tapes. Certainly we must plan instruments to handle far more data.

One should always know the calibration of his instrument, but actually this is vastly understating the problem. Too often we think of the calibration of an instrument as just one number, a number that expresses the full-scale reading of the instrument. There are many others, often overlooked, that are just as important to the understanding of the measurements, for example, the frequency response and the temperature characteristics. Often temperature characteristics are measured only by the zero shift of the output and disregard the effect on the original frequency response characteristics.

The stability or noise of the instrument is important. Here again we tend to describe this characteristic with one number, such as five cycles per day. This tells us that the instrument drift will not exceed the five-cycle range but does not tell us whether it has drifted uniformly at this rate or has fluctuated between the limit many times during the day. We need to know the spectrum of the noise of the instrument. The statistics of the noise determination of the instruments should be comparable to the statistics of the final data. In our next experiment we want to record tides. Since we must measure frequencies between six cycles per hour and one cycle per fortnight we should obtain one reading every five minutes for one year. We therefore should have one year, or a minimum of one month of stability data in order to measure the background of the instrument with comparable accuracy over the frequency range.

Too often instruments are built in reverse. If the engineer's problem is to obtain data, he should first decide exactly what measurements are to be made and understand clearly the problem at hand. Next, he must decide the best possible way to make the measurement from all known techniques. Then he should think about the cost of the instruments. The development of an inexpensive instrument can be very expensive. When we consider the cost of obtaining data, the price of the measuring equipment seems quite small compared to ship time, calibration of recorders, analysis of data, salaries, etc.

Since the problem of the engineer is to devise new techniques of making measurements, he should not be burdened with the task of obtaining data. His efforts should be put into building a good instrument and understanding completely its characteristics and its limitations.

Dr. Munk: Mr. Snodgrass referred to his transistorized tide gauge. This, I believe, is the first new development in the measurements of tides since Lord Kelvin passionately defended the use of a pencil as compared to a pen before the Royal Society. I am reminded of a statement by the inventor of the BT, that the ideal oceanographic instrument has less than one vacuum tube. This has now been realized in this age of transistorized equipment in a manner different than Dr. Spilhaus envisioned when he made this comment.

Concerning the difficulty of living with very large amounts of digitized data (and I think this is pertinent in particular to an oceanographic group), in general, one has a choice between putting one's efforts into getting numbers without mistakes, or finding ways of correcting mistakes. We find that with considerable care we can manage to get errors down to one in a thousand. The additional effort to reduce errors to one in ten thousand is enormous. The reasons for the errors are so varied that you cannot put your finger on them but something goes wrong to give you one bad number in a thousand even with considerable care.

The same experience has been noted in England by Sir Edward Bullard. So, if you take digital observations from ships and on the beach, you have to live with occasional errors. They tend in digital work to be very large errors, so large that if they are ignored, they will not only diminish the value of your observations but make them completely useless.

Our conclusion, then, is that one should find sophisticated means for detecting and patching errors. After a certain stage of effort to reduce errors to less than 1 per cent, one's efforts are better spent in finding how to live with them than in trying to reduce them further. When 50 million holes are punched in a tape, some of them will be punched in the wrong place. Dr. Tukey considers this problem a first-order intellectual challenge and not one to be disposed of as a nuisance.

There is very little background in mathematical

statistics, very little information on the problem of how one, in a sophisticated and considered manner, looks over data and finds mistakes without removing some of the essential information. This is a problem of great importance in this age of digital recording, particularly to people who have to do some of their recording under less than ideal circumstances.

The next speakers, Dr. Darbyshire and Dr. Neumann, have held different views on the description of waves by one and two dimensional spectra. I have the privilege, as Chairman, to ask Dr. Darbyshire why he is so completely enamored with *period* as compared to *frequency* as to insist in plotting spectra in terms of the nonlinear period scale.

Dr. Pierson: He doesn't do that any more.

Dr. Munk: In the talk he translated his results in terms of period wherever possible. I think even oceanographers have reached the point where they are able to obtain the reciprocal of a number.

Dr. Darbyshire: Mr. Chairman, Dr. Pierson answered your question for me. I do use frequencies now, very much against my will.

Dr. Cox: Even the mathematicians have learned to take reciprocals and, therefore, can use periods!

Dr. Darbyshire: For practical forecasting I prefer the period because you get the wave velocity by just multiplying it by three for the phase velocity and one and a half for the group velocity. It does make life simpler. I can do a reciprocal, as my latest paper suggests.

There is one point you did not mention, Mr. Chairman, about the height parameter. Mine is four times more than the one Neumann uses and eight times more than the one Burling uses. But it has some operational value. It does relate directly to the wave height from the crest to the trough. If you have a period interval, the value of H_f or H_t means that if all the rest of the spectrum were suddenly to disappear, then that would be the actual wave height of the sea that is left. It does have a physical meaning.

I will now talk about the one-dimensional wave spectrum. I feel that we should try to standardize and make more uniform methods of attack on this problem. Dr. Phillips has mentioned a very interesting point about some seas being really different from others. It is suggested that seas at positions "India" and "Juliet" are never very

quiet, and you get equilibrium more quickly than off the coast of the United States where, I am told, the sea is quiet.

But again, I am not too sure how reliable this is because even at stations "India" and "Juliet" it is quiet occasionally, particularly in the lower frequency range. My feeling is that we are not giving enough weight to the effect of the weaker winds. We don't have storms starting up like a discontinuous function; we have a gradual climbing up. It may be that the weaker winds pave the way for the strong winds and build up energy in the lower-frequency components. This might explain this mechanism of Dr. Phillips!

Regarding the synoptic network, one would like more and more observations for it. At the moment, of all the weather ships only one, or possibly two have a shipborne wave recorder. If they were all fitted with wave instruments, it would help considerably. I have made predictions of waves over all the North Atlantic, but it is absolutely impossible to compare my predictions with the observations. Often two ships in the same position give estimates of period and height differing by 100 per cent. We need direct instrumental measurements of waves.

On the wave propagation and decay problem, as far as I can see, there is no actual dissipation of energy in the cases of no wind and a following weak wind. It may be that there is some when there are cross winds and opposing winds. We don't have enough observations to verify this. In the simple case of calm and following light winds I think that the loss in height is due entirely to dispersion and the two-dimensional spreading of the waves. I have always used this hypothesis, and it seems to work out pretty well. We on the eastern side of the Atlantic have few examples of opposing winds as the winds tend to blow in our direction. So I have very few observations for studying decay when the winds oppose the waves.

Dr. Munk: Do you think it would be worthwhile and feasible to put considerable effort into taking directional recordings from weather ships with a simplified buoy? What do you think of directional recordings by wave stations along the Atlantic Coast? Should one really push a radio altimeter, as George Deacon emphasized in his introductory speech? Should one try to persuade the Polaris people to put their enormous tools to work on what (hopefully) may be the only profitable use to which they will ever put their equipment, namely, to measure the directional wave spectra?

Dr. Darbyshire: As far as I know, I am the only one who has published wave data taken by a radio altimeter. When we had the prototype flown over the Irish Sea, Dr. Deacon was in the air with it and that, as far as I know, was the only time it ever worked. That was in 1949. I was convinced of its usefulness then, and I have pressed all these years to get one but have had no success. This is by far the easiest way to measure the two-dimensional wave spectrum. The results would certainly be extremely useful. I study one-dimensional spectra because we don't have enough measurements of the two-dimensional spectra at the moment to study them (statistically). You cannot generalize very much from two or three measurements of the directional spectrum of wind waves. You can measure the two-dimensional spectra with splashniks and two-dimensional buoys, but the airborne method gives a more complete answer. With my new synoptic method I try to predict the two-dimensional spectrum based on the two-dimensional formula recently developed by Dr. Longuet-Higgins.

Dr. Munk: Thank you. And now Dr. Neumann.

Dr. Neumann: Our Chairman called our attention to the progress made during the last ten years in wave research. I think we all agree with him. In 1950, when I took wave observations, my instrumentation was a hand anemometer. I put it on a stick held aloft and went from the bow to the stern of a ship to find the best place to measure the wind and the waves with a stop watch! If we consider now what we have heard and seen during this conference on the development of instrumentation and techniques of analysis, then one can only say that it is marvelous.

Before I discuss the three points our Chairman has mentioned I would like to say a little about what people have done before us. It is always a pleasure for me to look into this old handbook of oceanography by Krümmel, the second part of which was written in 1911. In those days people really looked at the sea before they talked about it. Today, even if we have the best instrument, we should not just put it out somewhere, forget about it, and then come back a month later to pick it up and make an analysis of the record. One should also watch what happens during the time when the recording is being taken.

There is a figure in the second volume, of Krümmel's handbook, which is the first example of observed angular spreading. Krümmel gives a nice figure of swell recorded simultaneously. This is also a synoptic picture. He has gathered all the log books of the ships during that particular time and then plotted a map that shows where the swell was reported to have come from. This covers almost all the North Atlantic Ocean.

Now to return to the three points. The first — wave generation. I would like to combine that with point 3, synoptic observations. I think we have neglected the question of taking wave observations in the generating process. A good method is to go out with ships, as many as possible, and choose a well defined meteorological situation, let us say with an off-shore wind. From these ships, arranged in a line, wave observations are taken along this section.

The other question concerning wave generation is the growth of the waves in the initial stage. The question, what smallest wind is necessary to generate waves, is still open. Measurements of very small ripples as they originate are needed. For this purpose, capacitance probes or instrumentation such as Dr. Kinsman uses, are very helpful. More systematic observations and a subsequent detailed analysis will be necessary to give us some insight into the generation of waves.

At the same time we should not neglect to measure the micrometeorological conditions over the water surface. That is, we should take wind profile measurements, fluctuations of the wind itself, at two levels and try later to compute the Reynolds stresses. Measurements of the vertical temperature and humidity distribution are necessary to learn the vertical stratification and stability of the air, which will later be related to the wind stress.

The problem of wave decay and energy dissipation in a moving wave train is an important question, about which we know little. The eddy viscosity in the surface layers of the oceans is related to the wave motion itself. With the breaking of the waves there is a certain kind of stirring, and I believe it is agreed that if a storm sea is generated in one area and the swell of this storm sea travels through another area where there is a rough sea, then the decay of the swell is stronger than in the case where the waves travel through an area of calm. Would it be possible to get some instruments to measure this eddy viscosity or at least to measure turbulent fluctuations in the water? If so, it might be possible to get a quantitative value of the eddy viscosity coefficient.

I would like to mention some attempts by

Thorade in the beginning of the thirties to derive these coefficients from observations of wind-generated currents and to find a numerical relationship between the eddy viscosity coefficient and the wind velocity. His eddy viscosity coefficient increased very rapidly with increasing wind speed.

I made a similar attempt some years ago when I used the relationship between the energy input into the waves and the energy dissipation in the waves for a fully arisen sea. I must admit that this was a very crude attempt because we don't know much about the energy transfer from wind to waves. For the energy dissipation an expression derived by Lamb was used, and the molecular viscosity coefficient was replaced by the eddy viscosity coefficients. From this very crude attempt I arrived at eddy viscosity coefficients which are remarkably close to those derived by Thorade.

The decay of waves over shoaling water is an important factor, which we should study, if possible, on a synoptic basis. Statements of this kind were made, and Dr. Deacon pointed out the Agulhas Banks. There are other examples of this kind, and it is useful to look into the sailing directions and read the sailors' remarks on what they observed.

Here again I would like to cite the example, which was mentioned by Krümmel in his book, of the captain of a ship who observed that the sea was always rougher over the Wyville Thomson Ridge during storms in the area than it was north and south of the Ridge. The Ridge has a depth of 600 meters. It is hard to believe that a stormy sea is affected by a ridge 600 meters deep, but there may be something to it. We should direct our attention more toward such areas and such remarks by observers at sea.

The other point concerns the effect of currents on waves. Choppy waves do not occur over the whole area where we have tidal currents running, but only at the edge of the strong tidal current where there is a sheer. Maybe at the edge we have a sudden increase in turbulence, and the waves are in a stage of stronger dissipation.

We need to find good expressions for the wave spectrum under different conditions: the transient stage; the change of the wave spectrum when the sea comes in from the open ocean over shoaling water; the change of the wave spectrum when the waves approach the coast, the beach, and finally break and dissipate.

These are all open questions. However, the first question to be answered is, what is the wave spectrum in the open sea? I think from our conference we have found that we have a spectrum of spectra.

Dr. Munk: Thank you, Dr. Neumann, particularly for the impassioned plea for visual observations in this day and age of automatic recording. Prior to the invasion of North Africa I had to examine visual observations from the Island of Azores. I remember getting very poor results occasionally, and after plotting the visually observed wave height against time, I noticed a sharp peak in the wave height every Saturday night.

I will call next on the two great two-dimensionalists, Dr. Cartwright and Dr. Barber. Again I want to raise the question, can the two-dimensional buoys be simplified enough to become operational? Should we think in terms of operational two-dimensional stations on the shore line that could be run by non-specialists?

Mr. Cartwright: Of course measuring the two-dimensional spectrum is very important. Although it is mainly a matter of measuring technique, that in itself is a problem large enough to distract us from the fact that we are still (in this directional work) dealing with a linear theory, and, however elaborate our measuring systems, we may find a limit to our results until we can include nonlinear effects.

But to return to Dr. Munk's question, how might we make further progress with two-dimensional buoy measurements? Can this buoy (invented by Barber) be made an operational tool for routine observations? The instrumental difficulties would not be great, but a great quantity of data-handling and analysis would have to be done. Error detection, as was pointed out recently, is also important. This, of course, all depends on computing facilities and whether alternatively one could design an analog machine that would do the particular type of cross-spectral analysis more rapidly.

On the whole, I think we shall get best results with the instruments handled by research workers with special knowledge of and interest in the requirements and in selected weather conditions. One can then do an intensive analysis on good data, rather than analyze enormous quantities of data in a routine fashion.

The buoy has fundamental limitations in directional resolution, and we are considering possible improvements. One is to design a buoy system which measures curvatures as well as slopes. This should extend the directional resolution. We have a system devised in theory, and suitable apparatus is being designed, which we hope to try out at the end of this year. However, it may be that when one considers curvatures, one gets to the threshold where linear theories begin to be rather doubtful.

Another approach that has not been sufficiently explored is Barber's system of taking correlations between a line of recorders. This is being done by Harlow Farmer at the University of Washington. It is about the only type of array that could be used conveniently in deep water. One can't use a two-dimensional array there because it is so difficult to keep the distances correct. It looks in principle as if one could trail a line of recorders behind a ship (I believe Barber has done this) and with only four meters recording wave height obtain a good deal of directional information over certain ranges of wave lengths. If, in addition to measuring the heights, one measures the transverse slopes (another idea suggested in one of Barber's papers), then one gets almost as much information as can be hoped for with about four recording buoys. Of course, one can probably do better still with airborne equipment, as with the SWOP method, or with radar altimeters, but such methods are in a different category. For everyday practical purposes most people think in terms of records which can be made from a ship.

For coastal measurements one has the convenience of being able to use very large arrays, which can be spaced in fixed positions. It pays to have large numbers of recorders in such arrays; however, the size may be limited by the requirement of uniform depth over the area covered by the array.

All these are definite paths to progress which are still to be explored. In spite of the success we have had recently with the methods that have been described during this meeting, our information is still very limited in this field.

Dr. Barber: Mr. Chairman, when I left England in 1950 on my way to the Southern Hemisphere, it was with a feeling of relief that I should not need to think about waves any more. Such ideas as had occurred to me were worked out, more or less, and there were a lot of hard-core problems that I knew I would never solve. But it has not worked out that way. It is delightful to see how these hard problems, the nonlinear properties of waves and awkward things like that have been

happily solved. As for Dr. Neumann's point that you should look at things, we struggled along for six months in the Admiralty group until Deacon showed up — appalled that we had confined our attention to Lamb instead of looking at the waves. He said, "Look, you chaps, go down to Cornwall and just look at those waves for a bit." We took our bathing costumes and a little bit of scientific apparatus, and we did look at waves very closely. We took notes about the ripples on the sand and lots of other things. We were "looking," as Dr. Neumann says. We came back convinced that the only sensible thing to do was measure the wave spectrum.

Now what are we to do next? In this matter I am encouraged by the thought that if something is important, it is pretty obvious. You don't have to measure it to the fourth decimal place to see if it is important, provided that is, that you measure the right thing. Who tells us what the right thing is? I suppose the theoreticians are a guide, and a sensible engineer who looks at the process can tell what the right thing is. Once we have found the right thing to measure I feel that I would prefer to have a whole lot of bad measurements than one or two good ones; with a lot of data you get a lot of information.

You won't be surprised if I suggest that the important thing to measure now is the directional spectrum. I am following other speakers in emphasizing this. Here we want the instrumentalists to show us what is possible. I would like to see whole synoptic charts of the North Atlantic, giving not only winds and weather but also the directional spectrum of the waves.

Hidden away, I understand, in Pierson's 1952 paper, and more recently brought to light by Longuet-Higgins (and I thought a bit about it myself), is the way in which you can transfer the power spectrum from one point to another. It is delightfully easy; the rules are perfectly simple. So given a synoptic chart of the directional spectrum, the business of recasting it a day or two later is straightforward, provided there is no attenuation. This is how we may check attenuation. Of course, I would scarcely be saying this unless I had a pipe dream about how to get these directional spectra. But I am not an instrumentalist, so I won't explore that point.

I suffer from being misunderstood. It was very nice of Mr. Cartwright to associate my name with the N.I.O. buoy, but it was never in my mind that one should actually make the buoy, put it into the water, and measure anything. It was just an interesting theoretical consideration. At the time I was so misunderstood that Frank Pierce actually made the buoy. I never dared put it in the water. So 99/100ths of the work in that report is due to the authors.

Dr. Munk: Now we will call on two "generationists," Pierson and Phillips, for their views. First, Dr. Pierson:

Dr. Pierson: People have been thinking about these problems for some time. Dr. Neumann, Leo Tick, and I compiled a report (in SSC-124) a few years ago for some people interested in why ships broke in half.

The Hydrographic Office has also considered these problems. I think they now feel that they need wave records from weather ships recorded as a function of time at a fixed point, followed immediately by a spectral analysis aboard the ship, followed by radioing the spectral data to shore people in time for it to be used in the preparation of the next wave forecast. We have a time problem here too. It is not very useful to know two years later in a wave forecasting problem the spectral density in two variables for a particular sea condition. So if we want to go into large-scale directional spectra measurement, we have to know the directional properties of the sea in the source regions within an hour after the data are taken. This means that the data either have to be telemetered back to a receiving station, or they have to be analyzed on the ship and put into a useful form.

The real problem is a useful forecast. Meteorologists have complained in the past that they are overburdened by forecasting demands and have no time to be theoretical. There are also people who go to sea in ships and who do things on the surface of the sea, and they need better wave forecasts. We must also think of them. We, as scientists, can take x number of years to analyze the one-directional spectrum, but we should learn to give people at sea forecasts that are useful for tomorrow.

Here the experience of the synoptic meteorologist is valuable. I am tickled pink to see the progress that has been made in digital computer, ocean-wide wave forecasting procedures. We should soon see a whole hierarchy of wave forecasting systems.

Measuring the directional properties of waves is important, but we have dropped a factor. The observations that have been achieved to date are

for relatively low waves, 4 to 8 feet, and I submit that they are impractical for 50-foot seas or higher. This little buoy that Longuet-Higgins worked with can get flipped over on its back and sunk. You could never launch it, and you could never get it back under really high seas.

When I read the title of Dave Cartwright's paper, I thought, "He is going to tell us how to use his ship to determine the directional wave spectrum." He didn't. He solved the equally important problem of finding out what the shipborne recorder actually recorded under conditions when the ship is under way. But in big seas, a weather ship, hove to and just trying to maintain her position, is almost a buoy. The ship is perhaps 300 feet long, the waves 900 feet or a thousand feet long. She has an odd-ball response characteristic and a transfer function that the naval architects are a little worried about, but it is quite possible that we could get the frequency spectrum and a couple of intelligent numbers about the gross directional properties from data that could be taken on these weather ships and that would be useful in a synoptic picture. When the ship is trying to go somewhere, the problem is not quite the same as when she is hove to headed into the sea.

The problem of energy dissipation is also important. If the breaking mechanism is the big thing, is it an on-off type of mechanism? Sailors have described a type of sea condition as a "dead" sea for many years. What is a "dead" sea? It is the sea that you observe just after the winds die down and the breaking process has subsided to a large extent. It still looks like the big waves, but it is not breaking at the top. Perhaps the breaking mechanism is a form of dissipation that is an on-off type of thing. It works to limit or prescribes the form of the spectrum in a storm sea, but it does not act to attenuate swell.

There are problems about head and following light, low wind seas through which a swell passes that need to be checked, but we must be careful to determine whether or not this is an effect of lesser magnitude than the more dominant ones due to dispersion. If Walter can find a swell that came from half-way around the world, it certainly had gone through some opposing seas with breakers in them, and they did not knock the swell out completely.

We are now punching lots of holes in lots of paper and making measurements and getting all types of digital numbers. This is very useful for scientific work. We have at our disposal the biggest and the best computing machines. We have people who can write programs and talk to them and coddle them along and get out the answers. This is tremendously important. But after you have run the tape with all the holes punched in it through the machine, what good are the holes? These numbers are something you never use again. For a certain class of problems where we want large masses of synoptic data, we should reconsider very seriously analog techniques where magnetic tapes are used simply to record what is there as a varying signal. We get spectra, and we throw away or just simply file the tape in case somebody wants to look at the nonlinear properties.

With a large number of applications we are never going to use the numbers we digitize as numbers. We are never going to plot the curve. We are never going to do anything with them. Why get them in the first place if the answer you finally want is a *spectrum*? If the spectrum is not the answer you finally want, be careful. This is the question. What does the spectrum do? It takes three thousand numbers and converts them into sixty numbers that at times are a little bit easier for the human mind to comprehend and to apply to a particular problem. That is the only reason spectra are valuable.

Dr. Phillips: I enjoy reading science fiction. One type I like is that in which one extrapolates from past and present experience to the future. Let us recall briefly the situation of the subject in the nineteenth century. We had Lamb's hydrodynamics toward the end of the century, and we had a great deal of experience in looking at waves at sea. But the two aspects of the subject were quite divorced. There was no contact. Kelvin's work was interesting, but the sailor didn't care. Things began to get quite a lot closer about twenty years ago when the methods of statistical specification of the wave sea came into use. Here we had a way of describing what we saw. There was a great step forward. There began to be a feedback and interchange between the theoretician and the man who was observing waves. They could tell something to each other. But this was only half the story. It was the kinematic half. It was specification. It was not in any way an understanding of what *caused* the things we were seeing. We could describe them, but we could not explain them. I think in recent years the theoretician has begun to see elements of an explanation. This is where we stand right now.

What of the future? Let me just extrapolate on the basis of present trends. I believe that the dynamical theories will be able to predict quantities which will be observable. They may be wrong, so the theories will have to be modified. But with a continuous comparison between the predictions and the observations, such as has already taken place in the statistical description efforts, we will gain some confidence in them. We will see their limitations; we will see where modification is required. The sort of program that has been carried forward by the NIO is immensely valuable in this respect. In my more sanguine moments I hope that in perhaps ten years we will understand enough about what causes these waves to be able to feed back enough insight and knowledge to the chap who is trying to predict the waves to allow him to make a better estimate and prediction than is being made now.

I have said nothing about measurements because I am the worst man in the world to talk about measurements. I envisage some sort of continuous monitoring system. If we fill the whole North Atlantic with buoys every 200 miles, each sending out signals indicating what the sea state is at all times, we will have much better knowledge of what is going to happen if the wind starts to blow.

I would like to make a plea for measurements of wave decay. As far as I can see, it is rather difficult to explain the decay of a swell if it exists. This is a nebulous sort of problem. It is evident that the ordinary mechanisms which can dissipate short waves just don't work very well with long waves in swell in the open ocean. There is a possibility that the interaction mechanisms that Dr. Hasselmann talked about might provide a clue. He showed how this energy is being transferred from the large waves to the small waves, where they can be dissipated. Our problem is that we don't know whether this is a real effect. You cannot make theories in a vacuum. If you have nothing to explain, there is no point in deluding yourself into trying to explain it.

Dr. Munk: Thank you. One may ask, is it reasonable to regard these spectra as representing an instantaneous radiative balance between the generating and the decaying processes? If so, and if this is the view one wishes to take, the argument as to which spectrum is correct is really a rather meaningless one, because the spectra are not really the fundamental problem of our science. One does not ask *what* is the spectrum in the infrared of a black body, because different black bodies would have different spectra; one rather tries to find what the basic laws are and from those one can now rather accurately deduce spectra.

Our basic problem is, what is the radiation function? What is the energy propagated from each unit area — each infinitesimal area — energy per unit area, per unit time, per unit frequency band, per unit direction? This is the basic function that has to be understood from theory and from observation.

Darbyshire's work and Hasselmann's remarks make this quite explicit. There are the two theories we have discussed, the Phillips-type theory, which would make this "radiation function" a function of the local wind field only; and Hasselmann's type of theory, which makes it necessary to know the local wind field and in addition the wave spectrum already present. This makes the problem more complex. But inasmuch as these terms — "fetches," "finite durations" — are really great idealizations of the wind field over the sea, to try and write spectra for given fetches and finite durations is to endow these meteorological notions with more claim to reality than they deserve. The proper view of the future, especially for forecasting, will be to emphasize these radiation functions per unit area, evaluate them over a grid. In some instances the finite fetch and duration might be rather good idealizations, and we would end up with predicted spectra close to the present; in some instances it would be very different. I think this is a change in point of view from the one we held before this conference. This brings us to the final point of view that we want to present at the conference table today.

I have asked Dr. Tick and Dr. Longuet-Higgins to comment. Both have been particularly active in the field of nonlinear interaction. It is a very lucky thing for wave people that we have a good linear zero approximation. This is an asset which the turbulence people have lacked. It is an asset on which we all capitalize. It has made it possible to describe existing conditions from the point of view of linear theory with considerable success. But it fails completely when the problems of generation are involved. Those problems then call necessarily for a high-order theory, and the recent work has pointed in this direction.

I want to ask my friend, Michael [Longuet-Higgins], a somewhat embarrassing personal question! Ten years ago he wrote his Ph.D. thesis on

nonlinear processes, at which time he introduced the "bottom wind" improvement upon the Stokes theory. I have wondered since what has delayed this important development until today. The physical structure, the mathematical principles of this kind of development certainly were in existence a long time ago.

Dr. Longuet-Higgins: I don't know the answer to your last question. Maybe it is a problem of dissemination of information, but it seems now that the theory of the linear processes has been quite thoroughly explored and that the general feeling is that we should move on to study the nonlinear ones. It just so happens that the work that I did some years ago fits in with this objective. I agree that this conference has been a turning point in our studies. Until now we have been using integral formulae involving fetch and duration, etc. to predict wave spectra. No doubt these integral formulae will continue to be used, but the scatter of the various predictions shows that they are not absolutely satisfactory. I would hazard a guess that we shall never get much improvement in our wave predictions from this approach. I think the future lies with the approach which Dr. Hasselmann outlined in his remarks on Tuesday and which, in fact, Dr. Munk has just reemphasized. That is to say, we study the rate at which the spectrum is *changing* and the processes that are causing it to change. If we approached this observationally, it would mean that we would have to make synoptic measurements at fairly regular, brief intervals over the whole ocean and evaluate the difference between them. It is a very large observational program. I don't know whether it is practical. It means that we ought to have the directional spectra all over the ocean from a system of wave recorders. I believe it is possible to design the wave recording buoy so that it doesn't flip over.

I would like to go back to Dr. Hasselmann's equation which he wrote on the board and consider the various terms in this equation and how we will go about tackling each one of them. Perhaps this may be a more fruitful approach than trying to tackle them all together in the oceans. First, there is the input term due to the input of energy from turbulent pressure fluctuations. We really need to know much more about the pressure fluctuations in the atmosphere. The dearth of measurements of pressure fluctuations at sea is incredible. Of course, there is the difficulty of measurement, but we only just now know the order of magnitude for the first time.

We should have better measurements of the wind profiles. We have at the moment only a few good observations by Hay, Roll, and some others. I would like to appeal to all who have observations locked up in their drawers to consider whether they haven't enough confidence in them to put them into print.

Regarding the second term mentioned by Dr. Hasselmann, it is going to be very difficult to measure the "feedback" due to coupling between the air flow and the sea surface, which has been treated specially by Miles. I think we should try, but we should not be too confident that we can improve very much on our present estimates. It is more likely that we shall have to continue for some time to get this term from theoretical calculations, such as those of Miles.

There has been some controversy about the nonlinear interactions. We can study these interactions perfectly well on a model scale. Without going into the ocean I think we can get perfectly satisfactory answers for the tertiary reactions simply by doing model experiments. There is the very simple one that I have been engaged on, which has not yet been completed, and I think there is another one which could be tried in a rectangular wave basin; that is, to generate two wave trains crossing at an angle to see whether you don't get a third wave train coming out at another angle.

Next is the term due to breaking, which Dr. Hasselmann wrote down as N_b — delightfully simple! This can be studied also on a model scale. In fact, we have been experimenting for several months to determine under what conditions a spectrum of the sea surface will exhibit breaking waves.

We have a long wave channel. At one end we have a wave maker capable of putting in a sine wave of varying frequency. We can vary the amplitude of the wave while the wave maker is running. This is done by a system of gears. We plan to put in first of all the short waves in the spectrum, then gradually decrease the frequency, and create longer waves, which will catch the others at a certain point, or rather over a certain stretch. The point is not to put all the energy in at one go at the wave maker. The nonlinearities in the wave maker would cause breaking immediately in front of it, which one does not want. Our scheme is to build up the spectrum

over perhaps 20 or 30 feet on a model scale and for a few seconds duration, and see under what conditions breakers will occur.

The eddy viscosity term, which was mentioned by Dr. Neumann, cannot be estimated until we have further measurements at sea. I would like to point out that Dr. Phillips has done some calculations on the interaction of waves with the turbulent sea, and from his calculations it appears that the scattering by turbulence is very small. I would like to suggest that some of the decay which is observed when waves pass through a rough area is actually due to nonlinear scattering of energy into different wave numbers by the mechanism which Phillips and Hasselmann have described.

Then there is one term that Dr. Hasselmann didn't write down, which arises from the tangential stress. What we mean by tangential stress is perhaps difficult to define. But Miles made a crude estimate of it in his 1957 paper, and he estimated the effect at something like 20 per cent of that due to the shear instability mechanism.

Finally, although the subject is now growing so much that some degree of specialization will be forced upon us, we should have increased cooperation among theoretical physicists, instrumentalists, and engineers, because none of these three groups can get on without the other two. I hope there will be many more conferences and informal discussions of this kind.

Mr. Tick: I am glad that Dr. Munk brought up the point about the non-triviality of problems of dealing with large masses of scientific data. I wish to stress that scientific data are distinct from other volumes of data. They do present a peculiar problem, and we will all have to face up to it. I also want to say that a simple and formerly trivial arithmetic problem is now becoming serious. We deal with inexact numbers, and not numbers that are random but that are represented by a finite expansion because our instrumentation is of limited accuracy only. We are now attempting to use these numbers in highly refined theories. Rounding them off no longer becomes a trivial problem. It is quite easy to end up with nothing but "noise." Noise in computation travels in very strange ways, particularly through highly nonlinear operations.

Finally, I would like to refer to a report written by the late John Von Neumann, in which he examined the current state of turbulence theory.

He ended on a happy note. As you know, he was one of the foremost proponents of the use of large-scale computers in scientific work, and he felt that one of the great contributions that computers could make was to put an end to many debates that were going on in fluid mechanics. Problems could be formulated, the poles of debate agreed upon, a computational experiment set up, and the results computed in exact form. And from this a debate could be ended. This has never been realized in fluid mechanics as yet.

Dr. Munk: Thank you very much, Leo. Mr. Vetter, I think on retrospect I failed to carry out the task you assigned me by not paying enough attention to the very real problems of the engineer. I think it is a fair conclusion to say that those who are interested in the movement of sand, the disappearance of beach houses, the reflection of radar, the reason why a Texas Tower failed, and how sewage spreads into the sea have not really gotten tangible methods out of the great improvements that have taken place in our basic understanding of the physics of ocean waves. Though engineers have improved their own understanding a great deal and have adopted more sophisticated methods, the theorists have improved their approach even more, so that the two are further apart than ever. I wonder if I can strike a sympathetic chord in some of the people here who, like myself, are really not very bright and have difficulty in keeping up with things. I had just succeeded in grasping the one-dimensional power spectra analysis and the things involved with it, when I had to learn to visualize wave spectra in three-dimensional wave number space to be able to talk with my friend Barber. I just succeeded in having what I think is some degree of understanding of how to visualize waves in three-dimensional wave number space when I came to this conference and found that one really has to learn an awful lot about the nonlinear processes. Life is tough.

Dr. Deacon: We ought to emphasize our appreciation of the service which the National Academy of Sciences and National Research Council is doing here for wave research by fixing a date and place for the next meeting. To me, ten years seems to be about the right interval. The authorship of the *Encyclopaedia Britannica* article on waves passed from Vaughan Cornish to Walter Munk in ten years, and many of the ideas put forward at the NBS 1951 Symposium on Gravity Waves have reached maturity today. We could not have met in a nicer place than this. Everyone has enjoyed and profited from the friendly surroundings. Meetings with narrower terms of reference will be needed to keep pace with increasing specialization, but every ten years or so we shall need the same all-inclusive collaboration. It will be useful to have the old as well as the young, since both must derive much of their energy and direction from the central peak of activity. It will be very important to cover the whole range of interest from paper and pencil to heavy engineering, from sanguine theory to everyday application.

Perhaps we cannot ask the Academy here and now to arrange it, but we can ask Mr. Vetter to convey to the President and members our warmest thanks for this conference and to tell them of our belief that it marks and will sustain another great step forward in ocean wave research.

JOHN W. TUKEY

T W O

WHAT CAN DATA ANALYSIS AND STATISTICS OFFER TODAY?[1]

There are a few points involving data analysis upon which I should like to comment. These are treated conveniently under four heads: general statistical principles, choice of lag and spectrum windows, dealing with nonstationary situations, and dealing with non-Gaussian situations.

GENERAL STATISTICAL PRINCIPLES

As is inevitable, the papers presented here vary widely in their use of the knowledge and methodology of data analysis and statistics. A detailed review would profit us little, but a few specific points deserve attention.

First, Dr. Hicks, in his fitting of a specific functional form to the dependence of spectrum density on wind velocity, fetch, and frequency, appealed to the most fundamental basis we know for judging precision when he fitted it separately to several randomly selected subsets of his data. While some further gain could be obtained by a sophisticated modification of this process (cf. Tukey, 1958), his appeal to replication as the basis of confidence is both sound and praiseworthy. It may be well, however, to stress that even such fundamental procedures as this can assess only

precision and not accuracy. Probable or standard errors so obtained can allow only for fitting the chosen functional form to an infinite amount of data; they make no allowance for possible systematic errors in the chosen forms.

Second, the slides and diagrams that have accompanied the papers given here make it clear that oceanographers realize that relationship is more revealing than is a changing amount of variability, at least where y may be related to x in a simple graph. The same principle applies, however, to more complex situations. Thus, to learn which aspects of wind-field variation and change are most relevant to wave generation we should not expect to use factor analysis, when we can use multiple regression of measured wave generation upon a variety of aspects to help us select the more meaningful ones. Similarly, we should expect, as many have already confirmed by experience, that cross-spectrum analysis will be more searching and revealing than spectrum analysis itself. And as we go into the next stage of complexity, we can expect the cross-bispectrum to be even more revealing than the bispectrum. Relationship is a powerful tool.

Third, in his discussion Kinsman emphasized the dangers of "reduced information measures," and indicated that, although he knew it was impossible, he would really like to know the whole distribution in function-space. I would *not* like to know that. The whole distribution certainly

[1] Prepared in part in connection with research at Princeton University under Contract No. DA 36-034-ORD-2297 sponsored by the U. S. Army Research Office.

contains all the information, but I suspect it would be harder to dig the spectrum, for example, out of a total description of the distribution than to calculate the spectrum from a long wave record. What we need are *concentrated-information* measures.

The spectrum has served us well, but other measures, some simple, others complex, may also help. I, for one, place meaningfulness and understandability before efficiency or information content.

Fourth, Kinsman criticized the transition of X^2 from an approximation to a supposed precise fact. Others have indicated that the spectrum is good only for Gaussian ensembles because only then does it *completely* characterize the ensemble. These reflect two aspects of a single dangerous fallacy — a belief that we must be both precise and certain in our dealings with nature. The truth is just the opposite; we must remember, as my colleague Martin Wilk puts it,

"The hallmark of good science is that it uses models and 'theory' but never believes them."

Fifth, much discussion of dichotomies and olive branches has accompanied various formulas for wave height in terms of wind speed, fetch, etc., but I do not recall anyone admitting that his expression was an approximation, or indicating just what, for any situation, were the minimum statistical uncertainties in his fitted surface or hypersurface, or how this uncertainty changed for various combinations of the arguments. If wave generation is a nonlinear process, and I take it most agree that it is, it will have to depend at least somewhat upon the initial ambient waves in the generating area; and the two sides of the Atlantic are almost sure to have different behavior. But until we face the approximateness and uncertainty of fitting, we have no basis for judging how different this behavior has been established to be.

CHOICE OF LAG AND SPECTRUM WINDOWS

Dr. Barber has made a plea for rectangular lag windows. We have discussed the issues in private and have, I believe, come to relatively complete agreement. Uses of arrays, as in radio astronomy, where the number of detectors is the scarce commodity and sampling fluctuations can be easily waited out, are very different from spectrum analysis of time histories, where length of record is a scarce commodity and computations for a few more lags come relatively cheaply.

The uses of rectangular lag windows in the time-series situation still seem to me to be at best very dubious, but the array situation may be quite different.

The differences between the array problem and the time-history problem are made clearer if we ask what would be the precise array analog of the digital computations we habitually apply to time series. It would be to set out a few hundred detectors in a line, to choose one instant at which to record their instantaneous output, to combine these outputs in overlapping small groups, and to average the result over the groups. When are we ever likely to use an array like this?

Dr. Barber's discussion is thoughtful and careful, but a few points ought to be made for the record, two of them general:

(a) The "cosine" window considered by Dr. Barber is not the "cosine arch" or "hanning" window frequently used in data analysis (Dr. Barber tells me that he had no intention of selecting windows that were actually used in time-history practice). In particular, the "cosine" window has much higher side lobes than the "cosine-arch" or "hanning" window.

(b) The choice between windows depends very much upon the criterion used to judge among them, and the choice of criterion should depend upon the situation and the purpose of the analysis. (In a multipurpose analysis, and most analyses are multipurpose in this sense, the use of two or more different windows is quite natural.)

A few further words need to be said about each of Dr. Barber's concluding points:

(1) The correlogram can be zero outside a finite interval only if the spectrum extends to infinity (and does not decrease too fast), an unlikely event in the present instance.

(2) Arsac's result is correct, but if there are no narrow peaks, we can use a wider spectral window and gain an even greater reduction in error. The rectangular window may represent certain triangular spectrum peaks more closely than the cosine window, but this is not true for all triangular peaks. Quite the reverse. Extremely narrow triangular peaks are represented in the shape of the spectrum window itself, and as Barber's Figures 3-3-1 and 3-3-2 show, even the cosine lag window does better in such cases.

(3) Negative estimates are not in my judgment something to be shunned. I agree with Dr. Barber here. But a free hand in replacing them with zero implies a free hand in detaching the average

value of the estimates from anything in particular. If we go so far, why not farther?

(4) The display in Dr. Barber's Figure 3-3-4, showing mean responses of the two estimates, has limited meaning without some indication of possible differences in variability. The evidence here is incomplete.

I now have my own solution (Tukey, 1961a and 1961b) to the problem of choosing a window. It is to choose two windows, one with all positive side lobes and another with all negative side lobes. If both are used routinely in calculation, the difference of the corresponding spectral estimates makes clear where we ought to recalculate, usually after pre-whitening or elimination, if we want to avoid difficulty from lobes. Wonnacott (1961) has recently developed a negative-lobe window analogous to the triangular (Bartlett) window and has demonstrated some of its uses.

DEALING WITH NONSTATIONARY SITUATIONS

There have been requests for tools adequate to deal with nonstationary processes. The implication seems to be that there ought to be tools that would reveal to us everything about a nonstationary situation, exactly and without thought. (Since we have no tools like this for the stationary case, this seems a vain hope.)

There is probably some need for study of techniques for following a moderately rapidly changing spectrum, although oceanographers have done quite well following slowly changing spectra. (Munk and Snodgrass's detection in 1957 of 1-kilometer waves 1 millimeter high over a 10,000 mile fetch, for example, depended upon the changes in the spectrum.)

There is perhaps more need for a better use of the tools we already have and for small modifications in them. The discussion of the steepness of the down-frequency slope of the singly-generated wave spectrum is a case in point. It is clear that conventional spectral analysis can measure this slope better if (a) the record is filtered (probably digitally) to flatten out this slope before spectrum analysis, and (b) much longer records are analyzed. As the length of record analyzed is increased, some difficulty must arise. Change of cut-off frequency with time (i.e., nonstationarity) seems the most likely one.

At first glance, such a change might seem to be a bar to analyzing longer records, but this need not be the case. We know how to demodulate a single record into two records, low-pass filter the results, and remodulate the pair back to a single record, either preserving original frequencies or shifting them. (See Tukey, 1961, for a brief discussion of complex demodulation.) This technique, with shifted frequencies, is useful for examining narrow bands or, without remodulation, for the qualitative study of frequency constituents.

In the present situation we can alter it just a little, for example by using a slowly changing demodulating frequency and a constant remodulating one, and can keep the down-frequency cut-off in the resulting (synthetic) record at a constant frequency for a much longer time. (A much reduced remodulating frequency will also allow data compression with consequent saving in computational effort.)

In that a known procedure, useful in the stationary case, is modified somewhat to meet nonstationary needs, I believe this proposal is typical of the techniques that will help us most on nonstationary aspects of *data* in the near future.

DEALING WITH NON-GAUSSIAN SITUATIONS

The words "bispectrum" and "cross-bispectrum" have already appeared above without explanation. I believe they are the keys to the first step in treating non-Gaussian behavior and I would like to briefly explain why. To do this, it is well to begin with the spectrum itself and ask why we choose to use it.

The spectrum is a basis for the average values of quadratic (bilinear, if you prefer) functions of time histories drawn from stationary ensembles. The average value of

$$y(t + 17)y(t + 2) + y(t + 3)y(t - 7) + y^2(t + 13)$$

to take an over-simple example, is given by the integral of a certain kernel times the spectrum, where the same kernel is valid for any stationary process (and the fixed quadratic function).

There are many other functions, Jowett's serial variance function

$$\Phi(h) = ave \tfrac{1}{2}[y(t + h) - y(t)]^2 \qquad (1)$$

and the ensemble covariance function

$$R(h) = ave[(y(t) - ave\ y) \cdot (y(t + h)$$
$$- ave\ y)] \quad (2)$$

being only two, which are also bases in this same sense.

The unique feature of the spectrum is this: if $Z(t)$ is obtained from $Y(t)$ by a linear, time-shift invariant process (such as lagging, differentiation, integration, smoothing, or filtering), the value of the spectrum of Z for a particular argument (a particular frequency) is obtained from the value of the spectrum of Y at the same argument, no regard being given to the values of the spectrum of Y for other arguments (other frequencies).

No other basis for average values of quadratic functions has this property. This lack of entanglement under well-behaved transformation is the key property of the spectrum.

If we are to assess some of the non-Gaussian characteristics of a time history or, perhaps, detect some evidence of involvement with nonlinear processes, we are going to have to go beyond quadratic (bilinear) functions of the observations. The simplest step is to cubic (trilinear) functions and to bases for their average values.

These bases will be functions of two arguments, as illustrated by the analog of the covariance

$$R(h, k) = ave[y(t) \cdot y(t + h) \cdot y(t + k)] \quad (3)$$

Among them there is one whose values are not entangled when $Y(t)$ is subjected to a linear, time-shift-invariant transformation. Its arguments are pairs of frequencies. We can appropriately call it the *bispectrum*. It takes on complex values (like the cross-spectrum) rather than real ones (like the spectrum). Its argument can be regarded as either

(1) unrestricted pairs of signed frequencies, or
(2) triples of frequencies summing to zero.

The latter representation makes its symmetry properties more explicit. (As indeed the description of the argument of the spectrum as pairs of frequencies summing to zero does for the ordinary spectrum.)

Numerical estimation of the bispectrum seems to be quite feasible, though perhaps ten times as long a record may be needed for reasonable precision as for spectrum estimation.

Trial computations on synthetic records have been carried out under the direction of both Gordon McDonald and Leo Tick. The appearance of bispectra of real data cannot be long

delayed and may be expected to have interesting consequences.

The bispectrum is accompanied by a cross bispectrum, which involves *three* time histories, two of which may be alike, but all three of which may be different. It should be even more useful in revealing new things. (In due course we may have to dare to use the trispectrum, etc. There are generalizations of all degrees.)

Little has been said in print about the bispectrum, but an appropriate formalism and the transformation rule are set down in Tukey, 1959a, and 1959b.

REFERENCES

Munk, W. H. and F. E. Snodgrass, "Measurements of Southern Swell at Guadelupe Island," *Deep Sea Research*, IV (1957) 272–286.

Tukey, John W., "Bias and Confidence in Not Quite Large Samples (Abstract)," *Annals of Mathematical Statistics*, XXIX (1958) 614.

Tukey, John W., "The Estimation of (Power) Spectra and Related Quantities," *On Numerical Analysis*, p. 389–411, *ed.* Rudolph E. Langer. Madison, Wisconsin: University of Wisconsin Press, 1959a.

Tukey, John W., "An Introduction to the Measurement of Spectra," *Probability and Statistics*, p. 300–330, *The Harald Cramér Volume*, ed. Ulf Grenander. Stockholm: Almquist and Wiskell 1959b; New York: Wiley & Sons, 1959b.

Tukey, John W., "Discussion, Emphasizing the Connection Between Analysis of Variance and Spectrum Analysis, *Technometrics* III (1961a) 191–219.

Tukey, John W., "Curves as Parameters and Touch Estimation," *Proceedings of the 4th Berkeley Symposium on Probability and Mathematical Statistics*. University of California Press (1961b) 681–694.

Wonnacott, Thomas H., "Spectral Analysis Combining a Bartlett Window with an Associated Inner Window," *Technometrics* III (1961) 235–243.

COMMENTS

Dr. Barber (in reply to article by Dr. Tukey): The "cosine" lag window discussed in my paper, "A Plea for a Rectangular Window," is not, of course, that proposed by J. W. Tukey. I intended mine merely as one having properties in many ways intermediate between those of the rectangular window and those of the triangular window.

From the rather elementary standpoint of the present paper, the triangular window of M. S. Bartlett and the cosine window of J. W. Tukey have very similar properties. My own cosine window is not a serious proposal but is put up merely to be argued down, like an "Aunt Sally" in a fairground. I am trying to distinguish two problems. In the analysis of a single time series it is very clearly desirable to use either Bartlett's triangle or Tukey's cosine in preference to the rectangular window. But I argue that one should not carry over this conclusion to the case of the space correlogram obtained from an array of detectors. Here the rectangular window seems to have many points in its favour. Indeed Bartlett's triangular window (and by implication, Tukey's cosine window) seemed so unpromising that in Figures 3 and 4 I thought it fairer to the reader to omit them and to use some less extreme window (my own cosine window) to compare with the rectangle.

I agree with Professor Tukey that the distinction is in some sense an economic one. After the expense of making and using a large array, the expense of getting long averages in time is relatively small. The treatment of the correlogram then changes because stability has been already achieved.

APPENDIXES

VISUAL WAVE OBSERVATIONS

SEA STATE FOR ENGINEERS

CONFERENCE PARTICIPANTS

APPENDIX A

VISUAL WAVE OBSERVATIONS

An *ad hoc* group of experts, including Dr. J. Darbyshire, National Institute of Oceanography, Surrey, England, Dr. R. Dorrestein, Royal Netherlands Meteorological Institute, De Bilt, Dr. R. Gelci, Meteorologie Nationale, Paris, France, Dr. H. Walden, Deutcher Wetterdienst, Germany, Dr. G. Neumann and Professor W. J. Pierson of New York University, Dr. R. James and J. J. Schule of the U. S. Naval Oceanographic Office, considered a recent paper by G. Verploegh of the Netherlands and W. Shinners of the U. S. Weather Bureau that cited the inherent problems of the present coding procedure for reporting wave data by merchant seamen.

The group was in complete agreement that the present method of reporting wave height is inadequate and results in erroneous information in many instances. It was the consensus of the majority that (a) it is very difficult and often impossible for ships' officers to determine wave direction to the nearest 10 degrees, (b) it is not essential to report wave periods above 14 seconds because of infrequent occurrence, and (c) more value would result from reporting higher-frequency wave periods to the nearest second.

The group felt that to improve the reporting of wave data, wave code group $1\ D_wP_wh_wh_w$ should be considered, wherein D_w, wave direction is reported to eight points; P_w, wave period is reported by ten digits 0 to 9, where (0) is 5 seconds or less, (1) is 6 seconds, (2) is 7 seconds etc., and (9) is 14 seconds or more; and h_wh_w, wave height is the height in half-meter intervals.

353

APPENDIX B

SEA STATE FOR ENGINEERS

An informal, extra session of some forty members was held on Wednesday evening, May 3rd, at 7:30 P.M. to discuss "An Improved Description of Sea State for Engineers." After a brief mention of three previous meetings, Dr. Walter Munk described the confusion resulting from using a single number in contract specifications to describe the state of the sea and discussed his proposal that the energy spectrum density be used for frequency ranges applicable to the particular problem. A primer, to consist of about ten examples of problems in the low, middle, and high frequencies of ocean waves should be prepared. Examples in the low-frequency region, for mining problems, middle, for ship construction, and operation, and high, for radar problems, should be included in the primer.

Manley St. Denis noted that the Society of Naval Architects and Marine Engineers was deeply concerned with this problem. In a general discussion, plans were made to obtain volunteers to write the examples for the primer or for use in the final method chosen by SNAME. B. King Couper (Code 342C, Bureau of Ships, Navy Department, Washington 25, D. C.) will act as clearinghouse for the informal group preparing the examples.

APPENDIX C

CONFERENCE PARTICIPANTS

Mr. Ledolph Baer
ASW and Ocean Systems
Lockheed-California Co.
Burbank, California

Dr. N. F. Barber
Dominion Physical Laboratory
D.S.I.R.
Wellington, New Zealand

Dr. Charles Bretschneider
National Engineering Science Co.
1001 Connecticut Avenue, N. W.
Suite 725
Washington, D. C.

Mr. Marvin Burkhart
U. S. Naval Oceanographic Office
Marine Sciences Department
Washington 25, D. C.

Dr. R. W. Burling
Institute of Oceangraphy
University of British Columbia
Vancouver 8, Canada

Mr. Joseph Caldwell
U. S. Army Corps of Engineers
Beach Erosion Board
Washington 16, D. C.

Dr. D. E. Cartwright
National Institute of Oceanography
Wormley, Godalming
Surrey, England

Dr. Joseph Chadwick
University of Oregon
Eugene, Oregon

Mr. B. King Couper
Bureau of Ships, Dept. of the Navy
Washington 25, D. C.

Dr. Charles S. Cox
Scripps Institution of Oceanography
La Jolla, California

Dr. John P. Craven
Bureau of Naval Weapons, Dept. of the Navy
Washington 25, D. C.

Dr. W. E. Cummins
David Taylor Model Basin
Washington 7, D. C.

Dr. J. Darbyshire
National Institute of Oceanography
Wormley, Godalming
Surrey, England

Dr. Mollie Darbyshire
National Institute of Oceanography
Wormley, Godalming
Surrey, England

Dr. G. E. R. Deacon
National Institute of Oceanography
Wormley, Godalming
Surrey, England

Mr. Pasquale DeLeonibus
U. S. Naval Oceanographic Office
Marine Sciences Department
Washington 25, D. C.

Dr. Jacob E. Dinger
U. S. Naval Research Laboratory
Washington 25, D. C.

Lt. Cdr. R. P. Dinsmore
U. S. Coast Guard
1300 E. Street, N. W.
Washington 25, D. C.

Dr. R. Dorrestein
Koninklijk Nederlands Meteorologisch Instituut
De Bilt, The Netherlands

Dr. Carl Eckart
Scripps Institution of Oceanography
La Jolla, California

Mr. Harlow G. Farmer
Department of Oceanography
University of Washington
Seattle 5, Washington

Mr. R. Gelci
Meteorologie Nationale
2 Avenue Rapp
Paris (VIIo), France

Mr. Paul Golovato
David Taylor Model Basin
Washington 7, D. C.

Mr. George Hanssen
U. S. Naval Oceanographic Office
Marine Sciences Department
Washington 25, D. C.

Mr. D. Lee Harris
U. S. Weather Bureau
Washington 25, D. C.

Dr. K. Hasselmann
Institut für Schiffbau
Hamburg, Germany

Dr. Bruce L. Hicks
Coordinated Science Laboratory
University of Illinois
Urbana, Illinois

Dr. A. A. Hudimac
Naval Electronics Laboratory
San Diego 52, California

Mr. Lee Hunt
National Academy of Sciences
Washington 25, D. C.

Professor Takashi Ichiye
Oceanographic Institution
Florida State University
Tallahassee, Florida

Dr. Takeshi Ijima
Coastal Engineering Division
Transport Technics Research Institute
Ministry of Transportation
Yokosuka, Japan

Dr. Richard W. James
U. S. Naval Oceanographic Office
Marine Sciences Department
Washington 25, D. C.

Dr. Blair Kinsman
Chesapeake Bay Institute
Johns Hopkins University
Baltimore 18, Maryland

Professor Korvin-Kroukovsky
P. O. Box 8
East Randolph, Vermont

Professor E. V. Lewis
Maritime Administration
441 G Street, N. W.
Washington, D. C.

Dr. M. S. Longuet-Higgins
National Institute of Oceanography
Wormley, Godalming
Surrey, England

Mr. Sam Lum
Bureau of Ships, Dept of the Navy
Washington 25, D. C.

Mr. Frank C. Macdonald
U. S. Naval Research Laboratory
Washington 25, D. C.

Mr. M. S. Macovsky
Advanced Systems Engineering
Westinghouse Electric Corporation
Sunnyvale, California

Mr. Wayne A. Magnitzky
OP-07T14
Office of the Chief of Naval Operations
The Pentagon
Washington 25, D. C.

Mr. Wilbur Marks
Oceanics, Incorporated
114 East 40th Street
New York 16, New York

Dr. Arthur Maxwell
Office of Naval Research
Geophysics Branch
Washington 25, D. C.

Mr. James McGarey
Office of Naval Research
Geophysics Branch
Washington 25, D. C.

Mr. William T. McGuinness
Lamont Geological Observatory
Palisades, New York

Mr. Gaylord Miller
University of California
Institute of Geophysics
La Jolla, California

Dr. Charles E. Mongan
69 Dunster Street
Cambridge, Massachusetts

Dr. Walter Munk
Scripps Institution of Oceanography
La Jolla, California

Capt. H. G. Munson
18 Dodds Lane
Princeton, New Jersey

Dr. Gerhard Neumann
New York University
Department of Meteorology & Oceanography
New York 53, New York

Mr. Boyd Olson
U. S. Naval Oceanographic Office
Marine Sciences Department
Washington 25, D. C.

Dr. O. M. Phillips
Department of Mechanics
Johns Hopkins University
Baltimore 18, Maryland

Professor W. J. Pierson, Jr.
New York University
Department of Meteorology & Oceanography
New York 53, New York

Dr. David Price
Sperry Marine Division
Syosset, New York

Dr. R. R. Putz
Marine Advisers
La Jolla, California

Professor Robert O. Reid
Department of Oceanography
Texas A & M College
College Station, Texas

Dr. T. L. Russell
California Research Corporation
P. O. Box 446
La Habra, California

Mr. T. V. Ryan
Coast & Geodetic Survey
Washington 25, D. C.

Dr. Alfred Saenger
Hudson Laboratories
Columbia University
145 Palisade Street
Dobbs Ferry, New York

Mr. A. H. Schooley
U. S. Naval Research Laboratory
Washington 25, D. C.

Mr. M. D. Schuldt
Coast & Geodetic Survey
Washington 25, D. C.

Mr. John J. Schule, Jr.
U. S. Naval Oceanographic Office
Marine Sciences Department
Washington 25, D. C.

Mr. Willard Shinners
U. S. Weather Bureau
Washington 25, D. C.

Mr. A. E. Sik
U. S. Weather Bureau
Washington 25, D. C.

Mr. Frank E. Snodgrass
Institute of Geophysics
University of California
La Jolla, California

Mr. James Snodgrass
Scripps Institution of Oceanography
La Jolla, California

Dr. Manley St. Denis
Naval Warfare Analysis Group/Center of Naval Analyses
Washington, D. C.

Admiral E. C. Stephan
Commander
U. S. Naval Oceanographic Office
Washington 25, D. C.

Mr. Raymond Stevens
Woods Hole Oceanographic Institution
Woods Hole, Massachusetts

Dr. J. J. Stoker
New York University
New York 53, New York

Mr. Leo J. Tick
New York University
New York 53, New York

Dr. M. J. Tucker
National Institute of Oceanography
Wormley, Godalming
Surrey, England

Dr. J. W. Tukey
Box 708
Princeton University
Princeton, New Jersey

Dr. S. Uusitalo
The Marine Laboratory
Virginia Key
Miami 49, Florida

Mr. Richard C. Vetter
National Academy of Sciences
Washington 25, D. C.

Dr. H. Walden
Deutscher Wetterdienst
Hamburg 4, Germany

Dr. Stephen Waldron
Massachusetts Institute of Technology
292 Main Street
Cambridge, Massachusetts

Dr. Robert L. Wiegel
Associate Professor of Civil Engineering
University of California
Berkeley 4, California

Mr. Leo Williams
U. S. Army Corps of Engineers
Beach Erosion Board
Washington 16, D. C.

Dr. Basil Wilson
National Engineering Science Company
711 South Fair Oaks Avenue
Pasadena, California